THE HANDYMAN'S COMPLETE SELF INSTRUCTOR

ODHAMS PRESS LIMITED
LONG ACRE, LONDON, W.C.2.

CONTENTS

BUILDING

By Edwin Gunn

LESSON 1

The Foundations

SUCCESSFUL building is the result of a mixture of common sense, experience and knowledge, the last depending on familiarity with principles based upon the accumulated experience and research of others. These principles, of which at least an elementary appreciation is required, are those of mechanics, physics and the chemistry of materials; economics, too, must be considered.

Mechanical properties are con-concerned with such things as stresses and thrusts, and the inertia (or resistance) of materials having weight or mass to the disturbance liable to be produced by these forces. For example, it is useful to grasp the idea of triangulation, by which the tendency of a rectangular frame to distort under pressure is checked by bracing or strutting (Fig. 1, *right*), or the tendency of a pitched roof to spread unless the triangular form is completed by the insertion of the missing member, as in the "tie" shown in Fig. 2, *right.*

Physical properties relate to the internal structure of building materials, upon which their performance depends. For example, cast iron has a brittle and crystalline structure, while wrought iron tends to be fibrous; the former can therefore be used to support weights (in compression—subject to crushing pressure), while the latter has properties which enable it also to resist pulls or bending strains (in tension, bending or torsion—as in a tie-rod, a girder or an axle).

Chemistry will explain why certain materials have affinities one for another, while others tend to produce unwanted results if used in conjunction. For example, lead if laid on oak boarding may be attacked by the acid in the timber and in time reduced to white powder.

Economics is seen in the amount of money one can afford to invest in building. This must influence the choice of materials and methods so that the best results in each case are attained. For example, it might well be that the best results *in the abstract* would be obtained in a particular case by the use of 18-in.-thick stone walls and a roof of West-

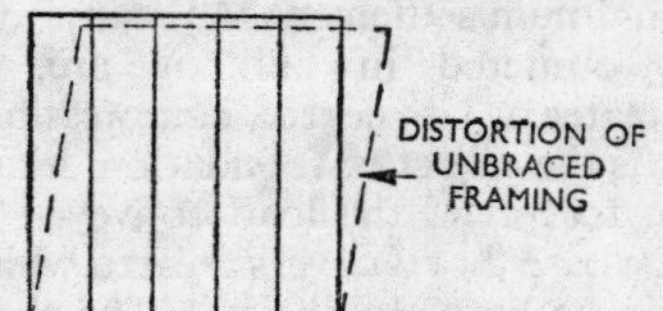

BRACE CHECKS
TENDENCY TO
DISTORTION

Fig. 1. *How the addition of a diagonal brace increases the rigidity of a frame.*

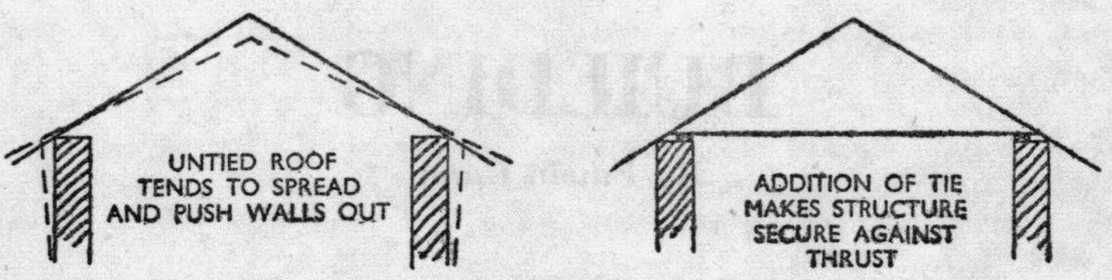

Fig. 2. *Spreading of a pitched roof is prevented by inserting a cross-tie.*

morland slates, but a sufficiently good, and much less costly, result might be reached in, say, 11-in. brick and machine-made tiles, or even in timber framing and cedar shingles.

Problems of Siting

Site problems are in the main two: the choice of site, and the placing of any building thereon when selected. When you are considering the suitability of any building site, examine it carefully on the following practical points: (1) It should not be subject to seasonal flooding; (2) its subsoil should not be likely to become waterlogged (as in some cases where an apparently good gravel soil overlies a bed of clay); (3) from its levels it should admit of good drainage with, alternatively, outlet to public sewers, or space within its boundaries to permit disposal of drainage upon the site (see Lesson 14); (4) it should afford a reliable foundation for any structure proposed; (5) it should not be subject to any likelihood of nuisance from adjoining or near-by properties; (6) liability falling on the owner for such matters as fencing, road work or maintenance should be clearly defined; (7) the existence of any restrictive covenants on the use of the land, or of any "easements" to other property-owners, or of liability for tithes or similar payments, should be ascertained.

Give careful study on the spot to determine the exact position on a site in which a building should be placed. In the case of a commonplace rectangular suburban plot, controlled by a "building line," one has little choice, but even in such circumstances there are occasions when, by retiring behind the prescribed line, advantage may be gained. It may, for instance, be possible to retain some natural feature such as a tree or hedge, or to place the house on higher land, or with side outlook clear of adjoining buildings, though it must not be overlooked that such retirement usually involves increased cost in paths and drains, and in water, gas and electric services.

On a rural or free-standing site the choice of correct position is of greater importance and allows greater latitude. Sites, however, vary so widely that detailed advice covering all eventualities is impossible; but the factors given above as to choice of site should each be weighed carefully.

Foundations

A good foundation is one which will sustain any load placed upon it either (*a*) without sinking, or (*b*) with an evenly distributed and minimum settlement. As many soils encountered in building are, in greater or less degree, compressible, it is the object of foundation design so to spread the load conveyed to the base that it covers an area which can be borne by the soil. The characteristics of the principal soils when used as foundations are as follows:

Rock (*including Chalk*). Incompressible and excellent as a foundation, needing only levelling, so as to counter any tendency for the complete structure to slide. This may be accomplished either by cutting down to a level, or by filling up uneven surfaces with the minimum quantity of concrete.

Gravel. Incompressible and good, provided the gravel bed is deep and does not overlie clay, in which case submerged pools are liable to form in wet seasons. In rare cases liability to shrinkage and settlement may arise from the drainage of water from the gravel bed, taking with it the finer sandy particles.

Sand can be an excellent foundation provided that it is *contained*, and thus prevented from escaping or washing away. To secure these conditions is often beyond the possibilities of minor building operations, and it is therefore to be distrusted.

Clay and loam are in greater or less degree compressible, but they are subject to shrinkage and distortion in periods of drought. In ordinary conditions they may be affected to a depth of 4 ft., but this may be exceeded in exceptional years. As a high proportion of building sites offer a clay foundation, this type will be the best for detailed consideration.

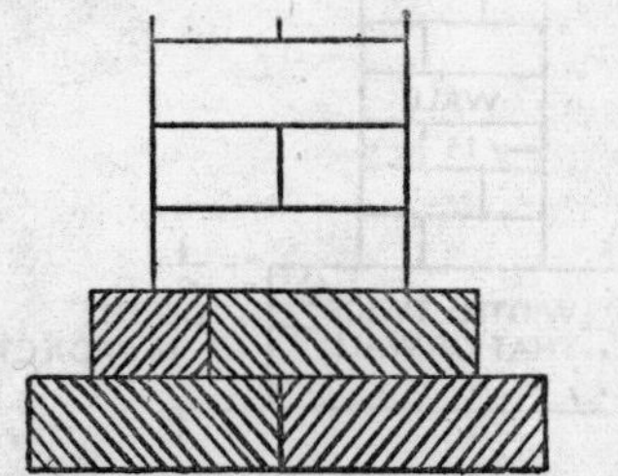

Fig. 3. *Formerly, brick or stone footings were used to strengthen the base of a wall.*

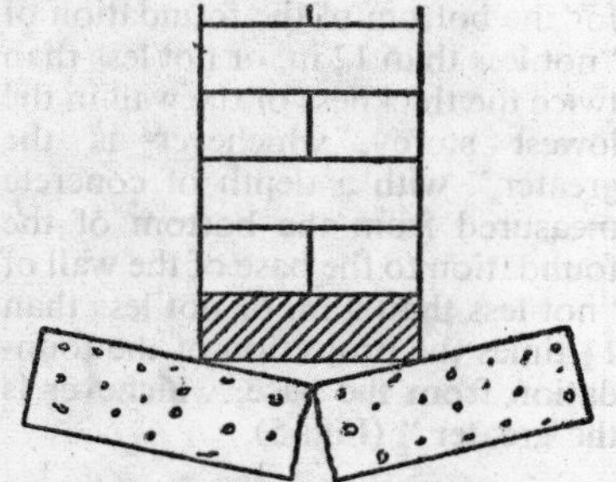

Fig. 4. *A cement concrete foundation slab may fracture if too thin to sustain the weight of the wall resting on it.*

Foundation design aims at an immovable base for building on, and may be divided roughly into two types: (1) that which attempts to reach an incompressible stratum, either in a continuous foundation trench or by a series of piers or piles; (2) that which (relying on a compressible soil) attempts, by spread of foundation and even distribution of the weight of the building, to secure a minimum and equal settlement. In its extreme form this second type may result in the "raft" foundation—a continuous platform beneath the whole building, the simplest form of which is the concrete floor-slab, on which may be built a light timber garden shed or garage.

Taking class (1), it was customary, before the introduction of Portland-cement concrete, to obtain the requisite spread and continuity of foundation at the base of a wall by projecting "footings" of brick or stone (Fig. 3). The convenience and economy of cement concrete as a foundation have made footings by means of brick offsets unnecessary, provided that the slab of concrete substituted is of sufficient thickness to sustain the central load of wall or pier without fracture (Fig. 4). The latest model bylaws issued by the Ministry of Health prescribe a width for the bottom of the foundation of "not less than 12 in. or not less than twice the thickness of the wall in the lowest storey, whichever is the greater," with a depth of concrete measured from the bottom of the foundation to the base of the wall of "not less than 9 in. or not less than 1⅓ times the projection of the foundation from the base, whichever is the greater" (Fig. 5).

Trench Foundations

When building on a clay soil with trench foundations, trench and concrete should be extended across any opening (such as a doorway) which reaches to ground level, and it is advisable to insert a few reinforcing rods across angles. Where the trench bottoms seem to be unequal in substance—softer in some parts than in others—it is wise to run such reinforcing rods continuously throughout; this is usually better than the alternative of taking out extra depth from soft places, as foundations on clay with their bottoms at different levels are apt to produce uneven settlement and fractures during drought.

In class (2), raft foundations require special care in design to ensure as nearly as may be an even distribution of loading and regularity of shape. A rectangular plan without projecting wings lends itself best to this type of base, and to prevent the loading being concentrated along the outer edge of the raft, it is advisable to plan fireplaces on internal walls towards the centre of the area covered (see cottage in Lesson 12). In the case of a raft which is too big to be completed in one continuous operation, the reinforcement should be left projecting where the join is to come, and the edge of the concrete exposed should be coated with a slurry of neat cement and water immediately before resumption of work.

Average safe loads on foundations are usually assumed as 4 tons per square foot on chalk, gravel or blue clay and 2 tons per square foot on yellow clay. Good cement concrete may be safely loaded up to 12 tons per square foot.

A concrete foundation does not (as many people appear to imagine) exercise any magical quality apart from its application on lines just described. The aim in good foundation concrete is to proportion the mixture so that a dense and solid substance without voids results. To achieve this, three components are needed—gravel or broken stone, sand or grit, and cement. The gravel

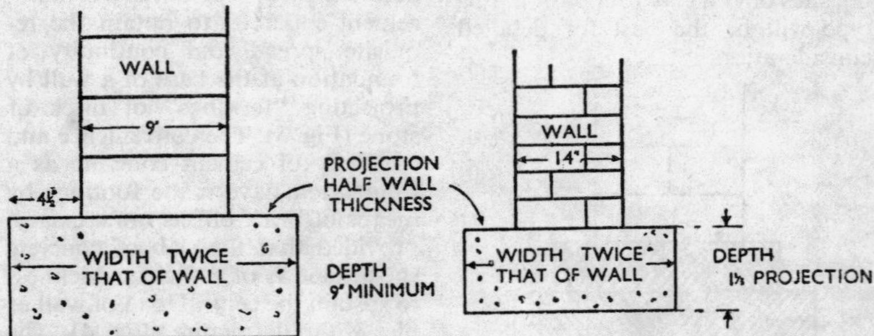

Fig. 5. *A concrete foundation should be twice as wide, and two-thirds as thick, as the wall it supports, with a minimum width of 12 in. and depth of 9 in.*

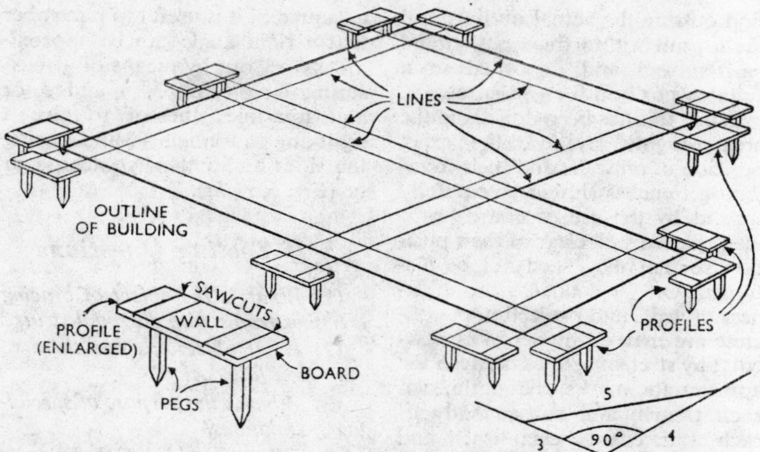

Fig. 6. *Positions of walls and foundation trenches can be marked on board profiles set as here indicated. Stretched lines mark outlines of trenches and walls.*

(coarse aggregate) supplies the substance and strength against compression or crushing; the function of the sand is to fill all the spaces between the individual stones, and the cement should be sufficient in quantity to ensure that every particle both of stone and sand is completely coated and in contact. In everyday use and with suitable clean materials properly graded in size you produce these conditions by using 6 parts of gravel, 2 parts of sand, 1 part of cement, with water sufficient in quantity to colour the mixture. Too much water will tend to separate the materials, or even to wash away the cement and weaken the concrete.

The important points in mixing small batches of concrete are, briefly: (1) the operation should be performed on a clean platform, which may be either of boards or on a cement-paved space; (2) the gravel and sand should be measured and well mixed dry; (3) the measured cement should be added and the whole mixture turned over at least twice dry, so that all material appears covered by cement; (4) water should be added by a fine rose without force, the mixture being again turned over so as to be completely moistened; (5) the concrete should be mixed in no greater quantity than can be placed in position within half an hour; (6) it should be deposited gently—not shot from a height—and gently rammed to a level. Too much ramming tends to bring the finer ingredients up to the surface, where they form a dusty deposit after setting.

Concrete in foundation-trenches will usually keep moist long enough to allow proper setting to occur; rafts or paving and cast concrete products such as lintels require to be kept moist for at least 48 hours, either by covering with damp sacks or by watering at intervals.

When the placing of a building has been exactly decided, the first step to be taken is soil-stripping. For this operation the shape of the building should be roughly marked, extending for a few feet in each direction outside the actual outline, and the topsoil within this area should be removed and deposited in a suitable position for garden use.

When this has been done, and the area roughly levelled, the exact position of all walls and their foundation trenches should be carefully set out by the use of board "profiles" placed well clear of their position so that they need not be disturbed. On these boards the thickness of walls and projection of concrete are marked by pencil or saw-cuts; by stretching lines between the appropriate marks the outline of each trench, and subsequently of each wall, can be established and worked to as required (Fig. 6).

To ensure all angles being right angles and the building "square," a long "set square" of boards is used, the longest straight line being first laid down and adjacent sides worked from that. In the absence of a "square," it is useful to remember that a right angle can be approximately set out by means of a measuring tape using 3, 4 and 5 or any multiples thereof to give a right-angled triangle—3 and 4 being the sides and 5 the hypotenuse or tie (Fig. 6, *right*).

Self Testing Questions

(1) *What is the object of bracing a timber frame with diagonal struts?*

(2) *What objections are there to clay as a foundation?*

(3) *What is the purpose of spreading foundations?*

(4) *What should be the aim in proportioning materials for concrete?*

(5) *What is a "profile" as used in setting-out?*

THE ANSWERS ARE ON PAGE 65.

LESSON 2

Wall Structure

WALLS, which are primarily for enclosure, have usually been made to perform at the same time the function of supporting floors and roofs. So long as aerial warfare threatens it may be necessary to vary this procedure. Two courses are possible as counter-measures to the effect of high explosives: (*a*) The use of heavy and solid masses which will resist effectively, and (*b*) independent support of floor and roof structures as frame construction (steel or reinforced concrete) with relatively thin panel enclosure walls that can be destroyed without wrecking the whole portion affected. As the first method would be too costly, it appears likely that the second may become general, unless world conditions improve greatly.

The problem of thin wall construction is twofold: the wall must be strong enough to stand and resist any stresses to which it will normally be subjected, and it must exclude the weather—wind, rain, frost and damp. The latter is the more difficult task. Walls may be built up of independent units—stone, brick, concrete blocks or slabs; or they may be cast in position from concrete, plain or reinforced—the latter seeking to reduce bulk by using embedded metal to supplement the

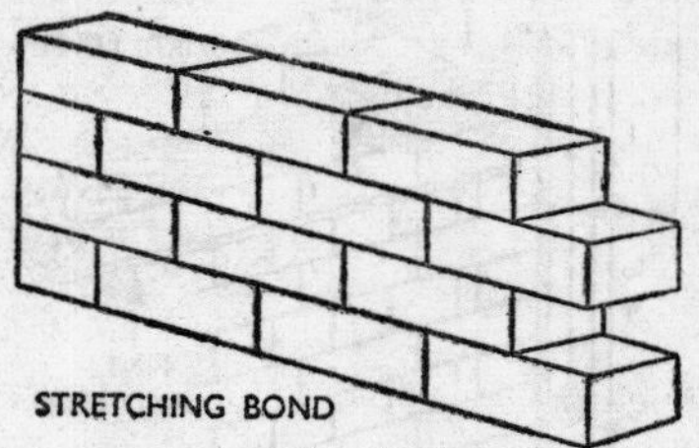

Fig. 7. *In stretching bond all bricks show their long face as "stretchers."*

concrete at its points of weakness.

Both types of wall consist of aggregate and matrix—the equivalent of bricks and mortar. The aggregate supplies the bulk or substance, and the matrix (or jointing material) cushions the separate pieces while plastic and unites them when "set." In brickwork, or any block construction, strength is obtained by "bonding," which is a self-explanatory term, and by well-filled joints. In concrete construction it is obtained by correct proportion of components (as already described) and by the right procedure in mixing, placing and ramming.

Bonding

The common brick with its adjacent joint occupies a space in the wall 9 in. long, 4½ in. wide and 3 in. high. The thinnest wall possible is thus 4½ in. thick. This cannot be expected to exclude dampness, besides being very cold. The "bond" of such a wall is the simplest possible, and is called "stretching" bond, all bricks used (except where cut for angles and openings) showing their long face, in which position they are known as "stretchers," the shorter end-face when shown being called "headers" (Fig. 7).

To obtain greater strength and increased resistance to penetration, we have the cavity wall, consisting of two entirely separate 4½-in. walls divided by a 2-in. cavity crossed only by twisted metal ties so that a layer of imprisoned air prevents the passage of moisture and insulates against fluctuations of temperature (Fig. 8). The metal ties *must* be kept clear of mortar-droppings. As an alternative to the cavity wall, which needs both skill and care in construction, walls may be built 9 in. thick and covered with water-repellent coatings of cement or roughcast, or they may be 14 in. thick or more, when they should need no protective additions.

Walls 9 in. thick or over require careful consideration to be given to "bond." There are two main methods in use, known respectively as "English" and "Flemish bond" (Fig. 9). In the former alternate courses consist each of headers and stretchers entirely; in the latter, alternate headers and stretchers are laid in each course with an arrangement on face so that each header lies centrally over the stretcher below. That is the essence of "bond," and complications only occur at angles, openings or other places which

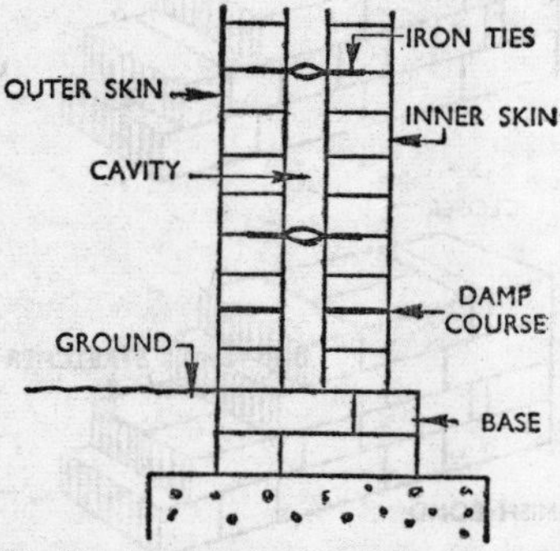

Fig. 8. *A cavity wall has two layers of bricks, each 4½ inches thick, enclosing a 2-in. cavity crossed by metal ties.*

cause regularity to be interrupted. It will be clear that, if all dimensions horizontally are designed as multiples of brick width (4½ in.) and vertically of brick height (3 in.), the simplicity of building is greatly helped. In straightforward work the bricklayer needs few tools; with trowel, level, plumb-rule, pins and line, most simple buildings can be competently built, and of these all but the trowel can be quite successfully home-made (Fig. 10).

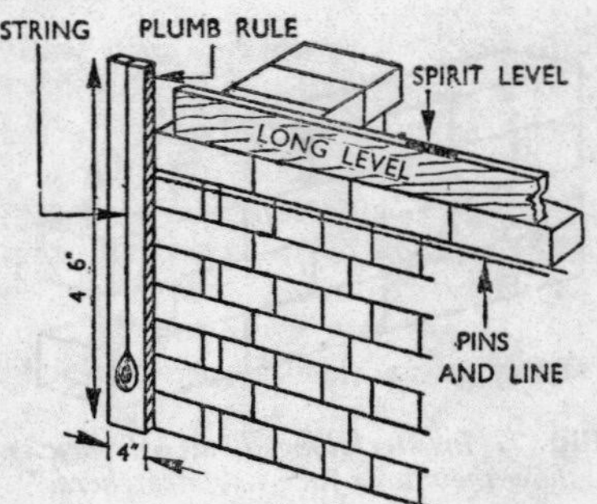

Fig. 10. *These, with the trowel, are the tools used in simple bricklaying.*

Mixing Mortar

The mixing and use of mortar can be greatly simplified by using modern means.

To make a mixture combining the advantages of lime-mortar and cement with ease in preparation and use, take ten to twelve measured parts (by bulk) of clean sharp sand and 3 parts grey stone lime. Mix them together with water on a clean platform, preparing a heap sufficient for the job in hand. This can be done best by making a ring of the sand, then placing the lime in the middle and slaking it with a moderate amount of water, finally turning them over together with hoe or shovel until well mixed. As each batch is to be used, 1 part of fresh Portland cement to 8 to 10 parts of the mixed mortar should be added and worked well in. By this means a bulk supply can be prepared. A more rapid initial set is given to the joints than would occur with lime mortar; while the "sharpness" and shrinkage usual with cement mortar are greatly reduced. Furthermore, if good mortar beds are laid and all joints well filled by tapping each brick well home so as to squeeze mortar beyond the face, satisfactory facework can be made without "pointing"—by merely scraping off superfluous mortar with the edge of the trowel as work progresses.

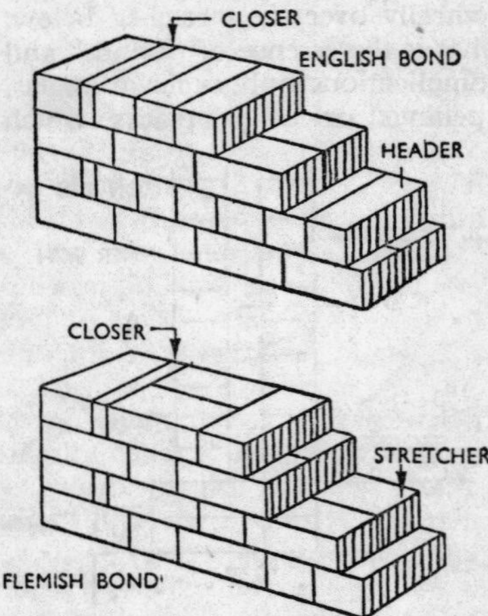

Fig. 9. *How bricks are arranged in English* (above) *and Flemish bond* (below).

Work built in this way is less subject to frost damage than if joints are raked out and pointed with mortar of a different consistency. The work also looks well in the mass.

Concrete Walls

Concrete walls built of cast blocks resemble brick walls in stretching bond to enlarged scale. This method of wall-making, however, is less speedy than one thinks, for the blocks are heavy to lift and put into place. All joints in such walls extend straight through without a break, so either special care or some form of block embodying a check is desirable to increase the strength. The *vertical* joints are the main source of weakness.

Concrete slab walls can be constructed on similar principles to brick cavity walls, using slabs 18 in. long by 9 in. high by 4 in. thick in two "skins." In such work it is advisable to use a dense concrete for the outside slab and a porous one (breeze or clinker) for the inner face. Iron ties are used as in brick cavity walling. Special care is needed to see that all vertical joints are well filled. Note, too, that mortar is apt to fall off the slab-ends during handling.

Cast concrete walls (in situ). Yet another method is to mould the walls directly from concrete. For this, concrete must be placed in shuttering or "forms" built up in the required position. Such walls have their own special disadvantages. The joints of ordinary brick or block walls, which are often thought of as a source of weakness, actually permit the unavoidable movements due to expansion and contraction caused by temperature changes and to minor ground sinkings to take place without ill effect. But in concrete work moulded *in situ* no such latitude exists. Hence, unless such walls include special "expansion joints" or metal reinforcements against the stresses developed, unsightly and troublesome cracks, which are impossible to repair permanently, are certain to arise in all but the smallest structure.

It is practicable, however, to make a concrete base-wall for a small timber structure, such as a shed or garage, without extensive precautions—see Fig. 57 later—but the design and construction of any building of greater complication are matters for highly skilled technical work in design and execution.

Skill and foresight are also needed for the contrivance and firm fixing of the timber "forms" in which the concrete is to be cast. This must not only be true in shape and unyielding to the considerable bursting-pressure caused by placing and ramming the concrete, but must also be easily removable, and should be capable of repeated re-use.

The properties of reinforced concrete may, however, be simply and

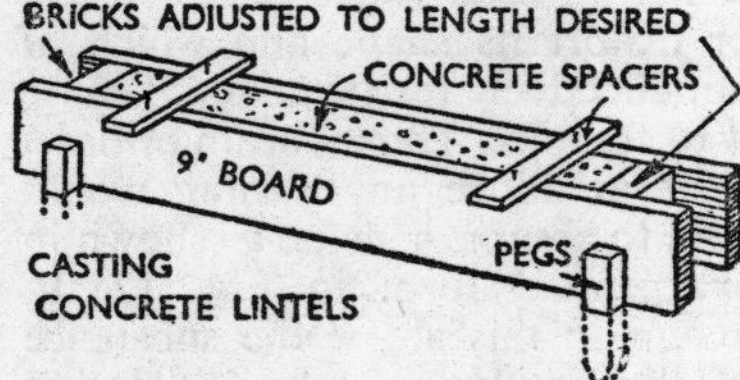

Fig. 11. *Casting concrete lintels on the ground.*

profitably utilised in spanning openings such as doorways and windows, whenever it is necessary to support upper-storey walls. Cast-concrete lintels in such positions are simpler to use than any form of arched construction which would involve timber "centring" and cutting and fitting the surrounding brickwork.

Concrete lintels may be cast in moulds on the ground and raised to their position when set, or, if their size would result in a weight difficult to handle, may be cast in position (Fig. 11). If made on the ground, care must be taken to mark clearly which is top or bottom, so that they may be fixed with the reinforcement in its correct position.

This is a convenient place to describe briefly the theory of reinforcement. Any beam, floor or pillar supporting weight may develop in-

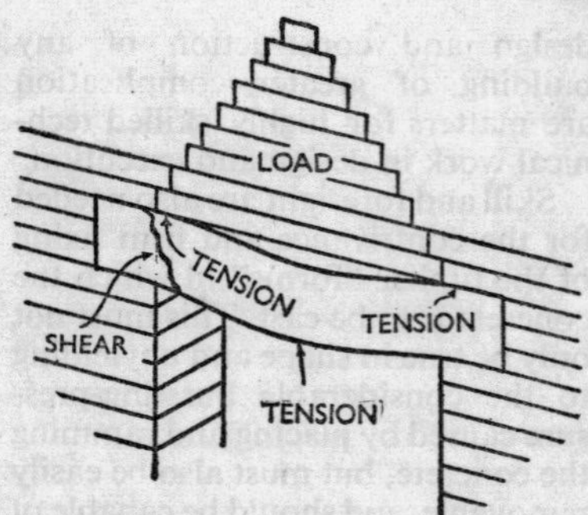

Fig. 12. *Without reinforcement, a lintel above an opening would tend to bend under stress and break at the arrow.*

ternal stresses, which tend to bend or distort its shape and which, if not effectively resisted, would cause it to fracture. Thus a beam or lintel built in above an opening would tend to assume a shape as shown in exaggerated form in Fig. 12. In assuming this shape the substance of the lintel would be in tension (*i.e.*, stretched) at its under-surface towards the centre of the span and in lessening degree towards each support, while at each end the upper surface would be in similar condition. The opposite surface—top or bottom in each case—would be in compression (squeezed), while intermediately the substance would be practically free from stress, the point in depth where tension passes to compression being known as the neutral axis. A further stress, known as "shear," is likely to develop immediately over each support. This tends to sever the beam or lintel more or less vertically on the line shown in Fig. 12. Concrete is itself strong against compression, and in the instance given is capable of resisting any compressive stress likely to arise. But it is relatively weak in tension, and the internal stresses from this cause are taken up by steel rods which may be bent to the line shown, or separately placed in independent lengths (Fig. 13). These rods are the reinforcement. It is usual to employ one rod to each $4\frac{1}{2}$ in. thickness of wall to be supported; *i.e.*, two rods side by side for a 9-in. or 11-in. wall. Shearing stress is not worth consideration in spans up to about 5 ft. with properly bonded walling above, the effect of bond being to reduce the actual amount of wall carried by the lintel to the triangle shown. For greater spans short lengths of reinforcing rod can be placed to counter the stress—as shown at *X* in Fig. 13.

Excluding Damp

It is at jambs and sills that dampness is most commonly allowed to penetrate, but it can be excluded by proper construction. It should be borne in mind that when window-frames are recessed in an external "reveal," all water which runs off the glass surface is caught by the brick or masonry sill, which it tends to saturate. If frames are built in towards the outer face of the wall, the oak sill which is part of the frame can be made to project beyond the wall face and thus throw water clear. The jambs of cavity walling are far too often built solid, thus defeating the object of disconnection at one of the weakest points. Either the cavity should be continued through to the jambs and subsequently closed by fixing slate up the jambs internally before

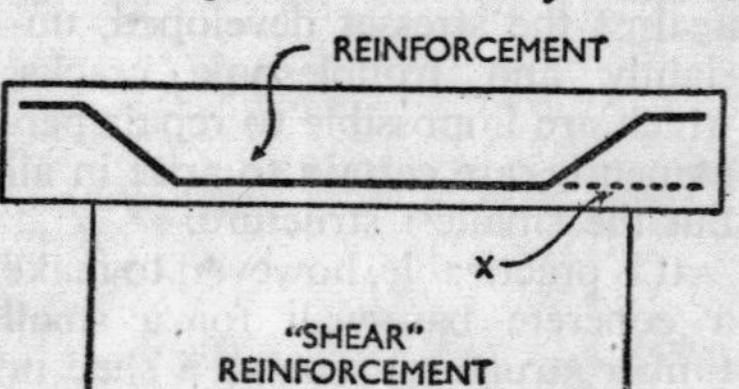

Fig. 13. *Bent steel rods arranged thus reinforce concrete against tension.*

plastering (Fig. 14 *a*), or a similar layer of damp-course material should be built up with the jamb (Fig. 14 *b*) during erection.

All walls should have a damp course at a level at least 6 in. above finished ground surface. In the case of solid walls this will extend through their full thickness, and may be either doubled slates set in cement or roll bitumen.

Cavity walling should have the cavity extended at least 6 in. below the damp course, which is thus divided (Fig. 8). Below that level the cavity may be either filled in with fine concrete, or the base of the wall thickened as shown in the illustration, the latter being preferable. The not uncommon practice of starting the cavity from the damp course extended for the full width of the base is asking for trouble, since the bottom of the cavity is likely to be filled by mortar-droppings which convey moisture across to the inner skin, thus defeating the object of the hollow, and exposing floors and skirtings to conditions favouring decay.

Ground floors constructed of joists and boarding must have the spaces beneath kept dry and ventilated. To secure dryness, the area within the walls should be covered with a layer of cement concrete at least 4 in. thick. On this will be built the "sleeper walls" carrying the timber "plates" to which floor-joists are nailed. These sleeper walls are built "honeycomb," leaving open spaces between the bricks to allow air circulation. Any internal partition walls dividing rooms should also have frequent openings below floor level so that circulation is complete.

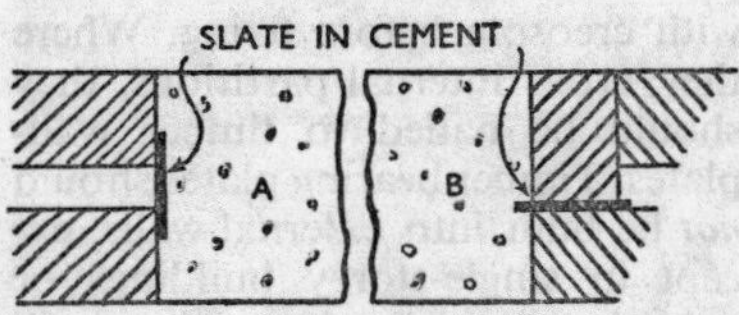

Fig. 14. *Slate is used, thus, to prevent damp from penetrating at window jambs.*

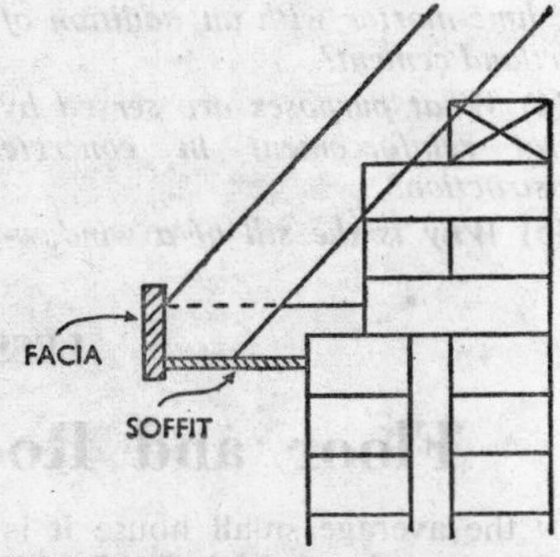

Fig. 15. *The upper courses of a cavity wall should be built over with solid brick.*

To admit fresh air, "air bricks" of cast iron or pottery are built into the external walls on each face of the building. The best position for these is toward the corners of the rooms, since air at the corners tends to stagnate, favouring the growth of fungus decay. Where the walls are cavity walls, the air-brick apertures should be sealed off from the cavities by slates set in cement to exclude mice and other vermin.

To stiffen the construction generally, and to ensure that the outer skin of cavity walls bears part of the load, the upper courses should be built over solid. If a close eaves (boarded-in with facia and soffit) is formed, this can be done as shown in Fig. 15, making the 2-in. reduction in thickness on the outer face. The construction shown is the simplest to execute and maintain.

Self Testing Questions

(1) *What are* (a) *headers;* (b) *stretchers?*

(2) *What are* (a) *English bond;* (b) *Flemish bond?*

(3) *What are the objects of gaug-*

ing lime-mortar with an addition of Portland cement?

(4) *What purposes are served by metal reinforcement in concrete construction?*

(5) *Why is the sill of a window-opening one of the weak spots against damp penetration?*

(6) *What measures should be taken to ventilate spaces below ground-floors?*

THE ANSWERS ARE ON PAGE 66.

LESSON 3

Floor and Roof Construction

In the average small house it is the upper floor which first brings the carpenter upon the scene, the construction of the ground floor being deferred until the building is roofed. This is because the upper floor joists bear upon the walls and partitions, which they do much to stiffen, whereas ground-floor joists which can be supported at close intervals by sleeper walls off the oversite concrete are independent of them and can be lighter in scantling.

Fir timber is usually employed in floor and roof construction, and this is marketed in sizes (called scantlings) varying customarily between 3 in. × $1\frac{1}{2}$ in. and 11 in. × 2 in., though irregular sizes are also obtainable. All such structural timbers are stronger and stiffer if so placed that their greater dimension is perpendicular to the chief stress which they are called upon to resist. This is mathematically expressed in the formula $W = C\frac{bd^2}{L}$, where W equals the weight to be carried, C a "constant" for the material used, b the width and d the depth of the scantling, and L the clear length between supports. From this formula it is apparent that while the strength varies in proportion to the width, it varies also in proportion to the *square* of the depth; *i.e.*, a joist 2 in. × 4 in. set on edge being taken as 2 × 4 × 4 = 32, one which is 2 in. × 6 in. will be proportionately 2 × 6 × 6 = 72, the increase from 2 in. × 4 in. = 8 in. in cross-section to 2 in. × 6 in. = 12 in., making the stiffness not *one and a half* times as much but *two and a quarter* times.

Floor joists are usually spaced 15 in. centre to centre, and at this distance apart and with domestic floor loads the following sizes are usual and sufficient:

Length of bearing in feet.	Size of joist.
Up to 5 ft.	4 in. × 2 in.
5– 8 ft.	6 in. × 2 in.
8–10 ft.	7 in. × 2 in.
10–12 ft.	8 in. × 2 in.
12–14 ft.	9 in. × 2 in.
14–16 ft.	11 in. × 2 in.

Floors having joists 7 in. × 2 in. or over and spans of over 8 ft. should be stiffened by lines of "herringbone strutting" to distribute loading and counter a tendency for joists to overturn.

The joist ends, where built into external walls, should be brushed with creosote before fixing. Where they cross internal partitions, they should be nailed to timber wall-plates. Timber bearing plates should *not* be built into external walls, except in single-storey buildings or gabled cottages, where they will come immediately below the eaves

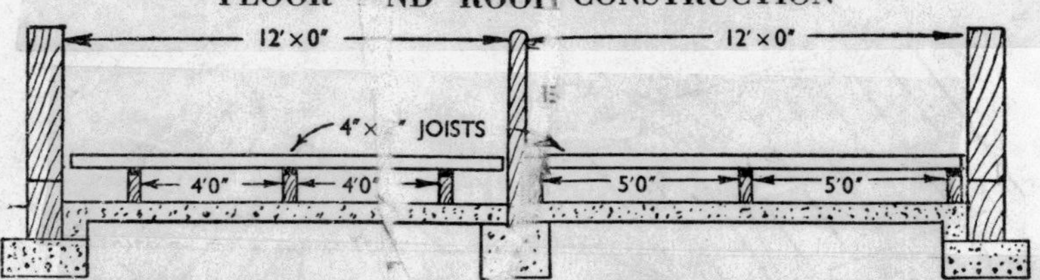

Fig. 16. *Spacing of sleepers. The arrangement at left, with the end sleepers arranged well away from the walls, gives a stiffer floor than that at right.*

and serve to fix the feet of rafters, as in Fig. 55.

The floor construction of most small buildings is what is known as "single"-joists, running one way without intermediate support by beams between walls. In many cases, however, it is better construction and more economical to shorten the span and reverse the direction of joists by introducing one or more beams, the latter also serving to tie the structure in a direction at right angles with the floor joists; an example is given later in Fig. 55.

Ground-Floor Joists

Ground-floor joists are seldom greater in scantling than 4 in. × 2 in., the sleepers being adjusted in spacing to comply with the necessity. The sleeper walls nearest the joist ends need not be close against the walls—in fact they are better not so. The joist ends can be allowed to overhang by any distance not greater than half the effective distance between sleepers; thus a 4 in. × 2 in. joist can project up to 2 ft. 6 in. By spacing sleepers as at Fig. 16, *left*, a stiffer floor is obtained than if the spacing at Fig. 16, *right*, had been followed.

Flat-roof construction resembles floor construction, with the difference that a slope or "fall" must be provided for. When the roof is to be covered with bituminous felt, which requires no "drips" (as customarily provided in lead or zinc roofs), this fall can be very slight—3 in. is quite sufficient for the ordinary house. If a slight departure from level is permissible in the ceilings below, this can be obtained by sloping the joists through a one-course drop from end to end. If a level ceiling is desired, the joists are fixed flat and "firred up" by nailing tapered pieces above each to receive the roof boarding, or, still better, by laying, above them and across, lighter joists either tapered or notched down to give the requisite fall, according to direction. This last has the double advantage that it allows free air-circulation around the timbers and permits the boarding to be laid lengthwise to the fall, so that any curling which may occur does not result in pools, but produces a series of channels toward the gutter edge of the roof (Fig. 17).

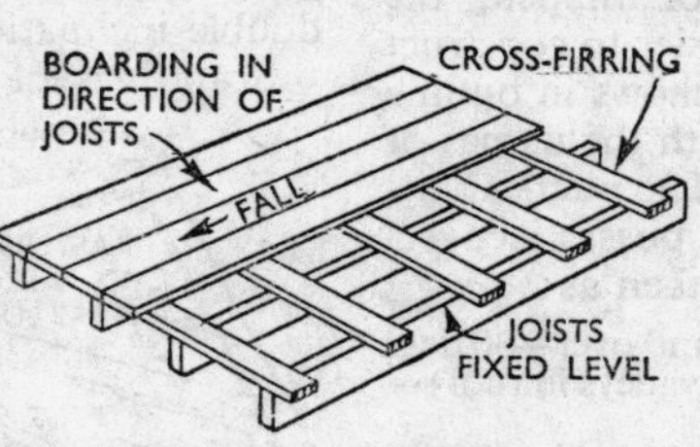

Fig. 17. *Fall in a flat roof over a level ceiling is secured by laying tapered "cross-firring" boards above and at right angles to the ceiling joists.*

Pitched roofs intended to be covered with slates or tiles introduce a new factor—if the rafters are not securely tied, their

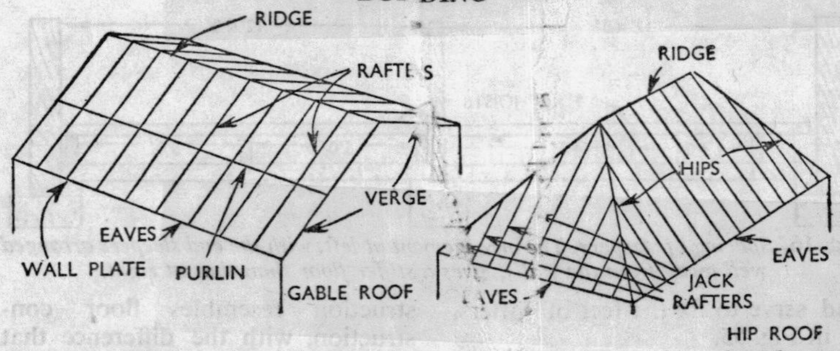

Fig. 18. *Parts in outline of* (left) *a gable and* (right) *a hipped roof.*

thrust will push the supporting walls outward; the flatter the pitch the greater the thrust, assuming the weight of the roofs to be equal. In minor building the roof thrust is usually tied by ceiling joists, either between the rafter-feet, constituting a "couple-close" roof, or at some distance above, the latter arrangement being known as a "collar roof." Rafters are supported intermediately by purlins, which are strutted by inclined timbers having a bearing on internal partitions or on beams. At the ridge, rafters are joined on a ridge-board, against which they are butted and nailed. In small house construction it is not usually necessary to include roof trusses composed of principal rafters, tie-beams, posts and struts, all of which support purlins which carry the common rafters. Simple roofs may be either gabled or hipped, the former being the easier to construct and cover. Fig. 18 shows in outline these two forms, with the names of their several parts. The pitches suitable to the various possible coverings are generally taken as:

Slates 16 in. × 8 in. and over—30 deg.
Plain tiles (without valleys in roof)—40 deg.
Plain tiles (with intersections producing valleys)—45 deg. but preferably 50 deg.
Pantiles, double Roman tiles and similar types (underlined)—30 deg.

In preparing roof timbers a level space of ground is required—a lawn or meadow is excellent. The scantlings are laid out, measured and marked, pegs driven temporarily being a useful aid. The bevels at head and feet can be determined and marked in this way, and subsequently cut to the marks made. Notches where the rafters are to fit over wall-plates are similarly marked and cut. The tools required are simple—measuring rod, adjustable square by which angles can be read and marked, and ripsaw complete the equipment (Fig. 19).

Jack Rafters

A hip roof produces further complication; the rafters abutting on the hips (known as jack rafters) vary in length, and the cuts at their heads are not easy to determine without geometrical skill, as they have a double inclination.

Scantlings of fir timber suitable

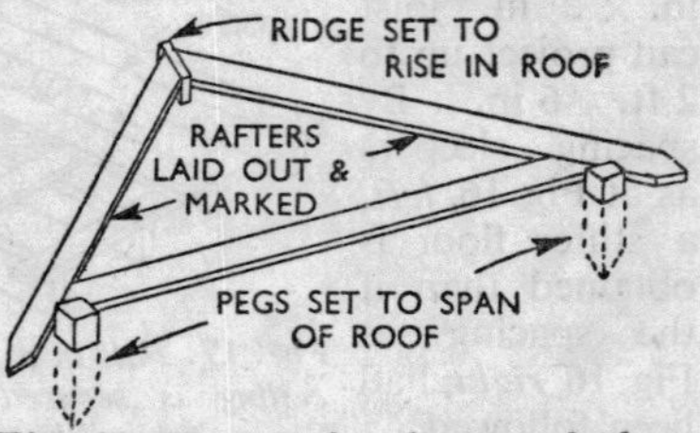

Fig. 19. *How roof timbers are laid out on a piece of level ground for marking.*

for simple roof structures, utilising stock sizes, may be taken as:

	Length of bearing (between wall-plates, purlins or other support).
Common rafters	6 ft. size 4 in. × 2 in.
	8 ft. „ 4½ in. × 2 in.
	10 ft. „ 5 in. × 2 in.

Rafters less than 2 in. on face are liable to split under nailing.

	Distance between bearings.	Spacing between purlins and sizes.
Purlins	6 ft.	6 ft.; 6 in. × 3 in.
		7 ft.; 6 in. × 4 in.
	8 ft.	6 ft.; 7 in. × 4 in.
		7 ft.; 8 in. × 4 in.

In erecting roof timbers it is convenient to raise two pairs of rafters

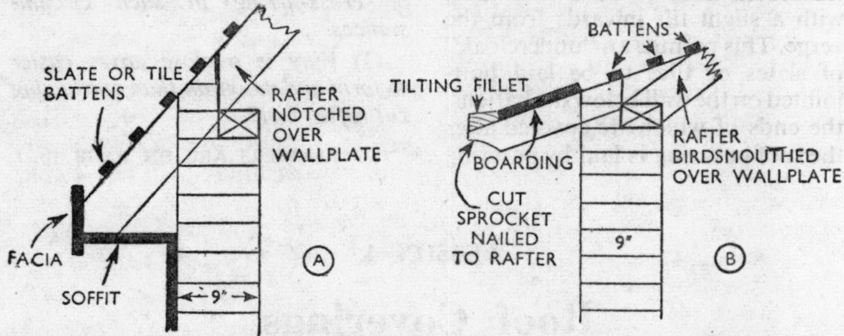

Fig. 20. *Two methods of forming a projecting eaves at the margin of the roof.*

(not necessarily in their final positions) which will support the ridge-piece, as a preliminary to the proper spacing and fixing of the remainder. The ceiling joists or collars may next be fixed, and the purlins finally placed in position, strutted and nailed. Ridges and hip rafters are not heavily loaded, and serve principally as a convenient means of joining common rafters which abut against them; valley rafters, on the contrary, serve to support the feet of all common rafters which bear on them. Hence ridges and hips may be relatively light, provided they are deep enough to receive the oblique-cut ends of rafters—7 in. × 1½ in. is usually sufficient. Valleys, except in short lengths such as might serve for dormer windows or small gables, need to be stronger—say 8 in. × 2 in. or more. It should be remembered that once *sufficient* strength and stiffness are attained in a set of roof timbers, any unnecessary increases in size and weight add to the load and possible thrust to be borne by the walls, so that heavier timbers than are required are not merely wasteful but may be harmful.

The design of the marginal finish of roofs should be carefully considered. A projecting eaves gives valuable protection to the walls and also to window-heads close below. The eaves may be formed by continuation of common rafters notched over the wall-plate (Fig. 20, *A*), or by the addition of separate lengths of timber (known as "sprockets") spiked to the rafters. In the latter case the eaves may be given a slight tilt or "bellcast" (Fig. 20, *B*), which allows greater height in the window heads and improves the lie of the slates or tiles on the roof. Sprockets are usually more economical in timber, but less so in labour, since shorter rafters are required, whereas the sprocket pieces can be cut from waste ends, but require separate preparation and fixing.

Eaves may be "open" or "close"; in the former the rafter feet are exposed and usually "wrought" (that is, planed smooth), with close-boarding in place of battens from gutter to wall (Fig. 20, *B*). Close eaves are formed by fixing facia and soffit boards as shown in Fig. 20, *A*—in the long run this is most economical, particularly if this eaves has to be painted—and it gives the easiest fixing for an iron eaves-gutter.

The verge treatment at a gable end is most simply dealt with by adjusting the end pair of rafters so that the slate or tile battens can run over the top of the gable end to within an inch or so of the face, with a slight tilt inwards from the verge. This permits an "undercloak" of slates or tiles to be laid butt-jointed on the wall below the battens, the ends of which are covered after the roof covering is laid by pointing up the space between undercloak and roof-covering, giving a thick strong verge not easily damaged (Fig. 21).

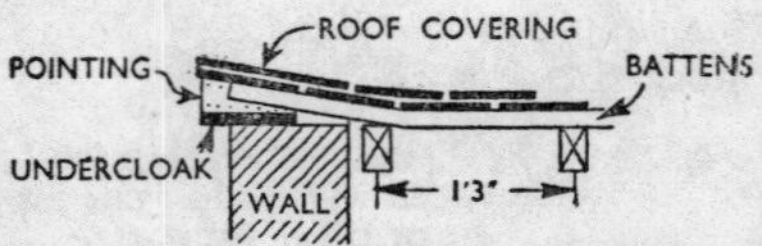

Fig. 21. *Treatment of verge at gable end, showing undercloak of tile or slate.*

Self Testing Questions

(1) *What is the action of herring-bone strutting used in a joisted floor?*

(2) *When are joists "firred up," and what are the relative advantages of cross-firring in such circumstances?*

(3) *Why is a close eaves easier to form and maintain than one having cut rafter feet?*

THE ANSWERS ARE ON PAGE 66.

LESSON 4

Roof Coverings

PITCHED roofs are covered so as to be water-shedding in a manner which can be simply described as natural—thatch follows the principle of an animal's fur, and slate or tile that of a bird's feathers. The important points to be ensured are lap, bond and freedom for minor adjustments due to structural movements. A grasp of these principles will enable any roofing problem to be overcome.

Slates are a natural product hand-split from slate-rock and dressed to shape. Customary sizes range between 12 in. × 6 in. up to 24 in. × 12 in., the commonest sizes being 20 in. × 10 in., known as "Countess," and the 16 in. × 8 in., known as "Ladies." Price varies according to stock, and it is unwise to insist on obtaining any special size—particularly "Countess," which is most in demand, and consequently dearer.

When fixed on a roof, slates are nailed to battens, usually 2 in. × $\frac{3}{4}$ in. in section. These are spaced to give adequate lap of each course of slates over the head of the next course but one below, the spacing being known as the "gauge," which is also equal to the "margin" or portion of each course exposed below the tails of the course above. The "lap" is consequently the balance of the slate length after reckoning twice the gauge—*i.e.*, slates 16 in. long set to a gauge of 6 in. would have a lap of 4 in.; 6 in. + 6 in. + 4 in. = 16 in. "Bond" in regular-sized slating is accomplished by breaking joint in each successive course so that the centre of each slate in a course lies over the side joints of the course below it. Where a verge is reached at a gable-end, wider slates, known as "slate and a half," should be used in alternate courses to maintain bond and avoid the use of narrow slips (Fig. 22).

Slates are fixed to the battens by nailing, the nails used being of copper or yellow composition; this is important, as the life of the roof depends usually on the permanence of the nails. Iron nails (even if galvanised) should be avoided, and zinc nails perish in many atmospheres. The nail holes are punched on the site, and are usually placed just above the centre of the slate's length, so as to come above the heads of the course below, and well covered by the lap. They are about 1¼ in. in from the edges. This method is known as "centre-

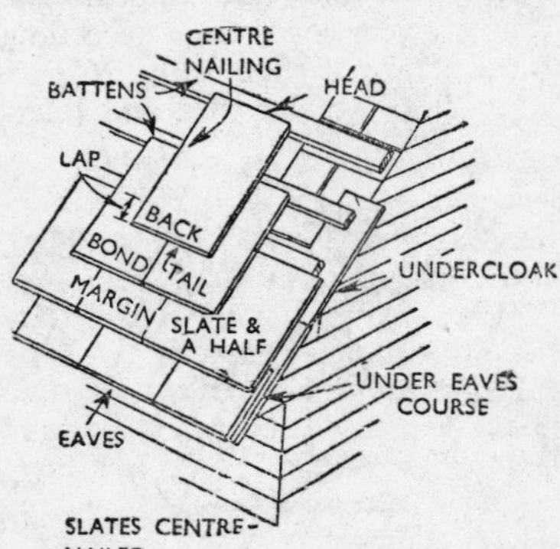

Fig. 22. *Terms used in roof slating, and the method of arranging slates, are here illustrated; note slate and a half at verge.*

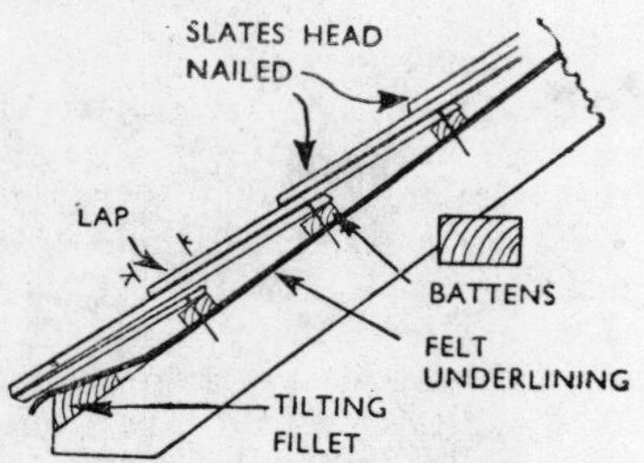

Fig. 23. "*Head-nailed*" (*as above*) *are less secure than* "*centre-nailed*" *slates.*

nailed." By an alternative known as "head-nailed" the nail holes are punched close to the head of each slate, but this method gives less secure fixing (Fig. 23).

In order that the tails of each course of slates may lie close upon the surface below and not "ride," slates must be given a good initial tilt at the eaves. A shorter course of slates is fixed here, known as the "under-eaves" course, and a similar course finishes the slating below the ridge, which is covered usually by tile ridging—preferably *not* red in colour, but blue or grey. Ridging of sawn slates and lead ridging are also in use.

Pitch, size and lap are closely related. A general rule which may safely be followed is: "the smaller the slate the steeper the pitch, and the lower the pitch the greater the lap." Taking 20 in. × 10 in. slates laid at 30° pitch with 3½-in. lap as standard, it should be possible to judge what variations are advisable as these factors are varied. All roofs are improved by underlining, and, with modern materials such as reinforced bituminous felt available, there is no excuse for omitting this inexpensive additional precaution against leakage, draughts and frost. The felt can be laid directly on the rafters and secured by the battens, and should be run

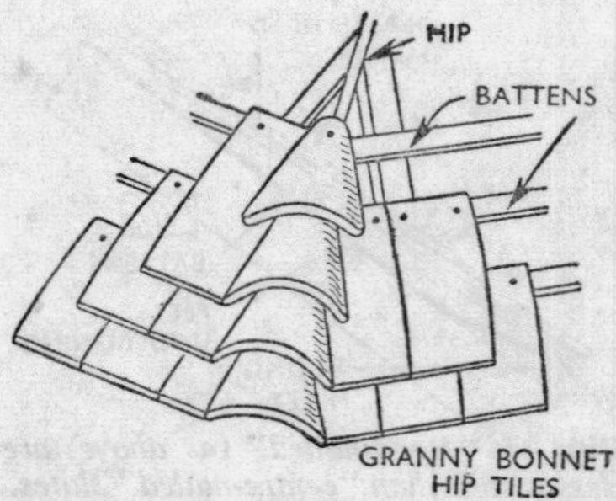

Fig. 24. *Curved intersection tiles are manufactured for covering hips.*

parallel to eaves and ridge, with a 3-in. lap in the direction of the fall.

Plain tiles $10\frac{1}{2}$ in. × $6\frac{1}{2}$ in. to 11 in. × 7 in. are laid upon similar principles of gauge and lap to slating, but, being constant in size, present less opportunity of variation. At usual pitches 4-in. gauge is customary.

Tiles, being plastically fashioned, are given a curvature or "camber" in length which assists the tails to lie close; nail holes and "nibs" are also fashioned during manufacture, and the possession of nibs has led to a practice of nailing only every fourth or fifth course, relying on weight and nibs for securing the remainder.

The special sizes required at eaves, ridge and verge (as in slating) are in tiling fashioned in manufacture, and, additionally, curved intersection tiles capable of covering valleys and hips are obtainable (Fig. 24). In slated roofs such junctions must be made by cutting to a line over a lead valley or to an independently covered hip. Battens for tiling are usually $1\frac{1}{2}$ in. × $\frac{3}{4}$ in., and similar provisions to those already described as to underlining and nails are advisable.

Asbestos-cement diagonal tiling is based on Continental slating practice and gives a light, cheap and waterproof roof, but also one subject to extremes of heat and cold.

The tiles are $15\frac{3}{4}$ in. square and have minimum lap of $2\frac{3}{4}$ in. at the edges alone, so that the greater part of the roof is covered by one thickness only, against the double thickness of slate and treble of plain tiles. The usual gauge is $8\frac{1}{8}$ in., and each tile is secured by two nails to the batten and by a copper rivet passed upward through its lower point and clinched above (Fig. 25).

Square-cover slates of shapes similar to natural slating are also made. Various colours are available, the cheapest being natural grey. Either this colour or russet-brown are preferable to the so-called "red," which is either a hot crimson or a sickly pink, and has created a great prejudice against this roofing.

Shingles or wood tiles, which have long been the common domestic roofing of America, are now gaining ground in this country. The best shingles are of Western red cedar, sold in bundles 16 in. long. They give a light, warm and windproof roof of reasonable durability and pleasant appearance. They are very easily fixed according to the arrangements in Fig. 26.

Pantiles, Roman tiles and inter-

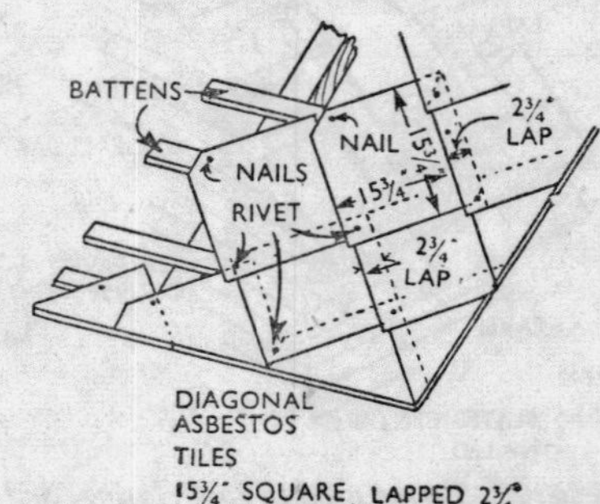

Fig. 25. *Arrangement of asbestos-cement diagonal tiles, showing fastenings.*

locking tiles of numerous types, all deriving from the ridge and furrow type, require considerable skill and judgment in adjusting design, and in laying. They are relatively large units with little facility for variation in lap or spacing, so that care has to be taken that the surface to be covered will accommodate an exact number of tiles in each direction. Thus used, the "double Roman" type makes one of the cheapest of permanent roof coverings. It is 16½ in. × 14 in. in size, and is laid

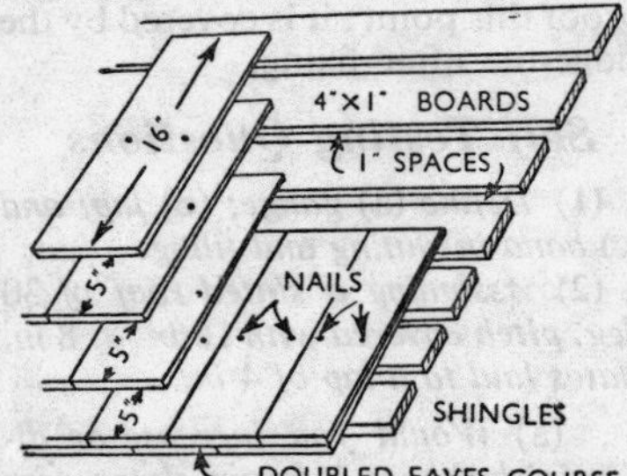

Fig. 26. *Method of nailing and arranging shingles or wood tiles.*

85 to the square (100 ft. super of roof) on 2 in. × 1 in. battens, which should be spaced only on receipt of tiles, as these are liable to vary slightly in burning. Underlining is almost essential, as only single lap is allowed with ridge and furrow types. An under-eaves course of plain tiles on which the big units can be bedded in cement mortar must be laid if draughts and sparrows are to be excluded (Fig. 27).

Flat roofs, once invariably metal-covered, are now more usually covered with some form of bituminous material—either roll felt or mastic asphalt. Bituminous felt is easier to apply, and, rightly used, makes a successful roof; asphalt is a specialist job requiring the transport of bulky plant which inflates the cost of small areas of roofing.

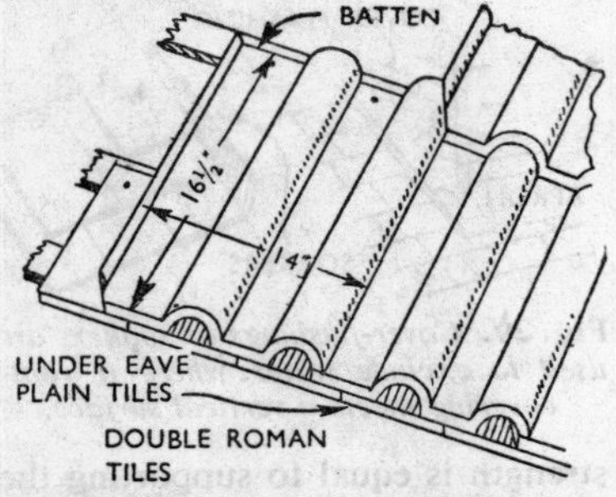

Fig. 27. *Double Roman tiles make a cheap yet permanent roof covering.*

Bituminous felt, under various proprietary names, is usually supplied in rolls 3 ft. wide × 72 ft. long, covering approximately 200 sq. ft. of roof-surface single thickness. Two or more layers should be laid breaking joint, and these are cemented together with a liquid bituminous cement and fixed at edges with ¾-in. galvanised clout nails. Felt should be unrolled and laid out to expand for some hours before fixing. The sheeting is turned up over a 3 in. × 3 in. triangular fillet next any parapet or other wall, and finished at any free edge over an eaves-gutter, as shown in Fig. 28.

If it is likely that the flat roof will be subject to traffic, paving can be laid over the actual waterproof membrane, and this can be either cement, tarmac, tiles or any similar material, provided that structural

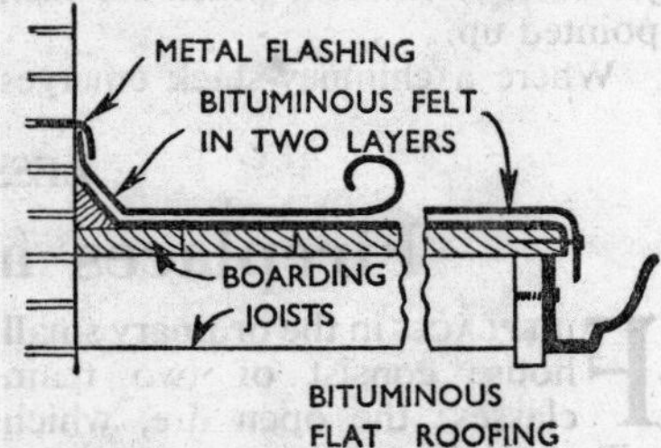

Fig. 28. *Method of finishing bituminous roofing felt over an eaves-gutter.*

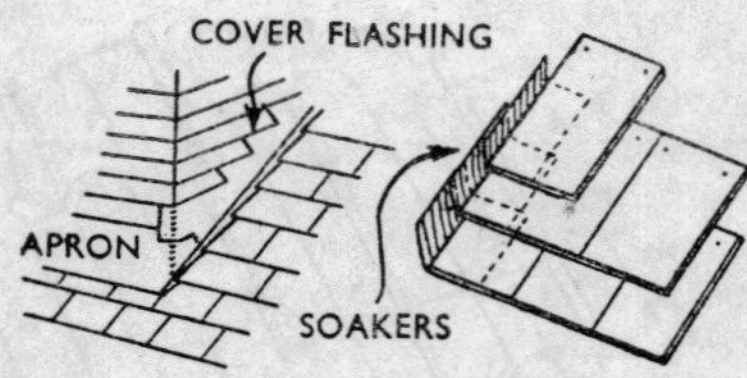

Fig. 29. *Cover-flashings or soakers are used to exclude water where a roof-covering meets a vertical surface.*

strength is equal to supporting the extra weight. Any such covering should lengthen the life of the roof, as the injurious cracking action of ultra-violet rays is prevented by the overlay.

Where a roof-covering abuts against a vertical surface, such as the brickwork of a chimney-stack or parapet, or the side or "cheek" of a dormer, metal soakers, aprons or flashings are required to exclude water. With slating or plain tiling the "soaker" and "cover-flashing" are the simplest expedients.

Soakers are cut out of 4-lb. lead, and have a length equal to the gauge plus the lap plus ½ in. or more for nailing, with a width equal to half the width of the slate plus 1½ in. to 2 in. for the turned-up edge against the wall (Fig. 29). They lie hidden between the slates or tiles, and the upstanding wing is covered by a stepped flashing of lead wedged with lead wedges to raked-out joints in brickwork, which are then pointed up.

Where a chimney-stack emerges from a roof other than at the ridge, some provision must be made behind the stack. The usual resource is a short length of lead gutter, but a better practice is to form a small gabled intersection to the roof-slope, diverting water flowing down the slope to either side of the stack. This is a simpler job if the roof is plain-tiled.

Where a roof-ridge at a lower level intersects a higher roof, a lead saddle-piece must be dressed over the intersection so as to waterproof this point; it is covered by the ridge-tile after fixing.

Self Testing Questions

(1) *Define* (a) *gauge;* (b) *lap; and* (c) *bond in slating and tiling.*

(2) *Assuming a slated roof of* 30 *deg. pitch covered with* 16 *in.* × 8 *in. slates laid to a lap of* 4 *in.*

(a) *Would you increase or diminish the lap if larger slates were used?*

(b) *If the pitch were increased to* 45 *deg., would you prefer larger or smaller slates?*

(3) *In what important characteristics do plain tiles differ from slates?*

(4) *What forms of covering are suitable to flat roofs, and why is one of them now most prevalent?*

(5) *What precaution against leakage is necessary when a roof is pierced by a chimney?*

THE ANSWERS ARE ON PAGE 66.

LESSON 5

Fireplaces and Chimneys

FIREPLACES in the ordinary small house consist of two main classes: the open fire, which still remains the most popular domestic warming device, and the cooker or boiler, which is of "self-setting" type, requiring merely a flue. Other appliances requiring flues for disposal of the products of combustion are gas fires and water-heaters. Electric appliances and gas cookers do not need chimney-flues for efficiency, but their provision is desirable for reasons of ventilation, whenever they can conveniently be planned.

Placing of Chimneys

Close consideration of the placing of fireplaces is a far more important factor in the planning of a dwelling than is commonly realised, and it is a defect of most amateur planning (particularly of bungalows) that single flues are apt to poke up in haphazard fashion, whereas grouping of flues attainable by greater skill results in increased economy and efficiency. It should be remembered that the sole motive power which causes a chimney to fulfil its purpose is the greater density and weight of cold air over hot. Though it is commonly said that hot air (and smoke) rises, this is due to colder and heavier air flowing in and forcing it up.

Pitched Roofs

A further point worth remembering is that chimneys of houses having pitched roofs are less likely to give trouble if they rise from the ridge rather than at eaves level, for the double reason that much less of their surface is exposed to cold and wet, and that the ridge position is free from many curious air-currents likely to cause down-draught in certain directions of the wind. Chimneys rising from eaves level are also often found to conduct moisture which causes damp patches on ceilings and walls immediately below, despite the formation of damp-courses in the actual chimneys above roof level.

Provision for an open fire during building too often consists of the formation of an opening about 3 feet square and 14 inches deep between brick jambs forming a "chimney-breast" and covered by a brick arch or concrete lintel. This customary width and height is a survival of the days when a cast-iron mantel interior was usual. They may profitably be reduced to a size more in accordance with the modern fire-clay component—say 18 inches wide × 27 inches high. If the jambs are less than 14 inches on face it is obligatory to provide a wrought-iron chimney-bar supporting the arch, and having its ends split and turned up and down to resist the tendency of the arch to push the jambs apart.

Flue and Hearth

This construction allows space within the breast above the fire-opening for a flue—usually 9 inches square—and the width of 3 feet is gathered in by a tapered "throat" to this dimension, being also swept to one side if there is a storey over so as to continue in one or other of the jambs of the fireplace above, this being increased to 18 inches on face to contain it.

At each floor level a hearth is formed in and around every fireplace, with the principal object of removing any timber or other inflammable material to a distance of at least 18 inches from the actual fire. Ground storey hearths are usually formed by building a "fender-wall" to support the floor construction and filling in the space enclosed with a hard core of broken brick or stone upon which rests the hearth of concrete and tiles. Upper storeys have their timber floor structures "trimmed" (see Lesson 12) and the hearth-space so formed filled in by a brick half-arch, or by a cast cement slab supported by the timber "trimmers."

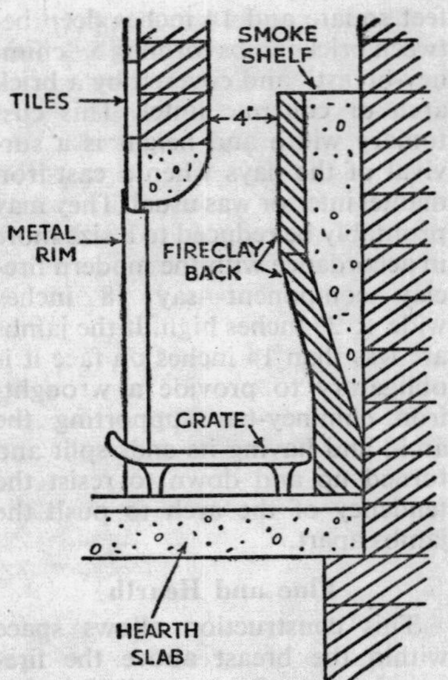

Fig. 30. *Section of fire-grate and flue inlet.*

Grates and Setting

A well-designed modern interior grate has its back and sides fashioned in fireclay on definite principles aimed at full combustion and at the radiation of the utmost heat outward to the room. It may have a movable iron grid bottom, or a base of dished fireclay in sections.

In setting such a grate it is important to observe the following points, neglect of which may cause a sluggish draught, smoking, or other drawbacks.

(1) The back and sides having been placed in position centrally in the opening and hard back against the brickwork, any cavities on either side should be solidly filled in. This may be done either by marking the outline on the base and building it solidly with rough brickwork before placing the fireclay interior finally in position, or by filling fine concrete (not *breeze* concrete, which is inflammable) into each space over the top of the interior in its place.

(2) The treatment of the space between the top of the fireclay interior and the chimney-flue is of vital importance. The aim in setting should be to make the entry to the throating in the form of a slit immediately above the fire and extending to the full width of the grate, having a superficial area equal to that of the flue. If the latter is 9 inches × 9 inches = 81 square inches in size, and if the width of the grate is 20 inches, a slit 4 inches wide (4 inches × 20 inches = 80 inches) will be enough. The height of the fire opening above the hearth has an important influence on the draught. The nearer the grate level this is, the more intense it will be—if too great it may be sluggish; if too little the fire may burn away too fast. A rough guide which has been found effective is to make the height from hearth to lip equal in inches to the height of the chimney top from the same point in feet. The space at the back of the forward-tilted fireclay mass over the fire should be formed into a flat ledge or "smoke-shelf" which is valuable in checking any tendency to down-draught. Fire-grates treated in this way, and with chimneys not grossly inadequate in height, can be relied upon to draw properly and not smoke (Fig. 30).

Chimney Flues and Stacks

In the construction of flues the greatest care is necessary to ensure no restriction in size or obstruction, particularly at bends. This is ensured by what is known as a "core," consisting of a bundle of sacking of the size of the flue suspended on a cord or wire and drawn up the flue as it progresses. Where a bend is formed, maintenance of the full cross-section is ensured by giving a rise of two brick courses to the upper side before gathering over. Flues should be rendered internally as built (known as pargetting), and this operation, which was formerly done with cow-dung mortar, is now usually done in cement and sand.

Where standing above the roof, the chimney is exposed to very trying conditions of alternating heat, cold, dryness, and soaking. It is usual to build such parts in mortar gauged with cement. A weathered cap should be formed to prevent rain and soot falling on the chimney top from streaking down the surface.

For a pot there is nothing sounder or better in appearance than a 9 in. circular flue liner, bedded in the cap so as to stand up about 2 in. above the weathering to prevent rain running down the flue.

Special points about boiler flues where coke is used are, first that unless lined internally with glazed drain-pipes, the sulphurous fumes and moisture will eventually disintegrate the jointing of the flue, and sometimes the brick also ; and, secondly, that it is advisable to provide a soot-door (preferably external) for clearing flue-dust.

Self Testing Questions

(1) *Give reasons why a position on an internal wall is preferable for any fireplace.*

(2) *What measures would you take to ensure the preservation of the full unobstructed size in a chimney flue during building?*

(3) *What precautions can be taken to avoid the risk of smoky chimneys?*

THE ANSWERS ARE ON PAGE 66.

LESSON 6

Wooden Buildings

THE prejudice still felt by many people against timber buildings is a legacy from the last war, following which many unsuccessful attempts were made to adapt Army huts, which had been hastily constructed, into comfortable dwellings. There is no reason why a wooden structure should not be as strong, as dry, and as comfortable as one of more permanent materials, and even on the score of permanence, given sound initial construction and reasonable care in upkeep, there is little to choose.

Even in wooden houses, however, brick, concrete or masonry should be used in base walls, fire-surrounds and chimneys. Apart from protection against fire, the presence of brick surrounds to fire-grates serves a useful purpose in conserving heat for gentle distribution.

Fig. 31 shows a simple design for a timber-framed bungalow such as might be built on a rural site and prove a comfortable home for a family.

A brief description of the order of construction is the best way to make the methods of timber-building clear.

Set out the lines of external foundation trenches and walls, and of the main cross-partition upon which occur the two chimney-breasts. Strip surface soil as described in Lesson 1. Then dig the foundation trenches. Care must be taken that surface water is not allowed to collect in the excavations. If these are shallow, dig a short trench from the lowest corner (few sites prove dead level) to an external temporary sump-hole slightly deeper than the trenches, into which water will drain naturally.

The corner of the building containing scullery, fuel-store, larder and E.C., which will have concrete floors, should be left bare for the present to consolidate; over the remainder of the enclosed space a layer of "oversite concrete" should be laid as soon as the foundation-concrete is in, so as to make a clean working platform.

The base walls and lines of sleeper walls are then built as shown on plan; there is no need to lay foundation walls beneath any of the short internal partitions, which can rest on the floor. The two chimney-breasts, with their fender walls, are built up at this time as far as ground-floor level, also the 4½-in. brick wall between scullery and larder, etc. The scul-

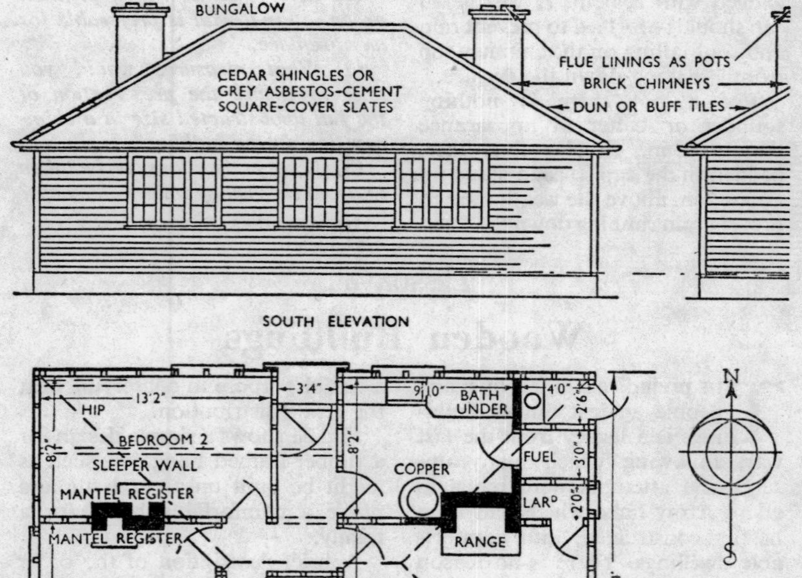

Fig. 31. *Plans and elevation for a timber-framed bungalow with slate or*

lery, etc., can then be filled up for future concrete paving. Following this, the sleepers and ground-floor joists are laid, the former running lengthwise of the building and the latter from back to front. The floor-boards, which should be grooved and tongued to exclude draughts, are then cut and laid reverse side up unfixed, to make a level platform for subsequent work.

Next the external framing is constructed and raised in position, the sills being secured to the base wall by ragbolts which have been built in during construction. If the base wall has been formed of concrete cast in position (as may prove simple and cheap if good gravel is available near at hand), the inclusion of ragbolts is rendered easier.

Each frame should be carefully drawn to a large scale as in Fig. 32,

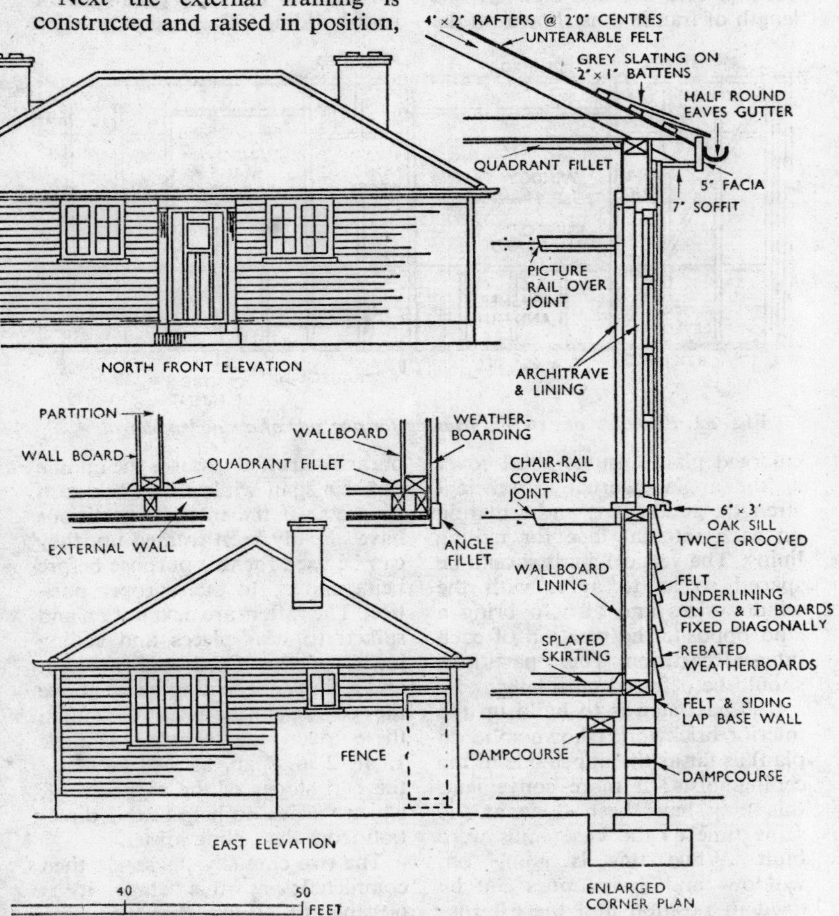

shingled roof. On the right are seen full details of materials and construction.

so as to make provision for window- and door-frames, internal partition junctions, situation of ragbolts, etc., and the sill, heads, studs and braces should be cut to correct lengths. The frames when erected should be temporarily stayed in true upright position by long braces (for which timbers subsequently to serve as rafters can be used), and the angles securely fixed by spiking or bolting. The doubled stud on one length of framing, as shown on the enlarged plan, ensures good cover at the angle externally, sufficient strength, good fixing and a margin on each internal face for nailing lining. The vertical studs should be spaced so as to agree with the window-sizes and also to bring a stud opposite the position of each internal partition. These partitions should be deferred until later.

The next step is to build up the interior brickwork (shown solid on plan) as far as the upper side of the ceiling joists; if more convenient, this may have been done at the same time as the base walls were built. While this is going on, window- and door-frames can be fixed in position and the external sheathing nailed to the framing. This layer of grooved-and-tongued boarding nailed on diagonally is important. Fixed in this way, it braces the framing in a similar way to inclined struts, and it secures a warm and draught-free interior when covered with felt or "building-paper" before the external weather-boarding is added.

The ceiling joists are next laid on the head-pieces of the framing, to form a working platform for roof-building. They may be temporarily strutted towards the middle of their span while this work is in progress; if the internal partitions have already been framed up, they can be used for this purpose before being moved to their proper position. The rafters are next put on and spiked to head-pieces and ceiling joists, purlins fixed and strutted, and a timber stiffening beam above the ceiling joists fixed to stiffen these over the centre of their 13 ft. 2 in. span, as well as tieing the end slopes of the hipped roof, which receive no help in this direction from the ceiling joists.

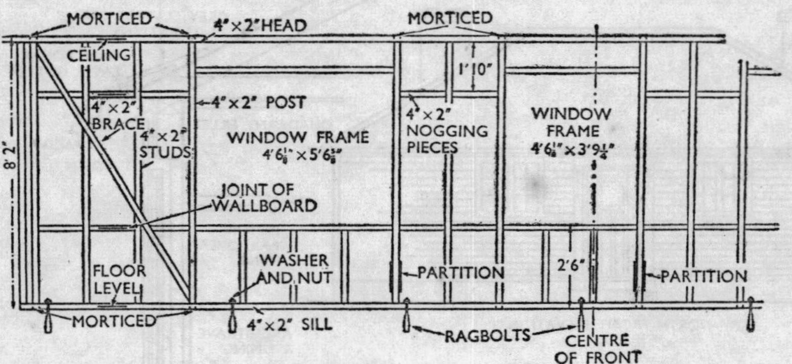

Fig. 32. *Elevation of external framing for one side of a wooden bungalow.*

The two chimney-stacks are then completed; at this stage it is possible to ensure that they rise clear of the hip rafters. The rafter feet can meanwhile be cut to a true line to receive facia and soffit, after which the felt, battens and roof-covering can be laid and guttering fixed.

The building is now closed in around and above, and internal work can proceed in any weather. Floor-boards are now reversed, cramped up and nailed, internal wallboard linings fixed to the ceiling and external walls, and the internal partitions placed in their proper positions. Labour is greatly reduced if this practice is followed, as there is no fitting of wallboard at the intersections if it is allowed to run through past each partition, as shown on the enlarged plan. When the partitions have been nailed in place from their end-studs through to the stud on external framing, their linings can be fixed and the joints covered by a quadrant fillet up each angle, as shown. It should be noted that wallboard supplied in 4-ft. widths is used throughout, and by spacing window heights as shown, and laying the board with its long dimension horizontally placed, one 4-ft. width is used intact, while the dado and frieze are cut by dividing another. This material is obtainable in overall lengths which are sufficient to avoid the need for end joints in rooms of no greater size than shown. "Nogging pieces" cut in between the studs must be fixed under horizontal joints. For these, waste ends of timber can be used. Felt or sisalkraft underlining can now be fixed to the diagonal sheathing, and the external rebated weather-boarding or "siding" fixed.

If Western red cedar can be obtained it is to be preferred, for its decay-resisting properties. The boards and felt should lap over the base wall by at least 1 in., as an open joint here would tend to admit wet and might rot the sill of the framing.

The building is now structurally complete and ready for internal fittings and finishings.

Self Testing Questions

(1) *What provision would you make for removing surface water from foundation trenches?*

(2) *What objects are served by the diagonally-fixed sheathing of grooved-and-tongued boarding fixed to external framing beneath weather-boards?*

(3) *Why are doubled studs with an intervening space used at the external angles of a framed structure?*

THE ANSWERS ARE ON PAGE 67.

LESSON 7

Windows and Doors

ALTHOUGH in the following pages a full description of the commoner types of windows and doors is given, the non-professional joiner would be well advised not to attempt to make these items, even for the simplest of buildings. Work which would occasion great expenditure of time and labour in the absence of tools and plant which are in the possession of joinery shops can by them be turned out with an accuracy, neatness and cheapness which cannot be rivalled. Moreover, the British Standards Institute has drawn up specifications covering quality, design and range of sizes by which windows and doors to meet any reasonable requirements can be ordered, and by adopting this method of supply, good results should be assured. For those who prefer metal windows, the extensive range of standard cottage casements, supplied by several makers, is also available. Ease in fixing and protection from damage in transit are both greatly increased if these iron casements are ordered in "wood surrounds" with projecting oak sills. Standard wood casements are embodied in the timber bungalow shown in Figs. 31 and 32, and metal casements in the brick cottage illustrated later in Fig. 55

Types of Windows

Windows as employed in this country are usually either outward-opening casements hung on hinges to solid frames, or double-hung lifting sashes hung on lines and pulleys to boxed frames. In both types the chief problem in detailed design is to secure easy movement without admission of draughts and rain.

Casement windows can be designed in any proportion of height to width by multiplying the number of "lights" divided by the vertical intermediate frames known as "mullions." If their proportion of height to width grows extreme, it is convenient to divide the height by a horizontal member known as a "transom," which serves as head to the casement beneath and sill to the one above. When embodying a transom care should be taken to see that it does not come at the eye-level of seated persons—which would be irritating. As an alternative to a heavy transom, it is often convenient, when top-hinged ventilator lights are needed, to include a mock transom by making a wider horizontal bar through the casement and dividing this with a rebated and throated joint. By this means the obstruction to vision as compared with a full transom can be reduced from perhaps 6 in. to 3 in. The solid frames of casement windows consist of rebated, throated and grooved jambs, heads (and mullions if two or more lights), and double-sunk, weathered, rebated, throated and grooved sills. The sills (and transoms if included) should preferably be of oak and projecting, and the grooving beneath should be more than a mere surface scratch. These members are put together by mortice and tenon joints, with a partial mitre if they are edge-moulded. The head and sill are both prepared about 6 in. longer than the full width of the frame, the projections being known as "horns." This is because the tenons are on the vertical members (jambs and mullions) and the mortices in head and sill. Before building in, the ends of sill and head should be sawn off true to even lengths, and if the horns on the head would show on face, they are best cut at an inward angle to secure the frame in position when fixed. These points may be followed by reference to Fig. 33.

Casement Frames

Each casement is composed of "stiles," top rail and bottom rail, and is either plain glazed or divided by bars or "astragals." The members are morticed and tenoned together, as with their frames, but the stiles are continuous top to bottom, and the other members fit between them. If panes are formed by bars, it is the horizontal bars which are continuous, the verticals being cut between them. In the standard range, casement frames are made in the following widths, each

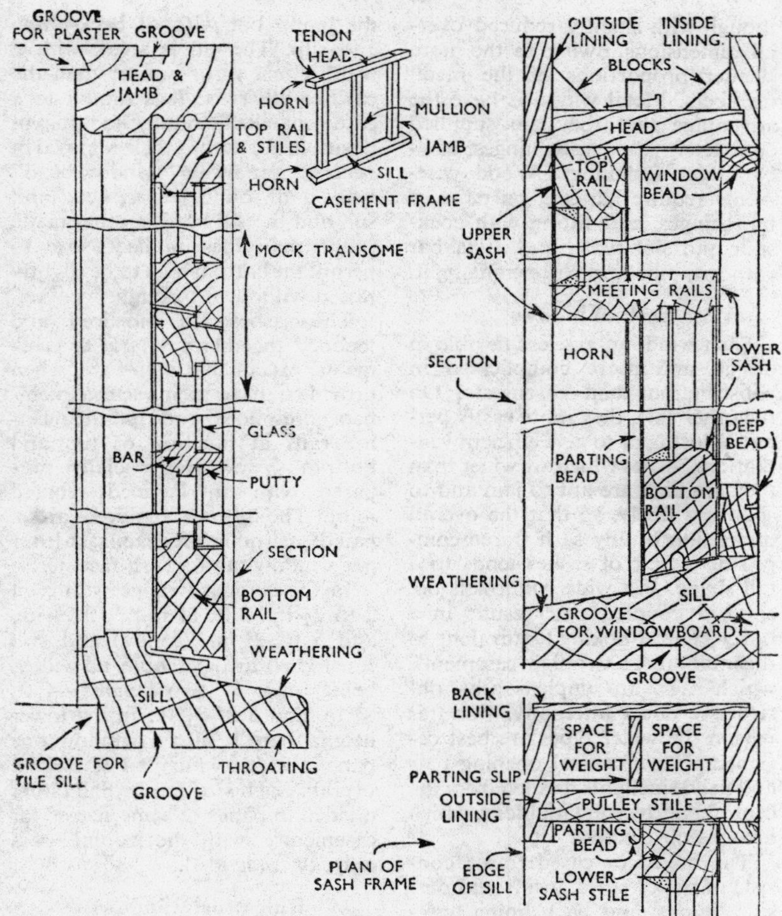

Figs. 33 and 34. *Details of* (left) *a casement and* (right) *a sash window.*

increase representing the addition of a "light" with an extra mullion: 1 ft. 11⅞ in.; 3 ft. 9¼ in.; 5 ft. 6⅝ in.; and 7 ft. 4⅛ in. In each width the following heights are obtainable, and all are available either divided by bars into panes 10¾ in. high × 7¾ in. wide, or with horizontal bars only, or undivided: 2 ft. 7 in.; 3 ft. 6⅝ in.; 4 ft. 6⅛ in.; 4 ft. 10⅞ in. (with transom); 4 ft. 8⅞ in. (with mock transom) and 5 ft. 10½ in. with transom. In the lower two heights there are also windows of one pane width, which are useful for such places as larders and W.Cs. From this series it is possible to select types suitable to all circumstances in the small house and lesser buildings.

The range of available sizes in standard metal casements is even wider, but on generally similar lines, though with slightly reduced overall dimensions, owing to the more slender proportions of the metal members. Metal windows have the advantage that they are supplied completely fitted with hinges, staybars and fastenings. Wood casements require hanging on pairs of butt hinges, and fitting with cockspur and slot plate, and a staybar with two pins to each opening light.

Sash Windows

Sash windows are less flexible in design and more complicated in construction than casements. On the other side, they more easily permit adjustment to give efficient ventilation. Sashes which are wider than they are high are apt to jam and to slide less freely, so that the overall dimension of any sash frame comprising a pair of sashes tends to a tall shape. If a wide window is desired, a coupled pair results in a bulky central boxing (equivalent to the mullion of a two-light casement), which has an unpleasantly obstructive effect internally. For this reason the wider types are best designed with a central opening pair and fixed sidelights divided from the central part by solid mullions, which are less obstructive.

The boxed or cased frame consists of pulley stiles, inside and outside linings, and back lining (constituting the jambs), which contain the pulleys over which operate the sash-weights and cords balancing the sashes and rising and falling within the casings. The weights are separated by a parting slip suspended in the casing, and the sashes by a narrow parting bead grooved into the pulley stile. A portion of each pulley stile is made removable in emergency for access to the weight when cords need renewal. The head is constructed similarly to the jamb, but without back-lining and slip. The sill is solid, with a width equal to or greater than the casing; otherwise it is similar to a casement sill. To retain the sashes in position, but permit their removal in necessity, an inside "window bead" is fixed all round jambs, head and sill, and the sill bead is often made deeper than sides and head, so as to permit the bottom sash to be slightly raised without a through opening.

The sashes are morticed and tenoned together similarly to casements, except that sash-bars, when provided, have their *vertical* members continuous, and that the meeting rails at junction of top and bottom sashes are specially prepared with an inclined rebated joint. The fittings required are a pair of sash pulleys for each sash (four per window) and a sash fastener.

In the standard range widths of 2 ft. $2\frac{1}{2}$ in., 2 ft. 11 in., 3 ft. $7\frac{5}{8}$ in., and 5 ft. $2\frac{5}{8}$ in. (central and two side lights) are available, all widths being made in two heights—4 ft. $8\frac{3}{4}$ in. and 5 ft. $8\frac{1}{2}$ in. In the lower height there is also a window one pane in width, which is 1 ft. $5\frac{13}{16}$ in. overall. Each size can be had either divided in panes of same size as for casements, with horizontal bars only, or undivided.

Rules for Windows

Finally, it is worth noting that by two simple observances the untidy and disordered appearance which characterises so much minor building can be avoided. The rules are two: (1) see that all window-heads in a storey are at the same level; (2) adopt a uniform proportion for window-panes throughout.

Doors in domestic and similar simple buildings may be classed as either external doors, which are hung to solid frames, or internal doors, which are usually hung to jamb-linings. There are three main types of door construction now current: (1) panelled doors made up from stiles, rails and muntins, with their spaces filled by panels fitted in grooves on the edges of the heavier members, which are themselves morticed and tenoned (or sometimes dowelled) together; (2) flush doors, having even faces of plywood upon a hidden skeleton framing; and (3) ledged doors, composed of vertical grooved-and-tongued boarding nailed to two or more horizontal ledges, with the desirable addition of inclined braces maintaining the rigidity of the whole. Types 1 and 2 are definitely workshop products, and can be bought for very little above what would be the cost of their materials. Type 3 can quite well be made.

Solid Door-Frames

Solid door-frames, constructed similarly to casement frames, consist of jambs, head and (when a mat is desired) threshold. These are usually prepared out of 4 in. × 3 in. or 2¼ in. fir (oak for threshold) rebated to receive the door, and are built in as the structure rises, with cramps or stout spikes on the back of the frame at intervals to hold them against loosening. The best external door is prepared by covering a panelled door, such as will be used internally, with a series of wide boards and cover fillets. A weather-board may be fixed at the foot, and a glazed panel inserted (Fig. 35).

Internal doors are hung to "linings" which are not fixed until a building is roofed in and ready for plastering. The openings are spanned by lintels of wood or concrete when building, and it is a manifest advantage if all these are set at the same level. There is no discoverable reason for the trade practice by which imported doors have added to their height an equal amount to each increase in width; British standard doors therefore adopt a standard height of 6 ft. 6 in., with widths of 2 ft., 2 ft. 4 in., 2 ft. 6 in., 2 ft. 8 in., 2 ft. 10 in. and 3 ft. The 2 ft. 8 in. × 6 ft. 6 in. size is suitable

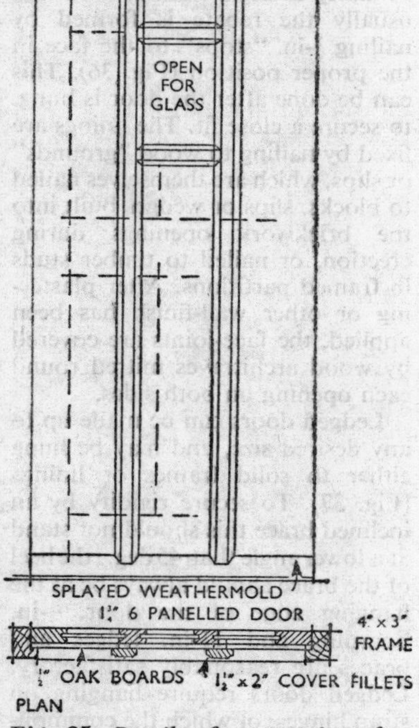

Fig. 35. *Details of construction of an external door with weather-board.*

for most living-rooms, 2 ft. 6 in. for bedrooms, and the lesser widths for bathrooms, W.Cs., larders, etc., into which bulky furniture has not to be taken. Panelled and flush doors are usually fitted with mortice locks let into their thickness. They are hung by a pair of butt hinges.

The "linings" to which they are hung are composed of wrot-boards

1 in. or more in thickness and of a width equal to the face-to-face thickness of wall or partition with its plaster coatings. The linings are grooved together at the head, and must be fixed with jambs truly plumb and head at exact right angles—otherwise door-hanging will not be satisfactory. Linings are sometimes rebated for the door similarly to solid frames, but more usually the rebate is formed by nailing ½-in. "stops" to the face in the proper position (Fig. 36). This can be done after the door is hung, to secure a close fit. The linings are fixed by nailing to wood "grounds" or slips, which are themselves nailed to blocks, slips or wedges built into the brickwork openings during erection, or nailed to timber studs in framed partitions. After plastering or other wall-finish has been applied, the face-joints are covered by wood architraves mitred round each opening on both sides.

Ledged doors can be made up to any desired size, and may be hung either to solid frames or linings (Fig. 37). To secure rigidity by an inclined brace this should not stand at a lower angle than 45 deg.; the heel of the brace should always be at the hanging edge of the door. ¾-in. boarding and 1¼-in. ledges and braces are reasonably satisfactory. Ledged doors require hanging on strap hinges, of which the commonest form is the "cross-garnet" which is screwed along the line of the

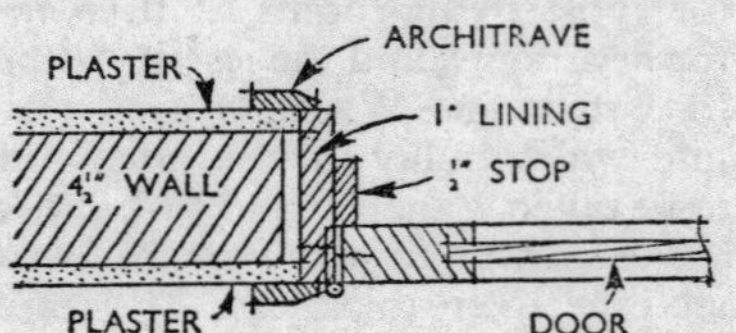

Fig. 36. *The rebate of an internal door is generally formed by nailing half-inch stops to the face, as here shown.*

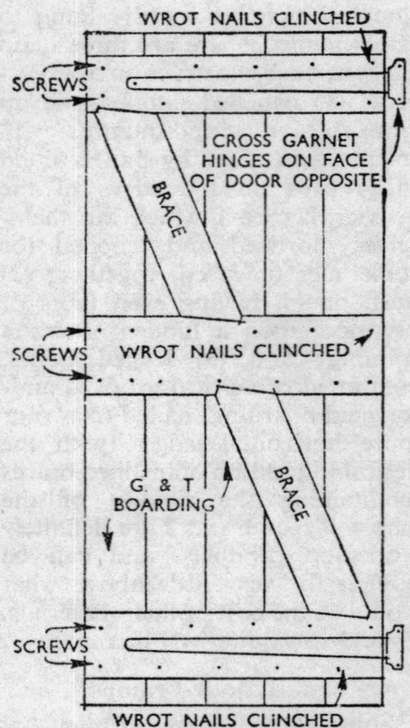

Fig. 37. *Parts and construction of a ledged door with supporting brace.*

ledges. Mortice locks cannot be fitted, and surface locks, called "rim locks," or latches of the Norfolk or Suffolk type are used. To secure durability, it is advisable that the board which forms the shutting edge of the door should be *screwed* to the ledges, and that these should extend to the full width, the rebate on the frame or lining being checked out to receive them.

Self Testing Questions

(1) *What do you consider are the relative advantages of sash and casement windows?*

(2) *What do you understand by "horns" on a frame? Give an instance.*

(3) *What is a "rebate" and where is it used?*

THE ANSWERS ARE ON PAGE 67.

LESSON 8

Interior Joinery and Fittings

THE amount of internal joinery work in the average small house (apart from that connected with doors and windows) is not usually large, but the care and skill with which it is executed have an exceptional influence in creating an impression of "finish" and consequent value.

The most important item is the stair, and while any complicated stair, including return flights or "winders," may well tax the ability of a skilled joiner, if this feature is restricted to a straight run it should not be beyond the powers of a careful man with average capacity in the use of tools.

Treads and Risers

In setting out such a stair, the first step is to determine the space available and to decide upon the size and proportion of "tread" to "riser" which can be adopted. The height from floor to floor will usually lie between 8 ft. 6 in. and 9 ft., and with either height thirteen steps can be taken as a minimum which is admissible, with fourteen or fifteen as a better allowance. Taking the height as 8 ft. 9 in., thirteen steps would give a riser of $8\frac{1}{3}$ in.; fourteen steps, $7\frac{1}{2}$ in.; and fifteen steps, 7 in. each. By a simple rule which depends on the human pace, "tread" multiplied by "riser" should lie between 60 in. and 65 in. Thirteen steps of $8\frac{1}{13}$ in. may therefore have 8 in. treads, while for the $7\frac{1}{2}$ in. or 7 in. rise, treads of 9 in. prove convenient.

In fixing plan-space there is always one tread less than the full number of risers, since the edge of the floor or landing constitutes the top tread. The plan-space of the steepest stair is therefore 12 times 8 in. = 8 ft. in length, with a width, in the case of the cottage shown in Fig. 55, which should allow 1 in. for latitude between walls so as to ensure getting in easily. The overall width outside the inclined "close-strings" between which the steps are framed is therefore 2 ft. 8 in.

Stair Construction

This particular staircase can, if desired, be entirely constructed of 9 in. × $1\frac{1}{4}$ in. boards, though 9 in. × 1 in. would be sufficient for treads and risers. Each string will need a board 12 ft. in length, upon which the outline of treads and risers with space for wedging must be marked out and recessed $\frac{1}{2}$ in. deep and right- and left-handed. By forming the treads and risers as shown, with the risers continuing downwards behind each tread, a stiff stair can be made out of boards of equal width, screws being driven from behind as shown at each joint (Fig. 38). All joints are glued up, and triangular blocks glued in the position shown increase stiffness, though not strictly necessary. In wider stairs these blocks (two in the width) should not be omitted, and at 4 ft. or over a central "carriage" or inclined joist, with brackets to take the weight, is advisable.

On the plan shown in Fig. 55 the foot of the stair is shown with a "newel" and "curtail step," but this complication can be omitted if desired. In that case a handrail on brackets might be fixed to the wall on right. The stair is fixed in position preferably either before plastering is commenced or after the first coat has been applied, and is secured by nailing through the strings to wood slips fixed to the brick joints, and by attachment to the floor at top.

Fixing Floor-Boards

When fixing. floor-boards it is essential that a close fit should be secured to minimise draughts. To obtain this result flooring cramps are used, by means of which boards are closely compressed edgewise before nailing. Without these appliances, however, very fair results can be obtained if a board at intervals is firmly nailed after measuring, so as to allow *slightly* less than the space occupied by those between, which are then placed in position as a sort of flat arch crossed by loose boards in at least two places. A heavy person standing upon each cross-board can then force the "arched" boards flat for nailing, and a tight floor results (Fig. 39).

The *architrave* covers the joint between wood linings and plaster. It is fixed by nailing to the edge of the linings, as shown in Fig. 36, and to the wood-slips built in by the bricklayer at the sides of door openings for nailing the "grounds" to which the linings are fixed. Architraves should be flattish in section and tapered from the door edge; otherwise they may restrict the angle to which the door may be swung back, or even force it off its hinges.

The *skirting* covers the junction of plaster or other wall-lining with the floor, and by its projection protects the wall surface from damage by furniture or sweepers.

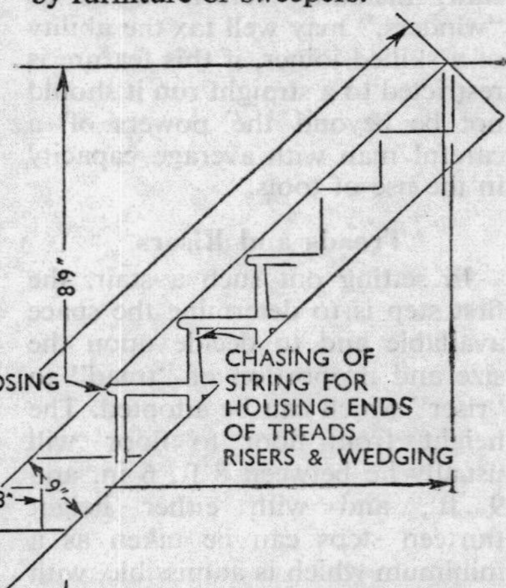

Fig. 38. *Parts of a staircase, with treads and risers constructed from boards of equal width and joints screwed behind.*

The *picture-mold* serves to divide wall-finish (paper or distemper) from ceiling-finish, and may afford means of lightening a room by extending the whiteness of a ceiling down the wall-face. By providing a hanging-rail for pictures it also saves damage by nails or other fastenings. Where wall-board is used it can be made to cover joints.

Dado-rails, which should be fixed at the height of chairbacks, may serve some of the purposes of the picture-mold, but are chiefly to take the knocks and grazes of chairs and similar furniture. Fig. 31 shows skirting, dado and picture-rail used with wallboard linings, and also the utility of small quadrant fillets in angles for covering joints. Whether the structure is brick or timber, the position of all these items of "trim" should be settled in advance, so that provision can be made for providing a fixing. In brickwork this provision often takes the form of breeze bricks built in at intervals, to which nailing is possible; but it may be made by ½-in. wood slips occupying horizontal or vertical joints at similar intervals. In wood framing, if it is not possible to nail directly to the studs or rails, special nogging pieces must be cut in and fixed, as provided in Fig. 32 for joints of wallboard.

Shelves

No house is complete or convenient without a liberal allowance of shelf space. Apart from the shelving provided in such places as larders and cupboards, it is generally a convenient practice to run a tier of shelving continuously over door-heads in the scullery. Such shelving may be either 7 in. or 9 in. wide, and supported either on metal or wood brackets at intervals of about 3 ft. In either case the wall member should be a wood batten firmly fixed to the wall. It is preferable for the back edge of any shelf to stand clear of the wall, so as to avoid a dirt-holding corner and allow the shelf to be cleaned without rubbing the wall. This practice also assists air circulation in larders. The ends of shelving abutting against walls are supported upon wood bearers nailed directly to the walls. Where tiers of shelving are fixed, the space

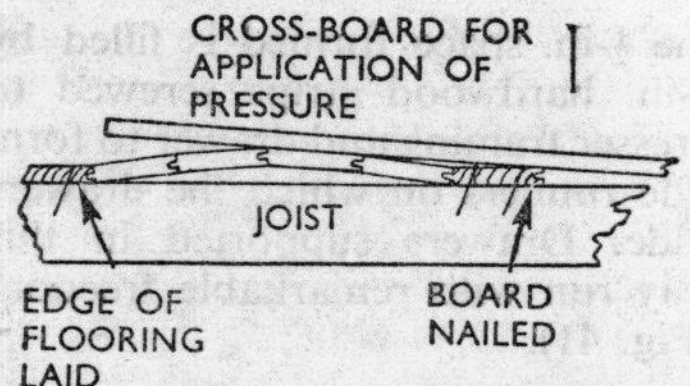

Fig. 39. *This illustrates the method, explained in text, of securing a close draught-excluding fit in floor-boards without the use of cramps.*

above described is easily formed if the wood battens which support the brackets are run continuously through the tiers, the shelves abutting against them without notching. In setting out tiers of shelving the mistake usually made is to allow much too wide a space between shelves, thus reducing usable shelf-space—10 in. to 11 in. for such positions as china-cupboards is ample, and 15 in. to 18 in. between the spaced batten shelving usual in linen-closets.

Fig. 40 shows details of a serviceable kitchen dresser embodying pot-board, two drawers, cupboard space below, and upper part enclosed by sliding doors. Sliding doors are preferable in this position, as when open they do not cause danger to the heads of incautious persons as hinged doors would. The space above the pot-board is left unenclosed, as the full width of this ledge should be available for use.

Making a Dresser

The construction of the dresser is relatively simple, except for the drawers, which should be dovetailed between sides and front, but as an alternative to this for those who may wish to avoid this rather finicky detail, the fronts may extend ½ in. beyond sides at each end and be screwed to them, while the ½-in. space formed is filled by ½-in. hardwood strips screwed to dresser framing and drawer to form side runners on which the drawers slide. Drawers supported in this way run with remarkable freedom (Fig. 41).

Draining-Boards

Every sink should have a draining-board at *each* side; this assists domestic routine, leaving one side for "dirties" and one for "clean." The space beneath may be closed by cupboard doors, but the space beneath the sink is perhaps preferably open, and may well be formed into racks for pails and other utensils (Fig. 42).

Draining-boards are usually grooved at intervals of 2 in., with a slight inclination towards the sink, and are made from teak, beech or other hardwood, but a modern

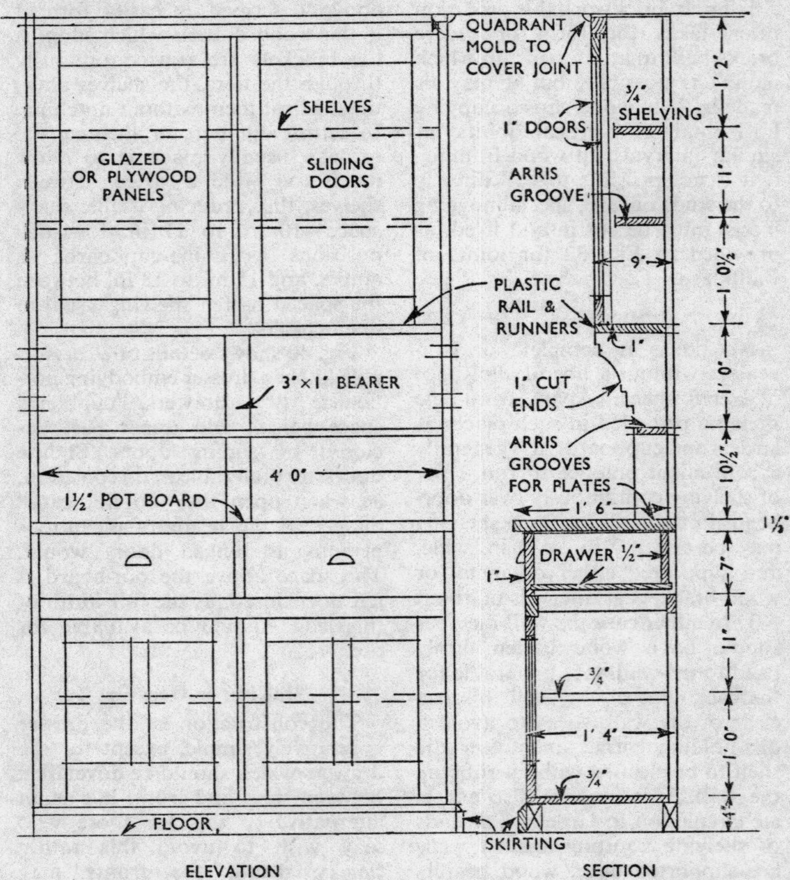

Fig. 40. *Elevation and section of kitchen dresser with panelled sliding doors to cupboard section, pot-board, grooved shelves and two drawers.*

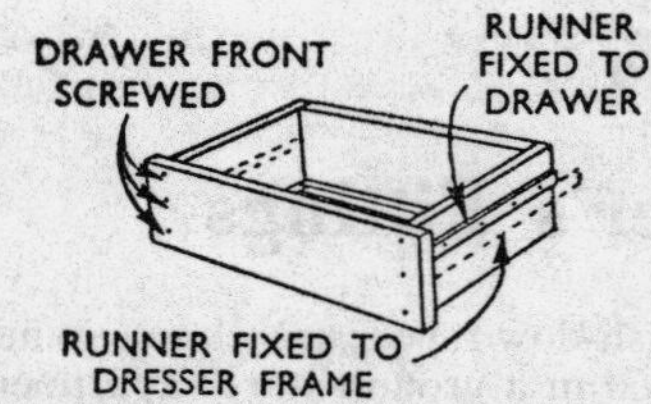

Fig. 41. *Method of constructing drawers for kitchen dresser.*

alternative which is pleasant and clean is to cover the surfaces with good plain linoleum fixed with adhesive to any sort of wood base, the front edge being covered and protected by a raised fillet as shown. A "drip" should be formed beneath each draining-board by grooving where it overhangs the sink ends; otherwise greasy water tends to run back below.

Fuel-Container

Coal can be shot up to about 4 ft. in height, and to secure full capacity for a fuel-house loose boards which can be removed singly should be provided across the doorway, with guides in which they can be slid. If the grooves of the guides are blocked for a height of 6 in. from the floor, giving an open space of this height, fine coal can be shovelled here, while lumps are picked out from above. Four 9-in. or five 7-in. boards then complete the enclosure up to about 3 ft. 6 in. high.

Self Testing Questions

(1) *How would you set about preparation for making a straight stair in minimum space between floors 9 ft. 6 in. apart?*

(2) *What provision for fixing would you make in the case of wooden "trim" applied to* (a) *a brick structure plastered internally,* (b) *a timber-framed structure?*

(3) *What reasons suggest the fixing of shelves with a space between their back edge and the wall behind?*

THE ANSWERS ARE ON PAGE 67.

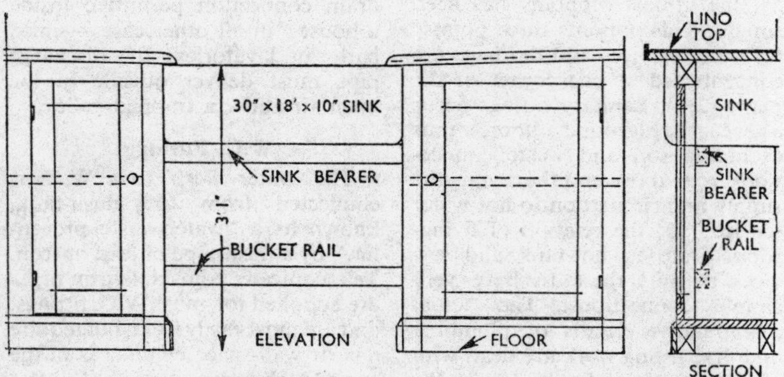

Fig. 42. *Design for sink with double draining-board over built-in cupboards.*

LESSON 9

Internal Plumber's Fittings

THE usual sanitary provision of the small house which possesses a drainage system either connected to a public sewer or to its own septic tank is W.C., sink and bath. A wash-basin in the bathroom, or in one or more of the bedrooms, is growing increasingly popular, and, where cost need not be cut to the minimum, is a desirable addition. It should not be overlooked, however, that apart from direct increase in cost, one effect of more widely distributed water services is greater liability to maintenance cost. Compactly planned water and drainage services are worth striving for when house design is in progress.

Economy of Fitting

In the cottage illustrated in Fig. 55, the utmost economy has been sought. This presents three points: (1) water services and drainage are concentrated at one corner of the plan; (2) no sanitary fittings occur above the ground floor, thus excluding soil and waste connections from above and shortening the supply and circulation to hot-water service; (3) the relation of living-room grate to hot-tank and services permits these to have very simple connections. The actual manipulative details of plumbing and pipe fitting work are dealt with elsewhere in this book, and in the following pages more general questions as to choice, placing and fixing of sanitary and water fittings will be discussed.

Every *W.C. fitting* used nowadays is of the kind known as a wash-down pedestal closet. When fixed in a ground-storey apartment from which it can be connected direct to the stoneware drains, it is of the type known as S trap (Fig. 43 *a*). Upper floor fittings, which are necessarily jointed to either cast-iron or lead soil-pipes, may either be of this type, jointed to an upturned socket on a cast-iron branch, or of the shape known as P trap, in which the arm projects more or less horizontally in place of the turned-down form (Fig. 43 *b*). In the instance shown on the plan, the 4-in. branch drain would be brought into the W.C. apartment, with an upturned bend just above floor level and in the right position for the S trap on the fitting to be jointed direct with a cement joint.

A W.C. connection is the only drain connection permitted inside a house; in all other cases—sinks, baths or lavatories—the discharge pipe must deliver outside in the open air above a trapped gulley.

W.C. Fittings

The water flush to a W.C. is connected from the flush-tank, known as a "water-waste preventer," by a flush-pipe of lead or iron. Telescopically adjustable iron pipes are supplied for most W.C. fittings, and are most easily fixed, but require a clear wall-space behind, as in the example shown.

A fashionable type of fitting at present is the "low-down," in which the flush-tank stands just above and immediately behind the pan; this is neat in appearance, but the flush loses some force and the position of the tank causes the fixture to project farther from the back wall and to occupy more space. The flush-pipe is connected at the rear of the fitting to a hollow "flushing rim," through which discharge occurs. Connection is often made with red-lead and rag, but a type of lead collar specially supplied for the purpose is preferable.

Flushing-tanks, which are syphonic in action, are of many types, but of two main kinds: (1) in which an upstanding trumpet-mouthed pipe leading to the flush-pipe is covered by a heavy, bell-shaped casting which is raised by the lever arm worked by the pull. On release it falls, and surges water over the rim of the pipe, so starting syphonic action (Fig. 44 *a*); (2) in which the pull-lever actuates a piston or plunger in a cylinder within the tank, so lifting contained water, which it forces into the syphon, the action continuing by the operation of a flap-valve in the piston (Fig. 44 *b*).

Note that type (1) action is produced by release, and type (2) by the actual pull. In both types water is admitted to the tank by a ball valve, and the noise of refilling may be reduced if from the inlet point a pipe is carried down to the bottom of the tank.

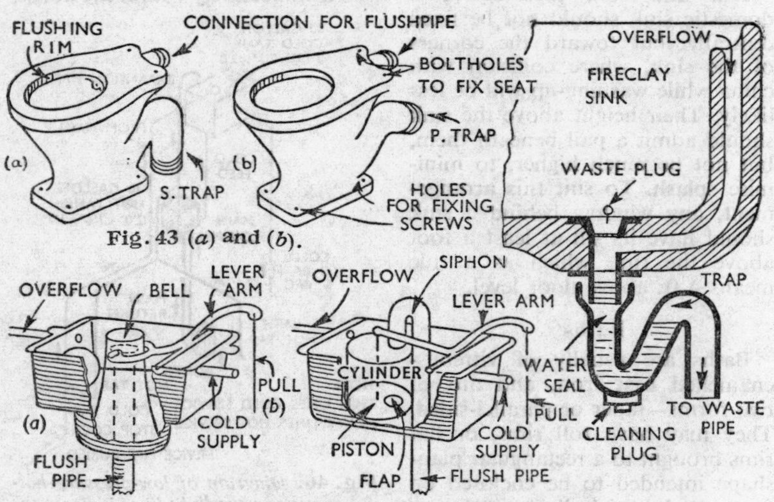

(Above, left) **Figs. 43** (*a*) **and** (*b*) *and* (below, left) **Figs. 44** (*a*) **and** (*b*). *Details of fittings of S-trap and P-trap types of W.C. pedestal, and both types of flushing cistern.* (Right) **Fig. 45,** *Fittings of scullery sink.*

An overflow or "warning pipe" from every flush-tank must be taken through an external wall to project 6 in. beyond.

A scullery sink, of heavy enamelled fireclay, will be fitted with a brass grating and waste-trap connected by lead or galvanised-iron pipe to a point over an external gulley. The sink will embody at one end an overflow channel formed in its own substance and communicating with the waste-outlet above the trap, which has its sleeve slotted so as not to obstruct the flow (Fig. 45). The trap will also be fitted with a screw-plug for access to the bend should any stoppage occur.

Position of Sink Taps

Hot and cold taps above a domestic sink should not be fixed centrally, but toward the corners of the sink, where collision with china while washing-up will be less likely. Their height above the sink should admit a pail beneath them, but not be much higher, to minimise splash. To suit this arrangement, any window behind a sink should have its sill at least a foot above the rim, which as a rule means 4 ft. above floor level.

Baths

Baths are usually of vitreous-enamelled cast iron, and are of two forms—taper or parallel-sided. They may have roll rims, or flat rims brought to a rectangular plan-shape intended to be enclosed on free sides by "risers" of metal, plywood or other sheet materials. The unenclosed "Roman" bath is less costly and more easily fitted, though the enclosed type looks smarter and has no inaccessible spaces requiring to be kept clean. Hot and cold bath-valves are usually fixed to the rim or end of the bath over the waste, and an overflow outlet is formed here as in the sink. The waste outlet and trap likewise resemble those for a sink, though the trap (to keep the bath rim lower) is generally shallower, and with its inspection cap at the side.

In the cottage plan shown, the bath waste-pipe is a 1½-in. galvanised-iron pipe laid in the floor-concrete as shown dotted, and discharges to the same gulley-trap as the sink. In the timber bungalow also (Fig. 31) bath and sink wastes are thus grouped.

Cold-water service from a public-service main must be brought into the house in pipe of a character and size approved by the Water Authority. There should be a stop-valve immediately within the house,

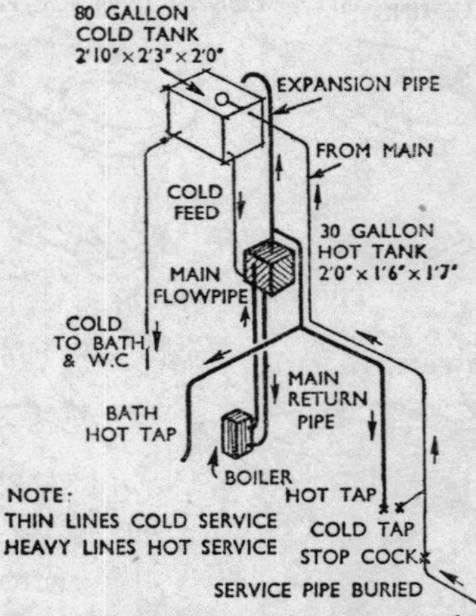

Fig. 46. *Diagram of low-pressure hot-water system: the light lines indicate the cold, and the heavy lines the hot service.*

and the pipe should then rise *on an internal wall* to the storage cistern. A branch should be run off this pipe direct to the sink for drinking-water. In the cottage illustrated the service pipe could conveniently enter below the sink draining-board nearest the fuel store, where the stop-valve would be fitted; it would then rise with a branch for sink-tap and continue against the end of the living-room chimney brickwork to feed the storage cistern over the stairs, this being supported on bearers between the brick partition next Bedroom 2 and the partition opposite, which bears directly on the substantial chimney-breast beneath. From this cistern a down service pipe would be taken to feed the hot-service and for supply to W.C. flush-tank and bath. A warning pipe from the cold tank, capable of exceeding the delivery rate of the supply pipe, must be taken outside as with the flush-tank.

The hot-water service in the example given would be simple. From the boiler in the living-room, flow and return pipes would be taken through the end of the brick fire-recess to the scullery, thence rising and crossing the scullery ceiling to a point immediately beneath the linen-closet above, where they would be connected to the sealed hot tank or cylinder.

Hot-Water Circulation

The circulation depends on the fact that hot water is lighter than cold. For this reason the flow-pipe is connected at the top of the boiler and carried to near the upper part of the tank or cylinder, while the return pipe leaves the bottom of the tank and enters the boiler low down. Hot water is thus found near the top of the storage. From this point a single expansion pipe would rise, with branches to supply sink, bath and any other fitting. Above the supply branches this pipe would reduce and continue above the level of the cold tank, over which the end would be turned down so as to drip therein. The cold feed-pipe from the cistern would be connected to the lower side of the hot tank or cylinder. At the lowest point of the main return pipe near the boiler (on scullery wall) a drain-cock for emptying the hot system would be fixed.

Low-Pressure System

The complete system as described is shown in diagram in Fig. 46, in which the cold service is shown in light lines and the hot service heavily. This is known as a low-pressure hot-water system, the pressure in the pipes being only that due to the head of water in the cold cistern, and it should be realised that the flow of hot water from the taps will be solely due to the inflow of the cold supply by the feed-pipe which is replacing it; also that as the hot storage cylinder and boiler with their circulating pipes cannot be emptied by any of the taps over the fittings, risk of accident is reduced. Nevertheless a safety valve fixed on the main flow-pipe is a wise precaution.

Where a circulating system is not intended, coppers of a type which allow heated water to be run to a bath are obtainable. Either of the two plans shown would admit of this simple arrangement, which is the cheapest possible.

Self Testing Questions

(1) *What arrangements for drain-connection are required for* (a) *a W.C.,* (b) *a bath?*

(2) *What do you understand by a warning-pipe, and how is it provided?*

(3) *What connections are made to the hot storage tank of a low-pressure hot-water supply system, and why are they arranged in definite relationship?*

THE ANSWERS ARE ON PAGE 67.

LESSON 10

Plastering, Rendering, Wall-tiling and "Finishings"

THE practice of internal lining for walls and ceilings has undergone extensions in several directions from the introduction of new materials and methods. At one time the almost invariable practice was to plaster walls internally with lime plaster in three coats, and to cover timber ceilings and partitions with wood lathing finished similarly with three-coat plaster. Lathing was originally cleft or rent from oak billets, the resulting laths having a thickness of about ¼ in., with a width of about 1 in. and considerable irregularity of surface.

From the nature of the material and its preparation these were tough and straight in grain. Rent oak laths, however, have been almost supplanted by sawn fir laths similar in dimensions, but of regular shape and liable to contain cross grain, which produces fragility.

Wood Lathing

Wood lathing is nailed up to the wood partition studs, floor or ceiling joists by galvanised-iron lath nails, one to each joist crossed, the laths being butt-jointed at their ends, which should be frequently varied in position so that straight runs of joint do not occur. On any timber over 3 in. in width counter-lathing below the sheet lath should be provided to ensure a "key" to the plaster (Fig. 47).

The undercoats of plastering consist of lime and sand, with an admixture of bullock's hair to secure tenacity while the material retains plasticity. Each coat is scratched while soft to give a key to succeeding coats. The final coat consists of lime putty gauged with plaster of Paris, and is usually trowelled smooth. This finishing coat is known as "fine stuff." The trade description is "render, float and set" on walls, and "lath, plaster, float and set" on ceilings.

Gypsum Plasters

A more recent introduction is hard wall plastering of various kinds, mostly prepared from gypsum (sulphate of lime), with additional ingredients to retard setting, which, as with plaster of Paris (a pure gypsum plaster), is too rapid for most processes. The best-known gypsum plaster is called "Keen's cement," but is not a proprietary article. There are, however, many variations, some of which allow quite good work to be obtained in two coats. Expanded metal and other forms of metal lathing are also available, and when used it is advisable to give the first coat in Portland cement, which will not attack the metal.

Other internal lining materials, which will undoubtedly gain in popularity from their greater ease and speed in application, are the numerous sheet materials which serve either as complete linings or as a substitute for lathing and undercoats, requiring only a surface skim of plaster. Roughly, three classes are available:

(1) Plaster-board, consisting of about ¼ in. of gypsum plaster between two surface layers of

paper. This is made in numerous sizes ranging between 36 in. × 28 in. and 48 in. × 12 ft., and it can be sawn or scored and broken quite easily. When nailed to joists or studs with the joints filled in with plaster, a final coat of plaster completes the lining, or carefully fixed, it can be papered direct.

(2) Fibre-boards, composed of wood-pulp or vegetable fibres, usually ½ in. thick and in sheets of 3 ft. to 4 ft. width and lengths of up to 14 ft. "Hard" boards are also made; these have a smoother surface and denser substance, having been subjected to severe pressure. Either of these materials, when fixed to joists or studs with their joints covered by wood strips, can themselves remain exposed as the complete ceiling- or wall-lining. If fixed to brickwork, wood battens suitably spaced must be fixed first for nailing to. Such treatment increases the heat insulation of the wall and gives a warmer interior in winter. If desired, the ½-in. boards can be given a setting coat of plaster similarly to plaster-board, but the joints should be covered first with "scrim," either of canvas or wire.

(3) Plywood, made up of three or more thin layers of wood, with their grain crossed, cemented together under pressure.

Mixing

Plaster consists of lime and sand (with hair in some cases). The use of lump lime, which requires to be slaked and handled with some caution, can be avoided by the purchase of hydrated lime, which is supplied as a dry powder ready for mixing. Undercoat (with hair if for use on lathing, or gauged with 1 part Portland cement to 4 parts of plaster if on metal lath) is mixed—hydrated lime 1 part; sand 3 to 4 parts: second coat, 3 parts undercoat mixture with 1 part plaster of Paris: setting coat, hydrated lime 1 part; fine sand 1 to 1¼ parts, with 1 part plaster of Paris to each 10 parts of the mixture.

Mixing is done with a hoe called a "larry," and, where cement or plaster of Paris is added, it should not be done until time of use. Plaster is applied from a "float"—a square of board fixed to a handle—

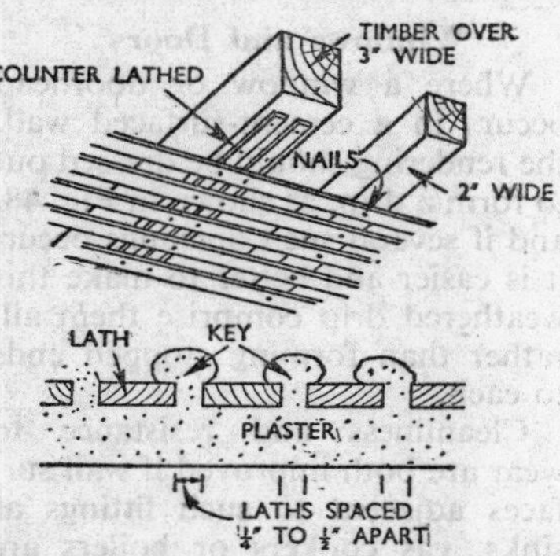

Fig. 47. Above, *arrangement of laths and counter-laths for plastering;* below, *how plaster is "keyed" to the lathing.*

and finished by trowelling smooth, but its application and finish require skill and proficiency. Watch a professional at work, if possible.

An external plaster coating may be intended to protect or to improve the appearance of a structural material such as concrete blocks or porous brick-work, and it is sometimes relied upon for water-proofing purposes. In all such cases Portland cement and sand are the materials used. If applied similarly to ordinary plastering, the process is known as "rendering," but with the surface coat roughened by disturbing it when first applied (with a stubby broom or other means) it may be "fine-cast," or, yet again, by dashing the moist surface with fine pebbles and cement, may be "roughcast." The rougher surfaces are generally found more satisfactory in repelling weather attack, External rendering has a tendency to shrink and develop fine cracks, in which condition it may do more harm than good as a water-proofer. There are proprietary substances sold for addition to cement which add considerably to its weather-resisting properties.

Windows and Doors

Where a window or doorhead occurs in a cement-surfaced wall, the rendering should be dressed out to form a drip, as shown in Fig. 48, and if several such openings occur, it is easier and better to make this weathered drip comprise them all, rather than forming stopped ends to each.

Cleanliness and resistance to wear are both improved if wall surfaces adjacent to such fittings as sinks, gas cookers or boilers are lined with glazed tiling. To fix such tiling securely, the surface is first rendered in cement, into which the tiles are pressed, being driven home to a surface level by tapping upon a length of board which will span three tiles. The tiles should be well soaked for 24 hours before use and picked straight from a bucket of water for fixing. The open joints can be filled by rubbing in plaster or Keen's cement, washing off any surplus immediately.

Floors of sculleries, external porches and similar places may be paved with quarry tiles, and the most practical internal window-sills are also formed of similar tiles, which can be obtained in 4 in., 6 in., 8 in. or 9 in. squares. The tiles are laid on a level cement and sand bed, known as a "screeding," and the treatment is generally similar to

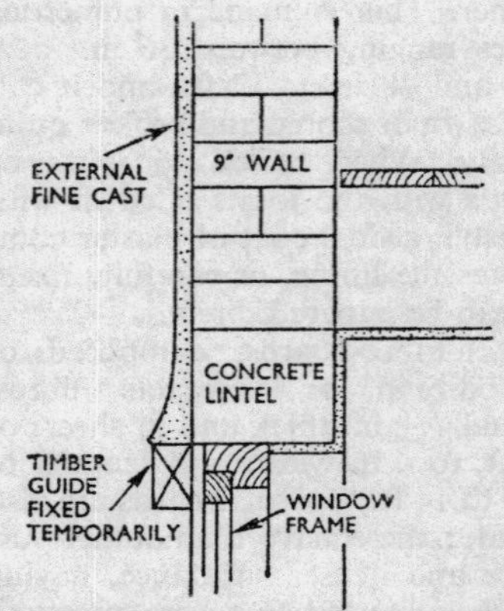

Fig. 48. *The rendering of a cement-surfaced wall should be dressed out over a window or doorhead to form a drip.*

wall-tiling, except that cement should be used for joint filling, and surface stains removed by washing with spirits of salt solution followed by clean water.

Ready-prepared paints are now so reliable that it is necessary to say little more than—"buy established brands and observe the makers' directions." It should, however, be remembered, when preparing woodwork for paint, that the correct order is "knot, prime, stop and paint"; the stopping of defects is often wrongly done before priming.

Staining does little to hide such defects in timber as knots or bruises, and careful choice and handling are required. Creosote stains such as Solignum or Cuprinol have a preservative effect, but painting has advantages for external joinery exposed to the weather, since its protective film covers the joints and excludes moisture in a way which no saturative solution can effect.

For floor-stain there is nothing to surpass a mixture of turpentine and Brunswick black, which dries quickly, does not wear off, is easily patched, and by regulating the proportions can give any tint between light nut-brown and sepia.

In glazing wooden windows ordinary glazier's putty is used; when glass is fixed to metal windows this fails to harden, and special putty is required. In either case care to provide a good back-puttying is essential, and sprigs or stubs should be inserted to hold the glass in position in the rebates; these will be buried as the outer putty is filled in.

Glass on roof-lights is best fixed with ample back putties alone, the upper side of glazing bars and about ½ in. of glass surface on each side being heavily painted.

Self Testing Questions

(1) *What is "counter-lathing" and why is it used?*

(2) *What preparation must be made for fixing wallboard and other sheet materials to brickwork?*

(3) *What are the relative merits of creosote stain and paint on external joinery?*

THE ANSWERS ARE ON PAGE 68.

LESSON 11

Handyman's Repairs

THE minor repairs which accident or ordinary wear and tear demand in almost every building can often be attended to by a handyman with less trouble than is caused by application to a landlord or endeavouring to secure the services of a builder.

Broken or displaced slates and tiles are among the most urgent repairs commonly necessary. Most of these require at least two ladders—one long enough to reach some 3 ft. above the eaves, and the second to lie on the roof-slope as far as the seat of the trouble. First, raise the long ladder against the gutter and rope it securely to the gutter or rafter feet; secondly, tie a loosely filled sack of hay or straw to the head of the second ladder, raise it and gently slide it into position resting on the stuffed sack. When in position, as shown in Fig. 49, it should be securely roped to the head of the long ladder, but lying to one side of it, so that it is possible to step from one to the other.

Slates, which are nailed throughout, are more difficult to replace than tiles. The slater has a special tool called a "ripper," which is used to cut or pull the nails from a broken slate, which can then be removed, but this requires skill and some force. Loose or broken slates can successfully be re-fixed by pressing them down on a strip of one of the bituminous adhesives

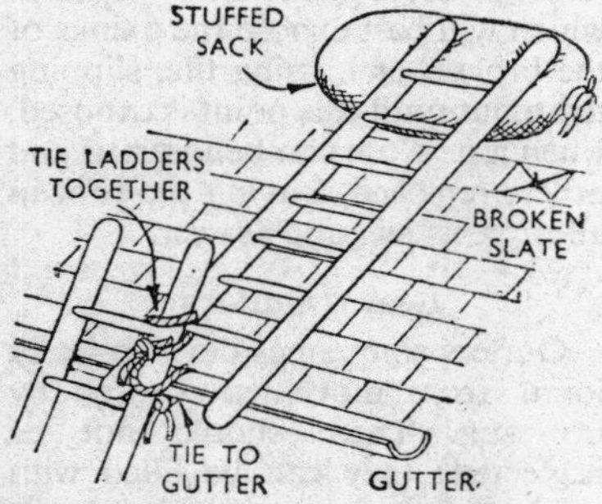

Fig. 49. *A ladder placed on tiles for roof-repairing should be arranged as indicated, and securely roped to the long ladder reaching the ground.*

under each *side* joint with the addition of a securing clip (called the "Perfik") wedged above the joint immediately under the tail of a slate to be secured (Fig. 50). If a missing slate has been head-nailed and has slipped out owing to decay of nails or breaking off of corners, a complete slate can be inserted and clipped provided its upper corners have been broken off clear of the nail-heads or corner-pieces remaining in place.

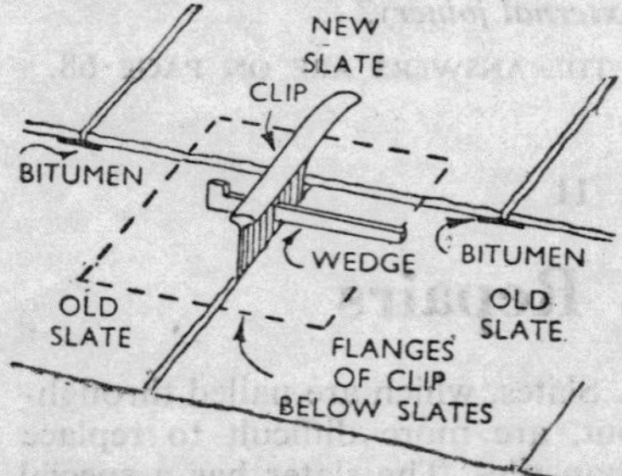

Fig. 50. *Loose slates can be affixed by means of bituminous adhesives and clips.*

Tiles hung in the usual way, with nailed courses only at intervals, are more easily replaced. All that is necessary is to test by pushing up the tails of several courses to locate the nailed one, and then carefully raising those un-nailed courses which will best expose the fixings of the broken or missing tile, slipping these out until this point is exposed, when a new tile can be inserted and others replaced, leaving the roof in all respects as good as ever.

Leaky Gutters

Gutters sometimes develop leaky joints from movement caused by hot sun. These should not be neglected; they can be filled with red lead putty and painted over.

Cracks in brickwork due to settlement are best left to expert attention, as the cause ought to be sought out, but minor repairs such as loose bricks can quite well be dealt with, and often the stitch in time will save the proverbial nine. The important points to remember in any such cases are; (1) to clean off all loose mortar, dust or brick-flakes from the surfaces to be jointed, (2) to saturate them with clean water before re-setting any loose parts, including the bricks to be inserted, (3) to keep the work moist and sheltered from wind or strong sun for 24 hours or so.

Repairing Grates

The fireclay interiors of sitting-room grates usually develop cracks and cavities after a few years' use, and these, as well as being unsightly, may be dangerous. They can quite easily be repaired with one of the plastic fire-cements such as "Purimachos" or "Pyruma."

To make good repair, the cracks and surrounding surfaces should be freed from soot, dust and loose pieces, and well soaked with water. The cement should be kneaded by hand to a roughly suitable shape and pressed well into place by the thumb, leaving a slight surplus, which should then be removed and the cement smoothed, using an old table-knife dipped in water. The cement will harden under heat and the original surface be completely restored. Open joints in boilers, and in iron or asbestos-cement flue pipes, can also be refilled with these materials. This does not, of course, refer to *cracked* boilers.

The efficiency of any fireplace, stove or boiler depends almost entirely on control of its air-supply, and many unsatisfactory ones could be easily restored to good working condition by dealing with them as suggested above.

Cracks and broken places in plaster should be "made good" by filling with hard stopping of Keen's cement. Any loose material should be raked out and the open crack well wetted by flinging water from a brush, after which the freshly mixed stopping should be well pressed in and smoothed off with a small trowel or old table-knife. If considerable pieces of plaster have been knocked off from projecting angles such as a chimney breast, a roughened undercoat of Portland cement and sand (1 to 2½ parts) should be applied first, to within about ¼ in. of finished surface, the final coat alone being of Keen's.

Floor-Boards and Stairs

The surface of floor-boards (and other wooden articles) is often worn into hollows by the movement of furniture, being then in a stringy condition. Such places can be effectively repaired by the use of "plastic wood," which when filled in and hardened can be painted or stained to match the original surface treatment.

Stairs which are worn hollow on the steps, usually towards the nosing of each tread, and in that condition may be dangerous, can be renovated with a little patience and ingenuity. The nosings should be neatly cut back to the line of the risers, and new, rather deeper, nosings screwed on, standing up about ¼ in. above the original tread so as to allow a new tread surface of plain lino to be fitted as in Fig. 51. If the hollow extends beyond the nosing on to the surface of the tread remaining, it should be levelled up with plastic wood before fixing the lino with adhesive. Stairs renewed in this way are quite good in appearance and comfortable in use without carpeting.

Little need be said on glazing—it is within the capacity of any intelligent person to remove and replace broken glass. It may, however, be worth mention that "weeping" around the edges of panes due to defective puttying, or to lack of cement in lead-glazed windows, can usually be stopped by marking the origin of the leaks when active, and running ordinary lead paint into the marked places when dry.

Protection of Pipes

A great deal of trouble might be saved if water-pipes in roof-spaces were wrapped or similarly protected. Felt is the best material for this, but lacking felt several thicknesses

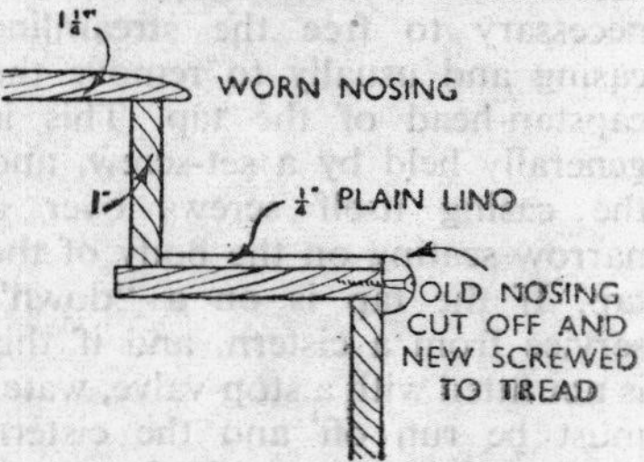

Fig. 51. *This method may be used for repairing a stair tread which has worn thin towards the nosing.*

of old newspaper secured with string can be quite effective, and in places where actual wrapping cannot be carried out, a packing of old clothing can help.

The prevention of drip from taps and ball valves by replacing defective washers is another task easily performed. An ordinary tap (known as a "bib-cock") consists of a screwed spindle which raises or lowers a washer of leather or composition, bearing when closed upon a seating. The washer is placed upon a loose "jumper" fitting the spindle, and by unscrewing the upper part of the tap (usually fashioned as a hexagon nut to accommodate a spanner) the interior can be withdrawn. The water-pressure must, of course, be shut off before beginning.

Another cause of dripping from taps and stop-valves is loose packing around the spindle. Immediately around this at the top of the body of the tap is a milled edge; this constitutes a gland or stuffing-box, and, by screwing down, compresses a fibre packing which makes the spindle water-tight in its bearing. Extra compression, or renewal of this, is not difficult. The modern "Easiclean" types of tap are similar internally, but to obtain access to the working parts it is necessary to free the streamline casing and usually to remove the capstan-head of the tap. This is generally held by a set-screw, and the casing itself screws over a narrow seating on the body of the tap. If the tap is on a "down" service from a cistern, and if this is not fitted with a stop-valve, water must be run off and the cistern temporarily prevented from refilling by holding up the ball-valve. This can be done by tying it up with string to a stick placed across the cistern.

Ball-Valves

Washers on dripping ball-valves are easily replaced; if the ball-arm is removed by pulling out the split-pin which secures it, the valve will drop out and can be re-washered and replaced without difficulty.

The amateur painter most often fails from one or both of two causes: (1) neglect to wash down the work to be repainted; (2) insufficient "rubbing down" with glass-paper to give a key to following coats. He should also remember that coats should alternate—flat and glossy—so that if a glossy finish is desired, the preceding coat should be flat, and *vice versa.*

Use of Lime-White

Lime-white for external use has a distinct value as a waterproofer on brickwork, plaster and roughcast. Properly mixed and applied, it serves to seal the minute cracks which intersect rendered surfaces, and to check porosity. To prepare a waterproof lime-wash which will stand the weather, take 20 lb. beef tallow and one bushel of unslaked chalk lime (or proportionate quantities) and place in a barrel. Add sufficient boiling water to slake the lime, but not to drown it, and cover the barrel with sacking to keep in the heat. When cool, dilute with sufficient cold water to make the mixture flow so that it can be brushed on. This will give a milk-white colour; if cream or buff is desired, small quantities of ochre can be added when first mixing. The wash should be strained to remove lumps before use.

Self Testing Questions

(1) *What difference in method of fixing makes tiles more easily replaced in case of breakage, as compared with slates?*

(2) *What successive steps would you take to replace a washer in a dripping tap?*

(3) *You intend to repaint an external door; how would you proceed?*

THE ANSWERS ARE ON PAGE 68.

LESSON 12

Sun-Parlour and Cottage

THE special value of a sun-parlour is *not* to be able to absorb the sun's rays in summer, but to enjoy their brightness and warmth in those days of spring and autumn (and occasionally winter) when chilly winds and perhaps damp ground would prevent sitting in the open. Aspect is therefore important.

A Sun-Parlour

The sun at midday in winter rises no higher than 15 deg. above the horizon, whereas at the same time in summer it appears nearly overhead. To obtain full benefit from sunlight when it can be welcomed, a sun-room should have a more or less south aspect; front and any open side should be chiefly of glass; the roof should be solid and heat-resisting (so that it may screen the interior from the high sun of midday in summer); and the depth of the shelter should not be greater than will allow the sun's rays at low elevation to reach to the back at head-height of a seated person.

It is also convenient to be able to open up a considerable proportion of any glazed side to admit pleasant breezes, according to the direction of the wind. Fig. 52 shows a sun-parlour attached to a house and open to east and south; the west aspect in summer is apt to be tiresome when the sun is low at the end of a grilling day.

The depth of the shelter admits deck chairs extended, with space for movement, the height allows sun at low altitude to penetrate, the roof is flat and covered with bituminous felt lime-washed (a valuable reflector and preservative) and lined below with insulating wallboard. The glazed sides are hung on an overhead track so that they can be folded back concertina fashion. If a less complete opening-up is desired, the complication and cost of the work can be considerably lessened by omission of the track and concertina sashes. In that case the front would be divided into four widths, of which the middle two would be hung to a fixed sash on either side so as to fold back flat when open. The side glazing might be fixed, with one opening casement for ventilation.

A Brick Cottage

Fig. 55 shows working drawings of a cottage of a type which gives maximum accommodation on the most economical structural scheme. The special features which make for economy are:

(1) simple rectangular plan without projections;

(2) unbroken gabled roof without interruption or cutting caused by hips or valleys;

(3) restriction of brickwork throughout most of plan to one storey in height;

(4) single chimney-stack with flues on internal walls; rising from ridge of roof;

(5) no space wasted on passages;

(6) drainage and water services (except for storage cistern) confined to ground level, and compactly planned;

(7) floor-spans small and beams act as stiffeners to whole structure in direction not tied by joists;

(8) roof-thrust completely tied by floor-joists, and rafters stiffened by the bedroom partition and ceiling-collars.

Other points in favour of this type (in rural situations) are that it is suitable to a raft foundation by reason of the even distribution of loading, and that the gable-pitch of about 53 deg. is the natural angle of racked brickwork, so that raking cutting of bricks is reduced to a minimum. It is also adaptable to any aspect by reversal, or by turning the plan either as drawn or reversed, so that the living-room gable-end faces south, the entry, if necessary, not facing the road front.

The procedure in building would be: (1) soil-stripping; (2) setting-out with "profiles"; (3) trench-digging; (4) concreting foundations; (5) building brickwork up to damp-course level. The plan shows 9-in. walls—if cavity walling is intended the overall dimensions each way should be increased by 4½ in.; (6) spread oversite concrete to living-room and bedroom 3 and make up levels to receive concrete under solid floors elsewhere so that filling may be consolidated; (7) build

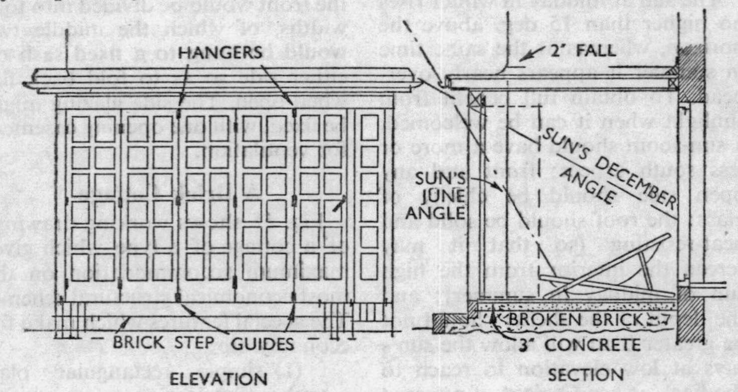

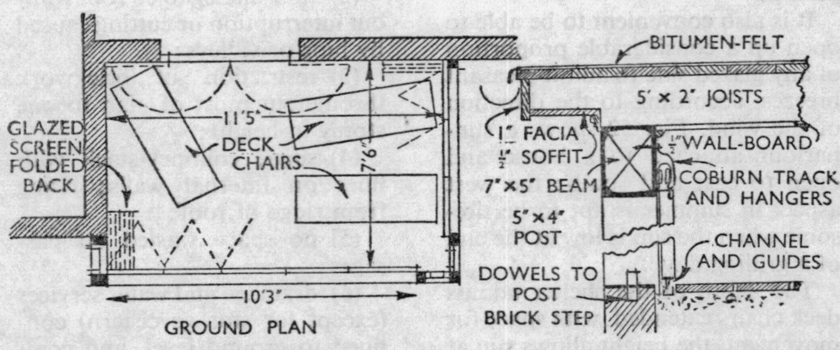

Fig. 52. *Plan and elevation of sun-parlour open on two sides. The glazed sides, hung on an overhead track, can be folded back, or one half of the glazing can be fixed.*

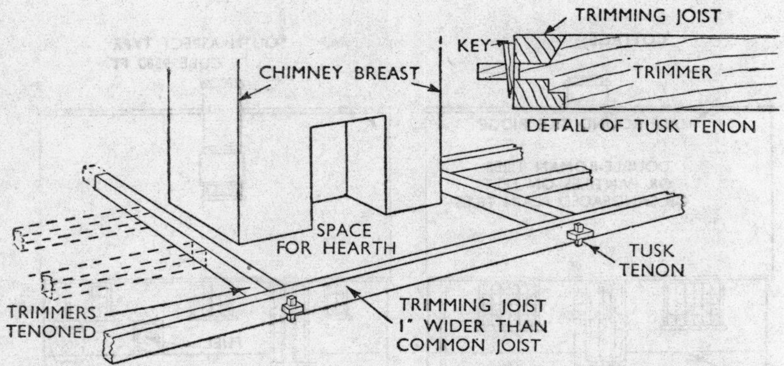

Fig. 53. *Floor joists near chimney flues and hearths must be trimmed, as here shown, to keep woodwork at a minimum of 9 in. away from flue.*

brickwork up to height for bedding first-floor joists, building in exterior door- and window-frames as the work rises, and bedding lintels; (8) fix beams and floor-joists. Joists around chimney-flues and hearth of fireplace in bedroom 1 must be "trimmed" as in Fig. 53, so that woodwork is no nearer than 9 in. to any flue; (9) set up a few pairs of rafters and the ridge, to act as a guide for brickwork of gables and chimney; (10) build gable-ends as high as first-floor window-heads, building in frames as the work rises; (11) make and fix timber-studded partitions forming upper bedrooms. These should be framed as shown in Fig. 54, when they will serve as trussed purlins to the roof; (12) fix remainder of rafters, each pair nailed securely to joist-ends at foot, to heads of bedroom partitions, and to ridge; (13) fix temporary guide below rafters and cut, fit and nail on collars at 8 ft. above floor; (14) fill in gablets above window-heads with studding and cover with felt and weatherboards; (15) raise chimney-stack through roof. The flues, where gathered over stairs, are supported on concrete lintels. By dropping a plumb-line from ridge, stack can be adjusted so as to lie at side of ridge-board and avoid necessity for a lead gutter. Tilted roof over small staircase window is set out to width of stack, and a projecting brick course is formed above this when building stack, to serve as a weathering; (16) fix staircase window, with lead apron fixed below sill to be dressed down over tiling when laid (Fig. 56); (17) cover in roof, including fixing undercloak at gables, and felt underlining. This should preferably cover whole roof surface, but in no case should be omitted from the space marked

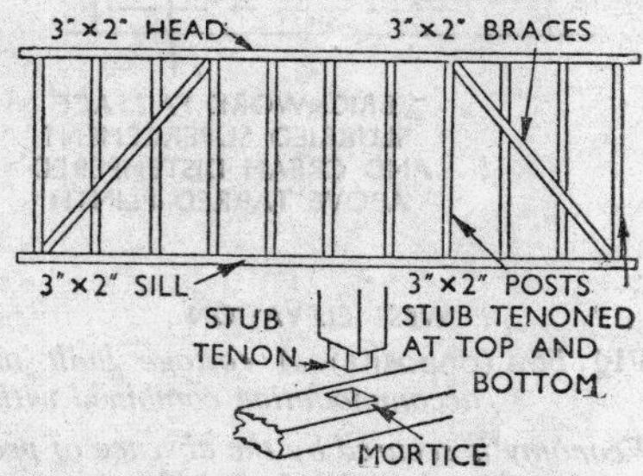

Fig. 54. *Partitions framed as here shown will form the upper bedrooms and also act as trussed purlins to the roof.*

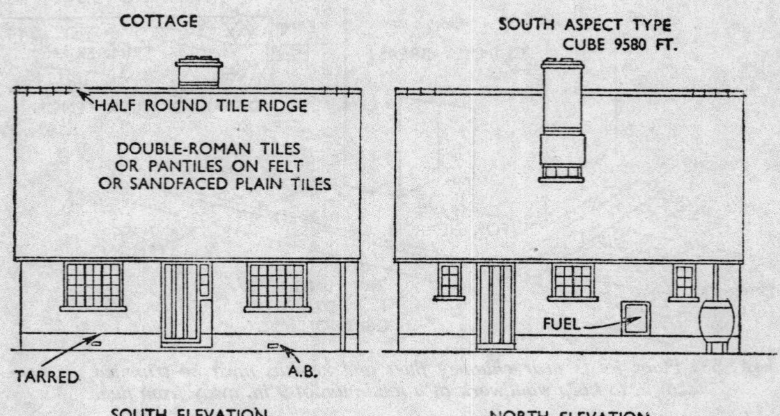

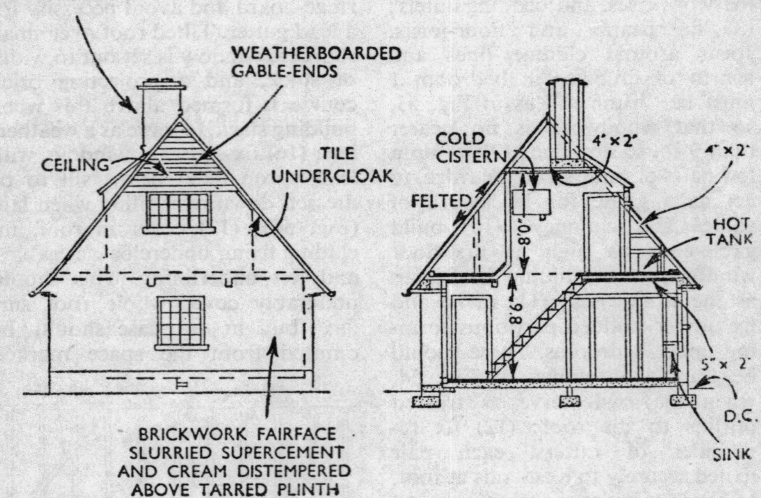

Fig. 55a (opposite). *A cottage built to these drawings gives the maximum of accommodation combined with economy of structural expense.*

Economy is secured by the absence of projections, uninterrupted roof, restriction in height of brickwork, single chimney-stack, confining drainage and water supply to ground level, and small passage area. It can be adapted to any aspect desired.

Fig. 55b. *End elevations and section of the cottage shown in Fig. 55a.*

SUN-PARLOUR AND COTTAGE

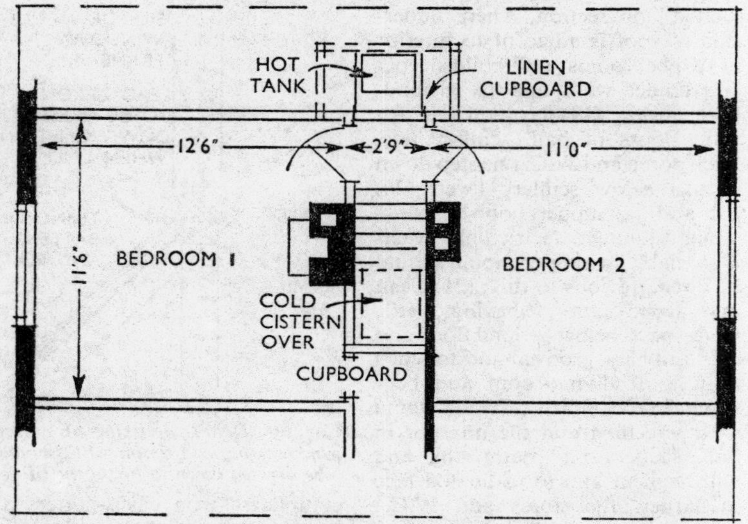

FIRST FLOOR PLAN

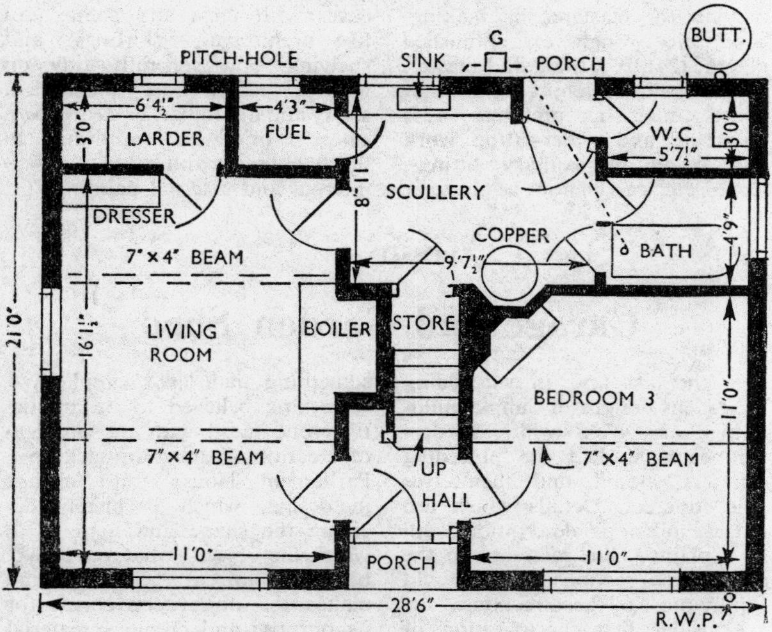

G
PITCH-HOLE
SINK
PORCH
BUTT.
6'4½"
4'3"
3'0"
LARDER
FUEL
W.C.
5'7½"
3'0"
8'11"
SCULLERY
DRESSER
COPPER
4'9"
BATH
7" × 4" BEAM
9'7½"
21'0"
16'1½"
LIVING ROOM
BOILER
STORE
BEDROOM 3
11'0"
7" × 4" BEAM
UP
7" × 4" BEAM
HALL
11'0"
PORCH
11'0"
28'6"
R.W.P.

GROUND FLOOR PLAN

"felted" on section, where underside of roof is adjacent to interior of two bedrooms; (18) build sleeper and fender walls and fix ground-floor joists; (19) lay concrete for solid floors of hall, scullery, etc. Back porch and W.C. one step down (6 in.) below scullery level; (20) cut and lay upper floor-boards—straight joint. If electric light or gas is available, wiring or piping should be done previous to this; (21) clean out wood chips, shavings, etc., from space below ground floor and cut and lay grooved-and-tongued flooring to living-room and bedroom 3; (22) finish off solid floors with screeding and tile quarries in hall, scullery and bathroom, and with cement and sand floated face in larder, fuel-stores and W.C.; (23) fix linings, stairs and grounds for other internal "trim," and prepare for plasterer by making-good any rough or unfinished places; (24) fix lathing and plaster, or fix strap-battening and wall-board linings as preferred; (25) plumbing and water-fitting work and fixing of sanitary fittings, stoves, etc., can be done as plasterer completes—iron eaves-gutters and down-pipes can be fixed at any time after carpenter has completed eaves with facia and soffit; (26) fix architraves, skirtings and shelving, and generally tidy up interior; (27) render in finecast, slurry and distemper, or clean down external brickwork (according to finish chosen), and carry on with internal and external painting.

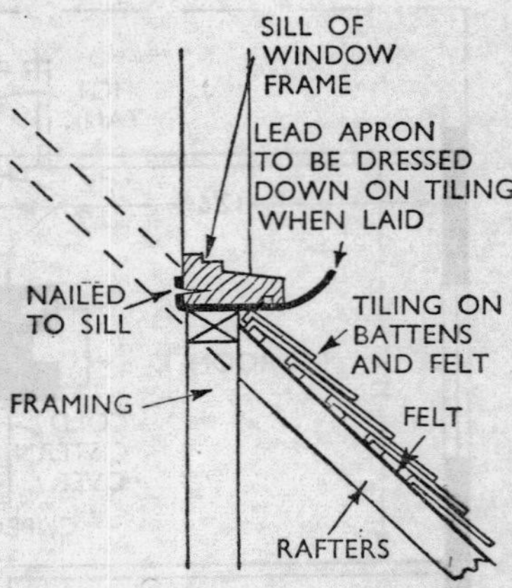

Fig. 56. *Details of fixing of staircase window: the lead apron will eventually be dressed down to lie on the tiling.*

LESSON 13

Garage and Garden Shed

In the last and in succeeding lessons designs of simple buildings are given which readers who have studied the preceding chapters should find themselves able to erect. Details which are outside previous descriptions will be explained, but reference to the appropriate sections above should supply most of the directions.

Consider first the question of design. Design does not imply something that lacks simplicity—something believed to be artistic. Everyone faced with the problem of creation—from a tin-tack to a Parliament House—must engage in design, which is merely deciding the shape and material in which the object—whatever it may be—shall appear. Good design makes the object convenient for its purpose and employs material to best advantage. In complicated subjects the skill and judgment required of the designer will obviously be high, and the ideal "straightforward" arrangement which in the result looks so natural may not easily be reached; but design is present even in the humblest of human works, and the endeavour should always be made to produce results which are proportionate, shapely and well organised.

Fig. 57 gives working drawings for a small garage capable of housing a light car or motor-cycle

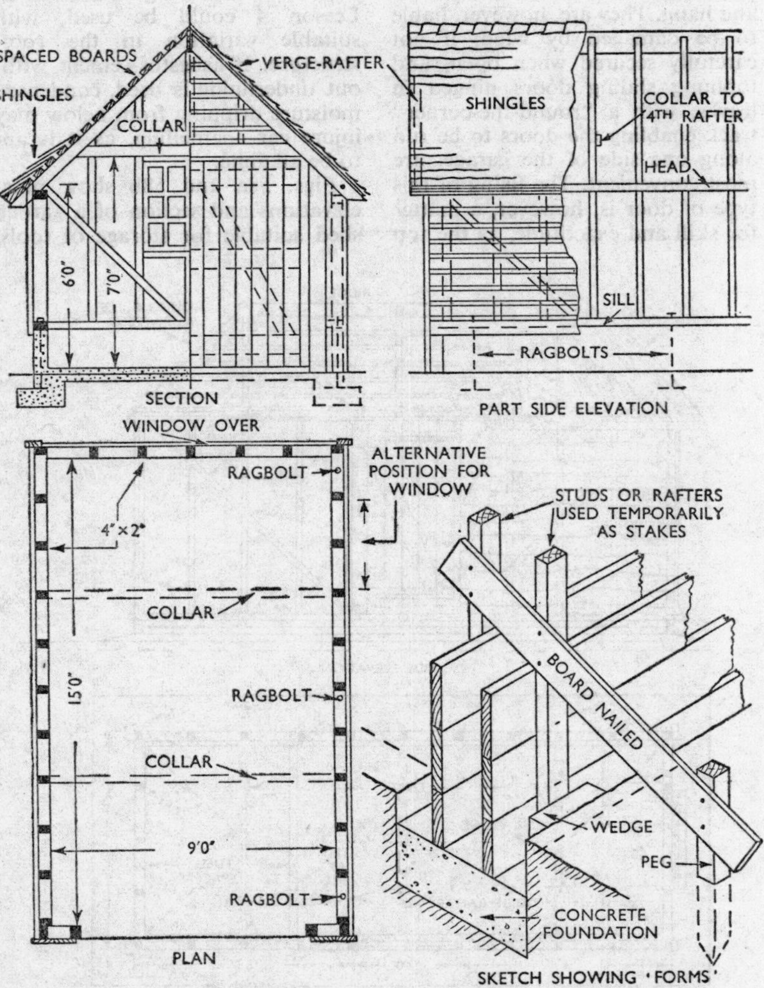

Fig. 57. *Plan, elevation and section of small garage for a light car or cycle. Top-hung sliding doors could be substituted for the double doors here shown.*

combination. The base wall below the framing is shown in concrete, and the sketch shows the way in which the casting in position may be conveniently done, with rag-bolts embedded for attachment of the wood sills. Double doors are shown, as these are easier to make and hang. They are, however, liable to be damaged by wind, if not carefully secured when open, and tophung sliding doors hinged in leaves, with a "round-the-corner" track enabling the doors to be run along one side of the garage, are most convenient. The fixing of this type of door is, however, a matter for skill and exactitude, as the top track and bottom guide must be in perfect alignment and parallel if the action is to run smoothly, and the track and hangers are considerably more costly than two pairs of strap-hinges.

The roof is shown shingled, but any of the coverings described in Lesson 4 could be used, with suitable variation in the roof-structure. If asbestos-cement without underlining is used, condensed moisture dripping from below may injure car enamelling, as it is apt to be alkaline.

Figs. 58a and 58b show plan, elevations and section of a garden shed suitable for storage of tools,

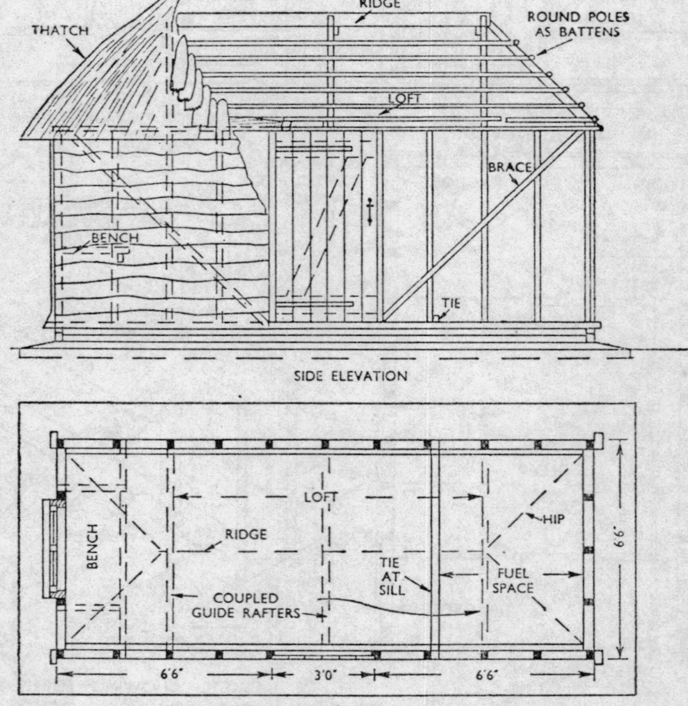

Fig. 58a. *Plan and side elevation of garden shed with thatched roof*

garden accessories, winter fuel and the usual odds and ends which cumber the average house. It is also adapted for use as a workshop for minor tasks.

The order of procedure for construction would be: (1) strip soil and level site; (2) set out lines; (3) lay concrete floor, which, if site should be on clay or loam, might be treated as a light raft, by embedding stout wire netting in its thickness. The large-mesh netting used for fencing sheep, pigs or deer is most suitable; (4) build brick base two courses high along sides (6 in. high) and continuous through doorway and one course on edge (4½ in. high) at ends. This difference in height allows side and end frames to lap at angles; (5) frame up the four sides out of 3 in. × 1½ in. fir timber, erect ends first and stay in place. Next get sides into position, their sills and heads crossing those of ends, secured to them by bolts or spikes when trued up; (6) cover external faces of framing either as described in Lesson 6 or as shown in Fig. 58, in which sawn elm boards are used. These are cheap to buy, easy to fix if nailed on "green," and harden on exposure, weathering to a beautiful silvery colour which is permanent; (7) cut off and nail together on ground three sets of guide rafters each having 3 in. × 1½ in. rafters, tie-joists and ridge-coupler preserving a space into which the ridge-board will drop when fixing. Raise and fix these coupled rafters in the position shown. Floor-boards 7 in. × 1 in. may be used for ridge and to form loft space on the tie-joists (useful for storing garden nets, pea-guards and similar light things); (8) fix hip rafters from angles to ends of ridge-board. For thatch roof these can be unsquared timber; small limbs of oak trees serve quite well; (9) cover the roof with round poles about 1 in. in diameter, well nailed on. Hornbeam bean-sticks serve admirably; (10) thatch roof with bundles of straw, laid butts downward and tied at ear ends with tarred twine, which is then passed round the circular "battens" and tied from

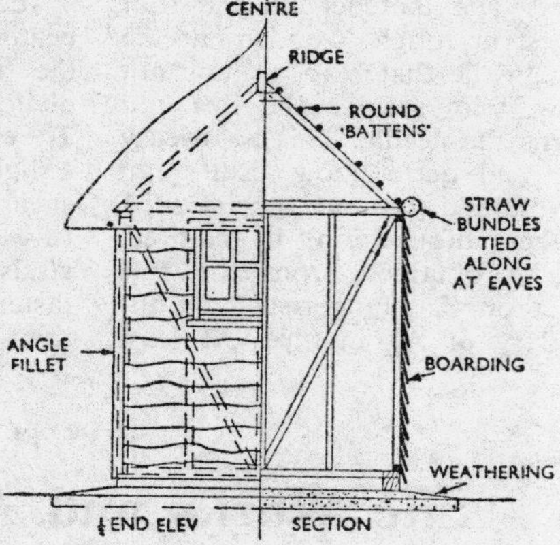

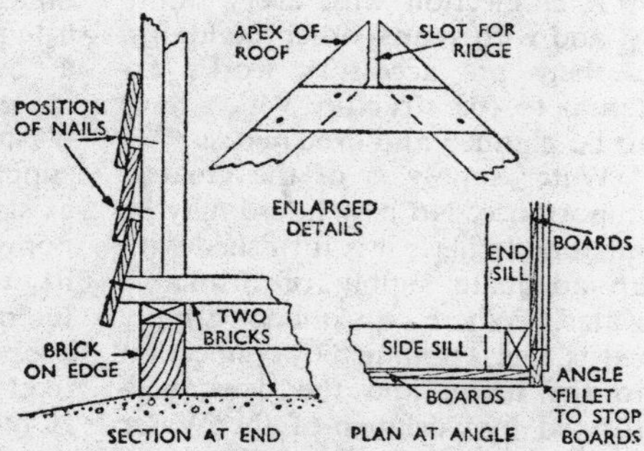

Fig. 58b. *End elevation and section and details of garden shed for tools, accessories and fuel.*

below. The thatcher on the roof pushes a rough wooden needle through the thatch to an assistant below, who secures the ties and returns the needle. This is an easy task, and quite good results can be obtained without special skill. Further information, if required, can be obtained from the free leaflet on thatching issued by the Ministry of Agriculture. At least a foot thickness of thatch, well beaten down, should be laid, and the surface lightly raked on completion to remove loose straws. The eaves soffit should be trimmed to a slightly undercut line with ordinary shears. (11) Fix bench, coalboards (if wanted) and shelving to internal studs; hang door and fix window fastenings, etc., and the structure is then fundamentally complete.

LESSON 14

Site Works and Accessories

In connection with every house and with many other buildings, there are accessory works external to the structure which have to be planned and executed.

Water supply is of the greatest importance. No new house may be inhabited unless it is furnished with an adequate supply of drinkable water. Where a public supply exists, this is obtained by connection to the main, and the work performed by workmen of the Water Authority, who will tap the main, insert a ferrule and bring the supply pipe (with an outside stop-valve for the Authority's use) into the building-owner's premises.

This connection is usually made in heavy lead pipe of small diameter, but in soft-water districts owing to the risk of lead poisoning it may be in galvanised iron of the quality known as "steam-barrel." The supply pipe is usually buried at least 2 ft. deep, and preferably more; mains are usually 3 ft. below ground. Whatever type of pipe is used by the Authority's workmen should be used in continuation as far as the storage cistern.

The water-supply branch is usually the first thing to be arranged on a building site, and is fitted with a temporary stand-pipe to serve as a "building supply" for water used in mixing concrete, mortar and plaster. When a sufficiently clean supply from a spring, well or pond exists, however, considerable economy can be effected by its use in building, as a Water Authority's lump-sum charge is usually out of proportion to the amount of water likely to be used for this purpose.

Where no public supply exists, water must be sought for and obtained by tapping a spring or by well-sinking—a subject beyond our scope. An ordinary suction pump will raise water 25 ft.; wells deeper than that require more complex apparatus. In some districts the only practicable source of water supply is saved roof-water; in such case large underground storage tanks are formed and the water is passed through a sand filter on the way to storage.

Drainage comes next in order of importance. Where a public sewer is available, connection will be made by the Local Authority in accordance with the plans, which must be deposited with and approved by them. Usually, and preferably, the branch drain will be brought within the site by their workmen on payment of a deposit.

The laying of the house-drain is started from this point, and works backward. The aim is to carry the piping in straight lines both for direction and grade or fall from point to point, with all changes in direction effected in manholes to which also any branch drains are connected. The work is carried out in glazed stoneware socketed pipes and fittings, comprising channel and channel-bends in the manholes, pipe-bends of varying radius for branches, gulley-traps for waste-water connections, and in most cases a "sewer-interceptor" consisting of a special form of trap with a "clearing-arm" fitted with a stopper between the lowest manhole and the sewer connection or septic tank. The pipes will in most cases be 4 in. internal diameter, which require to be laid to a minimum fall of 1 in 40, and they will be laid upon a bed of concrete at the bottom of the trench and jointed in cement and sand, with a "gasket" of hemp wrapped round each spigot so as to prevent the entry of the jointing cement into the bore of the pipes.

As each pipe is jointed and laid, the interior should be wiped out with a wet cloth to ensure freedom from obstruction. The joints are then "collared up" in cement and the whole drain preferably "benched" in fine concrete as shown in Fig. 59. Trench-filling should be carefully done to avoid damage.

A typical drain plan is shown, applicable to the cottage (Fig. 55); from manhole *A* the direction of the drain to manhole *B* may, of course, be varied to suit fall of ground or direction of outlet. Two connections other than inlet branches are obligatory on any house drain; these are a fresh-air inlet, fitted with a talc flap-valve, which is connected to a branch near the top of the manhole by the sewer-interceptor, and the vent-shaft connected as near as possible to the head of the drain. This latter is an iron pipe jointed in molten lead and gasket, and carried up in some convenient position to a height of 3 ft. above any window-head. Where W.C.s occur on upper floors, extension of the vertical "soil-pipe" which conveys their discharge is the usual means of providing this vent.

Rain-water drains should be

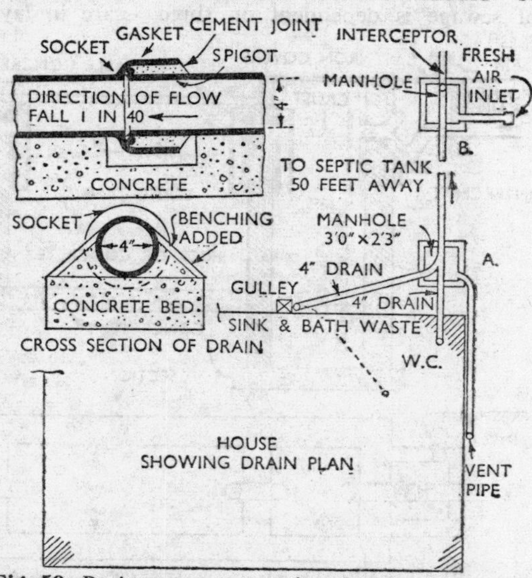

Fig. 59. *Drainage connections from house to public sewer or septic tank, and arrangement of concrete benching.*

separate from foul drains, either taken to "soakaways" 10 ft. from the walls or connected to a separate outlet. Where no sewer is available, house drainage must be disposed of on the building site and distant at least 50 ft. from any building. The water-tight cesspool or the septic tank are the alternative methods of doing this. The former requires frequent emptying by pumping out, which is an unpleasant and tiresome necessity, so that the alternative is preferable in all cases where surface filtration of effluent is likely to act. A cesspool with holes or other contrived leakage is *not* a septic tank, and is highly objectionable as a possible danger to water-sources.

Septic Tank

Fig. 60 shows a simple septic tank system which is suitable for a family of up to five persons, and should work well on any but a heavy clay soil. Bacterial treatment of sewage is dependent on three successive processes: (1) breaking down of solids; (2) fermentation by anaerobic bacteria; (3) purification by aerobic bacteria—the latter can live and work only in the presence of air, and are drowned in submerged or water-logged conditions. For this reason, filters or soakage areas, such as the radiating land-drains of the illustration, must be laid just beneath the surface in topsoil. Vegetation will grow freely in this area, and if rank growths of weeds are to be avoided, it should be cultivated and planted with things which will thrive on it, of which black-currants are the best example.

Gas and electric services, when available, are brought in by the authorities responsible, and the builder is concerned only in seeing that application is made in due time so that the work may be done without needless disturbance.

Paths are a necessity, which repay a little thought as to their lines and care in laying. The best material

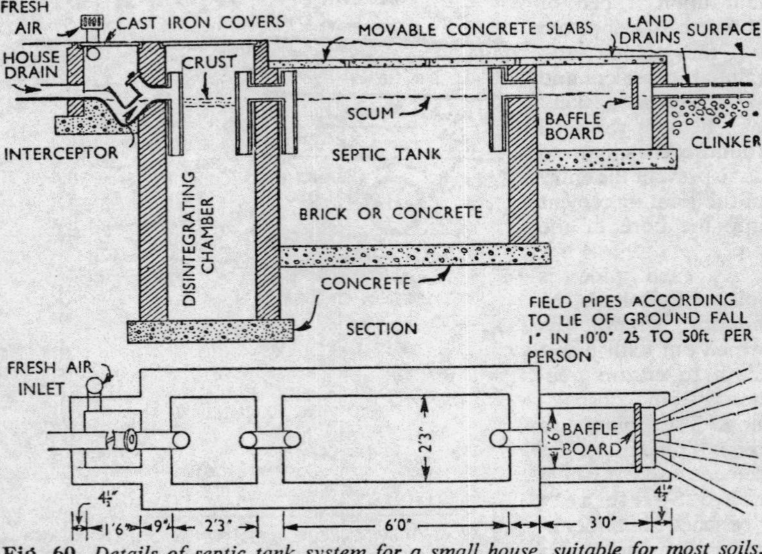

Fig. 60. *Details of septic tank system for a small house, suitable for most soils.*

available locally (which may be concrete, tarmac, gravel, clinker or stone) should be chosen. If clinker or gravel is used, stout creosoted wood edging and stumps should first be fixed. Clay soil presents the only real difficulty, as the clay is apt to work up through any porous material. Experience has shown that a reversal of the usual practice of bottoming in coarse material and surfacing with finer has greater success. A carpet of fine ashes followed by a layer of coarse clinker appears to keep a gravel topping much cleaner.

Fencing

Fencing usually causes trouble and expense far beyond its real importance. Wooden fences decay and collapse just when a garden is reaching maturity. In any rural, and in most suburban, situations a good hedge is greatly to be preferred. Choice should select a hedge-plant of strong growth which will need infrequent clipping, and give shelter in winter as well as summer. For this there is nothing to beat hornbeam (which most people take to be beech). Planted in zig-zag formation 9 in. apart and with rabbit-wire run straight and passing between the stems, hornbeam plants 2 ft. high clipped twice a year will in a year or two make a close, impenetrable hedge 4 ft. in height or more.

To secure the netting until the hedge is established, no more than rough posts about 9 ft. apart with a single or double line of wire is requisite—if the posts rot when the hedge has grown, they can be ignored. If rabbits are likely to be a nuisance, a trench 12 in. wide and deep should be formed first on the site of the hedge, and the wire-netting buried with a turned-outwards "foot," the hedge-plants being put in as the trench is filled.

If a permanent fence-line is required, reinforced-concrete posts with chain-link wire net have a life in excess of any timber fencing and will save much maintenance work.

Answers to Self Testing Questions

LESSON 1

(1) To form triangles, which resist distortion.

(2) It is liable to cause water-logging, and is subject to severe shrinkage during droughts, which results in unequal settlement.

(3) To distribute loading so that it is within the supporting power of the soil.

(4) To obtain complete density without voids, with all particles of aggregate coated with cement and the minimum quantity of water.

(5) A cross-piece of board nailed over two firmly fixed pegs. Upon it is marked the thickness of walls and projection of foundations, so that by stretching lines between each pair of profiles the positions of trenches and walls are defined.

BUILDING

LESSON 2

(1) (*a*) Bricks laid with their ends to the face of the wall;
(*b*) bricks laid with their long sides to the face of the wall.

(2) (*a*) English bond shows all headers and all stretchers in alternate courses;
(*b*) Flemish bond is laid with headers and stretchers alternating in each course.

(3) More rapid initial set, greater strength and easier handling result, combining most of the advantages of lime mortar and cement mortar.

(4) The metal meets tensile stresses produced by loading and resists shear. It also lessens the tendency of the concrete to develop shrinkage cracks.

(5) Because all rain beating against the window must run down over it.

(6) Air-bricks in external walls near corners of all rooms, honeycomb brickwork of sleeper walls, openings in internal partition walls to allow air to circulate.

LESSON 3

(1) It enables the two adjoining joists to help in supporting a point-load coming on any individual joist, and checks the tendency of deep narrow joists to overturn.

(2) To give a fall to a flat roof. Cross-firring allows freer internal air circulation within the roof space, and can be used to direct the fall along the run of boarding.

(3) The rafters need less preparation, and painting in future is much reduced.

LESSON 4

(1) (*a*) Gauge is the space between courses of slates or tiles.
(*b*) Lap is the extent by which the slates or tiles of any course overlap the heads of the next course but one below.
(*c*) Bond is the arrangement of slates or tiles by which the joints in each course break line so as to occur centrally between those of the course above and below.

(2) (*a*) The lap might be diminished: (*b*) smaller slates.

(3) They are cambered in length and formed with nibs and nail-holes.

(4) Metal (lead, zinc or copper), bituminous felt and asphalt. Bituminous felt is gaining ground, from its cheapness and easy application to either wood or concrete.

(5) Lead-work in the form of soakers and cover-flashings should cover the junction.

LESSON 5

(1) (*a*) Heat is not wasted on the open air by radiation from exposed firebacks.
(*b*) Grouping of fireplaces and flues results in economy and a better chimney-stack.
(*c*) In such a position the stack can be made to rise from the roof-ridge, where it is less likely to be saturated or to be subject to down-draught.

(2) (*a*) By the use of a core to preserve even size.
(*b*) By the exercise of care when forming bends or

sweeps, so that the cross-section is not constricted.

(3) (*a*) Sufficient height of chimney-top above roof.
(*b*) Formation of throat with "smoke-shelf."
(*c*) Solid setting of fireclay interior.

LESSON 6

(1) A short trench might be cut from lowest level to a temporary sumphole, or with outlet to a ditch or lower land.

(2) (i) The diagonal fixing stiffens the frames similarly to inclined struts.
(ii) The extra thickness with joints which cannot coincide with those of the outer lining assists in securing a warm and draught-free interior.

(3) On the outer side they permit an arrangement of sheathing and angle fillet which gives good cover without any through joints; on the inner side the arrangement secures a fixing for wallboard lining on both the surfaces which meet in the corner.

LESSON 7

(1) Casements allow greater latitude in width and are more adaptable where limited height is available. Sashes permit closer control of ventilation—especially during windy or rainy weather.

(2) The extension of any member beyond the actual width or height of the framing. The head and sill of a casement frame and the head of a door-frame are thus extended to secure the tenons on the jambs.

(3) A rebate is a rectangular sinking at the edge of a frame or lining into which a door, casement or similar inner framing fits or closes.

LESSON 8

(1) The total vertical rise, being 114 in., would give a result of fourteen risers each $8\frac{1}{7}$. With 8-in. treads (9 in. over nosings) the product 8 in. $\times$ $8\frac{1}{7}$ in. = $65\frac{1}{7}$ in., which would give just tolerable going. One extra step with risers throughout $7\frac{3}{5}$ in. would be preferable if space allowed.

(2) (*a*) Breeze bricks or wood slips would be built into the brickwork during erection.
(*b*) Fixing to timber studs, posts or rails would generally be available, but in cases where none served, timber nogging pieces would be provided.

(3) (1) Avoidance of a dirt-holding corner; (2) shelves may be dusted or washed without smearing the wall; (3) air-circulation is improved; (4) labour is reduced in the case of tiers of shelves, which need not be cut around the vertical bearers.

LESSON 9

(1) (*a*) A direct connection from the trap on the fitting to the house drain.
(*b*) A waste-pipe from the trap on the fitting discharging in the open air over a trapped gulley connected to the drain.

(2) A warning-pipe is the name

given to the overflow from any cistern or other fitting which contains water. On any cistern or tank filled by a ball-valve it is fixed so as to start flowing before the tank is over full, and it is carried so as to discharge visibly 6 in. clear of an external wall.

(3) Two main circulation pipes, the flowpipe reaching to nearly the top of the tank and the return pipe leaving near the bottom; a cold feed-pipe entering near the bottom; and an expansion pipe (from which hot water supplies are drawn) leaving the top of the tank and continuing to a level above the cold-service cistern over which it is turned to drip. The arrangement is due to two factors: (i) Heated water becomes lighter, so that hot water first accumulates near the top of any vessel containing it; (ii) it is the pressure of the cold replacement water which causes hot water to flow when a tap is opened; with connections as described, this cold water will rise in the hot tank, forcing the hot water above it into the expansion pipe, and so to the service branches and taps.

LESSON 10

(1) Strips of lath fixed to any surface wider than 3 in. across the direction of any lathing to be applied. It creates a space into which the plaster can be pressed to form a key.

(2) Wood battens, spaced 15 in. to 24 in. centres, to which the sheets can be nailed.

(3) Stain is a preservative solution, while paint is a covering film which prevents entry of moisture into joints and crevices.

LESSON 11

(1) Every slate is fixed by nails, which are not easily reached, whereas plain tiles are usually lodged against battens resting on nibs, with only an occasional course nailed, so that portions of the roof-covering can readily be removed to expose even the nailed courses if these are the seat of damage.

(2) (1) Close stop-valve on water service to shut off pressure. (2) Unscrew upper part of tap-body. (3) Remove damaged washer and replace. (4) Re-assemble tap and turn on water.

(3) First well wash down surface to be painted with plenty of clean water, using an old sponge; next examine the surface and decide number of coats required; make good any open cracks or defects with putty, and touch up. Rub down all over with glass-paper, and apply requisite number of coats, finishing glossy.

HOUSE DECORATING

By Edward Newman

LESSON 1

Hints on Modernising

THE clean lines of a modern room are coveted not only for their good appearance, but also for the work they may save in dusting.

For instance, the flush door has no mouldings to dust; whereas the much-panelled Victorian door may have as much as 26 ft. of moulding —sometimes more.

The Victorian fireplace can be literally a hotbed of labour. Embossed metal-work and tiles get very dirty—and hold the dirt. Blackleading is necessary—and unwanted. The modern hearth dispenses with these troubles.

A balustrade of the old-fashioned, intricately carved banisters is another creator of dusting work, which the encased balustrade is not.

Fireplaces

The fireplace is the dominating constructional feature in a room. If the fireplace is ugly it spoils all your efforts on walls and ceilings.

Sometimes the remedy is the simple one of painting. If the tiles are the wrong colour and the surround is rather grim, a coat or two of the oil paint you use for your skirting may do the job. The result is better when the walls are in the same colour, especially if it is a light shade.

Dead-white marble is an unpleasant fireplace surround for most of us to look at—especially when it is streaked with grey, and in a north room, where nothing so cold is wanted. If you rub the marble down so as to remove the gloss the paint will take better; though it can be applied to the more shiny surface.

Tiles

The tiles you cannot rub down: but apply the paint and keep some by you for touching up chippings. There are bound to be some in the course of using the fireplace, but not so many as to justify retaining the unpleasant colour you would like to hide. Coal fireplaces, thus painted, will stand up to wear over a long period.

If the jambs and mantel are ugly or over-ornate, you may encase them with thin sheets of wood which you can paint or leave plain to suit yourself. Make the casing detachable unless the house is your own. It can easily be fixed by brackets at each side if the case is made as a whole.

Should you want to make a case for a fireplace in which you wish to continue to burn a coal fire, it is advisable to call in an expert, unless you are going to leave exposed the original tile filling. There must be no risk of catching fire. Modernisation for an electric or gas fire can be more easily tackled. Non-inflammable sheeting can be got for the purpose. Asbestos sheeting, neat and paintable or

Fig. 1. *Old-fashioned, labour-making fireplace before modernisation. To case in such a fireplace with wood is a simple matter for the amateur carpenter.*

glazed in any colour and ready for fixing, is suitable material.

The construction of the frame is quite simple for the amateur carpenter who knows enough about joints to be able to make a frame to fit.

It may be desirable to build up the frame no higher than the underside of the mantel, leaving the shelf exposed if it is inoffensive by itself; but if the shelf has to be covered in, do not leave a dull square top to the casing, but step the top corner all round.

The opening for an electric fire must have its own framework as part of the whole frame to support the fire. When the frame is made, the sheeting can be screwed to it and the whole fitted over the existing fireplace and fastened by screws through brackets at the sides.

An electric fire for fitting into the opening is not difficult to buy. To ensure that the opening is the right size, you must acquire the fire before making the frame. And you must allow tubing to conduct your flex through the side of the casing from the nearest power-point in the room.

If the mantel projects very far, you may be able to make an extra opening, as for a bookshelf, above the opening for the fire as shown in Fig. 2.

The casing will look best painted to match the wall, especially if the fireplace is a large one.

Doors

Wallboard of various kinds, leather or rexine are suitable materials for covering in existing doors to give them the attractive and useful flush appearance (Fig. 6).

If you use board, do not forget to chamfer the hinge edge, or you may find a difficulty in opening the door.

A break must usually be made for the door-handle, unless you intend to replace this with something different. A snip-latch and a bar-handle are the easiest changes to make.

The door should be painted the same colour as the walls or woodwork (or both); if it is not, you must be prepared to change it every time you re-decorate.

The board can be obtained veneered with wood to match your furniture. But supposing you change the furniture? It will be more convenient if the ply is painted so that another coat is all that is needed if change there must be.

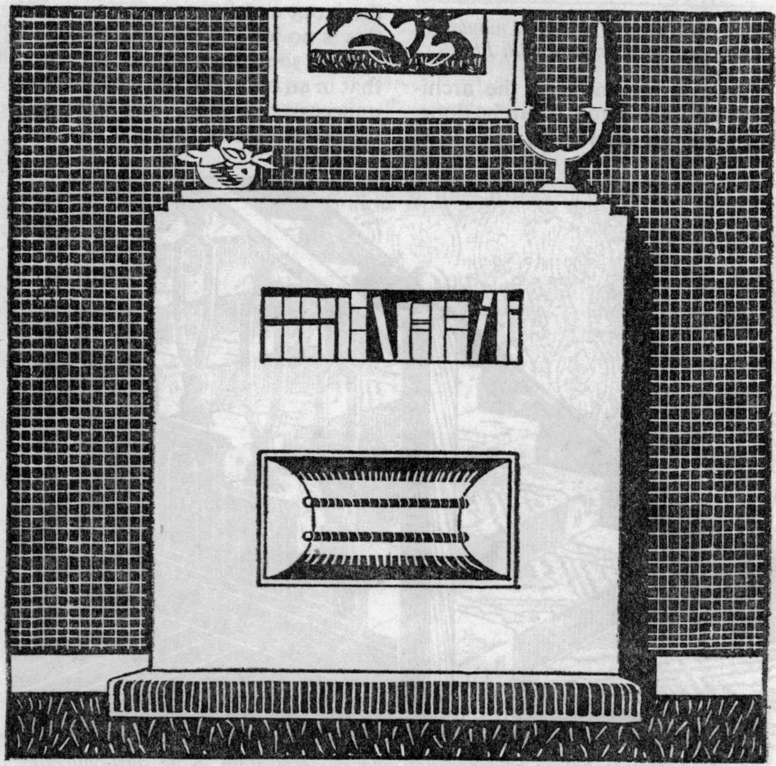

Fig. 2. *After modernisation: setting for an electric fire with book-space above.*

Fig. 3. *Old type of door: all mouldings need dusting. Compare with Fig. 6.*

Do not try encasing the architrave or door-frame. It can be done, but the effect is so bulky as to look worse than the original. The same, incidentally, applies to a heavy cornice; the old ornate affair painted to match the walls is less aggressive than the projecting rectangular beam that results when you box it in.

If you cover your door with leather or rexine it will be studded down with brass-headed nails all round, which can be quite decorative. But choose the material of a colour to match the walls or otherwise to agree with your scheme.

Windows

Little can be done to improve awkward windows except by taking them out and fitting new ones; and this is no job for the amateur.

It is sometimes found, however, that in an old room the windows are unnecessarily high, and that the room would look better if they were

Fig. 4. *Staircase before re-decoration and modernisation. Note dust-collecting, carved balustrade and stair-risers showing marks from being kicked.*

Fig. 5. *Staircase after re-decoration and modernisation: balustrade enclosed; stair-treads white while risers are dark in contrast for ease in seeing in poor light.*

made to appear less lofty. Where there is daylight to spare this can be done by fitting a perfectly plain pelmet board across the top of the window-frame and hanging the curtains from inside it. The board can be made the necessary depth, and should be painted to match the walls.

This would mean that the curtains could not overlap the window-frame; but, to cut out draughts, they could be fixed at the sides to the length of the frame.

If a sill projected, this idea would not be feasible.

If the pelmet has to be built out, it becomes more noticeable and less like part of the wall. You can reduce this effect by making it longer from end to end, as if the windows were wider, hanging the curtains to cover the extra space of wall at each side.

The "addition" to the width of the windows might, indeed, be desirable.

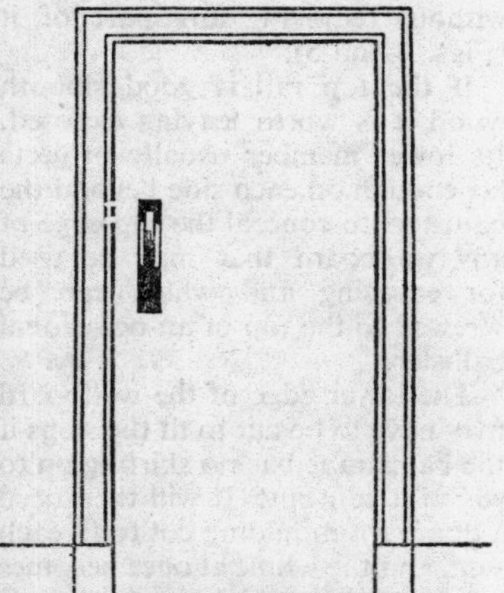

Fig. 6. *Door after modernisation: one smooth panel, which collects no dust.*

If you have two windows in the one wall and you wish to cut their height, another, though more extravagant, method is to build the deep pelmet right across that wall of the room, cutting off as much of the window as you wish, and hanging curtains that cover the wall as well as the windows, so that even when they are drawn back and the windows exposed, the wall between and flanking the windows is covered by curtain; at night the whole wall would be curtained.

Staircase

If you have no hand-rail on the wall side of your staircase, a simple way to achieve one without elaborate carpentry and fixing is to make one of rope.

The wall must be plugged at suitable intervals to take a ring through which the rope will pass. Each end of the rope will be knotted.

It is the balustrade, however, which in an old house gives rise to a longing for modernisation. And in some instances it is possible to enclose it to give a "solid" effect without removing any part of it (Figs. 4 and 5).

If the top rail is good smooth wood it is worth leaving exposed. Its lower member usually projects far enough on each side beyond the balusters to conceal the top edge of any wallboard that may be used for encasing and which can be screwed to the top of an occasional baluster.

The lower edge of the wallboard may have to be cut to fit the steps if the balustrade has no skirting on to which it can butt. It will then need a quadrant moulding cut to fit each step, and the whole at once becomes a more elaborate job.

If, however, there is a skirting to take the lower edge of the board, the work is easier. You may decide to fix the board on the run, taking its length along the balustrade, or you may prefer to cut it into sections to fix upright.

For the former method the width of the board may be too great for the depth of the balustrade, in which case a long strip will have to be cut from one edge of the board. The ends would also have to be diagonally cut to come upright against the newel-post when the board is lifted to the diagonal line of the balustrade. But there will be no joints, as in the second method, when sections are cut for fixing upright.

Joints must be carefully and closely butted. They can be covered with mouldings and the whole of the casing painted to match the wall. Or the casing can be papered to match the wall, dispensing with mouldings if the butting is well done.

The illustration which shows this modernisation of a staircase also makes another suggestion. The risers which get all the kicks are painted dark and treads light. This alternate dark and light—black and white if they fit the colour scheme—are not only decorative, but are helpful in a dark staircase by making the steps more clearly seen.

Bath

To encase a bath, it is not difficult to construct a frame as in Figs. 9, 10 and 11. Its top fits against the under-side of the bath-lip and projects at each side of the curved end to make the rectangular corners.

The sides can be covered with glazed asbestos sheets or sheets of wall-glass or even wallboard, if these are given a coat or two of glossy oil paint or enamel.

The top edge of the frame at each of the projecting corners must be

Fig. 7. *Bathroom before modernisation. The old type of bath, raised on four ornate feet, catches the dirt beneath it, and between its side and the wall.*

Fig. 8. *Bathroom after modernisation. The wooden casing prevents dirt from collecting either underneath or behind the bath. Note the squared linoleum.*

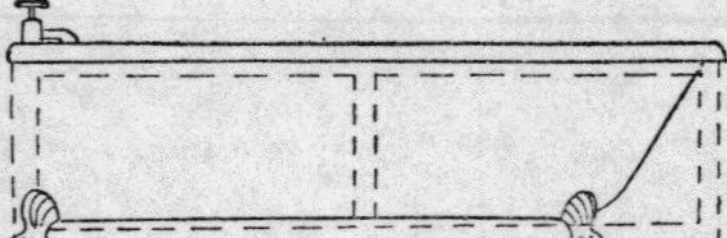

Fig. 9. *Long side of frame for bath.*

Fig. 10. *Top view of bath showing projecting corners of frame at round end.*

cut to allow a piece of the material used to cover the sides of the bath to be slipped in, so that its inner edge comes under the lip of the bath and its outer straight edges cover the top edges of the side and end panels.

The colour of the casing would depend on the colour scheme of the bathroom. The wall-glass and the glazed asbestos colour ranges are quite ample; and if a wallboard is used, or plywood, it should be well

Fig. 11. *Wood frame to take asbestos or board panelling for enclosure of bath.*

painted with glossy oil paint or enamel to give the effect shown in Fig. 8.

Self Testing Questions

(1) *Which parts of a house best lend themselves to modernisation?*

(2) *In casing a fireplace, what risk should you guard against?*

(3) *What are the advantages of a flat-surfaced door?*

(4) *Name some materials used in encasing an old-fashioned bath.*

THE ANSWERS ARE ON PAGE 114.

LESSON 2

Ceilings Are Important

THE ceiling is important in the scheme of decoration, if only because so many people neglect it, dismissing it with white, and concentrating all their scheming on the other surfaces of the room. The work itself, too, should be tackled before the walls and floor, because, with the greatest care, you may spill or splash your whitewash.

Consider the ceiling as one of the surfaces of the room just as much as floor and walls. It is less seen than the other surfaces, but is still very potent to affect the scheme.

It can affect the scheme by its colour; and it can affect the scheme by its size.

These are two points to consider before you make your decision. We will investigate them and another before passing on to the work of decorating a ceiling.

Have you ever chosen a light wallpaper for your walls in the hope of making your room look light, and then found when it was hung that neither paper nor room looked as light as you thought? Almost certainly this is because your ceiling is white or nearly so, and by contrast makes your walls look darker.

The best thing to do in these circumstances is to make the ceiling (and frieze) match the wall tint.

In fact, a ceiling *darker* than the walls will emphasise the lightness of the latter; but this is practical only in a lofty room (Fig. 14).

You cannot, of course, change the size of your ceiling, but you can change the appearance of its size.

Fig. 12. *Ceiling without cornice, which may be variously treated as shown in following diagrams.*

Remember that ceiling and floor are the two horizontal surfaces of your room; the walls are the perpendicular surfaces. If you want to make a lofty room look wider and of more comfortable proportions, you must paint part of the walls to match the ceiling (Fig. 15).

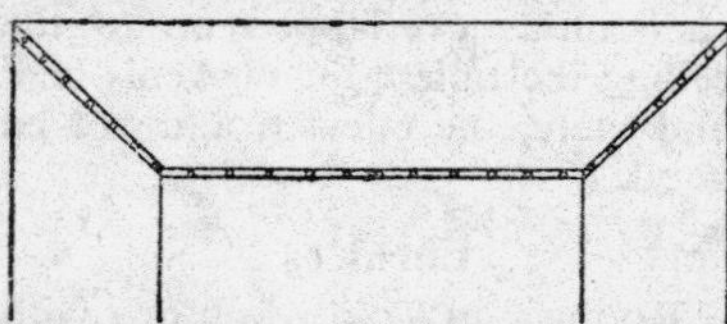

Fig. 13. *Moulding or paper border to make break between walls and ceiling.*

How you may decide upon the colour for your ceiling is explained in the Lessons on Colour Scheming.

Presence or absence of a cornice also affects the colour area of a ceiling. If there is a cornice, it is better to consider it as part of the walls than of the ceiling, and to decorate accordingly, when the walls are a plain colour. This need not apply if the room is narrow and you want to make it seem wider; but in that case you would probably

Fig. 14. *Ceiling painted a deeper tone in order to make walls look lighter.*

have a frieze to match the ceiling in a deeper tone than the wall, and then, of course, the cornice would be painted in the same colour. Neither need it apply when the cornice is more on the ceiling than

Fig. 15. *Frieze made by border or moulding and painted with ceiling a deeper tint than that of the walls.*

on the walls; for it is then painted to match the walls, or it will make the ceiling seem smaller—and the room too.

Many rooms, however, are made today with no cornice between walls and ceiling. And, indeed, a break is not always necessary.

Putting up a cornice, or even a moulding, to make a break is a job for the skilled workman. But there are ways of achieving a break without this.

A wallpaper border can be used; or the artistic amateur may be able

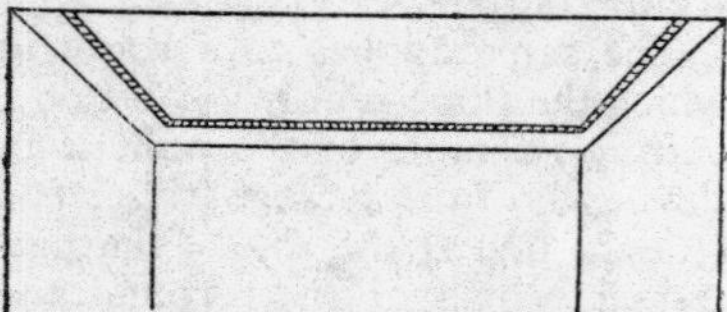

Fig. 16. *Ceiling border or moulding set in as a surround 6 in. from walls.*

to cut himself a stencil for making a patterned band of colours.

This border can be fixed at frieze level, at the top of the wall close to the ceiling, at the edge of the ceiling close to the wall or on the ceiling but set in a little from the wall—according to the requirements the room makes of its scheme of decoration.

Setting-in the border on the ceiling (Fig. 16), and painting the margin thus made, and not the rest of the ceiling inside the border, to match the walls, is one way of making the room look higher.

Rooms with a sloping ceiling present problems on which advice may be helpful.

A common question is "Shall we stop the wallpaper at the top of the upright wall or carry it on over the slope to where the horizontal ceiling begins?"

Rooms with Sloping Ceiling

The more you cover with the wallpaper, the more wall space do you suggest; which means, too, that there is less "ceiling." The less you cover, the more ceiling you have.

Do you want to make the ceiling look small and narrow? Fig. 17 shows a room with half its height cut by slope and a patterned paper carried up over this area as well as over the wall proper. Fig. 18 shows the same room with the patterned paper stopped below the slope. The slope, being plain like the ceiling, is less emphasised than when covered with pattern.

The same applies to a room in which the slope is only a short one, cutting no more of the walls than the depth of the average frieze. The straight line at the top of the patterned wallpaper right round the room at the level below the slope renders this feature less noticeable.

In both cases, too, the ceiling seems larger and the room more light and less closed in.

Incidentally, the same two illustrations show how the arrangement of pictures in a straight line, instead of going up in the middle, helps to lessen the effect of the inward slope.

Is a Break Necessary?

It is not, however, essential to have a line or border or moulding to "make a break" between the colours of wall and ceiling. In a room in which the proportions are satisfactory, the wall colour can quite well end at the top of the walls and the ceiling colour begin at the edge of the ceiling, the angle of the wall and ceiling being sufficient break.

This does mean, of course, that the painting and paper-hanging would have to meet in a perfectly even line. With paper on the walls and paint on the ceiling this should not be quite so difficult; but with paint on both, if the edge of the wall-colour overlapped on to the ceiling the tiniest bit unevenly here and there, the effect would not be good.

Cornices

Rooms in old houses with ornately moulded cornices and plaster decoration in the middle of the ceiling are best treated by the amateur quite plainly—not picking out these decorations in colours, but giving them the extra cleaning they will need because they hold a lot of the old whitewash; the ceiling ornaments being painted to match the rest of the ceiling, and the cornice, if it does not come too much on to the ceiling, to match the wall if possible, as already explained.

Old and uneven and cracked

ceilings may be better with a good lining paper before the whitewash or distemper is applied; but the papering of a ceiling is more difficult than whitewashing, and you would be well advised to call in the skilled workman to do it for you.

More equipment is needed—planks and step-ladders or other means of raising yourself to the necessary level to do the work without strain. The water you use in the washing off is apt to trickle down your brush and into your sleeve. The attitude in which you must do the actual painting is rather back-breaking, yet you must keep at it steadily once you have started.

Fig. 17. *Attic with patterned wallpaper carried up over the slope, and giving cramped effect. Compare with Fig.* 18. *Note "stepped" arrangement of pictures.*

Cleaning the Ceiling

So much by way of warning. If you must do the ceiling yourself, realise that the work must be divided into two parts:

(1) Cleaning and repairing. (2) Applying the whitewash.

For cleaning the ceiling of its old whitewash you will need two pails of hot water (one containing a little ammonia) and a distemper brush which has been used and is partly worn; a brush of the type in which the bristles are divided into two groups.

Get the pails up beside you on the planks. The one in which the water contains ammonia is for washing off. The other is for cleaning the brush occasionally during the work.

Dip the brush in up to the hilt and squeeze out excessive water, or it will run down the handle into your sleeve. Let your treatment of the ceiling be generous, and cover as much of the area as you can reach before moving your step-ladder. Let the water soak in well. A second soaking may be necessary. If you don't get all the whitewash and dirt off the first time, go over it again.

For the removal of stains, such as from smoke of fire or lamp or other such causes, use a solution of 1 lb. of soda to a gallon of water *after* you have otherwise cleaned the ceiling thoroughly. Then get rid of any signs of the soda by another clean-water wash.

Treatment of Cracks

Cracks, if they exist, may then be filled up with Keen's cement or with a mixture of equal parts of plaster of Paris and whiting. Level the edges first.

After this, when the ceiling is quite dry, comes the coat of Clearcolle made up of whiting and size. Soak concentrated size in water according to the directions on the packet and then add the same amount and half as much again of whiting—six ounces of whiting, for instance, to a quarter of a pound of concentrated size to make two quarts.

Whitewashing and Distempering

When Clearcolle has been applied and is quite dry, the ceiling can have its whitewash or distemper.

You can make your own white-wash, but it is better to buy a good brand—paste or powder—to which you have only to add hot or cold water. See that the whitewash is throughly well mixed, or you may find brush-marks showing in the finished work.

You will need a broad, flat white-wash brush.

When you have all your require-ments in the room, close the win-dows and doors, and keep them closed throughout the work. The reasons for this are: (1) to prevent the whitewash drying too quickly while you are applying it, and (2) to help it dry quickly when the work is finished.

Don't submerge your brush more than 3 in. in the whitewash. Be liberal in the application to the ceiling, but use the tip of the brush only, and do not press the whole of the bristles backward and forward against the ceiling. Use up all that is on the brush before dipping it again.

Work the brush evenly, and do your utmost to avoid brush-marks.

Most Economical Method

Begin with a band 18 in. wide right across the ceiling, and work as quickly as possible (without scamp-ing), so that the edge will not be dry before you start your next strip, or the wetness of the second band will show as an overlap on the dryness of the first. If you do an uneven, irregular, circular area, you give yourself more edge to dry and make the succeeding work more difficult.

Commence this first band so that you work away from the light.

When you have finished open the doors and do all you can to make the room dry quickly.

Self Testing Questions

(1) *What effect has* (a) *a dark ceiling against light-coloured walls;* (b) *a white ceiling against walls of a darker tint?*

(2) *In an attic room with a sloping roof what effect would you get by covering the slope with wallpaper?*

(3) *Why should the ceiling be treated before the walls or floors are done?*

(4) *How would you fill up the cracks in a ceiling?*

(5) *What is it that should be applied before the whitewash?*

THE ANSWERS ARE ON PAGE 114.

LESSON 3

Floors and Their Treatment

Not until you have emptied your room preparatory to decoration will you be able to make a thorough examination of the floor.

As a surface in the scheme it is not, of course, complete until it is laid with its rugs or carpet. But even these must be thought of now. Are you going to have a close-fitted carpet? If so, none of the floor will show, though some repairs may nevertheless be needed. Will you have only a rug or two? If so, a great deal depends on the condition of the floor as well as its colour. Is a carpet square your wish, so that a surround will be left showing the floor itself? If so, again condition and colour must be studied.

Floor Ventilation

Suppose your home is newly built. You may have heard that fitted carpets should not be laid to the floors of a new house because of the risk of damage from damp. It is true that there is much moisture to evaporate from a new building, and that nothing should be done to prevent the moisture coming out.

This, however, does not apply so much to the floors as to the walls; and, in any case, as far as the floors alone are concerned, if the house is well built, with proper damp-courses and ventilation to the floors, fitted carpets should be no hindrance.

You would not, of course, wish to lay fitted carpets on solid floors of parquet, wood-block or stone. With these surfaces there might be trouble through lack of ventilation. Linoleum or close-fitting pile carpet will produce on a stone floor moisture that may eventually rot the covering, while rough edges of flags or bricks will quickly wear it. If you already have plain carpet ready for fitting, think of making it into mats for the parquet or wood-block floors.

Grass Matting or Rugs

The best covering for a stone floor is sisal grass matting or coco matting. These provide comfort and the necessary quiet to the tread, and at the same time are porous enough to allow air to reach the floor. Even so, it is best not to try to fix even this covering, but to lay it unfixed, so that it can be taken up and shaken when the room has its weekly turn out. Pile mats and rugs may be laid on the matting—if it is plain enough and of a sufficiently neutral shade to make it a suitable background.

If you wish to have rugs on a new wood floor, think a little more carefully than most people seem to about staining. Whether it is of good boards, pine or oak blocks, or parquet, the assumption is that it must be stained brown or black.

It is worth knowing that good stains are available in a variety of shades, from which a careful selection might help you to make a much better colour scheme. For instance, if rugs are mainly green, there is more reason for a green stained floor than for a black one.

The question whether your room will look better with rugs, carpet square or fitted carpet depends upon several factors.

If you feel that the room is small and that everything must be done to make it look as large as possible, a completely fitted carpet or no more than one or two rugs on polished wood will better give an effect of space than will a patterned carpet square showing a surround; and the lighter the fitted carpet the larger will the floor appear to be.

Wise Use of Carpet

The carpet square has its advantages, but it does tend to make the floor seem no larger than itself, suggesting that the surround is an area not to be walked on. Rugs have not the same effect, because the predominating area is the polished wood.

If a carpet square must be used, let it be plain if possible, and have the surround covered in felt to match. This is the nearest you can achieve to the effect of a fitted carpet while retaining the carpet square.

Rugs are generally a nuisance in the dining-room, where a carpet square or fitted carpet is better. In the bedroom there is nothing to better the fitted carpet for comfort.

On the stairs, carpet fitted the full width of the stairs makes the staircase seem wider. The same applies to the hall. In hall and stairs, however, patterned carpeting is better, because this main thoroughfare of the house receives so much wear, and a close all-over pattern will show it less than will something plain.

In the average house much carpet is wasted by furniture permanently covering it. On the polished floor of a lounge it should be possible to arrange the rug and the furniture so that the latter does not greatly overlap the former.

In the dining-room the carpet under the table is little used, and is not a good surface for the crumbs that fall. On a polished dining-room floor, however, a runner can be laid the length of each side of the table, with a smaller mat at each end. The chairs and the feet of diners are then on a pleasantly soft surface, and the rugs can easily be removed for cleaning or polishing the floor.

In the bedroom all carpet under the bed is largely wasted, and chiefly collects dust. The amount of carpeting bought for fitting the floor of this room need not include any for under the bed. Alternatively, two rugs for the floor at each side of the bed and a long runner across the foot would be an economy.

Stairs can save carpet if the risers are not covered. This means a small mat for each tread—about half the amount of carpet usually used. Risers would be stained, polished or painted to match the floor of the hall or the skirting at the sides of the staircase.

Cleaning and Staining Floors

When you know how far you intend to cover your floors you can better consider how you will treat the surface.

New floors in good condition present no difficulty for staining right away. Existing stain and wax can be removed by a liberal application of hot turpentine, which softens the wax so that you can scrape it off. But remember while you are using it that turpentine is inflammable. Benzine is an alternative—also inflammable.

Soiled or stained floors can be bleached by a solution of oxalic acid in water, followed by a good wash down with plain water. In all cases allow the floor to dry thoroughly before staining.

Gaps can be filled with plastic wood. You can make your own composition for the purpose, but it is quicker, easier and more reliable to buy the plastic wood.

Straight-sided gaps and cracks may let the filling fall through later on when it is old and dry. So make the gaps V-shaped by chamfering a little away each side near the top.

Spirit-stains and oil-stains are generally considered to be better than water-stains, but a variety of colours are obtainable in all three.

Cheapest of all staining is with a strong solution of permanganate of potash. It goes on wine red and dries a pleasant shade of brown. Two coats may be necessary.

When you are doing your staining, brush the way of the grain. Keep the stain at an even consistency. Avoid overfilling the brush, or the stain will drip.

Work from the farthest corner to the door, or you will have to walk out of the room across the wet stain. Keep brushes in turps, supple and clean between jobs.

Fig. 18. *The same attic as in Fig.* 17, *looking lighter and more spacious with the wallpaper stopped below the slope, and the pictures arranged in a straight line.*

If it is a new, clean floor of good wood on which you intend to lay rugs or a carpet square showing wood surround, consider the possibility of polishing without staining. It makes a light-coloured floor, which looks more spacious than a dark floor; but the lightness is not impractical. Good polishing prevents marks showing unduly, and general wear, instead of spoiling it, helps to mellow its appearance. The natural colour of the wood is a good background for most schemes and furniture woods.

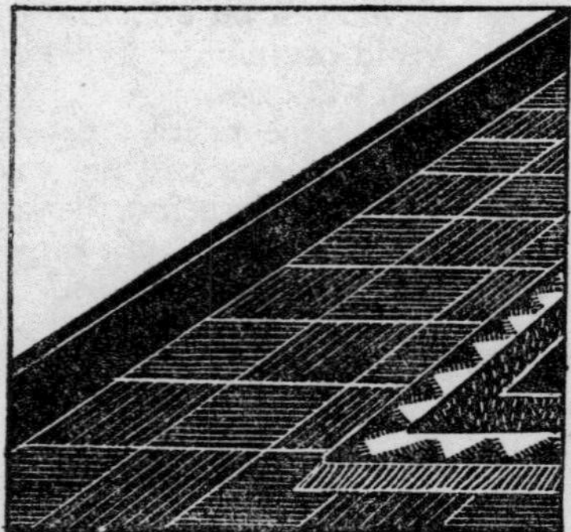

Fig. 19. *When using oak plywood, set the squares with the grain arranged to point in alternate directions.*

Fig. 20. *With oak strips the position of the joins should alternate so as to form a pattern resembling brickwork.*

On absorbent woods, however, such as deal boards or pine blocks, it is necessary first to apply a thin coat of size all over the floor. Application is quite straightforward with a distemper brush. When the coat has been allowed to dry thoroughly, the polish goes on quite easily. Without the size your polish would be too quickly absorbed.

Parquet and Plywood Squares

It is not advisable for any amateur to tackle the laying of a whole floor with what is commonly thought of as parquet—the herring-bone variety. But the newer, good-looking and fashionable squares are not difficult to lay.

They are obtainable in oak ply 9 in. × 9 in. or 6 in. × 6 in., and it is a simple matter to measure up your floor to learn how many you may require. Odd pieces for the sides have to be cut.

You can lay them on an existing floor. It is easier, of course, if the floor is perfectly even. On an uneven old floor glue is necessary to get a level and to hold. On the even floor the pins which are obtainable with the squares are all you need.

To get the best effect do not lay the squares with the grain all the same way. Alternate them, as shown in Fig. 19, and you will get a quiet, chequered effect.

Oak strips are easier to lay than the oak squares. You get them in 6 ft. lengths, 3 in. wide.

They are also fixed with pins and, on uneven floors, with glue. The effect is most pleasant. See that the end joints do not come all in a line across the floor, but rather as shown in Fig. 20.

These and the oak squares may be stained or not as you please, and of course will take polish quite well. Either can be used for the surround only, where a carpet square is being laid in a room.

Self Testing Questions

(1) *What is the best covering for a stone floor?*

(2) *What effect has* (a) *a patterned carpet in a very small room;* (b) *a carpet the width of the stairs in a narrow staircase?*

(3) *How should* (a) *soiled or stained floors;* (b) *waxy floors, be cleaned?*

(4) *Are there any alternatives to a brown or black stained surround?*

THE ANSWERS ARE ON PAGE 114.

LESSON 4

Woodwork and Walls

Too often the woodwork is regarded as though it had no bearing on the other parts of the room.

In many homes, whatever the wall colour, the woodwork is cream or dark brown. The only real reason for this prevalence seems to be that these two colours will "go" with anything. Actually the woodwork is part of the wall surface; and as both have to be decorated, why not consider them together and achieve a better-schemed room?

Woodwork which is a contrast with the walls emphasises the limitations of the room. Woodwork which blends with the walls helps to make the room seem larger.

Plain and Patterned Walls

If you decide to have plain walls in paper or paint, you will generally find it better to have woodwork painted to match. As well as making the room look larger, it has a more restful effect.

With patterned paper for the wall it is not always easy to decide the colour for woodwork. If you are in doubt you will usually be safe if you paint it to match the ground of the paper.

Sometimes a contrast is effective. A wallpaper with a very dark ground chosen for some particular background quality may be better with cream-coloured woodwork. But such wallpapers are not common.

Should you choose wallpaper or distemper for your walls? To answer this let us consider the merits of both. Washable distemper well applied will give you a surface which wallpaper cannot give. It will be entirely free from joins. Its smooth finish and its texture are qualities not obtainable in anything else but paint. And in it you have a great range of pleasant colours for plain surfaces.

It is easier to match the paint of woodwork to distemper than to wallpaper. It is washable if applied and treated in the right way. A single thin coat can be scrubbed away, but from a covering of two coats you will be able for some time to remove all surface marks by sponging or washing.

The coat of paint is only washable while it is there; so the thicker it is the longer will it be washable; and the rougher your washing the quicker will you remove not only the marks, but the coats of distemper too.

The value of wallpaper is that it protects the plaster surface, being a covering of different material.

Whether you should choose a plain or patterned wallpaper is discussed in the Lessons on Colour Scheming.

Mottled Wallpapers

Semi-plain wallpapers provide a good background without being quite plain. They may be finely streaked with mixed colours suggesting a Japanese grasscloth, or they may be mottled in a way which is otherwise obtainable only by more expensive and skilled painting. They are not washable, but they do not show marks so easily as the plain.

If you decide to have a patterned wallpaper, be careful how you

Fig. 21. *A room devoid of pattern on both walls and floor lacks interest.*

choose it. You will be shown a pattern book in which the samples do not generally show the pattern repeated, except in the case of very small designs. Also, you are looking down on it, and you are probably seeing it under a top light.

Thoughts about Pattern

It is worth while asking the salesman to bring out two lengths and to arrange them for you side by side on a stand. You can then get some idea of the repetition of the pattern and see whether it is good or bad; and the almost perpendicular surface the stand provides is more like the wall of your room than the page in the pattern-book on the table.

Repetition rightly used has a great value in decoration; but to bear repetition, a pattern must be pleasantly drawn and coloured, and of good proportions and well balanced. This is important, because every fault is accentuated by repetition. If the pattern is squat it may make the room look squat. If it slopes upwards to one corner, as many seem to do, when seen repeated you have a noticeably diagonal procession which results in making the wall appear to be out of the square.

For a small room do not choose a large pattern, however lovely it may seem in the shop. Look at the proportions of the unit. If they are square they will not, when repeated, look so pleasant as the unit which is somewhat longer than wide.

The pictures you wish to hang should also influence your choice of wallpaper. Etchings or drawings or prints without colour are usually better on a coloured or patterned background than on a plain wall as white as their mounts. If you have a set of pictures to hang, take one to the shop with you and have it held against the paper.

Fig. 22. *The same room with the simple improvement of the patterned wallpaper.*

If your room looks on to a lovely garden which contains flowers in bloom for much of the year, you will not want flowers on the walls of your room also. A town outlook on to streets where there are no flowers but masses of masonry rather asks for a flower-patterned paper. If you are fond of flowers and always have two or three vases in your room, a plain or semi-plain background is the best. And, of course, if you already have patterned curtains or carpet or chair-covers to use in the room, you will be wise to have plain or semi-plain walls rather than a patterned wallpaper (Figs. 34 and 35).

Cleaning Woodwork

The woodwork should be painted before the wall is papered, because it is easier to remove any marks of paper-hanging from the woodwork than paint-marks from the wallpaper. The same applies to distempered walls.

If your woodwork is in good condition and already in the colour you require, you may not wish to repaint it; but if this has to be done it must be cleaned first.

Do not forget to remove all door-knobs and finger-plates at the outset. If left on they may become marked in cleaning or painting.

The woodwork can be rubbed down with sugar soap and a fairly fine waterproof sand-paper. Or you can use a half pound to a pound of soda (according to the dirtiness of the woodwork) to a gallon of water, applied with a soft scrubbing-brush; finish with a sponge-down, and take care to get rid of all water, especially from the mouldings.

Your cleaning and rubbing down should leave the surface smooth and matt. A shining surface will not take the new paint. But if you leave either sugar soap or soda solution on too long they will soften the paint, which will then come away.

Allow the woodwork to dry for a whole day. Then fill up holes. This may be done with putty mixed with a little white lead and a touch of the colour the woodwork is to be painted. Smooth it with a stopping-knife, which is made for the purpose and can be bought from the painters' stores. Having finished the stopping, dust the surface thoroughly and it is then ready for the paint.

Use the best quality of ready-mixed paint. One gallon will cover about 540 square feet of woodwork. When you open the tin you will see the oil and turpentine floating at the top. Drain some of this off into another pot, or when you stir to mix the contents of the tin the oil and turpentine will slop over. After you have poured off sufficient, mix the remainder thoroughly, pouring back into it, while you stir, the excess oil and turpentine you took off.

When you go to buy your brush ask for a flat varnish brush. It should be about 2½ in. wide. Although it is flat, you can paint mouldings by using it sideways. Clean it first with soap and hot water or with naphtha or turpentine. With soap and hot water it may take a day or two to dry.

How to Paint

Most amateurs load the paint-brush far too heavily. The result is that the paint runs and makes "curtains" and is tacky. Do not plunge the brush into the paint; the tip is sufficient. And do not dip again until you have used the first brushful.

Brush up and down and then across, and finish gently up and down. In addition, on door panels and such surfaces end by drawing the brush upwards from the bottom to spread any paint that may have flowed down.

Open the window at the top to help drying when the work is done.

New walls are really better left without distemper or paper until the free alkali in the plaster is no longer likely to affect the colour.

As this may mean waiting for three years, however, a thin coat of distemper or a thin wallpaper can be applied in a light neutral shade such as stone or fawn, which will show disfigurement less than will a definite colour such as blue, green, yellow or pink.

Distempering Walls

The wall must be clean to begin with. Old walls should first be repaired, holes being filled with a mixture of plaster of Paris and whiting or Keen's cement. You can apply the distemper over existing wallpaper if the latter is clean and in good condition. But dust it first and stick down all loose edges firmly.

If the paper is to be removed, this can be done with the aid of a stripping-knife after you have thoroughly soaked the paper with water, and allowed plenty of time for the water to soak in.

Old distemper can be removed with a hot solution of vinegar and water.

To apply the distemper you will need a large flat distemper brush. Do not fill it too full, or you will make splashes all over the place. Use up what you take on to it before you dip again. Cover the floor and woodwork with sheets or paper. If you do splash any distemper, clean it up at once.

Commence work at the top of the wall, and go downward and forward as rapidly as you can (without skimping), so that the edges do not dry. Two coats with 48 hours between them is best.

It is not advisable to hang new paper over old, as this encourages insects. But if you must do so, rub down the old very thoroughly to remove dust, clean it if necessary with bread dough made without yeast and stroked one way only on the wall, paste down loose corners most carefully, and rub down lapped joints with sand-paper over a piece of hard wood; butted joints would not, of course, show so clearly through the new wallpaper.

The removal of old wallpaper with a stripping-knife has already been explained. The work should be done carefully, so as not to damage the plaster.

New walls are better without either wallpaper or distemper, but if a paper is to be hung, it should be a thin one, as this seals the wall less, and it should be of a light neutral shade, because this will show discoloration less than a definite colour. Do not hang wallpaper on damp walls.

Paper-Hanging

If the walls are distempered, the distemper must be thoroughly removed before papering, because paper will not adhere permanently over it and will eventually come away. Its removal is not difficult, as it requires only a good soaking with water, after which the distemper can be taken off by means of a brush in what is called a sweeping action.

When the old paper or distemper has been removed, examine the surface for holes. These can be filled, as already explained in the Distempering section, with a mixture of plaster of Paris and whiting.

Quantity of Paper

Next you must know the quantity of paper to order. Measure right round the room (including doors, windows and fireplaces to allow for waste), multiply this by the height to be papered, divide by 63, and you will have the number of pieces of English wallpaper required. Each piece of English wallpaper measures about 11½ yd. long by 21 in. wide. By including doors, windows and fireplaces you allow enough for waste. This will give roughly what you need for the area; and it is advisable, as a check, to calculate, too, how many cut lengths (21 in. wide when trimmed) will hang round the room.

Trimming

The selvedge must be cut off both sides of the paper if it is to be butt joined, or one side only if it is to be overlapped. It is better for the amateur to do this with long scissors the "dry" way, rather than with the knife after the paper has been pasted.

The professional way of trimming is the best. This is shown in the illustrations.

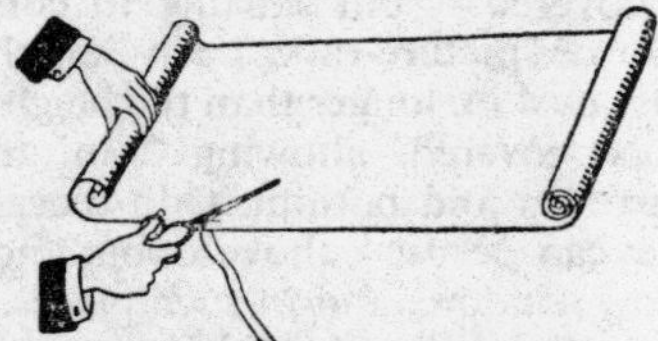

Fig. 23. *Trimming the wallpaper.*

You can sit with your legs outstretched but close together, so that the roll of paper can rest on your insteps. Take the end of the paper in your left hand, rolling it up towards your body as you cut off the selvedge with the scissors.

You can if you wish rest a paperhanger's board or a drawing- or other board of satisfactory proportions on your legs so that the paper can rest upon it.

In the first method your right hand as it wields the scissors has your leg as a support. In the second method it has the board.

You can buy your wallpaper ready trimmed at the shop; but although this saves you the labour of trimming, it defeats part of the purpose of the selvedge, which is to protect the patterned portion of the paper until it arrives at the house in which it is to be hung. For if between the shop and your home the edge of the roll became jagged, the pattern would be cut into if the paper had been trimmed; whereas, if the selvedge were still on, it would protect the pattern.

Whether you trim both edges and butt-join the paper—edge to edge—or trim only one edge which will overlap the uncut selvedge of the next place, is for you to decide. The overlapping method is found the easier by most amateurs.

Cutting

Now cut the paper into lengths according to the height of wall to be covered—from skirting to cornice or picture-rail. Each length must be 4 in. longer than the height to be covered, allowing 2 in. to spare top and bottom. Odd pieces over can be used above doors and below windows and in such places.

A paper-hanger's table helps the cutting. It is 6 ft. long and 2 ft. wide, so that if the length to cut is 8 ft. 4 in., you will have only 2 ft. 4 in. hanging over one end. But you will probably use your kitchen-table, or, if that is not long enough, your dining-table covered with oil-cloth, linoleum or several thicknesses of paper.

Take the roll in the left hand and unroll the paper with the right, drawing the unrolled part with slight pressure over the edge of the table to take out the "curl," and unrolling to the length of the table. Know the length of the table and push the unrolled end of the paper so far over the end of the table as to allow you to unroll the paper further, so that the remainder of the roll will come at the other end of the table, where it will act as a guide for cutting.

For instance, if your table is 5 ft. 6 in. long and the length of paper to be cut is 8 ft. 4 in., you will have 2 ft. 10 in. hanging over.

Then cut across the paper close to the roll, and repeat this unrolling and cutting process on top of each cut length until you have the required number of lengths all face upwards on top of one another.

Roll up all the lengths together from left to right, turn them over on the table, and unroll them from left to right so that they are face downward. They are then ready for pasting.

Before you actually paste the paper, make sure you know exactly where you are going to start hanging it.

Where to Begin

If it is a plain paper you can start in a corner of the room. If it is a patterned paper centre the pattern in the middle of one unbroken wall-space or in the centre of the most important wall, hang the first piece there and the others from one side of it right round the room until you get back to the other side of the first piece. If you are starting from a corner choose the lightest and work towards the darkest.

Whichever way you do it begin with a straight line. Use a plumb line, draw the string across a stick of chalk so that it becomes white, fix the top of the string in the position desired, hold the bottom of it against the skirting, see that top and bottom are pressed close to the wall and with your free hand take the string by the middle, pull it away from the wall an inch or two and let it snap back so that it leaves a white line on the wall.

Paste and Pasting

The strongest paste is made from paste powder, which you can buy where you buy your wallpaper. It is easy to mix according to the directions given with it.

Your cut pieces are lying on top of one another face downward on the table. Apply the paste generously so that the paper will not stick too closely when folded back on itself, and so that it can be more easily adjusted when on the wall.

Keep the fingers of the left hand between the top piece and the piece below to prevent paste getting on to the latter.

Fig. 24. *One end of the cut piece of wallpaper pasted and turned back.*

That part of the top piece lying on the table must now be folded (see Fig. 24), so that the whole can be moved along to draw up the length hanging over the end of the table.

When this remainder has been pasted, fold it back likewise to meet the end of the first part already folded back, as shown in Fig. 25. Do this accurately; the sides of the paper throughout the folds must be exactly over one another. Bend back each end by running your finger underneath, so that both ends stand up like lips, as seen in Fig. 25.

Throughout the proceedings have a towel by you to rub off any paste from your hands as soon as it gets on.

See that your steps are in position. Take the pasted and folded paper

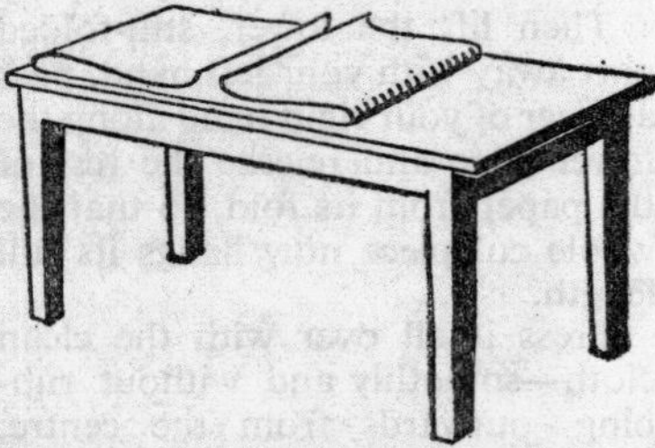

Fig. 25. *The other end of the cut piece pasted and turned back. End edges are turned up so that they almost meet.*

and hang it over your left arm. Mount the steps. With the thumb and forefinger of your right hand take hold of the lip nearest to you and, supporting the paper with the second finger under the fold, draw it toward you off your left arm until with your left thumb and forefinger (and other fingers under the paper for support) you can hold that end of the near lip in the same way as the other.

Then withdraw the fingers which have been supporting the paper so that you are left holding the paper by the thumbs and forefingers of each hand.

This removal of the supporting fingers will let the paper drop as far as the first fold and present the pasted side to the wall. The paper must then be placed with one edge against the chalk line on the wall and the lip edge 2 in. above the picture-rail or cornice, whichever is the upper limit of the area to be papered.

The lower portion of the paper still remains folded, helping you by keeping that part of the pasted surface from the wall while the upper part is straightened in position as in Fig. 26. Press the upper part against the wall with a clean cloth, evenly all over.

Applying to the Wall

Then lift the lower, still-folded part away with your left hand, pass a finger of your right hand along the lower edge and release the rest of the paper from its fold, so that the whole cut piece now hangs its full length.

Press it all over with the clean cloth—smoothly and without rubbing—outwards from the centre. Take care to avoid getting air bubbles under the paper.

You now have the 2 in. over top and bottom to remove. Press the side of the scissors along the paper just under the moulding of picture-rail or cornice to mark the cutting line, then ease the top of the paper from the wall, cut off the 2 in. across with great care and press the paper back into position.

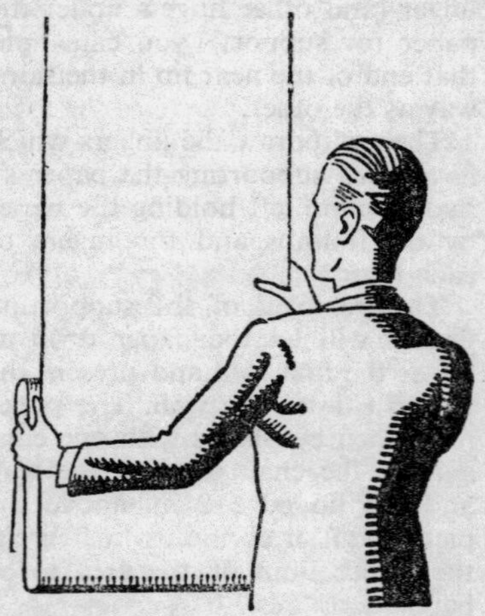

Fig. 26. *The lower part of the paper is still folded up, while the upper part is being placed against the wall.*

Fig. 27. *Trimming off the excessive 2 in. at the lower end of the paper.*

Do the same at the bottom of the paper against the top of the skirting to remove the 2 in. at that end (Fig. 27).

Follow on by pasting your other cut lengths in the same way. If you are overlapping, remember that the cut edge of the second piece will overlap the pasted-down selvedge of the first piece; and so on.

Do not forget that if you are starting from a corner you should choose it so that you are working from the lightest toward the darkest. When you come to the next corner you may find that the piece you are hanging does not finish there, but can go on round the corner on to the wall at right angles. Make sure that corner pieces are well stuck down.

Self Testing Questions

(1) *What is the effect of woodwork that matches the colour of the walls?*

(2) *How do you calculate the number of pieces of wallpaper required for a room?*

THE ANSWERS ARE ON PAGE 114.

LESSON 5

How to Make Your Own Colour Schemes

GOOD colour scheming need not be a strain on the brain or the purse; but it is an asset to health and happiness. Here are simple principles to help you achieve it.

The first step is to decide upon colour. At the same time you must consider the aspect of the room. Whatever you choose may be made the main colour in either of two ways:

(1) As the background, *i.e.* on walls and perhaps ceiling or floor, with relieving colours kept to furnishings.

(2) As the main colour in carpet, chair-covers and curtains, with relieving colours kept to the walls, woodwork and ceiling.

If a room gets little sun, the main colour should be of the warm and cheerful red, yellow or red-yellow shades.

These used either in furnishings or on the walls, according to strength, will give the cold room warmth. How to decide where to use various colours is explained further on.

Some light yellow-green shades are also useful here, but only in conjunction with another warm colour, and never with blue. Examples will be given.

Blue shades, blue-greens, blue-reds, purples and such colours should not predominate in cold rooms, for they are cool colours, but may do so in sunny rooms—with other shades as relief.

You will find the Scheme Chart on page 94 of the utmost value in deciding what colours will best harmonise, and in what proportions they should be used in decorating a room. Study the Chart and the examples given in the text, and you will soon be able to draw up colour schemes for yourself.

How to Use the Scheme Chart

The main colours are set out in column (1) of the Scheme Chart.

Among the contrast colours chosen to set off the main colour, there may be touches of pink or other red shades in the blue room; and there may be even touches of blue in the cherry or peach room, but as this would be a sunless or cold room, a light sunny green would be better.

Having then decided upon the main colour in your scheme, the next thing you need to know is whether it should be deep and full or only a light shade, such as a pastel.

These points would generally be settled by the size of the room and whether it is a dark or light room. As a rule, full, deep colours make the small room seem smaller. There are exceptions, but generally it is advisable to use light colours for the small room. One which faces north, for instance, could have for its wall colour pink-tinted cream, introducing both warmth and lightness, while a large sunny room might be done, for instance, in midnight blue, blue-green or blue-grey. Dark

HOUSE DECORATING
SCHEME CHART

Essentials			Optional
(1) MAIN COLOURS.	(2) CONTRASTS.	(3) NEUTRALS.	(4) POSSIBLE ADDITIONS.
Reds, Pinks.	Blues, Greens.	White, Cream, Pink-tinted Cream, Straw, Stone, Beige, Fawn, Brown, Grey.	Yellows, Orange.
Yellows.	Blues, Purples.	As above.	Reds, Pinks, Orange.
Blues.	Reds, Pinks, Orange.	As above.	Yellows, Purples.
Orange.	Blues, Greens.	As above.	Reds, Pinks, Yellows, Purples.
Greens.	Reds, Pinks, Orange.	As above.	Yellows, Purples, Blues.
Purples.	Yellows, Greens.	As above.	Reds, Pinks, Blues, Orange.

To draw up a colour scheme for a room, choose a colour from column (1), *as the predominant tone, and at least one from each of the corresponding parts of columns* (2) *and* (3). *Touches of colour may be added as desired from column* (4) *as well as from those colours left in the corresponding lines of columns* (2) *and* (3).

rich shades can be very effective on the walls where the room is of good size and proportions and well lighted.

If you have chosen your main colour well, the other colours in your scheme should be subservient, but so arranged as to set off the main colour to its full advantage. They will also have to be suitable for the aspect, size and light of the room.

Relieving Colours and Neutrals

The relieving colours may in each case be divided into two groups. In one you will have the contrasting colours needed in the scheme in just sufficient quantity to keep the main colour "alive." In the other group are all the neutral shades. Both are set out in columns (2) and (3) of the Scheme Chart. How will you choose each?

The contrasting colours are not difficult to choose if you remember that touches of blue or green shades throw up red, blue and red shades throw up yellow and orange, red and pink shades throw up blue or green, as shown in the Scheme Chart.

The neutrals will be chosen by relationship. With the red and/or yellow schemes from cherry through orange to peach, you would choose a neutral that would be warm, such as cream, rather than cold, such as grey. With the cherry, the cream might be a little on the pink side; with the orange it might be a little on the yellow. Remember that this colour would perhaps have to be the colour for walls, woodwork and ceiling, while the orange or red would be the main colour kept in the furnishings.

Thus we see that the scheme must consist of a main colour (column 1), at least one contrast (column 2) and at least one neutral (column 3). Suitable other colours you may wish to add are shown in column 4.

Black, White and Brown

Black, as a general rule, should be introduced in tiny quantities only, especially in a small room. Black is often used as a relief, nearly always wrongly. It should be less than the colour it is to relieve, for any touches of black in a room are always the heaviest and most noticeable. Black or any dark colour painted in as a line or band or for the moulding of a room is so outstanding and noticeable that it makes the limitations of a room at once obvious.

White is definitely valuable as a relief in the majority of schemes, but it should not be overdone. It is too commonly used for ceilings where it is not always the best colour for the room below. The ceiling is dealt with in the examples of schemes given later on.

Brown is not a colour, but a mixture of colours. Therefore there is no contrast for it in the scheme. It can be used as a neutral quite as much as grey.

Before we select schemes according to the chart, there are two other factors to consider. They are related, for pattern is composed of line. We must separate them, however, because for the most part pattern will be of the repeat variety, as in wallpaper, fabrics and carpets; whereas line covers other items such as lines formed by mouldings, picture-rails, panels, the levels of a number of windows and the doors, etc.

These may to some extent govern the placing of your colours.

Line and Pattern

Take stock of the "general line" of the room. Is it a low, wide room suggesting more the horizontal, or is it a lofty room emphasising the perpendicular?

In the low, wide room you will not want *more* horizontality, or you will make the room look squat. Any additional lines and pattern, therefore, should be predominantly perpendicular; they will make a low room look more lofty.

Conversely, perpendicular lines make the lofty room seem narrow and high.

The difference between the effects of perpendicular and horizontal

USING THE CHART

Essentials			Optional
(1) MAIN COLOUR.	(2) CONTRASTS.	(3) NEUTRALS.	(4) POSSIBLE ADDITIONS.
Peach Pink.	Light Yellow-Green.	Pink-Beige, White. Pink-tinted Cream.	Pale Yellow.

A Specimen Scheme for a north room compiled from the Scheme Chart.

lines—as in a striped or banded wallpaper in the same room—is shown in Figs. 28, 29, 32 and 33.

If in a low room you find its horizontality emphasised by the lines of dark-painted chair-rail, dado-moulding or picture-rail, the best way to mask them is to paint them to match the rest of the wall. If the wall is to be in patterned paper, this would not be so easy.

Dividing a Lofty Room

Line may also be used in conjunction with colour to divide a room. For instance, the lofty room which you wish to make seem more wide can be divided by careful addition of line and the use of two colours. You could make one of the horizontal surfaces (the ceiling) seem larger in area and the perpendicular planes of the room (the walls) seem less high by running a moulding round the walls at a suitable distance from the ceiling, or making use of an existing picture-rail if it is at the right level, and painting the ceiling and that part of the wall above the moulding all in the same colour—darker than the walls, which should be so much lighter as to make something of a contrast. An example of this is given in two of the illustrations (Figs. 28 and 29), showing the same

Fig. 28. *This old-fashioned room looks narrow and lofty and not very comfortable.*

Fig. 29. *The same old-fashioned room, modernised now, looks wider and more attractive. The upright lines are gone, and the height is reduced by the frieze.*

lofty room wrongly treated in one of the sketches, while in the other the room has a dark ceiling and frieze and light walls.

The "line" in this case is the moulding, and it should be painted to match the wall below rather than the ceiling above.

You could use the main or the contrast colour for the ceiling.

An example is a lofty north room with orange as the main colour. It could be used plain for the curtains, and predominate in the pattern of the chair-covers, in the lamp-shades and cushions. Walls up to and including the moulding might be in ivory yellow: the wall above, and the ceiling, could be in the contrast colour of green, not too dark and a little on the yellow side; yellow would be present in small quantities in the pattern of the chair-covers too. A carpet in brown, which might be second neutral, and present in the chair-covers also, would complete the scheme.

Although the ceiling is one of the largest surfaces in the room, the colour in it would not have a predominant effect because one sees less of the ceiling than the walls and the floor. That is why it is perhaps preferable to use the contrast colour of your scheme rather than your main colour on the ceiling; for the colour you have all over the ceiling can hardly be widely introduced into the walls or furnishings of the room as well.

To make a long, low, narrow room seem wider and perhaps less low, line will help again. A wallpaper of perpendicular lines or stripes could be used on the two narrow ends of the room and be brought about 2 ft. or 3 ft. along each of the side walls as well, leaving the rest of the side walls plain to tone. Or a darker paint could be used on the long side walls, with the exception of the sections made at each end by the perpendicular dividing moulding, beyond which they would be painted in a light contrast to match the end walls.

Floors. Pink-Beige Carpet.
Woodwork. Pink-tinted Cream.
Walls. Pink-tinted Cream.
Ceiling. Pink-tinted Cream.
Curtains. Peach.
Covers. *Patterned:* Peach, Green, Pale Yellow, Beige.
Cushions. *Plain: Some* Peach, *some* Green, *some* Yellow.
Lamp Shades. Peach Pink.
Accessories. *Pictures in colours and covers,* White *in mounts, frames and vases.*

Application of selected scheme for room decoration given on page 95.

Position of Pictures

Width and height can also be helped or hindered by the proportions and arrangements of pictures and furniture, as may be seen by the two illustrations (Figs. 28 and 29) where high furniture and long, narrow pictures and the general "upward" arrangement make the lofty room seem narrower.

Pattern has practical as well as decorative values. Remember that it is available for floor-covering, walls, ceiling, chair-covers, curtains —though not for all in one room. Perhaps its greatest practical value appears when it is small and close-covers a surface which will not then show marks so easily as if it were plain.

Again, a larger pattern may make the area of the surface seem smaller, be it floor, walls, ceiling, covers or curtains; a small pattern does the reverse.

An appreciation of pattern is necessary before you choose your colours and allocate them to the various surfaces; because, generally speaking, any room requires some pattern in its decoration.

A room of all plain surfaces—no matter how well colour-schemed — lacks interest if it lacks pattern. It is like satisfaction for the senses and none for the intellect. Plain surfaces need the relief of a pattern somewhere, just as a main colour needs a contrast to keep it alive.

But pattern is introduced in too many surfaces (Figs. 34 and 35). If you want to play for safety, have it in one only; though it should not be too difficult to have it in two.

Because of its practical value already mentioned, think of the surfaces that receive the most wear. These, of course, are the chair-covers and carpet.

Conflicts

You can go wrong if you choose patterns for both without due regard for the possible conflicts. To see that the same colours are present in both and that no colour in one hurts any colour in the other is not sufficient. The pattern in one must not hurt the pattern in the other.

A carpet with an all-over flower pattern of about the same size as the differently designed flowers in the chair-covers would present an unpleasant hiatus. But an Indian carpet with much expanse of plain green ground, a centre medallion and decorated corners could well take chairs in natural linen with green, and the other colours of the carpet in a smaller and close repeat pattern.

All pattern is not of the repeat variety. You may have a decorative panel in which nothing is repeated; but if it *is* a decorative panel and is well chosen as part of the decoration of a room, and not on its own merits only, then it will have pattern value.

Value of Pictures

Pictures hung in any quantity also have a pattern value in the room by the way they are arranged. A set of prints can be arranged in a straight line, a stepped line, a square or a circle to make a feature on any one wall. The same applies to decorative china plates or a collection of brass. If any of these are items which you intend to use, remember them in scheming your room, and do not arrange too much pattern in addition.

This consideration influences both colour and line or pattern.

A room with a garden full of flowers for its view all summer does not require gaily floral curtains. Have these for winter if you wish, and plain curtains for the summer.

A room facing the sea with very little landscape in the foreground should avoid having, exclusively, plain sea blues and greys and greens for a scheme, even though the sun streams in all day. More yellow and touches of warm colours should be introduced and there should be pattern.

Outlook on to nothing but brick walls requires careful handling of the colour scheme. Net curtains—even-patterned net—may be justified, completely covering the window, and then the heavy curtains would naturally be plain, pattern coming again in chair-covers, with further suitable pattern in the carpet to keep the interest in the room. Or with the same window treatment, patterned walls and a contrast between plain covers and plain carpet.

In the next lesson we shall make selections from the Scheme Chart. Our chief examples will be for rooms where there are no existing furnishings to consider and where everything will be new. This will show more clearly the working of the principles which must guide us.

In each case we shall assume that we are going into an empty room the walls and ceiling of which are uncoloured plaster and whose woodwork is in its natural state.

We shall know whether the room is large or small; we shall know its aspect and its view.

After we have dealt with these examples, we will deal with rooms for which you already have some furnishings, or a troublesome fireplace or a desire for a colour which is not good with the aspect.

Self Testing Questions

(1) *Which of these colours are most suitable for a cold room: greens, reds, greys, browns, purples, blues?*

(2) *How would you use the main colour in a scheme?*

THE ANSWERS ARE ON PAGE 114.

LESSON 6

More About Colour Schemes

For convenience in writing, the schemes in this lesson are given for sitting-rooms, but they can be adapted for bedrooms or dining-rooms. If you have a bedroom in mind, read bed-covers for chair-covers. You can use plain fabric suggestions for bed-covers and patterned fabric for curtains. In dining-rooms patterned fabric can more frequently be used for curtains, while the seats of the chairs can be plain in the contrast colour of the scheme.

North Room Schemes

Our first room is of satisfactory proportions—so that we have not to change the appearance of its shape in any way. Its aspect we know. The view is across a garden to houses on the other side of the road.

Let us take cherry-red as our main colour.

As *Main Colour* this can be lovely, not quite so sunny, perhaps, as orange, but not so dark as the deepest red cherries, which in certain lights look almost black.

Green as *Contrast*, not darker than mid-green, and a little on the yellow side, sets off this colour admirably.

White is good as *Neutral* with cherry-red, but too cold for a north room. The ivory-yellow of billiard balls is better here—a warm, mellow, sunny white.

If a second neutral is required, let it be a good dark rich brown. It is warm and, generally speaking, when the main colour is such a full colour as this cherry-red, the neutrals should be either very light or very dark—not just medium; so that if there are two let one be light and the other dark.

From the column of possible additions we had better choose one or two colours to have by us, because if a patterned fabric comes into the scheme, it is not likely we shall find one containing only our main and contrast colours and the two neutrals.

Orange is the one colour in the possible additions column in the chart which might appear in small quantities in any patterned fabric we choose. Blue would be quite safe with cherry, but must be in the smallest quantities, because it is in a north room, and blue is cold. It could be used because it is one of the colours in the contrasts column; but it should be no heavier than the green. Contrast colours can usually be as light as the main colour is deep; and cherry-red is on the deep side of medium.

For any extra neutrals there are plenty given in the neutrals column. More than one of these are bound to be present in small quantities in the patterned fabric we buy for the room.

Walls and Ceiling

Which of our chosen colours shall we have upon the *Walls*? Our main colour is hardly suitable. The dark brown would be possible, but it is a little extreme, and might better be justified if the room seemed too large and we wanted to make it look smaller. The contrast green would be good; so would the ivory-yellow, our main neutral. Let us work out a scheme for both.

With green walls we will have a

green *Ceiling*. As so much green is to be used, it would be only sensible to keep it light; and do not forget that it must be a little on the yellow side.

With ivory-yellow walls, the ceiling would also be ivory-yellow.

Woodwork and Floor

Woodwork should be painted to match the walls—green or ivory. Do not forget that a contrast in the woodwork emphasises the limitations of the room, and as this room is not too large, we do not want to do that.

With the green or ivory walls and ceiling the *Floor* would be in natural parquet polished or dark brown-stained parquet polished, having in either case rugs of Persian design with the red predominating over minor touches of deep brown and perhaps a little blue, or rugs of modern design in deep brown with a simple line design in cherry-red. Alternatively, the floor could be covered with a fitted carpet of cherry-red or deep rich brown.

Accessories

Curtains could be plain cherry-red.

Covers might be of patterned fabric containing cherry-red, plenty of our green, a little of our blue, some of the dark brown, and any of the other neutrals that might be present.

You do not want patterned cushions on patterned covers—one kills the other; so have all cushions quite plain, but some in green and some in blue.

Lamp-shades against the green walls and ceiling should not be cherry-red, because a reddish-coloured light on green walls has a dull effect; in paints, remember red and green mixed give a black. You would not want them in the green, in case they cast the same unpleasant effect on the cherry-red curtains. But you might have them in the ivory-yellow, with cherry-red bands top and bottom.

Pictures in almost any colours can hang on green walls, and certainly on ivory walls.

Vases that are to hold flowers should not be chosen for the scheme, but for the flowers they are to hold. Ivory and stone-coloured vases are safe for most flowers; so is plain glass. Pale green is a safe colour—but dark green is not so good.

According to the patterned fabrics and the rugs you would choose, the foregoing two schemes are capable of variations, such as the use of the green on the ceiling, and ivory-yellow for the woodwork and walls.

Alternative Schemes

Or from the neutrals column, we might have chosen pink-tinted cream for woodwork, walls and ceiling. The curtains might be in patterned fabric, while the chair-covers could be in cherry-red, though this would be neither quite so pleasant nor so useful.

Orange or rust-red could be substituted for cherry-red throughout the foregoing schemes except in those in which pink-tinted cream is used for the walls and ceiling.

Japonica-red could be substituted too, even with the pink-tinted walls, and so could rose-red and peach.

Yellow and Green

You may wonder whether yellow and green can be used to make a scheme for a north room. Both can be sunny colours; but if they predominate in a scheme, though they may add something of an effect of

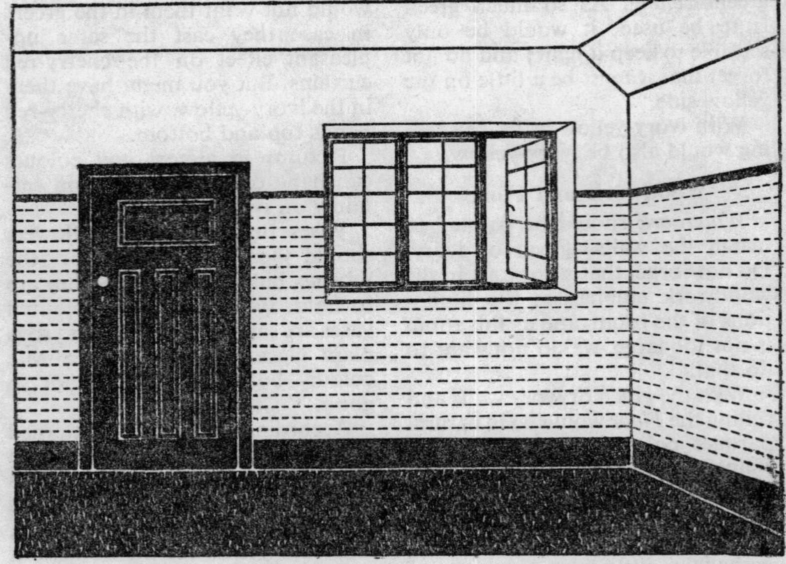

Fig. 30. *The different levels of the door and window in this room are unduly emphasised by the bad placing of the picture-rail, which is too low.*

sunlight they give little warmth. In any case they cannot complete a satisfactory scheme, for neither is a complete contrast to the other and neither is a neutral.

For the north room they would require one of the red shades, used as a main colour, such as those in the schemes just outlined.

This being the case, the arrangement of colours would be along the same lines: yellow or green or one of the neutrals for the walls, the red shade becoming the main colour in the same way.

Pastels

This is a name which has been given to soft and somewhat powdery shades—whether they are always like pastel colours or not. When we come to these shades in our main colours we obtain further possibilities in the same north room.

If the shade of red is so pale that it be called a soft shade of peach, it can be used all over walls and ceiling, if desired, and the contrasts and neutrals will occupy other parts of the scheme.

The carpets or rugs could be in deeper shades of peach or in pink-brown with curtains to match. Chair-covers would have the neutral for their ground and the contrast green abounding in their pattern, with peach shades present in minor quantities only.

Cushions could be plain, some green, some peach, or in plain cream piped with green or peach. The green should be a little on the yellow side.

In a north room the use of brown can also be demonstrated. Let it be the chosen neutral, with cream coming second.

We could have walls in a soft

Fig. 31. *A better effect in the same room is obtained by different placing of the picture-rail, which when raised no longer calls attention to the varieties in level.*

autumn brown, with woodwork in mellow cream, and carpet or rugs patterned in green, brown, orange or rust or copper, wine and golden-yellow. The richest and warmest and sunniest of the shades lends itself admirably to plain curtains—a deep rich orange more mellow than strong. Chair-covers could have warm cream for their ground and the colours in the carpet for their pattern. These colours would be repeated in plain-covered, odd cushions. Lamp-shades, orange or deep cream.

Picture-Frames

The brown walls would be good for a few pictures with frames in oak (dark-stained or natural), gilt, or cream painted wood, but not black or white. Where mounts are used, let them be in gold or cream, or in a tint best chosen to suit the picture, in which case the picture-frame could be painted to match.

If you want a patterned wall-paper, it would mean choosing one in the colours of the scheme as given for the patterned fabric of chair-covers or curtains, and having the latter plain.

Patterned Paper in North Room

Now let us decorate a room with the same aspect and view, but so lofty that we want to make it appear a little lower and wider.

How can we do it with one of the cream and cherry schemes?

One of the pictures (Fig. 29) shows how a room may have its height lessened by a frieze and ceiling contrasting with and deeper than the walls.

In this case the green contrast in the scheme could be used for both ceiling and frieze. The walls, mould-

Fig. 32. *A low room; incorrectly decorated frieze, coloured like the ceiling, reduces the already low height of the walls. The parallel lines are too strongly emphasised.*

ings and woodwork would be in cream. In the carpet or rugs the cherry colour would predominate, as in examples already given, which would also be the guide for curtains, covers, cushions and lamp-shades. The curtains you would probably have in plain cherry, keeping pattern for the covers or carpet or both. This arrangement would also apply to walls in pink-tinted cream, which would look well under a frieze and ceiling in a soft yellow-green in a north room.

Alternatively brown or beige could be used for the frieze and ceiling, with patterning in cherry, brown, beige and cream, and the chair-covers cherry-red on the outside and beige on the seat, inside of arms and back, or all beige with cherry cushions.

In the scheme in which orange takes the place of cherry you could also use brown as an alternative to green for the ceiling and frieze.

Above a patterned wallpaper the colour for a frieze and ceiling would be chosen in the same way as for a room with plain walls of the same colour as the ground of the paper.

A Low North Room

To make it seem as lofty as possible do not have the walls darker than the ceiling, or they will seem to shrink. This means using one of the light neutrals in the various schemes we have chosen on both walls and ceiling.

Do not have a frieze.

If you have a wallpaper, let it be in a perpendicular pattern, stripes if possible. These stripes could be in two shades of the colour which has been chosen for the walls.

A Narrow North Room

Try the treatment of "stealing" from the long walls to add to the short walls, thus making the room seem as if it were wider.

If you are having a wallpaper, choose one in which the pattern is markedly horizontal or in bands of various shades of the colour chosen for the walls. You may like to use the paper on the narrow end walls and the stolen pieces of the side walls, having the remainder of the side walls painted or plain-papered in the darker colour in the banded paper.

Rooms of a southern aspect are usually sunny. But even in the absence of sunlight, the light is warmer than in rooms absolutely north. Therefore, while cooler colours may be used, your aim should be to provide a southern room with a scheme which is never too warm on a sunny day, but not too cool on a cold day.

A Blue Scheme for a South Room

We will take a room of satisfactory proportions with a sunny aspect and a view across a garden to houses beyond. Here we shall have no need to change the appearance of the size of the room; and the view is a fairly common one.

Blue is perhaps the most popular of all colours, and we can make it the *Main Colour* in this example—a pleasant mid-blue neither so pale as to be washy nor so deep as to be dark. The deeper forget-me-nots have the colour.

Our *Contrast* shows that we must also use a little of some red shade in the scheme. The more we use of it the paler it should be.

From the *Neutral* column we will take cream—not white, for that is too cold with a colour that is already cool. The 2nd, 3rd and 4th columns show that we can also have yellow, green, brown and purple shades for the small quantities of any additional colours required.

Shall we let our first blue scheme use its main colour on the *Walls*?

Fig. 33. *The same low room made to appear higher by narrow upright panels contrasting with the rest of the wall. These, with the pictures and the rearrangement of the mirror over the fireplace, emphasise perpendicular lines.*

Then the woodwork and the cornice can be painted to match and the ceiling can take the cream.

We cannot very well continue blue on the *Floor* without a break between it and the walls, for this would make the room too blue. The golden yellow of polished natural parquet would be good with rugs in which blue predominates over plentiful touches of soft red shades and purple or wine colours.

Accessories

Chair-covers would have a cream ground and be patterned with plenty of blue and the pink or wine shades and touches of a golden yellow, the colour of the parquet, and perhaps a little green. In such a patterned fabric, indeed in most of them, you would almost certainly find some touches of brown and green. A small quantity of the former does not matter in most rooms; that is why it is included in the column of additional colours in the Scheme Chart. And it will almost certainly be introduced into the room by the wood of the furniture.

Curtains could be in plain cream piped in the red or pink or wine colour in the covers (you can do the piping yourself) or in cream and gold damask or other material of a cream and golden-yellow design. If you have a second set of curtains for the winter they could be in the warmer rose or wine, as in velvet, linen, or other plain material, but not too dark.

Alternatives

To change the scheme a little, have a blue fitted carpet. The walls could remain blue so long as the carpet is slightly deeper and is separated from the walls by cream-

Fig. 34. *The bad, heavy effect produced by much pattern—floors, walls, chair-covers, cushions, curtains. The effect is fussy and makes the room look small.*

Fig. 35. *The same room with pattern now confined to chairs and curtains. The unnecessary picture-rail has been removed. The effect is larger and more restful.*

painted woodwork. The rest of this scheme could be the same as before.

In either scheme you could have plain chair-covers with piping, and use the patterned fabric for the curtains. Cushions could be patterned with plain chair-covers so long as the pattern did not clash with the curtains. With patterned chair-covers they could be plain, and each in a different one of the colours in the scheme, or some blue and some rose.

Lamp-shades, if near the blue walls, should not be coloured with anything more than cream, perhaps relieved by gold or red edging. Shades on standard lamps nearer the centre of the room could be in pale rose or peach, or whatever soft red colour you have in the rest of the scheme.

Blue is not a difficult background for coloured pictures. If they contain a number of blues (with other colours, of course) they may be better with cream mounts and frames. Gold mounts and gold frames are not impossible; and some pictures, such as landscapes in oils or water-colours, or reproductions of either, may dispense with mounts, providing the background blue does not hurt them. Do not use a blue frame; a frame of any colour that is in the picture is rarely good for the picture itself, however well it may blend.

Now let us use the main colour in the furnishings and the neutral for the walls.

One of the neutrals available from column 3 in the Scheme Chart is the pink-tinted cream. This would look well on woodwork, walls and ceiling with a blue carpet and curtains, and chair-covers patterned in peach, blue, green and cream with touches of some soft brown shade. Cushions, plain blue. Lamp-shades, peach-pink edged with blue.

Do not forget that wallpaper, as well as paint, gives other alternatives. You could have it patterned in the colours suggested for the chair-covers in either of these blue schemes.

Green Schemes

These can be composed for sunny or sunless rooms. The sunnier your room the cooler can be your green and the colours you use with it.

Take, for instance, a soft shade of spring-green—the lightest and sunniest green, and not at all blue. With this on the walls and ceiling the woodwork could be cream and the carpet a slightly purple-blue such as you see in hyacinths or delphiniums, or it could be in a purply-wine shade. Chair-covers could have a cream ground well patterned in blues, greens and wine colours, with perhaps touches of more pink shades and some soft brown, and piped green. Cushions, green and blue.

Curtains could match the colour of the carpet; or be woven or striped in this colour and cream.

Lamp-shades, cream, edged green.

If you preferred a plain green carpet and curtains, the woodwork, walls and ceiling could be pale yellow or cream or, with a soft blue-green carpet and curtains, they could stand the warmer contrast of pink-tinted cream. In this case chair-covers could be patterned as before.

Note that yellow walls are generally better with white woodwork and touches of white in accessories.

A bluer green could be used throughout the foregoing green schemes in a sunny room. But in a sunless room the green should remain light and yellow; and orange, copper, japonica or cherry would be used with blue reduced to a minimum and an increase in a brown shade.

Here again patterned wallpaper would mean the use of plain carpets or rugs and plain curtains.

Lofty Rooms, S., S.E., and S.W.

These would be dealt with as already indicated in the section on *Line and Pattern* and in the treatment given for lofty north rooms, except that you would use the colours for the sunnier aspects in the blue and green schemes we have just been discussing.

The ceiling and a frieze both in a darker colour than the walls would mean using one of the lighter neutrals for the latter, or you could have pale yellow. The ceiling and frieze would have the contrast colour, such as rose or peach pink or pale wine. Curtains or carpet could be in blue or green—whichever is your chosen main colour; and the chair-covers could be patterned in all the colours of the scheme.

Patterned wallpaper with a ground in any of these light colours could take the same scheme, except that the chair-covers would be plain blue or green. Or they could have a slightly deeper shade of the wallpaper cream or yellow for their seats and inside their arms and backs, with the plain blue or green of the carpet or curtains for their exteriors.

Dark Blues and Dark Greens

There is one possibility for rooms of these aspects and loftiness which does not apply to lofty north rooms. The main colour here, being blue or green, could be applied in a deep rich shade to woodwork, walls and ceiling, while the light neutral is kept solely for the floor.

This is not quite so impractical as it sounds. Light stone, light fawn, beige, or gold colours are examples of light neutrals suitable for a carpet in rooms of any aspect. Or the floor could be in the golden colour of natural oak or pine, polished, and could have rugs to match as nearly as possible, with only the slightest of pattern, and this a touch of the wall colour.

Curtains could be a paler shade of the floor or carpet colour, and the chair-covers patterned in rose, wine or other pink shades and other colours mentioned in the blue and green schemes already given, but having a ground to match the light neutral of the scheme—the colour of the curtains. Accessories would be as already described for rooms with lighter blue or green walls. See that they are not too small or too many.

Thus the lighter part of the room is the carpet, and this lightness low down in the scheme draws attention away from the upper part or the loftiness. For a narrow, lofty room, however, the treatment is not to be recommended, because the darker walls may also seem nearer; and although you want the ceiling to seem lower, you do not want the walls closer in.

It would be as well to let some touch of the pink contrast colour be noticeable against the walls to keep the blue or green at full value. For instance, the curtains could be piped with this colour; so could the lamp-shades matching the curtains. Coloured pictures should contain plenty of this shade too, and would look well against the dark blue or green walls with cream mounts and cream frames.

Any room with a plain view, whether it is of plain brick walls, unbroken hills or downs, or the sea, is the best case for patterned walls or for walls in a colour contrasting with the view.

If you prefer plain colour for your walls, use the colour in your scheme which most contrasts with the view in so far as you can do this while at the same time meeting the other requirements of your room.

With Other Views

When the view is mainly greens and blues and greys, as in hills or sea, then the yellow or pink-tinted cream or any of the warmer light neutrals or brown in the various schemes could colour the walls. If the outlook is on to red-brick walls, then your room could have blue, green, cream, ivory, or yellow from the scheme for the walls if plain; but this is also a case for patterned wallpaper and glass curtains of net or casement silk, in addition to the heavier curtains. Drape the net, if you like this treatment, and let it have frills piped in the main colour of the scheme. Have a wide, low trough of flowers on the sill. Do all you can to add interest to the walls or to the room generally, and to keep eyes away from the view. Such a room asks for a delicate but naturalistic design of flowers rather than a formal pattern.

Grey

This seems to be one of the most difficult of the neutrals to use successfully. There are many shades of grey which appeal to the eye at first glance without the aid of any other colour to show them off.

Grey is cool, if not cold. It certainly should not prevail in any room which receives no direct sunlight. Yet this does not greatly help its use in a sunny room scheme.

The blues and greens which present the chief of our many

colours for rooms of this aspect take soft pink shades, fine reds, purples and yellows for their contrasts and additional colours, while their neutrals are also warmer, such as the various cream tints or even brown.

Grey can nearly always be included in the extras for a sunny room, as in the colours you might have in a printed fabric chosen for the scheme. But though blue and grey are popular together, yet with these as the principal colours the room would be rather cold.

But if you particularly like the blue and grey combination add rose and purple or amethyst and touches of jade-green and, to give a little warmth, deep cream or ivory or parchment as the main neutral for your walls and ceiling. Grey and the other colours are so happy together it is difficult to go wrong in arranging them in your carpet, covers, curtains and accessories, providing you observe the advice to avoid too many patterned surfaces. Incidentally, rose and old rose are not hot shades of red; old rose might be called a cool colour.

Odd Uses of Grey

Grey is useful in special schemes such as you may have to make for rooms in which you already have some of the furnishings. For instance, if you have copper-coloured curtains—or almost any other shade of red—to use in a sunny room, and you rightly feel that the colour is too warm, grey can be your neutral in a light soft shade and can be used for the walls and woodwork under a cream ceiling. The floor could be polished and have Persian rugs, chiefly blue with touches of copper. Chair-covers could contain blue, grey, green, cream, copper and soft brown. Or you could have a grey carpet and cream woodwork.

Grey can also be used in another way. Remember that it is so cold that your main colour or your main neutral should counteract this part of its effect. It is sunless, having little yellow in its composition. This at once suggests that yellow be used with it.

If it is a sunny room keep the yellow as light as possible. Do not use either of its chief contrasts—red or blue. Blue would first occur to you because this is a sunny room; but, as we have already seen, there is a contrast between the grey and the yellow. Red would, so to speak, be more wrong than the blue because of the aspect. So we come to green—the blue combined with the yellow already chosen. For an extra we can take cream which will set off both the grey and the yellow.

Different Arrangements

There are many different arrangements for the three colours. Here is one. Walls and ceiling, soft grey; woodwork, cream; floor, natural oak parquet polished to a golden-yellow shade and having modern rugs of grey patterned with a simple line or two of yellow and lime-green; curtains, primrose-yellow, piped lime-green; chair-covers, mainly yellow, patterned with plentiful touches of grey, green and cream (other colours avoided or kept to the minimum) and piped grey; cushions, grey, piped with lime-green and pale yellow; lamp-shades, yellow with grey and green decoration.

Inevitably touches of some red shade would come into the room by way of pictures, accessories or flowers, if not in the patterned fabric. Try to have them the cooler shades and not too noticeable.

According to the aspect of the room, choose your warm or cool

Fig. 36. *Light neutral ground of carpet and curtains is here repeated on the walls and woodwork. The figure below shows the effect of a simple change.*

Fig. 37. *A richer effect in the same room by using the brown or any other of the colours in the carpet and curtain pattern for the walls. The darker colour throws up in strong contrast the relative lightness of the pictures, curtains, and carpet.*

Fig. 38. *The combined effect of dark paint-work, paper and an ornate frieze make this hall gloomy and close. For better treatment, see Fig.* 39.

main colour and let it predominate in carpet, curtains and covers. If, however, you intend ultimately to use this colour on the walls and not in the curtains, let these latter be in the contrast or in the neutral. In the neutral they will match the walls; but this need not make the room dull, for their texture can have a richness as in the case of velvet, furnishing satin, damask linen, or an artificial silk and cotton fabric, or even a dull-faced material of noticeable and interesting weave that will show up against the matt surface of the wall. Curtains matching the colour of the wall also help to make a room look larger.

Individual Problems

Perhaps a rose-coloured carpet is your problem. having to use it in a sunny room and feeling that it is too warm. But you can use it with one of the blue wall schemes.

Suppose you have a carpet with blue predominating over touches of red and cream, and you want to use it in a north room for which you feel it is rather cold because of its blue, use the cream as the colour for your walls, woodwork and ceiling, and bring up the red in curtains and chair-covers, where there could also be cream and a little blue and plenty of brown.

A room which you have decorated and furnished carefully in shades of blue and green against cream walls, feeling this to be a good scheme because the aspect is south, now seems unaccountably dull. It needs touches of rose or peach or some such pleasant shade of red. Plain cushions of this colour with blue piping might cure the trouble, or the lamp-shades might introduce it; the accessories certainly could.

If you take over a house with orange-coloured tiles in the fire-

Fig. 39. *The same hall redecorated. It now looks wider and lighter because of light woodwork and walls, and the slightly deeper tone on the ceiling.*

place in a sunny room, paint the tiles the colour of your walls or woodwork as chosen for your new scheme; unless you prefer to enclose the fireplace as suggested in Lesson 1.

Have you a white marble mantelpiece you do not want to paint, though you find it cold in a north room? Paint the woodwork white to match it as a foil to sunny yellow-green walls which would be the contrasting colour for cherry or orange curtains. The rest of the scheme to enliven this north room and to counteract the marble white would include chair-covers in cherry or orange with yellows, greens, and browns, and touches of white, and gold-coloured mats on a polished wood floor. The ceiling could be in a paler shade of green.

If you have inherited Victorian furniture with the room it could quite well be used with this scheme. The chair-covers would have to be of a chintz or other floral design, not necessarily of the period, but something a little more pleasant that would agree with it.

Let the Chart be your Guide

These examples all show the use of the principles laid down in this course. You can always find what is wrong with an existing scheme by studying the chart and comparing your room with the examples given for the same aspect; and you will then be able to make the necessary corrections.

Exercise

Using the chart in Lesson 5 work out for yourself suitable colour schemes for sitting-rooms, bedrooms, dining-rooms. Work out a scheme for a southern sunny room and for a northern cold room.

Answers to Self Testing Questions

LESSON 1

(1) Doors, fireplaces, balustrades and baths.
(2) Against the danger of the new structure catching fire.
(3) It has no mouldings to catch dust, and gives a modern effect of simplicity and compactness.
(4) Glazed asbestos sheeting, wallboard or wall-glass.

LESSON 2

(1) (*a*) It emphasises the lightness of the walls; (*b*) by contrast, it makes the walls look slightly darker than they are.
(2) It would diminish the effect of having too great an area of ceiling in the room.
(3) Because it is impossible to avoid spilling paint or distemper when ceilings are being done.
(4) Clean ceiling with hot water and ammonia. Fill the cracks with Keen's cement or with a mixture of equal parts of plaster of Paris and whiting.
(5) A coat of Clearcolle, made up of whiting and size.

LESSON 3

(1) Grass matting or coco matting, with an occasional rug on top.
(2) (*a*) It makes the room look smaller; (*b*) it makes the staircase seem wider.
(3) (*a*) They can be bleached by a solution of oxalic acid in water, followed by washing with water; (*b*) they can be cleaned with turpentine or benzine—both inflammable.
(4) Surrounds can be stained red or green, etc., in harmony with carpets or colour schemes; they can also be of natural polished wood or of parquetry.

LESSON 4

(1) It is more restful and helps to make the room look larger.
(2) Find the total area of the walls (height × length) in square yards and divide by 63.

LESSON 5

(1) Reds and browns.
(2) *Either* on walls and perhaps ceiling and floors, *or* as the main colour in carpet, chair-covers and curtains.

WOODWORK

By Anthony Edwards

LESSON 1

Tools—Their Use and Care

For ordinary straightforward work you will need at least two saws. Others are desirable, but you can start with a couple. First comes the cross-cut handsaw, which you will use for the preliminary cutting up of timber. A useful size is 20 in. with, say, nine or ten teeth to the inch. This is sufficiently fine not to tear out the grain unduly without being too slow in cutting. It can be used for cutting both with and across the grain. Normally the wood to be sawn is supported upon trestles or upon the bench; if on the bench, a cramp is used to hold it firmly. Begin the cut slightly to the waste side of the marked-out line so that the edge can be trimmed later. Hold the saw as in Fig. 1, with the index-finger pointing forward.

When beginning the cut, place the left hand at the end of the board with the thumb bearing against the blade, to steady it. Make a few short

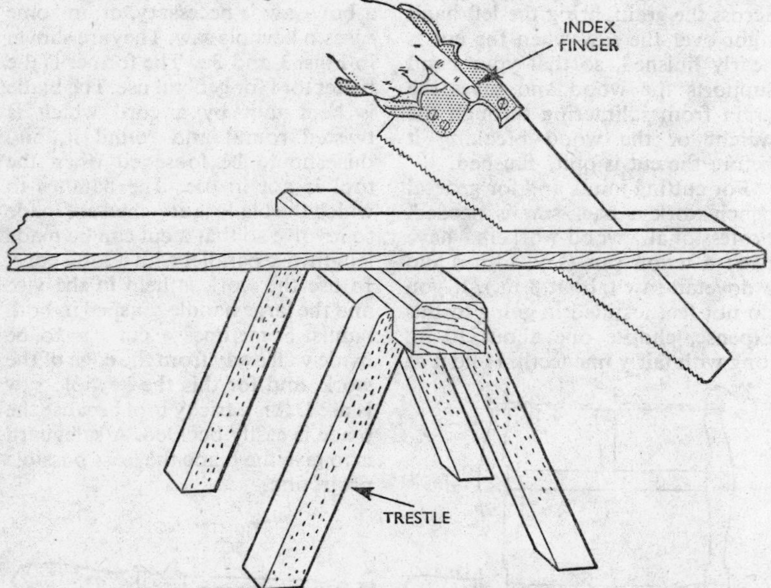

Fig. 1. *In sawing a plank supported on trestles or a bench, the saw is held as above, the index finger of the right hand pointing forward parallel with the edge.*

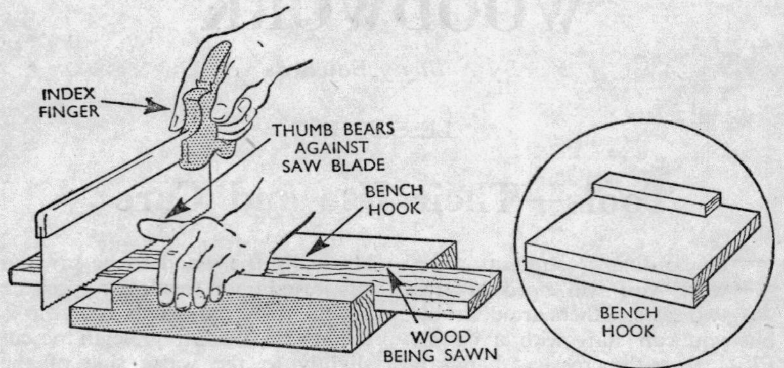

Fig. 2. *The back-saw, used for cutting joints and general bench work, is held as here shown, with the wood held in place by a bench-hook* (inset).

strokes up and down until the saw has made a reasonable start, and then work with full, long strokes. Never force the saw: like some human beings, it is easily led, but hard to drive. If you are cutting across the grain, bring the left hand right over the saw when the cut is nearly finished, so that your hand supports the wood and saves the grain from splintering through the weight of the wood breaking it before the cut is quite finished.

For cutting joints and for general bench-work a back-saw is needed. Professional wood-workers have two: a tenon saw (say, 14 in.) and a dovetail saw (about 8 in.). If you do not feel justified in going to this expense, choose one about 10 in. long with fairly fine teeth. Hold it as shown in Fig. 2, the index-finger pointing forward and the wood held upon a bench-hook. The latter is really a necessity in order to keep the wood steady.

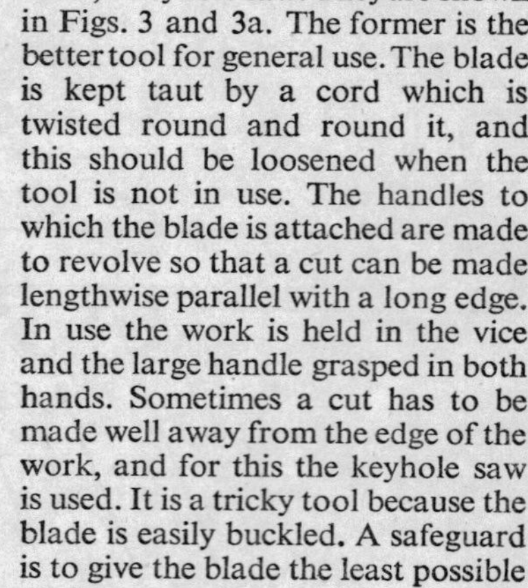

When you come to shaped work a bow-saw is necessary, or, in some cases, a keyhole saw. They are shown in Figs. 3 and 3a. The former is the better tool for general use. The blade is kept taut by a cord which is twisted round and round it, and this should be loosened when the tool is not in use. The handles to which the blade is attached are made to revolve so that a cut can be made lengthwise parallel with a long edge. In use the work is held in the vice and the large handle grasped in both hands. Sometimes a cut has to be made well away from the edge of the work, and for this the keyhole saw is used. It is a tricky tool because the blade is easily buckled. A safeguard is to give the blade the least possible projection.

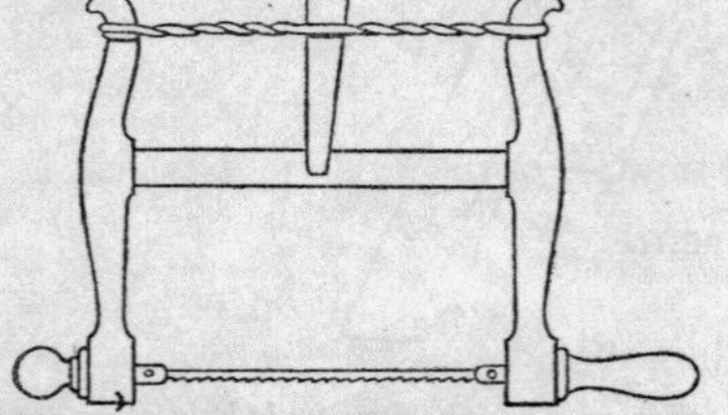

Figs. 3 and 3a. Left, *bow-saw;* right, *keyhole saw. Both are used for shaped work.*

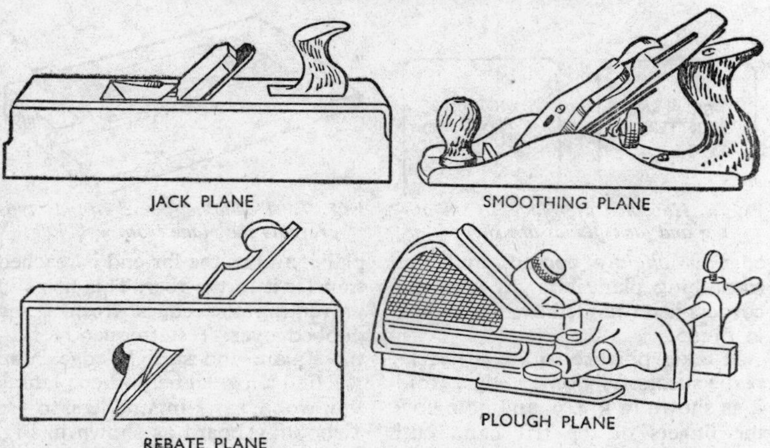

Fig. 4. *The serious woodworker needs a plane of each of the types shown.*

One last word about saws. When they become blunt have them sharpened by a professional sharpener. It is a difficult job, and the novice will do more harm than good.

Planes

For serious woodwork you need one fairly long plane to enable you to true-up long edges, and one for cleaning up. You can choose either wood or metal planes. The former are cheaper, and perfectly good work can be done with them. Metal planes, however, are more easily managed, and for certain work they are more satisfactory. You cannot do better than select a wood jack-plane 16 in. long, and a smoothing plane of metal with a 2-in. cutter. Other planes you will need later are a rebate plane, in which the cutter reaches right to the edges, and a grooving plane. All these are shown in Fig. 4.

First a word about sharpening. Remove the cutter and unscrew the back-iron. You will see that the edge is roughly ground. Hold it with the bevel flat on the oilstone and then raise the hands *slightly* so that the edge alone touches. Work it to and fro until a burr can be detected when the thumb is drawn across the back of the cutter. Now reverse the cutter, holding it this time *flat*, and rub it once or twice until the burr is removed. Finally strop both sides on a piece of leather until the burr drops off. You can tell when the edge is sharp by looking at it. If there is a line of white it is still blunt. A sharp edge is invisible.

When you replace the back-iron it should be about $\frac{1}{16}$ in. from the edge in the case of the jack-plane, and $\frac{1}{32}$ in. or less for the smoothing plane. The purpose of the back-iron is to break the shaving as it is formed and so prevent the grain from being torn out. Adjustment to the wood plane is made by tapping the back of the cutter or the striking knob as the case may be. The metal plane is adjustable by means of a screw knob and a lateral lever. Hold the plane over a sheet of white paper, when the cutter should appear as a thin black line. The jack-plane cutter

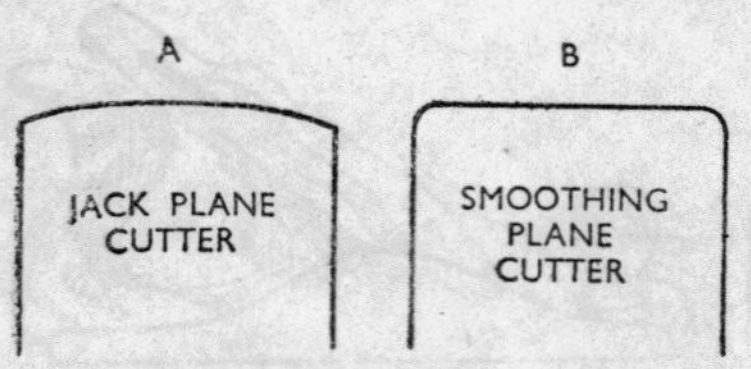

Fig. 5. *How the cutter edges of smoothing and jack planes are shaped.*

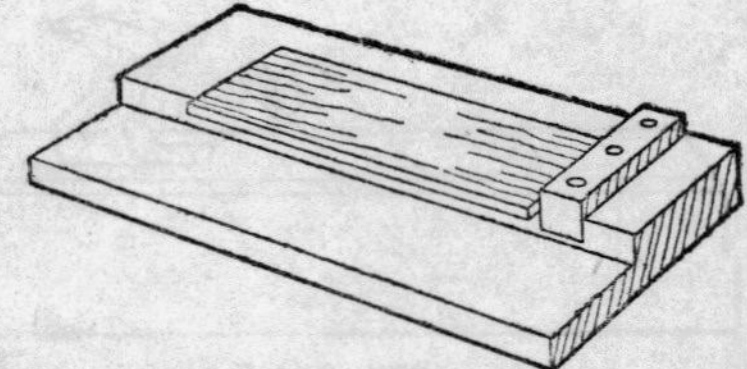

Fig. 7. *A shooting-board of this type prevents the plane from wobbling.*

edge is *slightly* curved, and the smoothing plane straight with the corners just rounded over as shown in Fig. 5.

It takes practice to use the jack-plane successfully on an edge. Hold it as shown in Fig. 6, and note how the fingers of the left hand curl beneath the plane and bear against the wood. They act as a sort of fence and help to keep the plane in its course. When beginning the cut exert pressure on the front of the plane, and as the far end is reached transfer it to the rear. This helps in preventing the edges from being dubbed over. Test frequently with the square and straight-edge. You will find it a great help when planing thin wood, say $\frac{1}{2}$ in. and less, to use a shooting board as shown in Fig. 7, as it keeps the plane from wobbling. It is also invaluable for trimming the ends of wood.

As its name implies, the rebate plane is used for working rebates.

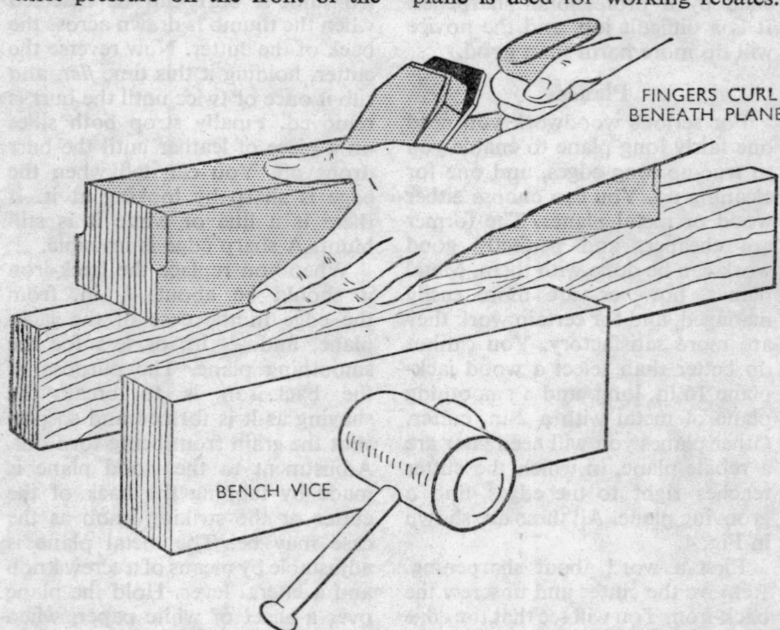

Fig. 6. *When using the jack-plane on an edge, hold it as shown, letting the fingers of the left hand bear against the wood, and pressing down with the thumb.*

Fig. 8 shows how it is held. The fingers of the left hand pass beneath the plane as a guide in keeping it parallel with the edge. If preferred, a strip of wood can be fixed down on the work as a guide. In the case of end-grain a cut must first be made with the saw, otherwise the grain will tear out.

When you want to work a groove you need a special grooving plane, and a useful little plane to work grooves $\frac{3}{8}$ in., $\frac{1}{4}$ in. and $\frac{3}{16}$ in. wide is obtainable in metal. Unless you have larger work to do than this you will find it very handy. It is shown in Fig. 4—the plough plane.

Chisels

The chisel is one of the essential tools of the wood-worker. It is a sort of maid-of-all-work. There are various kinds; the firmer, the bevelled edge and the mortise. Of these the firmer is the most useful for all-round purposes. It is sturdily built, and can be used for fine paring, or it can be struck with the mallet for chopping out. The bevelled-edge type is for fine paring only, being a slighter tool with the upper edges bevelled, enabling it to be used close into corners and acute angles. As the name suggests, the mortise chisel is for chopping out mortises and is a heavily built tool.

All are sharpened in the same way. The ground bevel is placed flat on the stone, the handle raised a trifle, and the tool worked back and forth until a burr is turned up. This is removed by reversing the chisel *flat* on the stone and rubbing it once or twice. It is of the utmost importance that it is held flat in the latter operation.

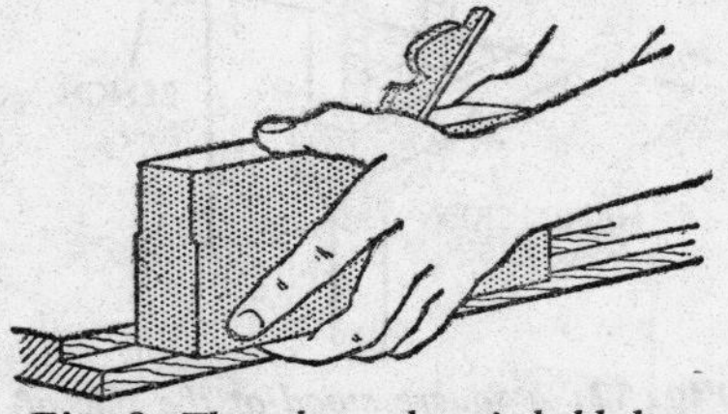

Fig. 8. *The rebate plane is held thus.*

For a start a 1-in. bevelled-edge chisel and a $\frac{1}{2}$-in. and a $\frac{1}{4}$-in. firmer chisels are recommended. Others can be obtained later as required.

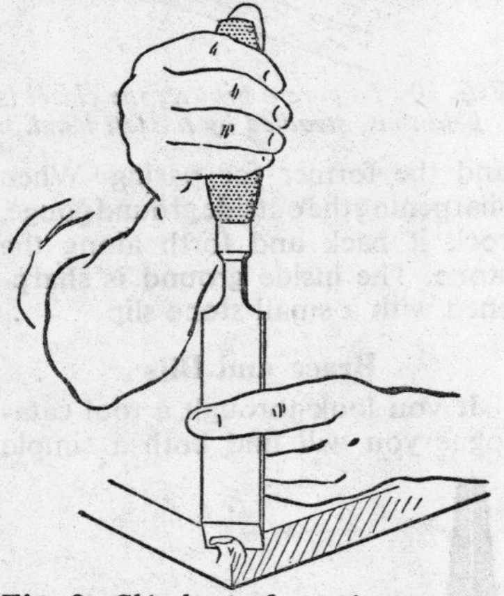

Fig. 9. *Chisel grip for paring a corner.*

For the mortise chisel the most useful is the $\frac{5}{16}$-in. size, because it is right for $\frac{7}{8}$-in. wood, the thickness most generally used for frames, doors and so on.

The golden rule when using a chisel is this: keep both hands behind the cutting edge. It will save many an accident. Fig. 9 shows how it is held when paring a corner. The right hand presses down, and the finger of the left hand curls around the blade to steady it. For paring a groove it is held as in Fig. 10, the work being either held in the vice or cramped down on the bench.

Gouges

There are two kinds of gouges; inside ground and outside ground. The latter comes in for general work

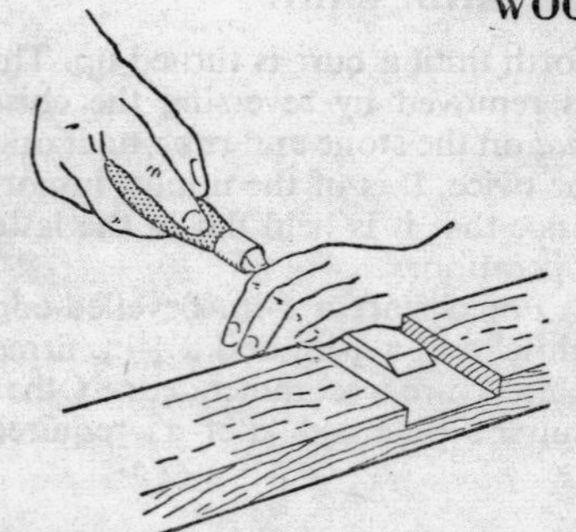

Fig. 10. *To pare a groove, the chisel is held thus, steadied by the left hand.*

and the former for paring. When sharpening the outside ground gouge, rock it back and forth along the stone. The inside ground is sharpened with a small stone slip.

Brace and Bits

If you look through a tool catalogue you will find both a simple brace and a ratchet brace. Choose the latter for preference because, although it costs more, it is useful for working in corners. One with a sweep of 8 in. is the handiest. For the bits you should have the following for a start; others you can buy as occasion arises. They are shown in Fig. 11. *A* is a $\frac{3}{8}$-in. auger bit which is used for dowelling and for boring deep holes generally. This form of bit has the advantage of not being liable to drift with the grain. *B* is a centre bit used for holes bored in comparatively thin wood. A $\frac{3}{4}$-in. or 1-in. size can be selected, according to the use for which it is likely to be required. When the hole has to pass right through the wood it is advisable to bore through from one side until the point just emerges beneath, and then finish it from the

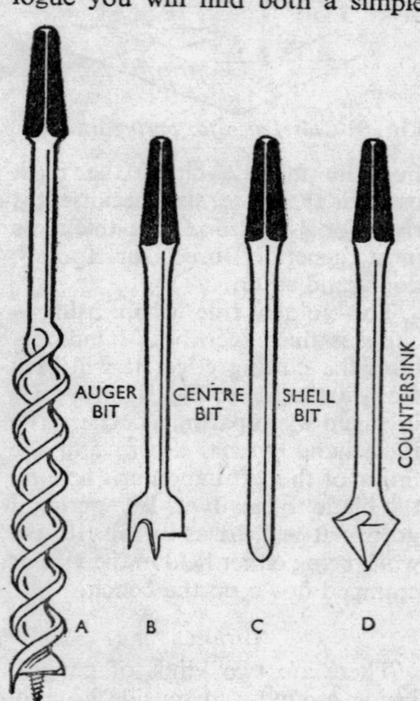

Fig. 11. *Four essential types of bit.*

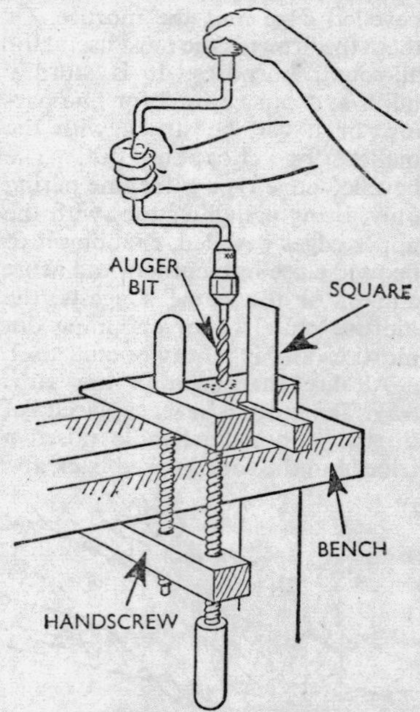

Fig. 12. *A square stood at the side of the work makes a good guide for the bit.*

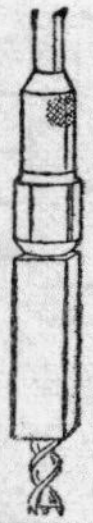

other side. For boring holes for screws the shell bit at *C* is used, and for recessing screw-heads, the countersink at D.

DEPTH GAUGE

Fig. 13.

Generally, a hole should be as upright as possible, and a square stood at the side of the work is a good guide, as shown in Fig. 12. Sometimes two squares can be arranged at right angles so that the vertical can be observed in both directions. Frequently you will have a number of holes to bore all the same depth. One method is to count the number of turns made by the brace (this applies only to the auger bit). Another is to stick a piece of paper to the bit and cease boring when the paper reaches the surface of the wood. A third method is to use a depth-gauge, as in Fig. 13. This is a piece of wood with a hole through it, and of a length to allow the required projection of the bit at the end.

Great care must be taken when sharpening the auger bit. Use a fine file with a safe edge, and avoid damaging the thread. Follow the bevel of the cutters and nickers. Unless a nail is encountered, however, the bit seldom needs touching.

Another handy boring tool is the bradawl. The cutting edge should always work at right angles to the grain, as this helps to prevent splitting. It can be sharpened on the oilstone. Its chief use is in boring holes when screwing. Many sizes are available; select a size for the work in hand. The gimlet is handy for boring deep holes, but it should not be used for thin wood or near the end of a piece, as it is liable to split the grain.

Marking-Out Tools

The tools mostly needed for this are the rule, square and cutting gauge. Others that will soon be needed for serious work are the straight-edge, mortise gauge, dividers, mitre square and the bevel. Taking them in order, the rule can conveniently be the 2-ft. folding type. When using it, place its edge on the wood so that the markings actually touch it, thus making for accuracy. The square is a necessity both for marking out and for testing. The 6-in. size is the handiest, though a larger one—say 12 in.—will be needed for larger work. Two kinds of gauges are available: the cutting and the marking type. The former is the more useful, in that it can be used for marking as well as for cutting thin wood. It always seems to be a tricky tool to use. It is held as shown in Fig. 14. The thumb presses forward, the index-finger exerts a downward pressure and the others press the fence tightly against the edge of the wood. The latter is most important if a clean line is to be produced. When setting the gauge, hold the rule with its end against the fence and, when the cutter is approximately opposite the required mark, tighten the screw. Then, by tapping one end or the other of the gauge on the bench, the fence will jump in the direction required.

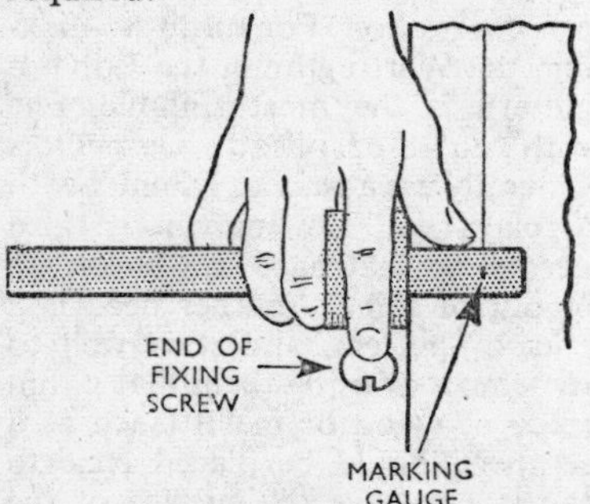

Fig. 14. *This is how the marking gauge is held: the thumb presses it forward.*

You can make a straight-edge yourself out of a piece of ½-in. wood. To test it place it on a piece of wood and draw a line with a pencil. Now reverse the straight-edge and see whether it lines up with the mark. If you propose to do much in the way of making doors or frames, you will need a mortise gauge. This has two markers, one of which is capable of being moved independently. When setting it, place the mortise chisel against the markers and move the free marker until the two line up with the chisel width. It is then just a matter of setting the fence until the marks are central on the wood.

Dividers are invaluable for spacing out marks at odd equal distances apart. For instance, if a length of, say, 10 in. has to be divided into seven equal parts, the whole can be stepped out by the trial-and-error method. The mitre square is similar to the ordinary square, but the blade is set at 45 deg. It is used mostly in mitreing. The bevel is a similar tool, but the blade can be set at any angle. It is not usually needed for straightforward work.

Tools for Nailing and Screwing

The hammer is an obvious tool in this connection. For furniture-making, the Warrington or the London pattern is the most suitable, one with an 8-oz. head. Carpenters generally use a heavier hammer with a claw-head. A punch is also needed so that nails can be driven in out of sight. Another need is a pair of pincers, and it is well to remember in using them that a thin piece of wood or metal (such as a scraper) should be placed beneath the jaw to save the surface of the wood from damage. For fine work panel pins are the most suitable for indoor woodwork. Oval brads are useful for heavier jobs. They have small heads and do not show badly.

Fig. 15. *When a joint is held solely by nails, give them a dovetail grip.*

When nails are driven in near an edge it is a wise precaution to bore holes first with the bradawl to save splitting. Then again it is an advantage to stagger nails whenever practicable—that is, avoid placing them in line along the grain. To obtain the maximum strength in a joint that relies purely on the nails, knock them in at alternate angles. This gives them a dovetail grip, as shown in Fig. 15. But you must drive in the first nail straight, as otherwise the angle may cause the top piece to slide along the other.

You will be well advised to get two screw-drivers, a little one for small screws such as are used for hinges and a large one for big screws. When you buy screws, remember that the length of flat-head screws is the over-all size, whereas the length of the round-head type is measured from the point to beneath the head. Many people make the mistake of boring holes that are too small for the screws. The hole into which the screw portion is driven should be equal to the diameter of the centre part of the screw inside the spiral. Remember that it is only the latter which holds in the wood. The upper piece of wood through which the plain part of the screw passes should be an easy fit. It is just a clearance hole. Thus when screwing together two pieces, bore the clearance hole

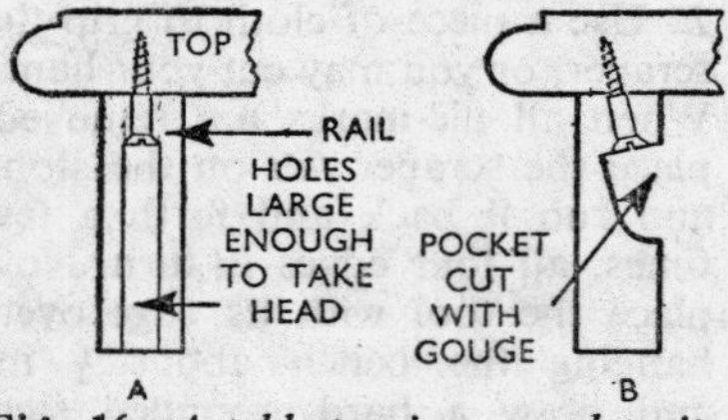

Fig. 16. *A table-top is screwed to its rails by* (A) *recessing in the rail, or* (B) *pocket-screwing from a gouge-cut.*

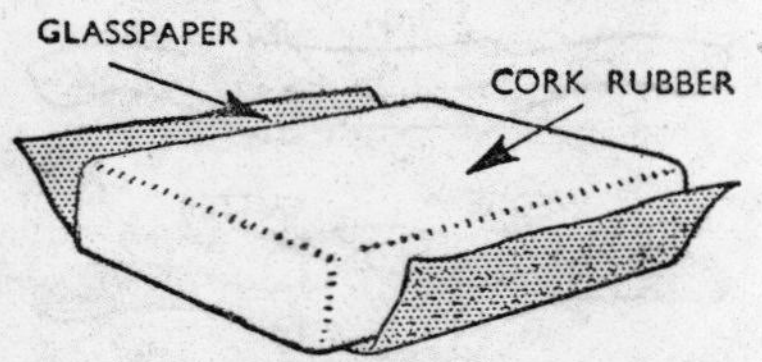

Fig. 17. *Ridges in softwood are removed by treating them with glass-paper stretched over a cork rubber.*

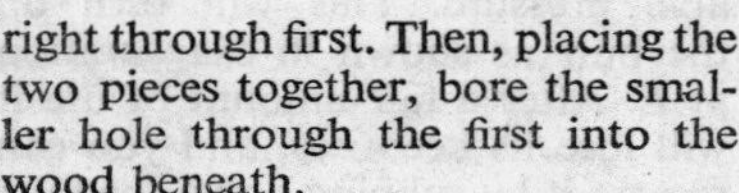

right through first. Then, placing the two pieces together, bore the smaller hole through the first into the wood beneath.

As a general principle, the thinner piece of wood should be screwed to the thicker, as this allows a greater length of the thread to engage. This is not always practicable, however, as when a table-top is being fixed to the rails. In this case the screw can be either deeply recessed in the rail as at *A*, Fig. 16, or it can be pocket-screwed as at *B*.

You have seen that one of the purposes of planing is to smooth the surface of the wood. If, however, you gave it no further treatment and tried to polish it at once, you would find that the surface showed a series of ridges owing to the cbtter digging

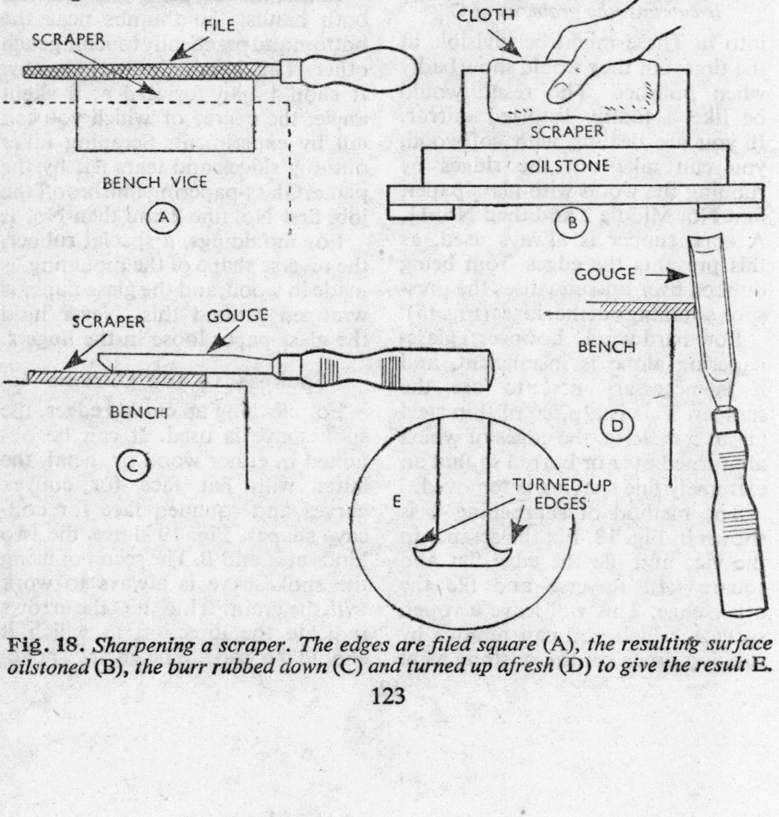

Fig. 18. *Sharpening a scraper. The edges are filed square* (A), *the resulting surface oilstoned* (B), *the burr rubbed down* (C) *and turned up afresh* (D) *to give the result* E.

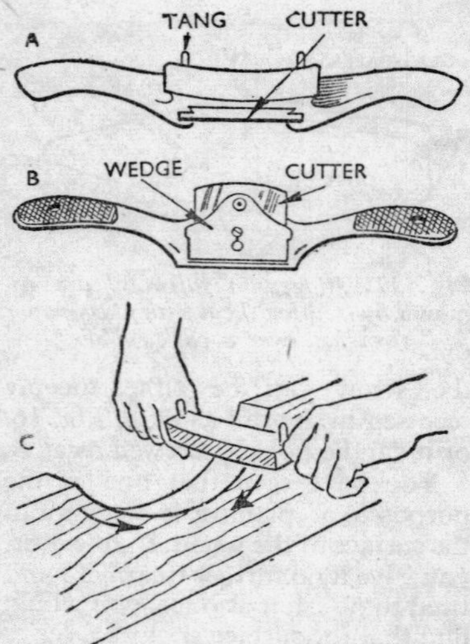

Fig. 19. *Wood* (A) *and metal* (B) *spokeshaves. In using either type the wood is cut* with *the grain, as at* C.

into it. These might be invisible at the time, but they would show badly when polished. The result would be like a faulty distorted mirror. If you are dealing with softwood, you can take out the ridges by rubbing the wood with glass-paper, first No. Middle 2 and then No. 1½. A cork rubber is always used, as this prevents the edges from being dubbed over and equalises the pressure, so taking out the ridges (Fig. 17).

For hardwood, however, glass-papering alone is insufficient, and it is necessary first to use the scraper. This is a piece of thin steel about 5 in. long, the edges of which are turned over or burred so that an extremely fine shaving is removed.

The method of sharpening it is shown in Fig. 18. Fix the scraper in the vice and file the edge flat and square (*A*). Reverse and file the other edge. This will leave a rough surface, which you can remove by rubbing down on the oilstone as at *B*. Use a piece of cloth to grip the scraper, or you may cut your hand. When all file-marks are removed, place the scraper *flat* on the stone and rub it back and forth a few times, all four edges in turn. Now place the tool with its edge overhanging the bench about ½ in. and draw a hard, rounded steel tool, such as a gouge, along the edge at an angle as at *D*, using considerable pressure. This will turn up the burr as shown in exaggeration at *E*. After a fair amount of use it will lose its keenness, and you can restore it by rubbing down the burr as at *C*, holding the gouge *flat* on the surface. It is then turned up afresh as at *D*. You can repeat this several times, but after a while it will be necessary to rub down again with file and oilstone.

In use, the scraper is grasped with both hands, the thumbs near the bottom and practically touching each other. This bends the tool slightly. It should lean forward at a slight angle, the degree of which you can tell by experiment. Scraping takes out any ridges and tears left by the plane. Glass-papering finishes off the job, first No. fine 2 and then No. 1.

For mouldings, a special rubber, the reverse shape of the moulding, is made in wood, and the glass-paper is wrapped around this. Never hold the glass-paper loose in the fingers.

Spokeshave and Oilstone

For cleaning up curved edges, the spokeshave is used. It can be obtained in either wood or metal, the latter with flat face for convex curves and rounded face for concave shapes. Fig. 19 shows the two kinds at *A* and *B*. The secret of using the spokeshave is always to work *with* the grain. Thus at *C* the arrows indicate the direction in which it should be used. The metal spoke-

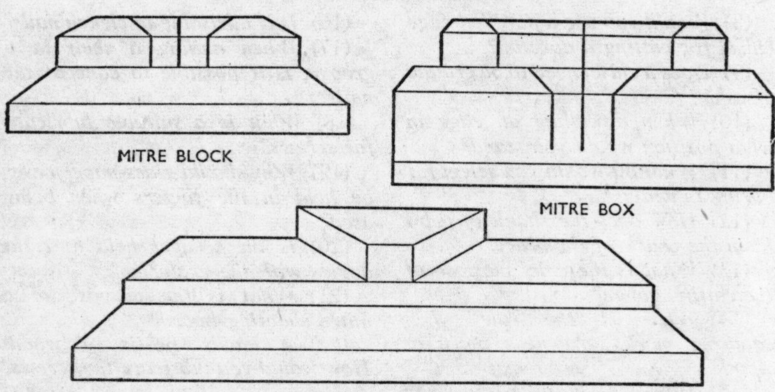

Fig. 20. *These appliances, needed for mitreing, as will be explained in a later Lesson, can easily be made by the home wood-worker for himself.*

shave cutter is sharpened similarly to a plane-cutter, but that of the wood type, having projecting tangs, must be sharpened either with a stone slip or on the edge of the oilstone. It is always sharpened on the inside—that is, the bevelled side—and, although the burr can be removed from the face, it must be held flat so that the edge is not dubbed over. For extra quick curves the wood file can be used, the marks being taken out afterwards with the scraper followed by glass-paper.

The oilstone has been already mentioned. Buy a good one. A poor stone is of little use, and it soon loses its cut. Good makes, such as the "Carborundum," the "Indian," or the "Washita," are reliable. Use a good-quality machine oil, and wipe it clean when finished with. A case for it is easily made, and a good plan is to stick a piece of leather beneath each end to save it from moving when in use. Treat the stone slip for sharpening gouges and wood spokeshave cutter as you do the oilstone.

Other tools or appliances which you can make yourself are those required for mitreing—mitre block, mitre box and mitre shooting board, all of which are shown in Fig. 20.

Finally a few cramps are needed. There is the sash-cramp for dealing with doors and frames, for which a length of 3 ft. is handy. Then there is a variety of *G* cramps, thumbscrews and handscrews for smaller work. These are best obtained as occasion arises.

Self Testing Questions

(1) *If you are buying one handsaw, what type would you choose?*

(2) *What lubricant would you use for a saw?*

(3) *Why is the index-finger pointed forward when sawing?*

(4) *If an edge is not square would you tilt the plane to correct it?*

(5) *How can you prevent the corner from splintering out when planing end grain?*

(6) *If one corner of a plane-cutter sticks out, how would you put it straight?*

(7) *What special point is there to look for when buying a wood plane?*

(8) *Would you use a bevelled-edge chisel for cutting a dovetail?*

(9) *Does a chisel need to be ground afresh?*

(10) *When dowelling an edge in what position would you stand?*

(11) *What bit would you select for boring in end grain?*

(12) *How does the shank of a bit fit in the chuck of the brace?*

(13) *What is the chief purpose of the cutting gauge?*

(14) *What is the rule when squaring marks around a piece of wood?*

(15) *How can you ascertain when the markers of a mortise gauge are central on the wood?*

(16) *Is it advisable to clench nails?*

(17) *When nailing a shelf in a groove, is it possible to conceal the nails?*

(18) *What is a suitable lubricant for screws?*

(19) *Why should glass-paper never be held in the fingers when being used?*

(20) *Is the scraper held at right angles with the grain?*

(21) *What is the purpose of a mitre shooting board?*

(22) *A handscrew is of wood. How would you lubricate the screws?*

THE ANSWERS ARE ON PAGE 178.

LESSON 2

The Wood You Use

BROADLY speaking, there are two kinds of timber used in woodwork: hardwoods and softwoods. Hardwoods are used for the show-parts of furniture, and include such woods as oak, walnut, mahogany and the various Empire timbers. Softwoods come in for parts which are not normally seen—shelves, backs, concealed rails, and so on, and are largely used in outdoor woodwork. In addition, there are the made-up materials, such as plywood and lamin-board.

A custom has arisen in recent years for retailers who supply amateurs to sell all woods at so much per foot run. That is, the price is fixed in accordance with the width and thickness, and the buyer, requiring a piece of, say, $\frac{7}{8}$-in. oak 7 in. wide has only to look up in the catalogue and see the cost per foot run of that size and multiply by the length he requires in order to arrive at the exact cost of the whole.

In the trade, however, although softwoods are sold in this way, hardwoods are priced at so much per foot super. In other woods the area, which is the length multiplied by the width, is the basis of the calculation. Suppose you need a board 4 ft. 6 in. long by 9 in. wide and $\frac{7}{8}$ in. thick. You are told that the price of $\frac{7}{8}$-in. stuff is 1*s.* 6*d.* per foot super. What you have to do is to find the area in square feet and multiply the price by it. First find the area. The rule is to multiply the length in feet by the width in inches, and divide by 12 (the latter to bring the width to feet instead of inches). Thus we can set it out:

Length $4\frac{1}{2}$ (ft.) $\times$ width 9 (in.) $\div$ 12
$= \frac{9}{2} \times \frac{9}{1} \times \frac{1}{12}$, or $\frac{9}{2} \times \frac{3}{1} \times \frac{1}{4} = \frac{27}{8}$
$= 3\frac{3}{8}$ super ft. or $3\frac{1}{2}$ super ft. @ 1*s.* 6*d.*
$=$ 5*s.* 3*d.*

There is a quicker method used in

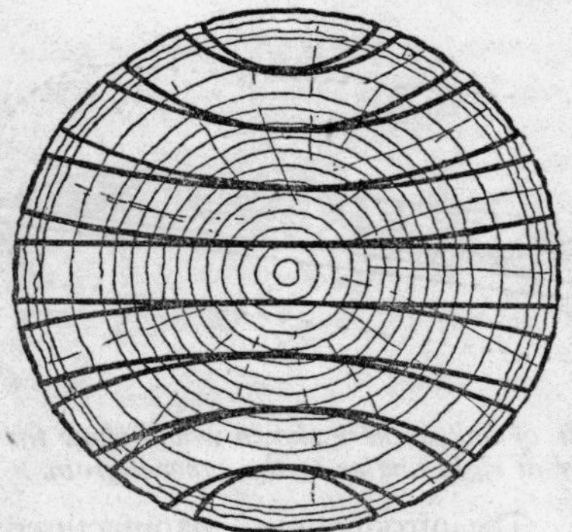

Fig. 21. *Boards cut from a log are apt to warp, because the bulk no longer prevents the rings from contracting.*

the trade, but from your point of view this will enable you to find out nearly enough the cost of your timber.

Apart from price there is the question of thickness, which sometimes confuses the amateur. You may order a piece of, say, 1-in. timber and find that $\frac{7}{8}$ in. is the thickness delivered. The reason is that when a log is converted it is usually cut up into 3-in. thicknesses, and when this is cut down to "1-in." boards, the latter measure under 1 in., because so much wood is lost when the timber is planed. It is advisable, therefore, to calculate on your stuff finishing $\frac{7}{8}$ in. This, however, does not normally apply to retailers supplying amateurs. They usually list the actual finished thickness.

To understand how figure is produced you have first to understand how timber is made up. If you examine the end of a log of oak you will find that there are a large number of concentric "circles," and also a series of light lines running radially. The former are the annual rings, and the latter the medullary rays. In some woods, such as oak and beech, the rays stand out very clearly and play a large part in producing figure. In others they are invisible except under a magnifying-glass.

Softwoods have no visible medullary rays, and consequently all figure is derived from the annual rings. Fig. 22 shows a typical example. If the tree were perfectly straight the figure would appear as a series of dark parallel lines, closer together at the outside. Since no tree is perfectly straight, however, the straight saw-cut runs across them, producing the more or less elliptical markings.

In the case of oak, however, a board cut as in Fig. 23 would exhibit the medullary rays, and they would appear as a series of flakes running across the general grain. At the same time note that the board runs radially from the centre—that is, parallel with the rays. A board

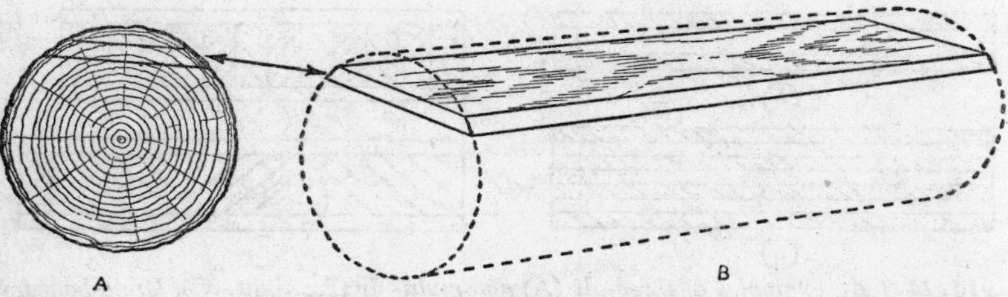

Fig. 22. *All figure in softwoods, which have no visible medullary rays, is that derived from the annual rings.*

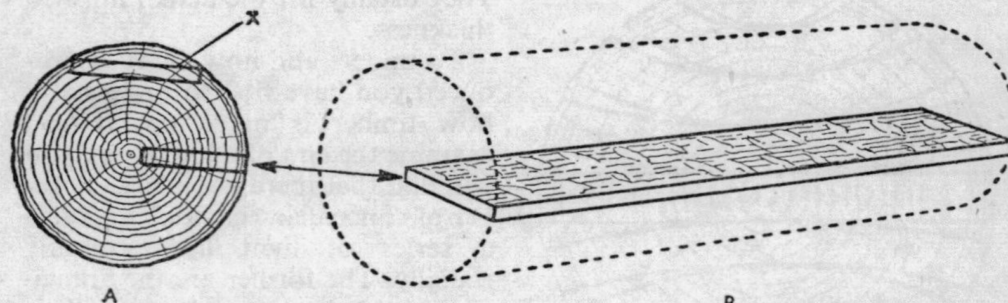

Fig. 23. *A board cut radially from a piece of oak as here shown would show the medullary rays as flakes running roughly at right-angles to the general grain.*

such as that at *x* (Fig. 23) would not show the medullary rays, because the latter would run through it instead of lying flat on the surface. You now realise the difference between figured and plain oak.

An understanding of the features just mentioned will help you to understand why some boards are liable to warp. A log as it dries out shrinks around its annual rings. They are trying to contract, but are largely prevented from doing so by the bulk of the timber in the centre. This is why a log is liable to split radially towards the centre. If cut up into boards the stresses are largely released and the individual boards are apt to curl as shown in Fig. 21. Note that the nearer the boards are to the centre the less likely they are to twist. That is why a figured oak board is less liable to curl than a plain one—because it runs radially to the centre, or nearly so.

The introduction of manufactured wooden materials has probably done more to alter design in furniture than any other cause. The reason is partly that they do not shrink in either length or width so that no allowance has to be made for shrinkage, and partly because of the great widths in which they can be obtained.

Plywood and Lamin-Board

Plywood varies tremendously in quality. Some is suitable for nothing better than tea-chests, while more expensive varieties can be used in the best cabinet work.

There are many thicknesses of ply available, from about $\frac{1}{64}$ in. up to 1 in. The thinner kinds, up to about $\frac{1}{4}$ in., consist of three layers, the centre one being thicker than the outer ones. Its grain runs at right angles to the others. Thicker ply, usually known as multi-ply, may have any odd number of layers, and

Fig. 24. Left, *examples of three-ply* (A) *and multi-ply* (B); right, (C), *lamin-board, and* (D), *block-board, in which the outer layers are cemented on at right angles to the centre strips, which are stuck together side by side.*

its stiffness is about equal in both directions. All kinds are sold in various standard sizes of panels. Fig. 24, *A* and *B*, shows examples of three-ply and multi-ply (in this case seven-ply) wood.

Lamin-board is more expensive, and, for work which is unsupported (flush doors for example), it is ideal. It makes an excellent ground-work for veneer. It consists of a centre core of narrow strips, stuck together side by side, with outer layers cemented on at right angles. Fig. 24 at *C* shows a section through a piece of lamin-board. In block-board (*D*) the centre core is made up of wider pieces. It is therefore not so reliable.

Self Testing Questions

(1) *How do you calculate the price of timber sold at per foot run?*

(2) *What is the area of a piece of wood 9 ft. long by 3 in. wide?*

(3) *What part do the annual rings play in the growth of a tree?*

(4) *How must an oak board be cut to show figure?*

(5) *What are the chief advantages of plywood?*

(6) *What is lamin-board mostly used for?*

THE ANSWERS ARE ON PAGE 178.

LESSON 3

Construction—The Joints Used

THERE are several important things to bear in mind when you make a door. You know, of course, that wood is likely to shrink or swell in accordance with the humidity of the atmosphere. Consequently the door must be so made that shrinkage will not adversely affect it. You just have to accept shrinkage and allow for it.

Doors and Frames

Now, if you make a door out of a solid slab of wood, you are faced with the probability of its shrinking across its width, so showing a gap at the closing edge and probably twisting as well. Narrow doors are sometimes made from the solid slab, but the precaution is taken of using perfectly seasoned timber and of polishing or varnishing both sides of the door to seal the grain.

It is safer to adopt what is known as the "framed-up" method of construction shown in Fig. 25. You see

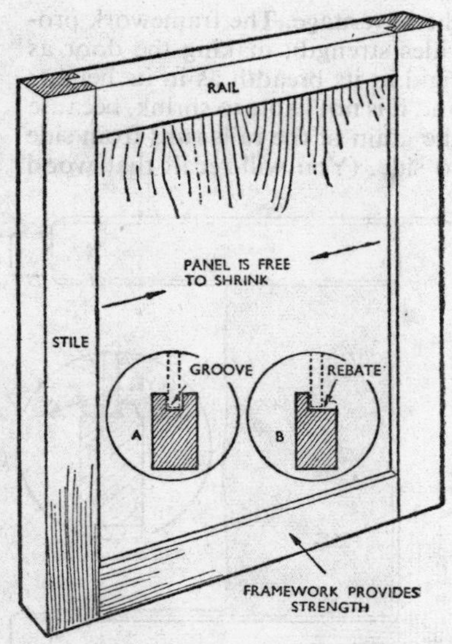

Fig. 25. *"Framed-up" construction for doors combines strength with absence of shrinkage. Inset, how panel is fitted.*

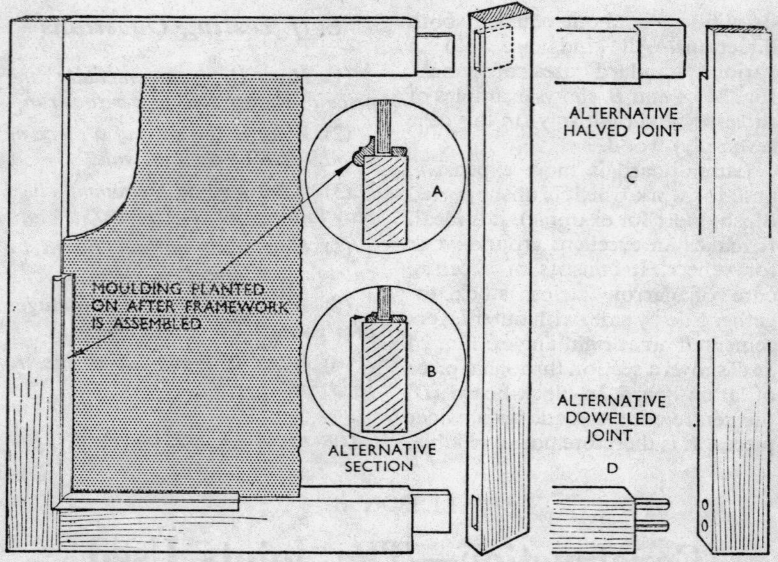

Fig. 26. *In this, the simplest form of door, a moulding is mitred round the inner edge of a plain framework, forming a rebate in which the edge of the panel fits.*

the advantage. The framework provides strength, making the door as rigid in its breadth as in its height; and it is not liable to shrink, because the grain of the rails runs from side to side. (You will recall that wood does not shrink in its length.) As for the panel: this fits in either a groove or a rebate (see Fig. 25, *A* and *B*), and, since it is not glued, it is free to shrink without affecting the door as a whole. Note that this

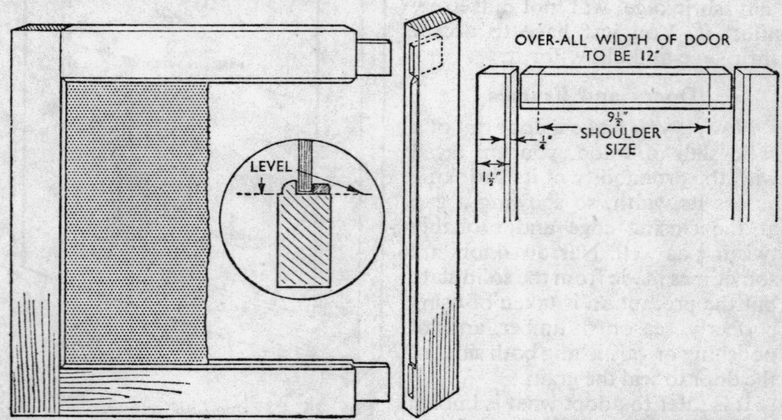

Fig. 27. *The moulding of a door may be made on the framework itself.* Inset, *how a flat surface is left after the moulding has been cut away to form the mitre.*

applies to all panelled work. Panels are never rigidly fixed with glue or nails. If they were they might split, since the glue would oppose any shrinkage.

Turn now to the way in which the framework is made. The method of securing the panel largely affects the type of joint used. Fig. 26 shows the simplest form of door. It consists of a plain framework with a moulding mitred around the inner edge, so forming a rebate in which the panel fits. Alternative sections are shown inset at *A* and *B*. A bead is nailed to the framework at the back of the panel, so holding the latter in position. Alternative joints for the framework are given at *C* and *D*. These are simpler, though not so satisfactory.

An excellent form of door is that in which the moulding is worked on the framework itself instead of being made separately and applied. It is shown in Fig. 27. Note how the bottom square of the moulding is made level with the rebate so that when the moulding is cut away to form the mitre a flat surface is formed (see inset). One important point to note when marking out the door is that the shoulder length is taken up to the rebate, not the overall width of the uprights. This is made clear to the right in Fig. 27.

If a door has a rebated-in panel but no moulding, the joint shown in Fig. 28 must be used. See how the back shoulders of the rails are longer than those at the front by the depth of the rebate. Incidentally, one of the advantages of the rebate as compared with the groove is that, since the panel is fixed after the framework is made, it can be polished separately, thus obtaining a much cleaner finish.

A door with grooved-in panel is given in Fig. 29. Note how a haunch is allowed at the outer edge of the tenon. This fills in the gap made by the groove in the stile and helps to prevent the wood from twisting away. One other point is that, since the groove necessarily

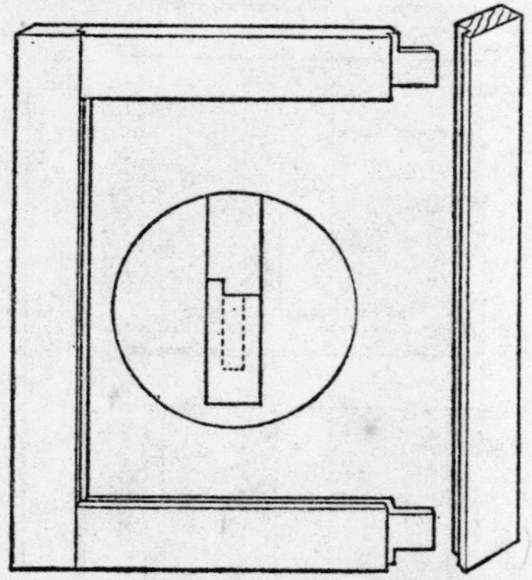

Fig. 28. *This joint is used for a door with rebated-in panel but no moulding.*

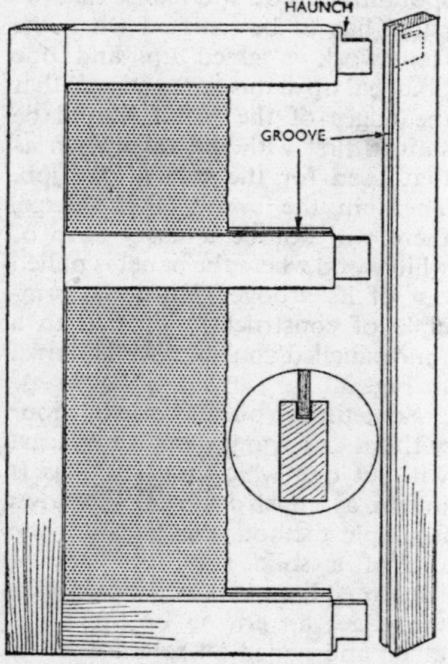

Fig. 29. *Door with grooved-in panel, inserted when the frame is glued up.*

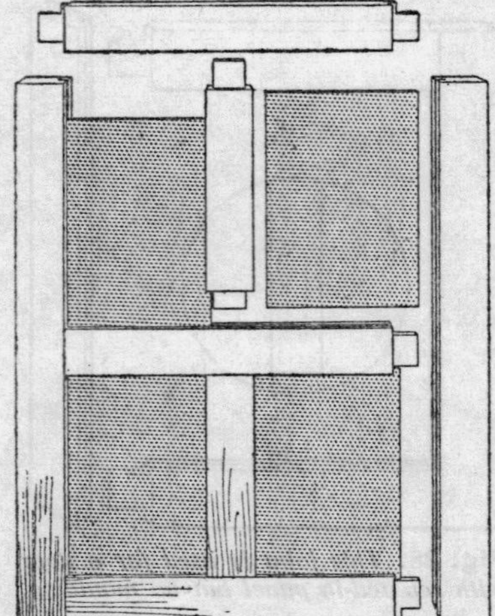

Fig. 30. *Exhibiting the principles of construction of a four-panelled door.*

cuts away the side of the tenons, reducing their width, the size of the mortises must be reduced correspondingly. You will realise that the panel has to be inserted when the framework is glued up, and one practical tip in this connection is that the edges of the panel should be stained first with the same stain as that used for the rest of the job. Then, in the event of shrinkage, there will not be a nasty strip of whitewood where the panel is pulled out of its groove. The same principle of construction applied to a four-panelled door or back is shown in Fig. 30.

Sometimes you may need a door without any framework, or at least without one which shows. This is known as a flush door. Fig. 31 shows a simple method which avoids the use of a solid slab. A piece of laminated board is used. To conceal the edges an edging or lipping is glued and nailed all round and the whole veneered over. The grain of the veneer is at right angles with that of the laminated board. Fig. 32 shows another method, in which a centre framework is made up with plywood glued on both sides.

Drawers and How to Make Them

Since one of the greatest stresses a drawer has to withstand is that of being pulled out, the joints must be of a kind that will stand the strain. The most satisfactory is the dovetail, because the wedge shape of this directly opposes the pull. Fig. 33 shows a drawer in which the sides are dovetailed to the front and back. The bottom is fitted in grooved slips glued to the sides at the bottom (see *B*). The advantage of this is that the slip increases the wearing surface of the bottom edges of the sides, and saves unduly weakening the sides by working the grooves directly in them. At the front, the bottom is grooved into the drawer front.

This involves certain peculiarities in the joints. For instance, at the

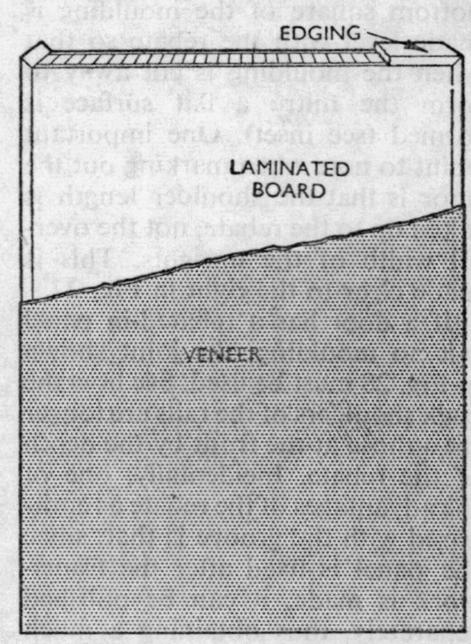

Fig. 31. *Employing veneered laminated board for an unframed or "flush" door avoids making use of a solid slab.*

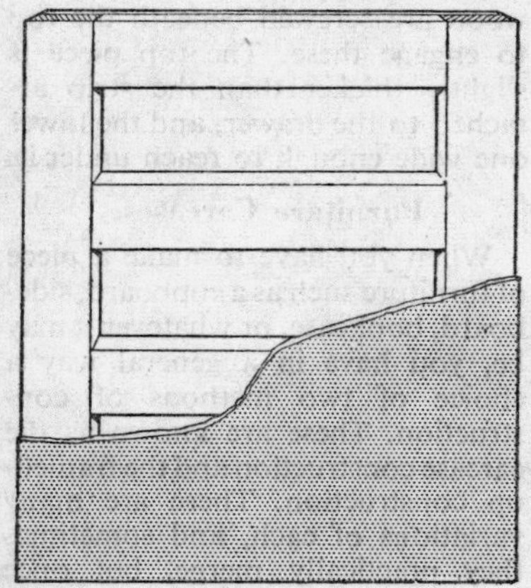

Fig. 32. *Centre framework of a flush door made up from glued plywood panels.*

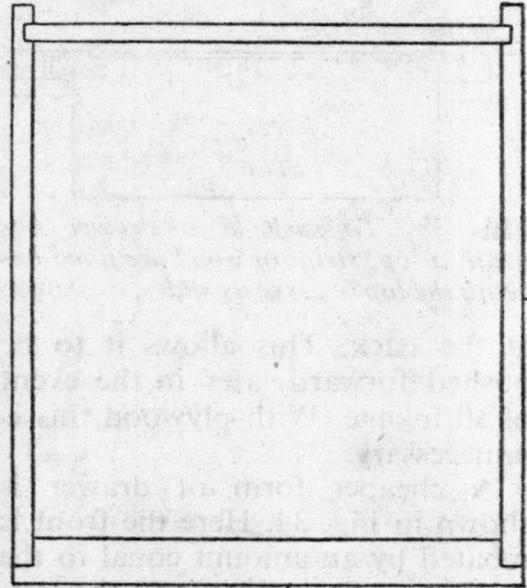

Fig. 34. *In this cheaper drawer the rebated front is fixed to the sides by glue and nails.*

front the bottom dovetail must be low enough to contain the groove within it (see *A*). Otherwise the groove will show at the ends. Note, too, that the dovetails are lapped so that they do not show at the front. Another feature is that the pins are narrow, this giving a neat appearance. So far as the back is concerned, the width of this extends from about ¼ in. beneath the top of the sides down to immediately above the bottom, the latter fitting under and being screwed to it. This is shown at *C*. If solid wood is used for the bottom, the grain should run from side to side and the bottom be allowed to project about ¼ in.

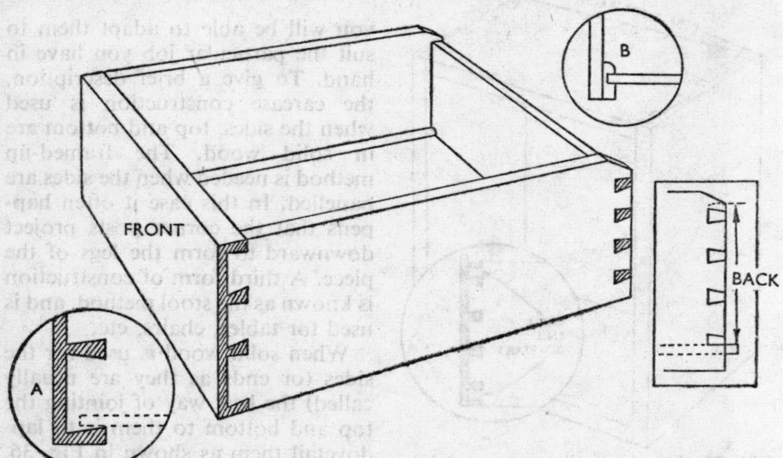

Fig. 33. *The sides of this drawer are dovetailed to the front and back, so that the joints directly oppose the opening pull. The bottom fits neatly in grooved slips.*

Fig. 35. *To suspend a drawer beneath a top, strips of wood are fixed beneath the top to serve as slides, as shown.*

at the back. This allows it to be pushed forward later in the event of shrinkage. With plywood this is unnecessary.

A cheaper form of drawer is shown in Fig. 34. Here the front is rebated by an amount equal to the thickness of the sides, and the last-named fixed with glue and nails. At the back the sides are grooved a little way in and the back is fitted in the grooves. The bottom is supported by grooved slips as before.

Sometimes it is required to suspend a drawer beneath a top. The simplest way of arranging this is shown in Fig. 35. Strips of wood are fixed to the outer surfaces of the sides along the top, and two pieces of wood are screwed beneath the top to engage these. The top piece is slightly thicker than the strip attached to the drawer, and the lower one wide enough to reach under it.

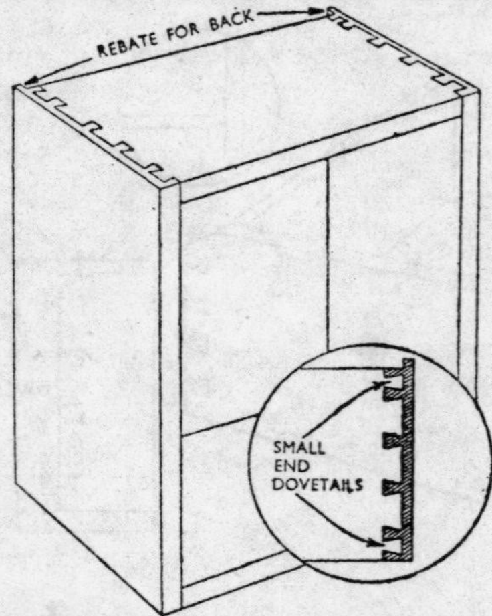

Fig. 36. *Lap-dovetailing prevents joints from showing at the sides or at the top in such articles as bookcases.*

Furniture Carcases

When you have to make a piece of furniture such as a cupboard, sideboard, bookcase, or whatever it may be, you have in a general way a choice of two methods of construction. These are known as the carcase construction and the framed-up construction. There are many variations of each, and sometimes they practically merge, but once you grasp the main principles of each

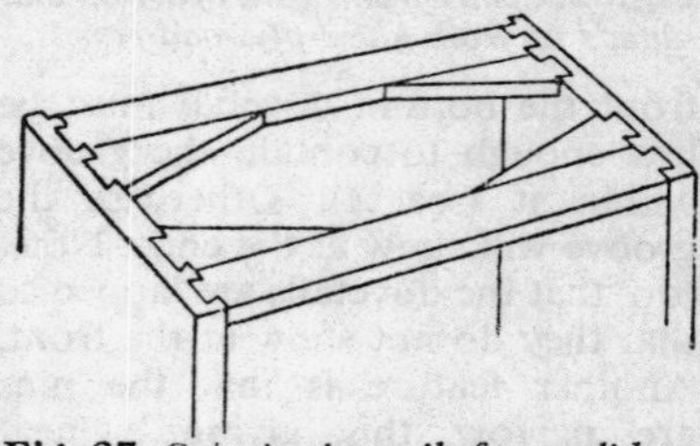

Fig. 37. *Substituting rails for a solid top in, say, a wardrobe economises material.*

you will be able to adapt them to suit the particular job you have in hand. To give a brief description, the carcase construction is used when the sides, top and bottom are in solid wood. The framed-up method is needed when the sides are panelled. In this case it often happens that the corner posts project downward to form the legs of the piece. A third form of construction is known as the stool method, and is used for tables, chairs, etc.

When solid wood is used for the sides (or ends as they are usually called) the best way of jointing the top and bottom to them is to lap-dovetail them as shown in Fig. 36. The advantage of this is that the joints are not visible at the sides; and, since there is always a separate top in addition, the dovetails cannot be seen from above. At the bottom they cannot be seen in any case. The inset drawing shows the setting out, and it will be seen that the dovetails at the ends are specially small. These prevent the sides from curling away in the event of the wood warping. One point to bear in mind is that the back invariably fits into rebates worked in the sides, but is screwed or nailed directly to the top and bottom. This means that the last-named are not so wide as the sides, but finish flush with the rebates.

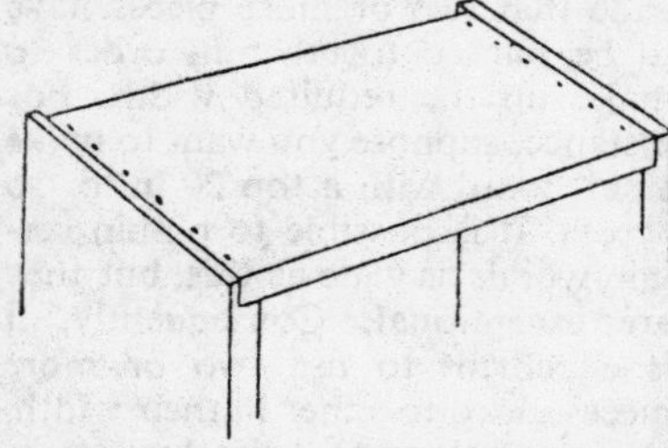

Fig. 38. *The lapped joint, fixed with glue and nails, serves for unpretentious work.*

It is possible to effect an economy in timber by substituting a couple of rails for the solid top as in Fig. 37. As these would leave the centre unsupported, however, triangular pieces of wood are glued first to the inner edges of the rails. These are then dovetailed in as a whole. The bottom, of course, would have to be a solid piece.

All of us at times want to do a quick job or make something of no great importance; the lapped joint shown in Fig. 38 can then be used. The parts are glued and nailed together. Such a joint would never be used in good-class work, but is handy on occasion.

An example of framed-up construction is given in Fig. 39. Suppose you have to make a simple cupboard with short legs and with doors at the front. The legs can conveniently run right through to the top and form part of the main construction. The rails are joined to the legs with mortise and tenon joints, the mortises meeting in the thickness of the wood and the tenons being cut off at an angle so that they

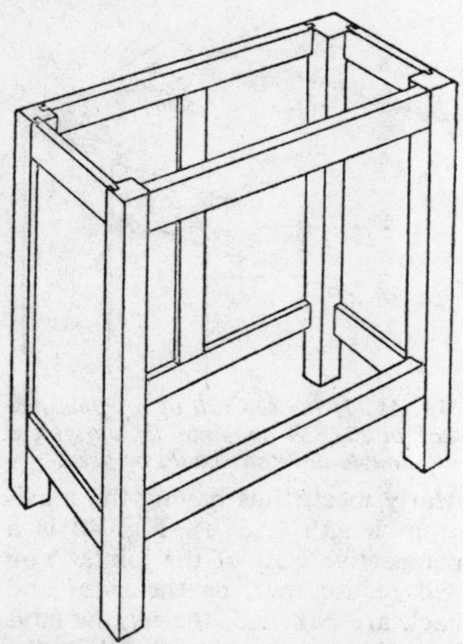

Fig. 39. *An example of "framed-up" construction, in which the legs run all the way through to the top of the frame.*

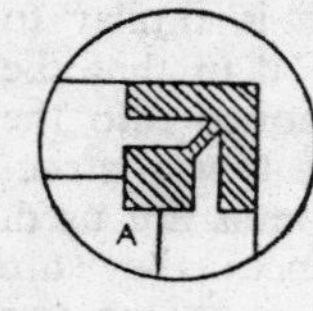

Fig. 40. *Perspective view of the joints of the frame shown in Fig. 39. Note the haunches in the top tenons.*

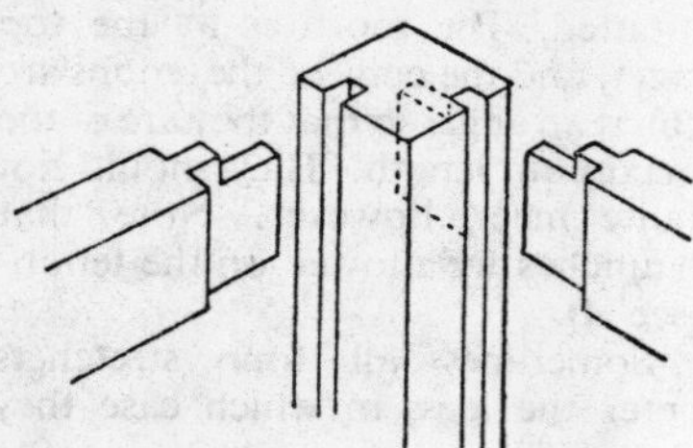

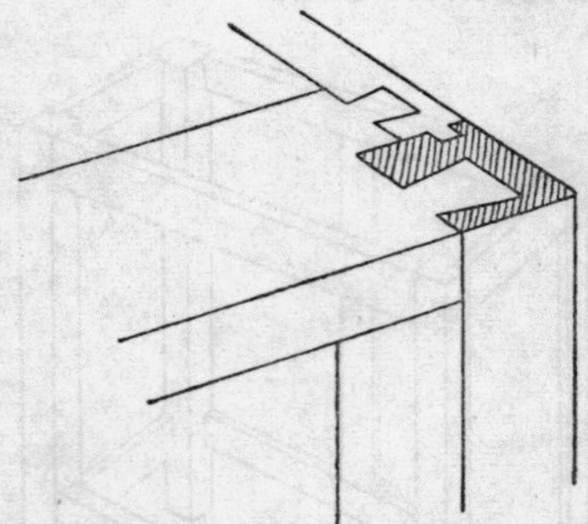

Fig. 41. *If the top rail of a frame like that in Fig. 39 does not lie upright, a double dovetail should be used.*

nearly meet, thus having the maximum length (see *A*). Fig. 40 is a perspective view of the joints. You will realise that, as the sides and back are panelled, the tenons have haunches at the top to fill in the gaps formed by the grooves. Just as the undersides of the top rails are grooved to hold the panels, so are the tenons automatically cut away. This means that the mortises must be reduced in length by a corresponding amount. Occasionally the top rail has to lie flat instead of standing upright, and in this case a double dovetail is used as shown in Fig. 41. This joint is cut *after* the side frames have been glued together.

Stool construction is similar to the framed-up method in that the various rails are tenoned into the legs. Fig. 42 shows a typical structure. Here stretcher rails are used, but in some instances they are omitted. The mortises at the top meet, and the ends of the tenons are cut at an angle so that they are of the maximum length. They should not quite meet, however. Note that haunches are allowed on the tenons (see *A*).

Sometimes all four stretchers enter the legs, in which case they are tenoned in. In the example given, only the end stretchers meet the legs. A centre stretcher running lengthwise is dovetailed to these. Note how the dovetail stops short at the top so that it cannot be seen from above. When you make a table like this, remember that the shoulder length of this rail must be longer than that of the top rails, because it has to reach right up to the side stretchers, which are set to the centre of the legs.

Tops, Panels, etc.

Under this heading we include all kinds of furniture parts which are so wide that two or more pieces have to be jointed together in order to make up the required width. For instance, suppose you want to make a sideboard with a top 20 in. or so across. It is possible to obtain certain woods as wide as this, but they are exceptional. Consequently, it is expedient to use two or more pieces glued together in their width. One point that immediately emerges is that for visible surfaces it is desirable to use pieces of wood similar in

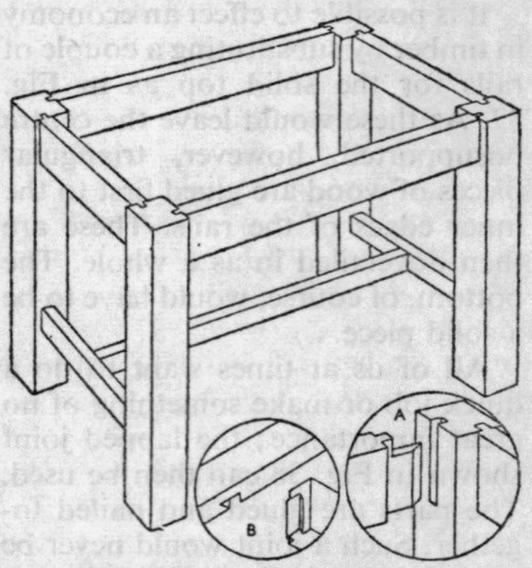

Fig. 42. *Construction of a stool fitted with stretcher rails. The tenons at the top, which may be haunched, are cut at an angle so as to be of maximum length.*

grain, because, although a well-made joint is scarcely visible in itself, the difference in the grain is bound to show up. This can be minimised by a careful matching of the wood.

Let us consider Fig. 43, which might be a top for a side-table. The simplest joint is known as the rubbed joint. The edges are planed to make a perfect fit, and the one piece fixed in the bench-vice. Both edges are glued, and the upper piece placed in position and rubbed back and forth with a steady downward pressure so that all surplus glue is squeezed out. When set, the surfaces are cleaned up and the ends

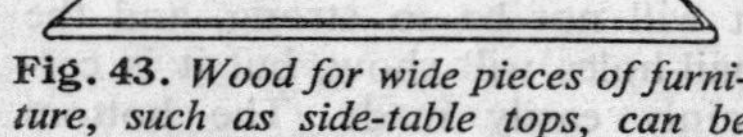

Fig. 43. *Wood for wide pieces of furniture, such as side-table tops, can be joined by the rubbed joint* (see *text*).

levelled. Any moulding at the edges is then worked. When using extra long pieces plane the joint a trifle hollow—say $\frac{1}{8}$ in. in 3 ft.—and put a couple of cramps across the whole towards the middle.

Rubbed joints of this kind are quite satisfactory for woods which hold the glue well, like mahogany, pine and walnut, and for work which is not subjected to any great strain. Sometimes, however, it is desirable to strengthen the joint, especially when the part is not supported in any way—the leaf of a gate-leg table, for example. One method is to use dowels as shown in Fig. 44. This has the advantage of simplicity and of being entirely invisible. Holes are bored at intervals on both edges and dowels are glued in. The inset at *A* shows how the holes are slightly countersunk to allow for any slight accumulation of glue at the base of the dowels. Note, too, that a saw-cut is made along the length of each dowel to enable the glue in the holes

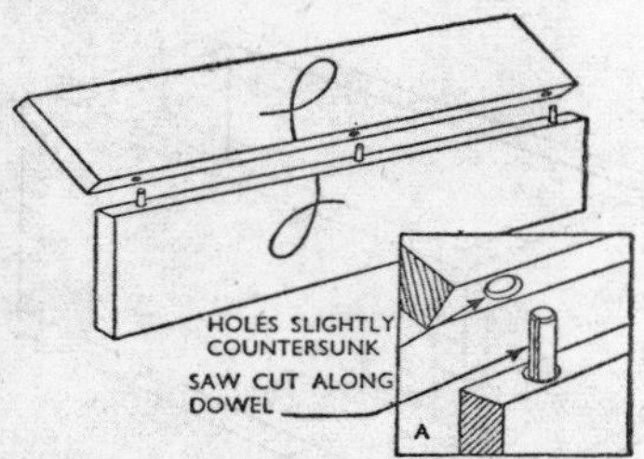

Fig. 44. *The use of dowels gives a stronger fixture than the rubbed joint. Care must be taken lest the glue, squeezed tight by the dowel, splits the wood.*

to escape when the dowels are knocked in. If this is not done the imprisoned glue may split the wood.

Another and stronger method is that in Fig. 45, in which both edges are grooved and a loose cross-grained tongue let in. This makes a very strong joint, but it has the disadvantage of showing at the ends. Sometimes this is not an objection, but it is inclined to disfigure any moulding that may be worked at the edges. Both this joint and the dowelled type need to be cramped when being glued up.

Boxes

Boxes may vary from small cigarette or trinket boxes to a large tool-chest. Dealing first with the former, observe that the way in which the corners are jointed depends on the design of the box itself.

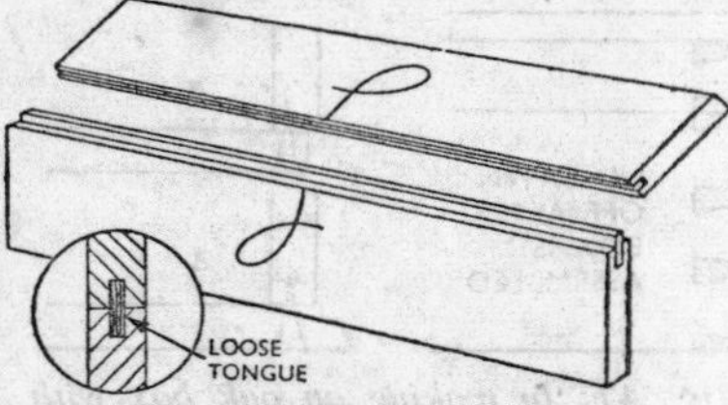

Fig. 45. *The joint here illustrated, made with a loose tongue let in grooves, is even stronger than the dowelled joint.*

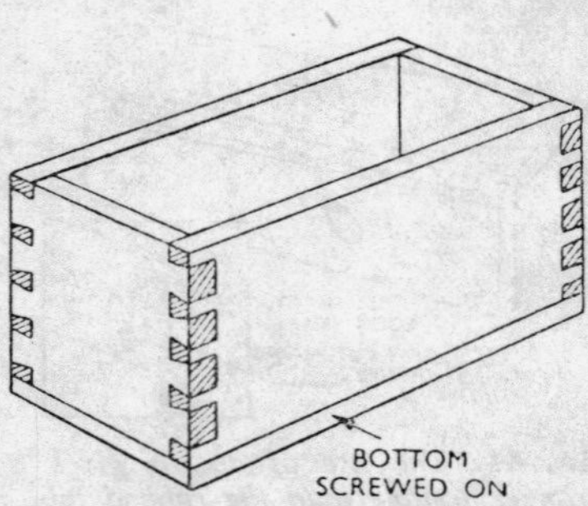

Fig. 46. *This through dovetail joint, though always visible, is a strong method of fixing the corners of boxes.*

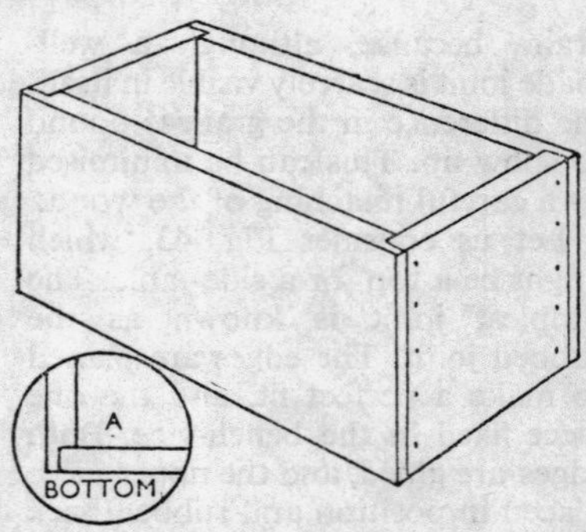

Fig. 48. *The lapped joint is handy though less strong than the dovetail.*

For instance, when there is no objection to the joints showing, the through dovetail in Fig. 46 is extremely strong and really looks very neat. In fact, a box made in oak is the better for candidly showing the joints which hold it together. If it has a lid with an edging, it is best to make the whole thing in one, and saw off the lid afterwards as shown in Fig. 47. A small dovetail must be arranged at the top, which will be entirely in the edging. Made in this way the edging is bound to fit the box exactly. Furthermore, the grain will match. As for the bottom, this can be fixed by one of the methods given in Fig. 47, *A* and *B*. *A* is slightly recessed, while *B* is moulded.

If you want to make a box without going to the trouble of dovetailing, you will find the lapped joint in Fig. 48 handy. Naturally it will not be so strong, and the nail-holes will show, but it is certainly easily made. The bottom can be fixed by either of the methods shown in Fig. 47, or, if it is to be concealed, it can be screwed or nailed in a rebate as in Fig. 48, *A*. In this case make the rebate in line with those of the sides which form the lapped joints.

Veneering is popular nowadays. Take particular care in the joints you select, because, owing to shrinkage, the line of the joints is liable to show right through the veneer in course of

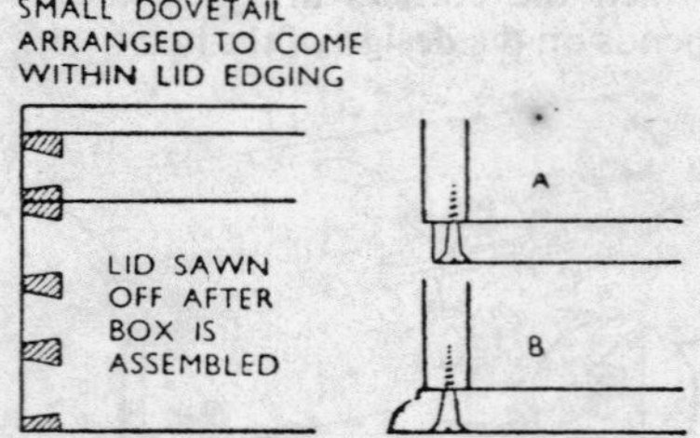

Fig. 47. *In making an oak box with edged lid, it is best to construct the whole at once, sawing off the lid afterwards.* (Right) A, *recessed;* B, *moulded.*

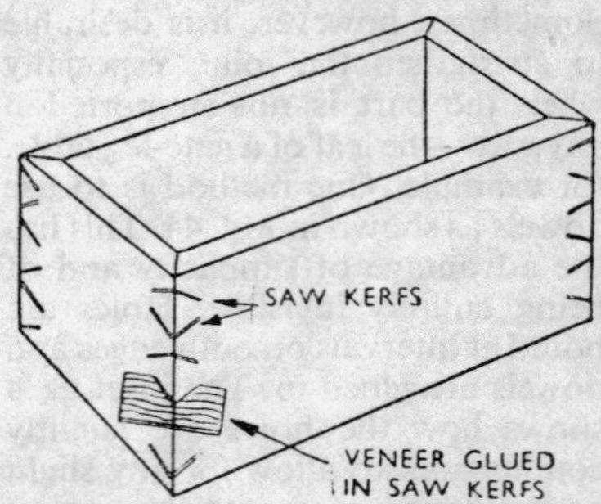

Fig. 49. *This illustrates the method of preparing a box for veneering. The corners should always be veneered and levelled down before the sides.*

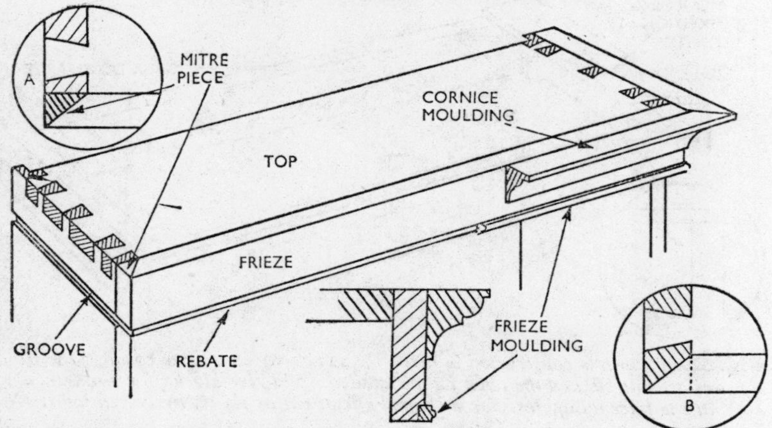

Fig. 50. *How the frieze is fixed along the front of a fixed cornice. To prevent the end-grain showing, a mitre piece is fixed at the ends, as at* A.

time. A satisfactory method is given in Fig. 49. You mitre the corners and glue up the whole thing, using string and wedges to draw the joints closely together. When the glue has set you make cuts with a tenon saw right across the corners in dovetail fashion, and in each kerf you glue in a little slip of thick veneer. After levelling down you can safely veneer over the sides.

Cornices and Plinths

Large boxes, such as chests of various kinds, should always be dovetailed, because there is considerable strain and the dovetail is easily the strongest joint.

Cornices are of two kinds, fixed and loose. Generally the latter is the more satisfactory, but it depends on the particular design. Fig. 50 shows an example of the fixed kind, and here it should be noted that the way in which the frieze is fixed depends on whether the doors are in front of the cabinet sides or are contained between them. In the former case it is obvious that the frieze must be fixed on the face of the cabinet top so that it lines up with the doors. In the event of the doors being con-

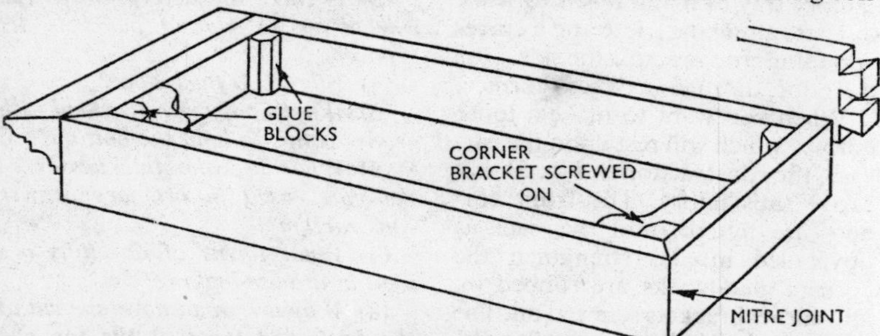

Fig. 51. *Construction of a loose cornice. The front corners are mitred, and the back dovetailed in. The moulding should be mitred as with a fixed cornice.*

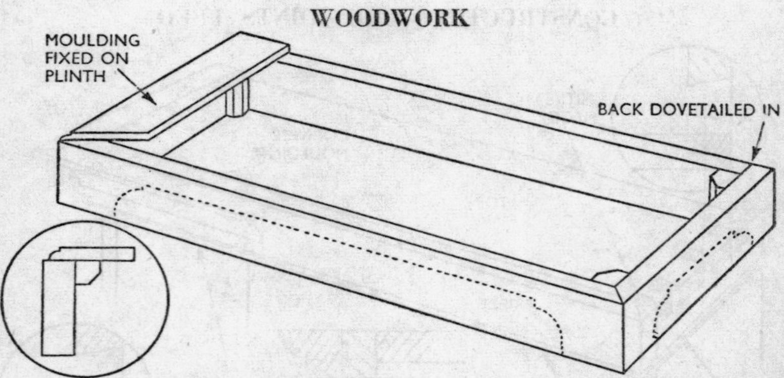

Fig. 52. *A plinth is constructed in much the same way as a loose cornice: the front corners are mitred, and the back lap-dovetailed. Add glue-blocks for strengthening at the internal angles. For a shaped effect, cut as shown by dotted lines.*

tained between the sides, the cabinet top is recessed by an amount equal to the frieze thickness and the sides mitred as shown at *B*, Fig. 50. Otherwise, the construction is much the same.

Fig. 50 shows how the frieze is fixed along the front of the top. You will realise, however, that unless special provision is made the end-grain would show badly at the ends. This difficulty is overcome by fixing a mitre piece at the ends, as shown enlarged at *A*. The cornice moulding itself is mitred round and is glued in position. Generally a frieze moulding is required at the bottom edge, and the most satisfactory way of fixing this is to work a rebate along the frieze and a corresponding groove across the sides. *B* is a section through a typical cornice.

When you want to make a loose cornice which will rest upon the carcase, the construction in Fig. 51 will prove satisfactory. The front corners are mitred, and the back is dovetailed in. To strengthen the corners glue-blocks are rubbed in, and corner brackets screwed on. The moulding is mitred round as before.

In many ways a plinth is similar to a loose cornice. Fig. 52 shows how the front corners are mitred and the back ones lap-dovetailed. Glue-blocks should certainly be added at the internal angles. The moulding, it will be observed, is mitred round on top, and glue-blocks rubbed in beneath make a strong job. If a shaped effect is required, the same construction is followed, the shape being cut as shown by dotted lines before the whole is put together.

Self Testing Questions

(1) *What joints are used for the framework of a panelled door?*

(2) *How is a door-panel held in its framework?*

(3) *Is there any exception to the rule never to glue a panel in its groove?*

(4) *What is a flush door?*

(5) *Why is a drawer provided with grooved slips to hold the bottom?*

(6) *What are the thicknesses of the parts used in ordinary drawer construction?*

(7) *What forms of dovetails are used in drawer-making?*

(8) *Why are small dovetails cut at the back and front of the top and bottom of a carcase?*

(9) *How does the grooving of the rails and posts of a framed-up job affect the mortise and tenon joints?*

(10) *What are the approximate sizes of timbers used in the parts of a dining-table?*

(11) *Are the stretchers of a table purely for decorative purposes?*

(12) *Why is a long joint usually planed slightly hollow?*

(13) *What size of dowel would you use for a* $\frac{3}{4}$*-in. or* 1*-in. top?*

(14) *Should a loose tongue fit tightly?*

(15) *Have any special precautions to be taken when making a dovetailed box the lid of which has an edging?*

(16) *Why should the rebate for the bottom of a lap-jointed box line up with the rebate of the joints?*

(17) *Why is it advisable to avoid dovetails when making a box to be veneered?*

(18) *Why are mitre pieces needed at the ends of a frieze which stands out from the sides?*

(19) *How is a loose cornice held in position?*

(20) *How would you fix a loose plinth?*

THE ANSWERS ARE ON PAGES 178–9.

LESSON 4

In the Workshop

You can either buy your timber in the rough—that is, straight from the saw—or you can get it machine-planed. In the former case you are giving yourself a lot of work, though you will save something in cost. Apart from the saving in work, machine-planed timber has the advantage that it is brought to an even thickness. At the same time, the show or outer surface will have to be hand-planed to produce a really good finish. It is wise to buy machine-planed timber.

Cleaning Up Timber

Since machine-planing exerts a certain amount of pressure on the wood, it is advisable to damp the surface before planing, as this releases the stresses. Otherwise marks are liable to show through later when the work is stained. When dry, the surface can be cleaned up with the smoothing plane. First, however, it should be cut to size and trimmed. Plane the front edge straight and square, using a long plane—a trying plane if you have one, or, failing this, a jack plane—and put a mark against it as in Fig. 53. Now plane one end perfectly square with it, chiselling off the back corner to prevent the grain from splitting out. The finished length is next squared across and this end trimmed to the line. Finally the width is marked parallel with the front and this planed.

When planing the surface set the plane fine with the back iron $\frac{1}{32}$ in.

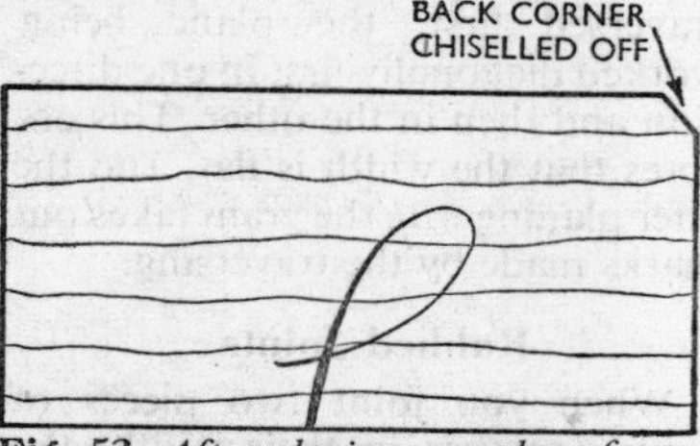

Fig. 53. *After planing one edge of your timber with a trying plane, mark it thus.*

or less from the cutting edge, and go over the whole surface *with* the grain. Examination of the edge will generally reveal the best direction in which to work, though many woods are apt to tear out in parts, however the plane is used. These tears and inequalities must be taken out afterwards with the scraper. Finally a thorough scouring with glass-paper wrapped around the cork rubber is given—first a medium, then a fine grade. Always work *with* the grain.

Particular care must be taken when you clean up parts which have been glued up, such as door-frames,

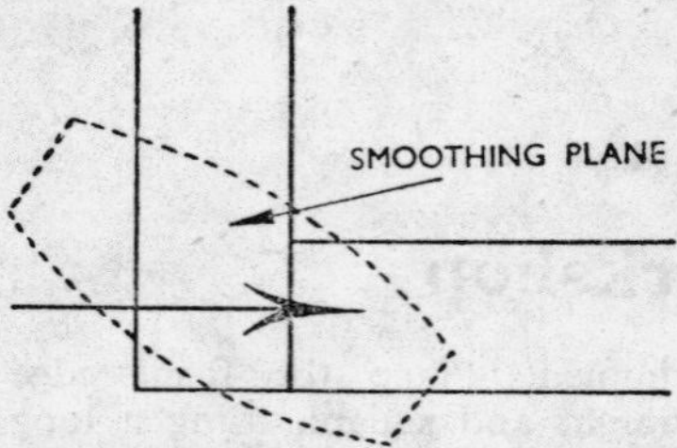

Fig. 54. *When cleaning up glued parts, first work across the joint thus.*

because the plane has to be taken partly across the grain. First work across the joint as shown in Fig. 54, with the plane held at an angle so that it takes a slicing cut. When level, work the plane in the direction shown in Fig. 55. Glass-papering is done in the same way.

In the case of a wide surface which has been jointed up—a table-top, for example—the surface should be traversed first, the plane being worked diagonally first in one direction and then in the other. This ensures that the width is flat, and the later planing *with* the grain takes out marks made by the traversing.

Rubbed Joints

When you joint two pieces of wood together in their width, the edges must be in close contact

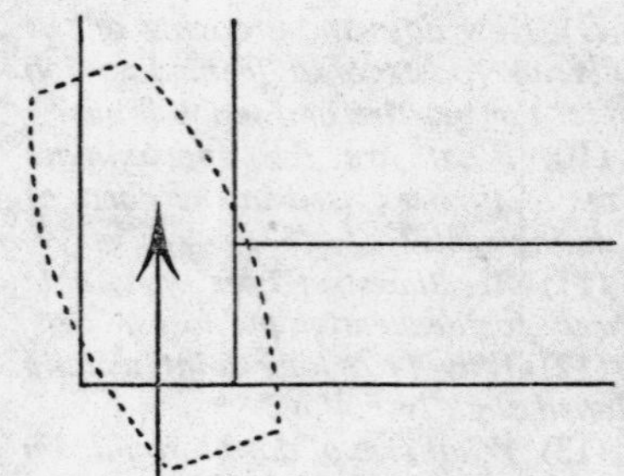

Fig. 55. *After levelling the glued joint, work the plane along as here shown.*

throughout their length—at any rate when the joint is fairly short. Longer joints can be a trifle hollow and have cramps put on near the middle. When treating the joint, put one piece in the vice and, setting the plane fine, plane the middle until the plane fails to remove any more shavings. Then take one or two shavings right through. Treat the other piece in the same way and try them together. If the plane is fairly long, a perfect joint should result. A test is to swivel the two ends back and forth. If the joint is round, it will

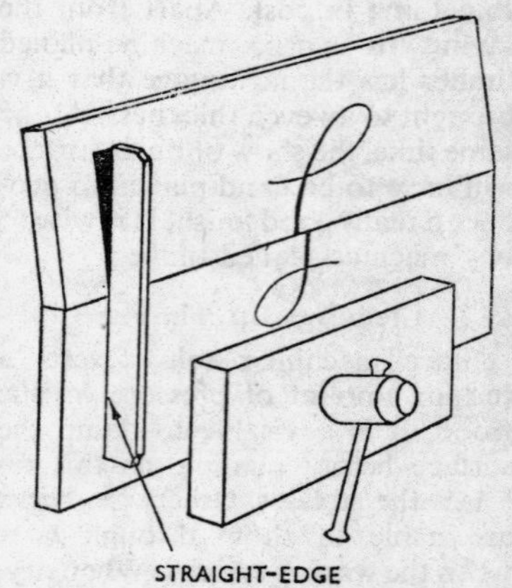

Fig. 56. *Use the straight-edge to test alignment of two pieces of wood joined widthwise. Look at light through joint.*

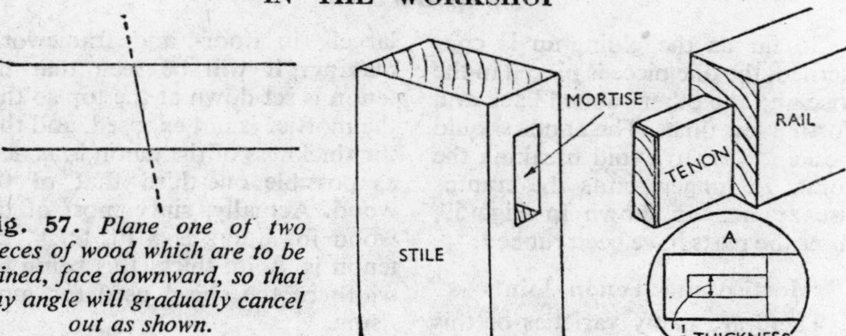

Fig. 57. *Plane one of two pieces of wood which are to be joined, face downward, so that any angle will gradually cancel out as shown.*

pivot easily at the middle and is faulty. You can tell when the centre is too hollow by looking through the joint towards the light. It is, of course, necessary for the two pieces to be in alignment, and this is tested by holding a straight-edge across the two pieces as in Fig. 56.

When the wood is too thin to be planed in the vice, the shooting-board is used. To ensure the parts being in alignment, one piece is

Figs. 59 and 60. *Simple form of mortise and tenon joint, used for doors and frameworks. The tenon is $\frac{1}{3}$ the thickness of the piece of wood.*

planed with the face side uppermost, and the other with the face side downward. The reason for this is that if the shooting-board or plane is not quite square the angles of the two will cancel each other out, as shown in Fig. 57.

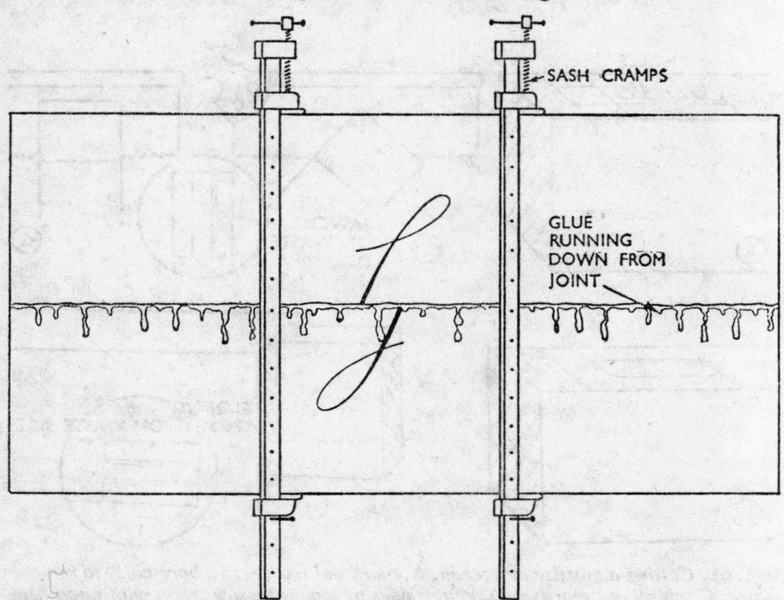

Fig. 58. *When you want to glue up two lengthy pieces of wood such as these, the cramps should be applied thus after the parts have been well rubbed.*

So far as the gluing-up is concerned, the one piece is placed in the vice and the other rubbed back and forth a few times. The hands should be kept low, to avoid breaking the joint. In longer joints the cramps are applied as shown in Fig. 59, after the parts have been rubbed.

Mortise and Tenon Joints

There are many varieties of this joint, but the principle of cutting is much the same for all. That shown in Fig. 60 is a simple form used largely in door- and framework-making. It will be seen that the tenon is set down at the top so that the mortise is not exposed, and that the thickness of the tenon is as near as possible one-third that of the wood. Actually, since most of the wood for doors is $\frac{7}{8}$ in. thick, the tenon is $\frac{5}{16}$ in. thick, this being the width of the chisel used for mortising.

Taking first the stile (the piece to be mortised), the marking-out is shown at *A*, Fig. 61. You will see

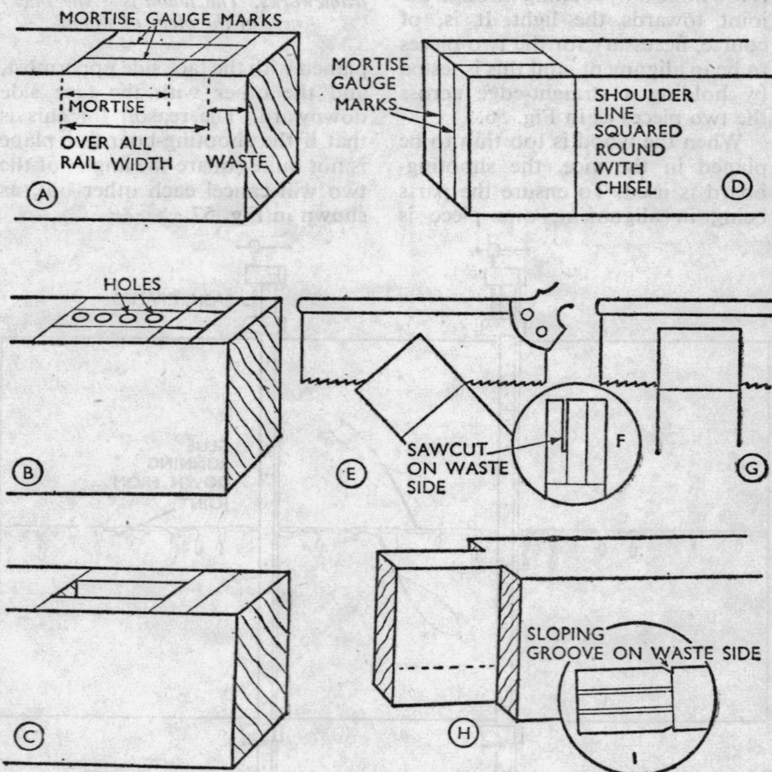

Fig. 61. *Cutting a mortise and tenon.* A, *mark out mortise;* B, *bore holes to remove waste;* C, *chisel out mortise;* D, *gauge sides of tenon;* E, *saw tenon with wood held in bench vice at an angle;* G, *reverse wood upright and saw down to shoulder line to finish off;* H, *cut in the tenon as shown by dotted line. See also Figs.* 59 *and* 60.

that the whole mortise is set in from the end, so that the wood is not liable to split when being chopped. The over-all width is squared across with pencil and a third line added showing the mortise length. It should be noted that when two or more pieces have to be mortised in the same positions, as in a door, the parts are cramped together and the marks squared across. The pins of the mortise gauge are next set to the chisel width, and the fence arranged so that the marks are central. The gauge is used always from the face side for both stile and rail.

When you cut the mortise, cramp the wood over a solid part of the bench, and bore several holes as at *B*, using a bit slightly smaller than the mortise width. This removes much of the waste. Now start the chisel at about the centre and strike it with the mallet. Work gradually towards one end, and then reverse it and work to the other end. The waste can be largely levered away with a smaller chisel. A piece of paper stuck to the mortise chisel will serve as a guide in working to the required depth.

Now for the tenon. Square round the shoulder lines with the chisel, keeping the butt always against either the face side or face edge. The sides of the tenon are then gauged as at *D*. When you saw the tenon, hold the wood in the bench-vice at an angle as at *E*, as this exposes two surfaces and enables you to keep to the line. Hold the saw on the waste side as at *F*, so that the lines are just left in. Finish off by reversing the wood (upright) as at *G* and sawing down to the shoulder line. Before you saw the shoulders cut a sloping groove with the chisel as at *I* to form a channel in which the saw can run.

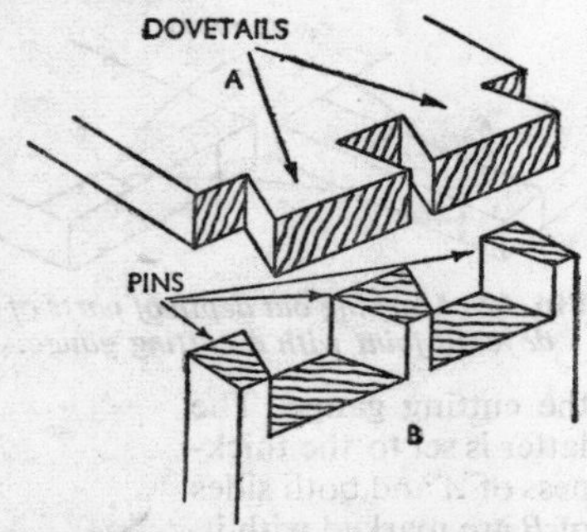

Fig. 62. *Example of through dovetail joint: dovetails in* A, *pins in* B. *The two pieces are often of the same thickness.*

It now remains to cut in the tenon as shown by the dotted line at *H*. Hold the tenon over the mortise and mark it with the pencil. When fitting, test the tenon length by noting the mortise depth with the pencil and trying against the tenon. The joint should make a hand-tight fit, and should fit straight from the saw. It is as well to take off the end edges of the tenon as in Fig. 60.

Dovetail Joints

The method of cutting dovetail joints is much the same for all types. It is only in detail that they vary. For instance, in the lapped dovetail a lap has to be allowed on the pins, but this merely necessitates setting the gauge accordingly and chopping down only to the gauge-line. The example we have chosen is a through dovetail (Fig. 62), and it will be seen that the one piece, *A*, has the dovetails, and the other, *B*, the pins. Frequently the two pieces are the same thickness, but we have shown *A* thinner than *B* in order to make clear the principle.

Your first job is to plane the ends of both perfectly square. Now, since they have to fit flush when assembled, the depth of the parts can be marked out conveniently with

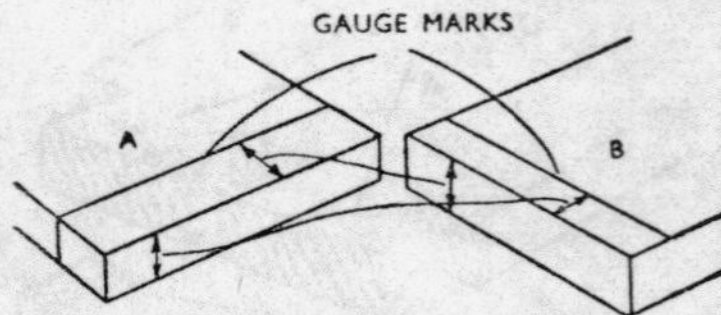

Fig. 63. *Marking out depth of parts of a dovetail joint with a cutting gauge.*

the cutting gauge. The latter is set to the thickness of *A* and both sides of *B* are marked with it. *A* is then marked similarly with the gauge set to the thickness of *B* as shown in Fig. 63. Note that the gauge is taken also round the edges of *A*, but not of *B*.

You will have to take care to keep the dovetails at the correct slope, because, if the angle is too great, the sides may chip off; if too small, the joint will not hold well. Fig. 64 shows how to mark the best angle. Measure 3 in. along one side of a right angle and ⅝ in. along the other. A line joining the marks gives the slope. A good plan is to make a template as shown inset at *X*, the edges being planed at the required angle. The small projecting piece at the top bears along the top edge of the work. Fig. 64 shows the spacing. When they are pencilled in, the lines can be sawn.

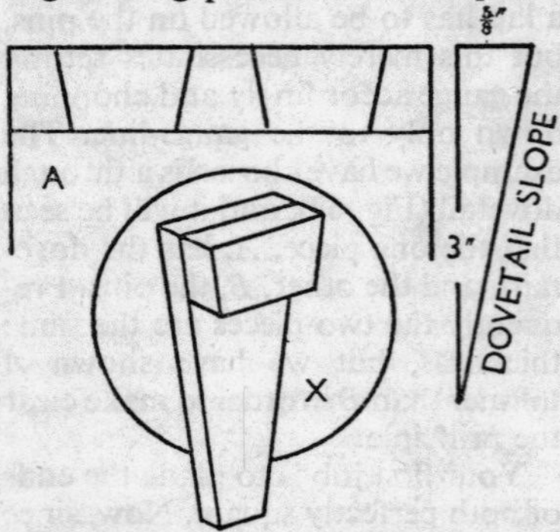

Fig. 64. *Illustrates method, explained in text, of marking angles for a dovetail joint. Drawing shows the correct spacing.*

To transfer the marks to piece *B*, place the latter in the bench-vice and hold *A* upon it so that it is flush all round (Fig. 65). Place the saw in each

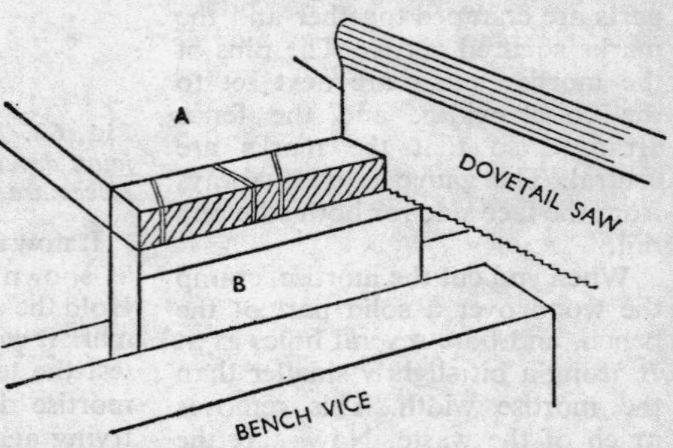

Fig. 65. *How the dovetail marks are transferred from one of the pieces of wood to be joined to the other.*

kerf in turn and draw it backward with a downward pressure. This will make marks on the edge which are an exact replica of the dovetails. If, however, the saw were placed exactly on these when cutting the pins, the joint would make a loose fit. It is therefore held *on the waste side* as shown in Fig. 66 (dotted lines). The cuts are made down square.

The waste pieces of both are removed by chopping with the chisel, half-way through from each side. Cramp the wood down on the bench

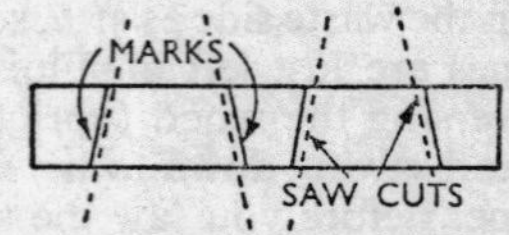

Fig. 66. *When cutting dovetail pins, the saw is held on the waste side of the marks, thus avoiding a loose joint.*

and cut a little sloping groove at the gauge-line where the waste is to be chopped as given inset in Fig. 67. Holding the chisel about $\frac{1}{16}$ in. from the gauge-line, chop downward, striking the chisel smartly with the mallet. The second cut is made horizontally *with* the grain. Do not try to reach the full depth with one cut. When practically down hold the chisel right on the gauge-line in the little groove already cut. In Fig. 67 the left-hand cut is short of the gauge-line. It is taken right up to it in the right-hand cut. Now reverse

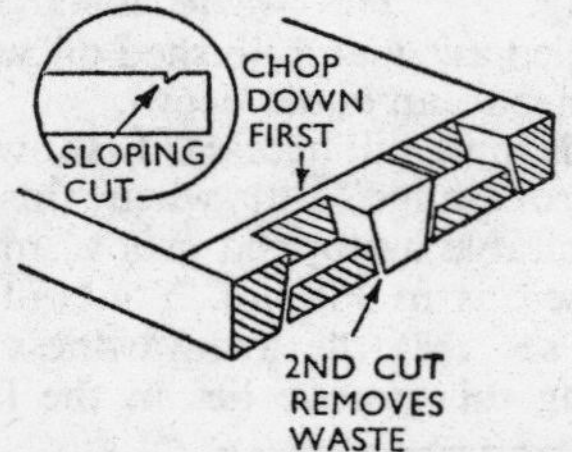

Fig. 67. *Method of removing waste from dovetail cuts. A sloping groove is first cut, as shown in the inset.*

the work and repeat the process so that the waste is removed entirely.

Dovetails should not be tried together before gluing, because this loosens them. They should fit straight from the saw; hence the necessity for careful cutting. Matters can be helped by taking off the lower edges of the dovetails where they will be concealed when assembled, as this helps to start them when being knocked together. Never strike the dovetails directly with the hammer when gluing-up, because this is liable to bruise them. Instead, place a piece of waste wood over them and strike this.

Lapped Joints

These angle joints are mainly used in making boxes and in less important carcase work. They are not

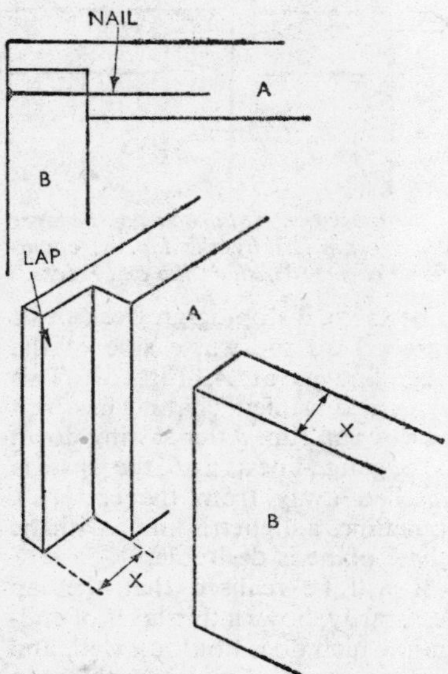

Fig. 68. *A lapped joint, as shown here, must be nailed as well as glued. The nails must be driven in the direction shown here, or they will grip badly.*

first class for any purpose, but they are handy on occasion. The lapped joint shown in Fig. 68 is the stronger of the two, but has the disadvantage that it must be nailed as well as glued. Note the direction in which the nails are driven. If they were put in the other way and punched in they would pass almost entirely through the lap of piece *A* and would have but little grip.

To cut the rebate which forms the lap of piece *A*, set the cutting gauge to the thickness of *B* and mark across the face of *A* (see *XX*). The thickness of the lap is also gauged at the edge. Since the cross-grain has

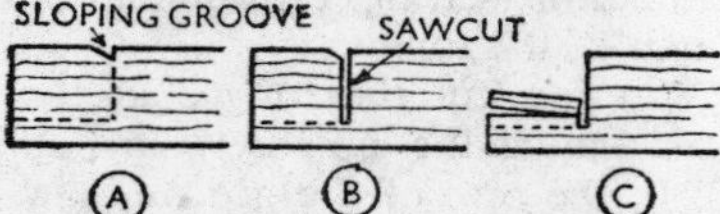

Fig. 69. *Method of cutting the rebate for the lap of piece* A, *Fig.* 68 (*see text*).

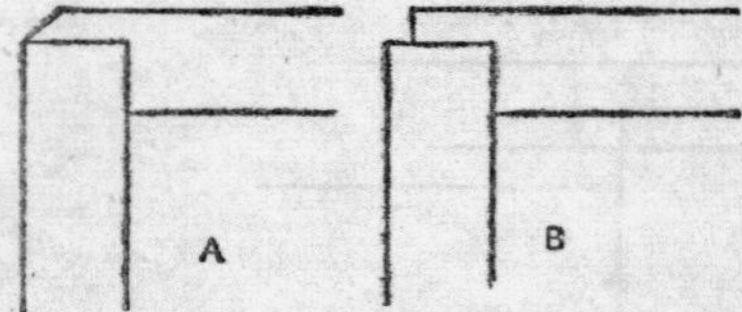

Fig. 70. *Two ways of disguising the layer of end-grain left by the lap.* A, *chamfered corner;* B, *short lap and recess.*

to be sawn, a sloping groove can be chiselled on the waste side of the gauge-line as at *A*, Fig. 69. This forms a convenient channel in which the saw can run. After sawing down to the gauge-line as at *B*, the waste is chiselled away from the end (*C*). Sometimes a slight trimming with the rebate plane is desirable.

It will be realised that the lap necessarily shows a thin layer of end-grain which does not look well, and two ways of disguising this are shown in Fig. 70. At *A* the corner is chamfered so that the joint is scarcely noticeable. At *B* the lap is short, giving a square recess.

Grooved Joints

Although the grooved joint in Fig. 71 does not need nailing, it shows a wide edge of end-grain, and the groove creates a narrow strip of cross-grain which is weak, being liable to crumble. Having squared the edges, the cutting gauge is set to the thickness of *B* and the face of piece *A* marked with it (see *YY*). It is then re-set to allow the thickness of the tongue, and both pieces marked as at *XX*. The depth of the groove is also gauged, and the outer surface of *B* marked with the gauge at the same setting, thus giving the length of the tongue.

You can cut the tongue in the same way as the lap shown in Fig. 68. In the case of the groove, saw both sides to depth and remove the waste with a narrow chisel.

When you have to fix shelves in a carcase or put in partitions, the housed joint is generally the simplest joint. A groove, the thickness of which equals the thickness of the shelf, is cut across the side of the carcase. The joint should make a hand-tight fit. The sides of the groove are sawn down as far as a gauge-line. It is a good plan to square across the marks with a chisel so that sloping channels can be chiselled on the waste side, thus forming convenient grooves in which the saw can run as shown inset in Fig. 73. The waste is largely chiselled away and finished off with a router to an equal depth.

This joint will necessarily show at the front edge, and when this is undesirable a stopped groove must be used as in Fig. 74. You will at once see that the awkwardness of cutting this groove lies in the fact

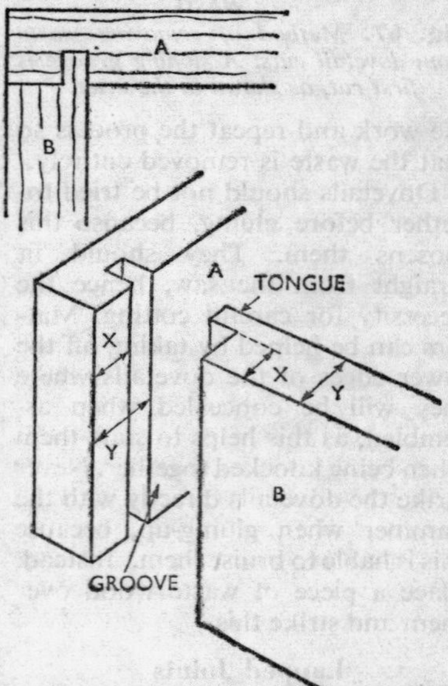

Fig. 71. *A grooved joint of this type needs no nails, but the strip of cross-grain is weak and liable to crumble.*

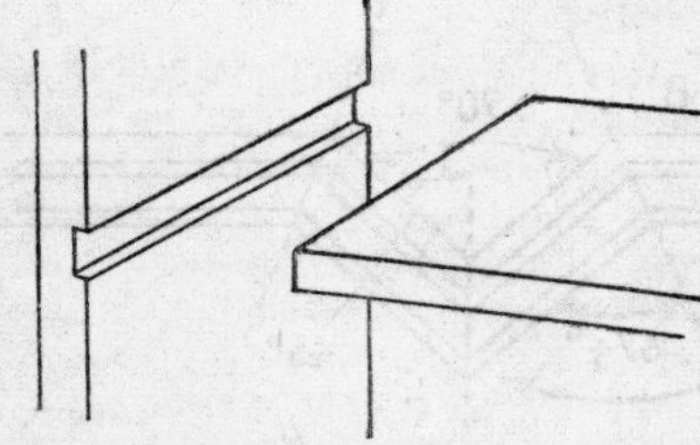

Fig. 72. *In this through groove the saw can be taken right across the wood.*

that the saw cannot be taken right across as in the through groove shown in Fig. 72. To get out of the difficulty a recess is chopped out with the chisel immediately next to the stop (Fig. 75). This allows the saw to run out at the recess, and so be worked back and forth in short strokes. When the sides have been

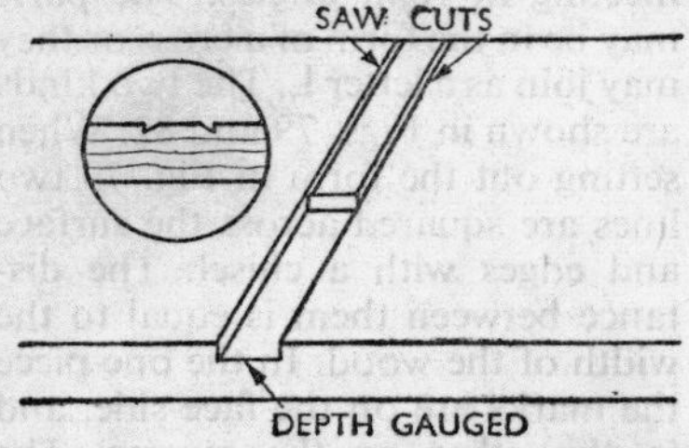

Fig. 73. *Channels for the saw-cuts can be chiselled as shown here on the waste side of a housed joint marking.*

sawn the waste is removed as before. The corner of the shelf, of course, has to be cut back as shown in Fig. 74, so that it will fit around the stop.

Mitred Joint

Bear in mind one rule and you will never go far wrong with the setting out of a mitred joint: the mitreing angle is always one-half that of the complete angle formed by the parts being mitred. Since most parts join at right angles, it follows that most mitreing angles are at 45 degrees; hence the fact that mitre-blocks and other mitreing appliances are made to cut at this angle. You will grasp the principle from a study of Fig. 76. At *A* the mouldings meet at right angles, and consequently are mitred at 45 degrees. The same thing applies at *C*. At *B*, however, the meeting angle is 90 degrees plus 45 degrees—that is, 135 degrees. The mitreing angle is therefore 67½ degrees. The same principle applies at *D*, the two angles being 60 and 30 degrees.

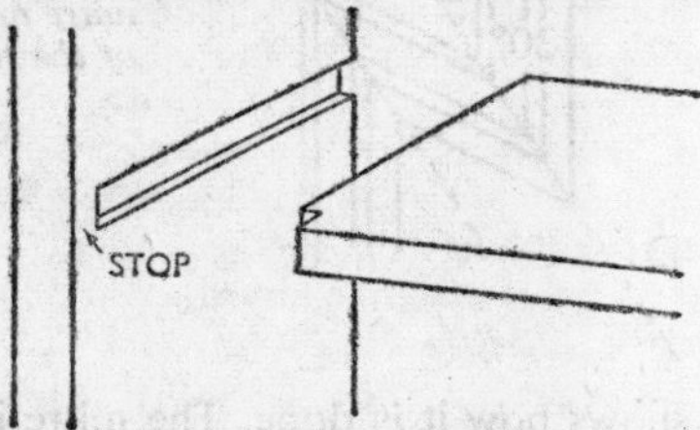

Fig. 74. *A stopped groove, made as above, will prevent a housed joint from being visible at the front.*

Turning now to the practical cutting: use the mitre-block for small mouldings, etc., and the mitre-box for large ones. If necessary, the joint can be trimmed afterwards on the mitre shooting-board. This applies to all work mitred in its width as in Fig. 77. A different procedure is necessary when the work is mitred in its thickness as in Fig. 78, because it would be too wide to be sawn in the mitre-box. Fig. 78

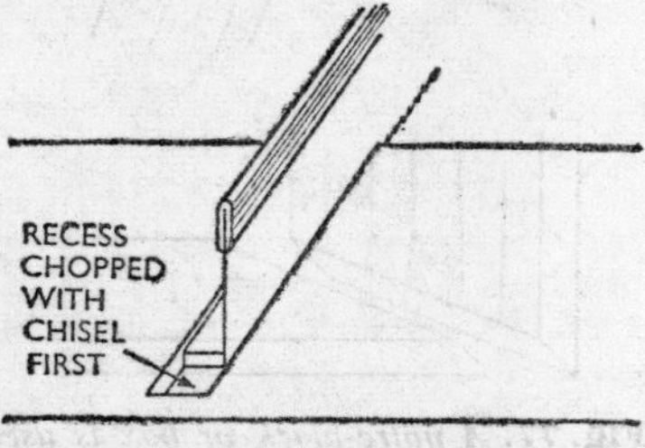

Fig. 75. *Chop out a recess for the saw before cutting a housed joint groove.*

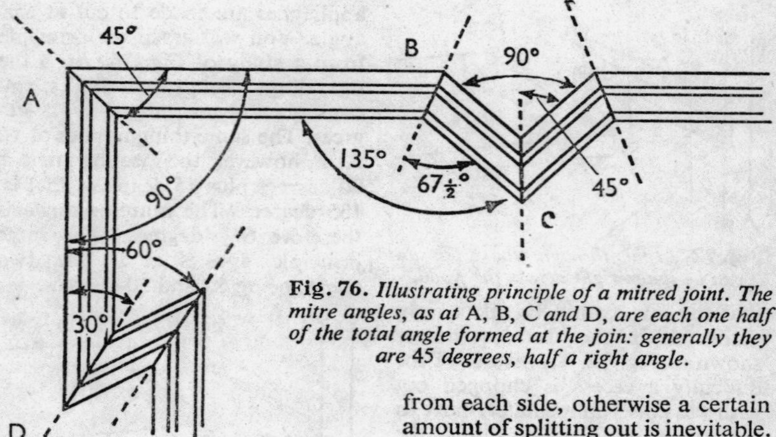

Fig. 76. *Illustrating principle of a mitred joint. The mitre angles, as at* A, B, C *and* D, *are each one half of the total angle formed at the join: generally they are* 45 *degrees, half a right angle.*

shows how it is done. The mitre is marked at both ends, and the work placed so that it overhangs the bench slightly, as in Fig. 78. The far corner is then chiselled away down to the mitre-line, so that the plane can be used without the corner splitting out. Before the complete depth is planed, however, the plane should be taken half-way through from each side, otherwise a certain amount of splitting out is inevitable.

Halved and Dowelled Joints

The halved joint is used for pieces meeting at right angles. The parts may be in the form of a cross or they may join as a letter L. The two kinds are shown in Figs. 79 and 82. When setting out the form in Fig. 79 two lines are squared across the surface and edges with a chisel. The distance between them is equal to the width of the wood. In the one piece the marks are on the face side, and in the other on the reverse. The depth of the groove is marked with

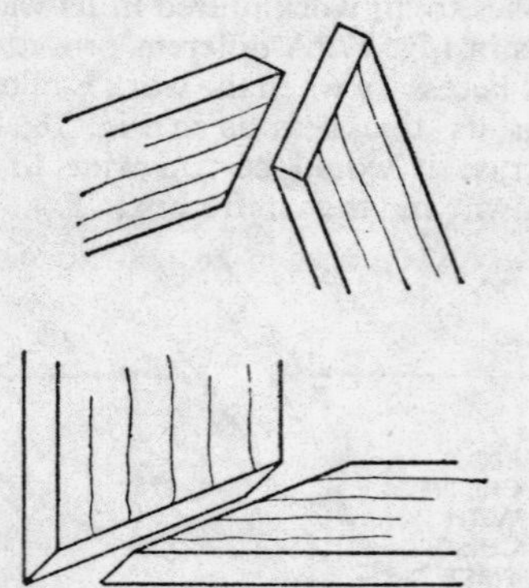

Fig. 77. *A mitre-block or box is used for work mitred in its width* (above); *for work mitred in its thickness* (below) *the procedure of Fig.* 78 *is followed.*

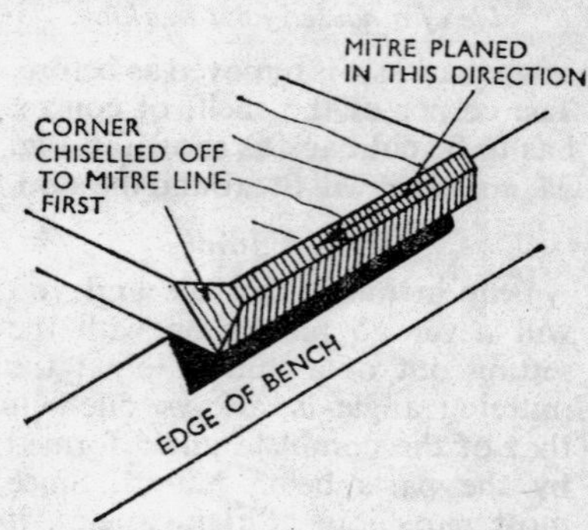

Fig. 78. *How mitres are cut in the thickness of a work-piece: for explanation see text.*

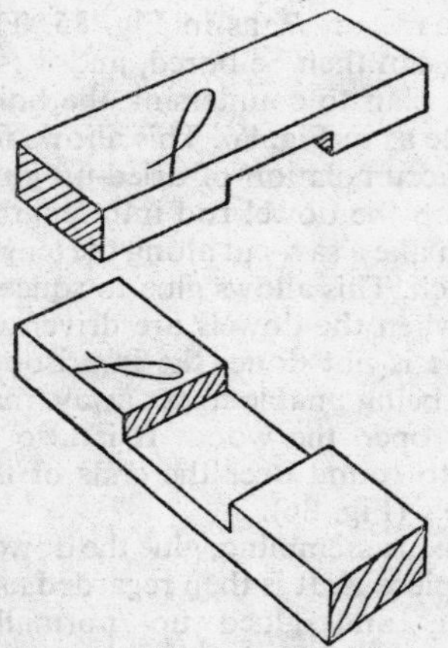

Fig. 79. *Halved joints are of two kinds: one, as above, gives the form of a cross.*

the gauge, this being used from the face side in both cases. Sloping grooves are cut on the waste side as shown in Fig. 80, to provide channels in which the saw can run. Saw carefully down the sides, taking care to stop the saw at the gauge-line. The waste is chiselled away half from each side. Fig. 81 shows the first side cut. The parts should make a hand-tight fit.

When parts have to join together in the form of an L, the depth is gauged at the end and both sides (from face side in both cases). The waste can either be entirely sawn similarly to a tenon, or the cross-grain can be sawn and the wood

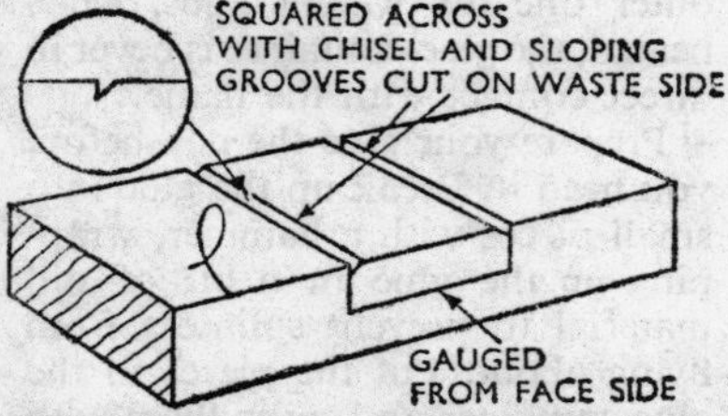

Fig. 80. *For the cross-shaped halved-joint, sloping grooves are cut on the waste side in which the saw can run.*

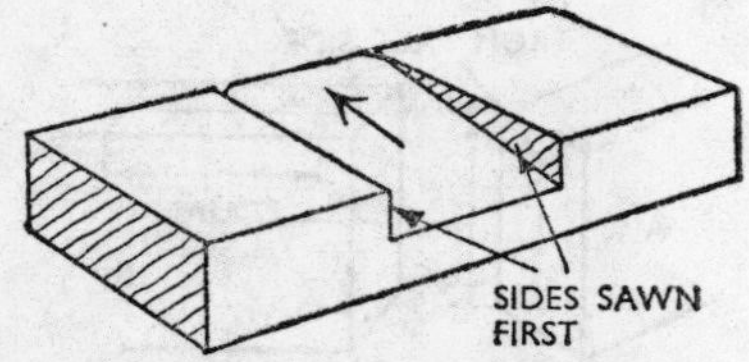

Fig. 81. *A halved-joint cross groove after it has been chiselled from one side.*

then chiselled away. If the saw is used, the gauge-line should just be left in. It will be realised that the ends should be trimmed square first. These joints are usually screwed as well as glued, as shown in Fig. 82. Note that the screws remain visible.

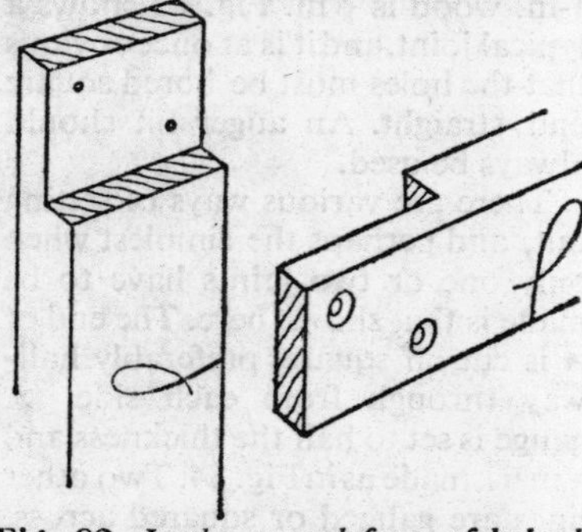

Fig. 82. *In the second form of halved joint the two pieces are L-shaped, as above.*

The dowel joint is often used in place of the mortise and tenon joint in expensive work, though it has its more legitimate uses as well. At least two dowels should be used to each

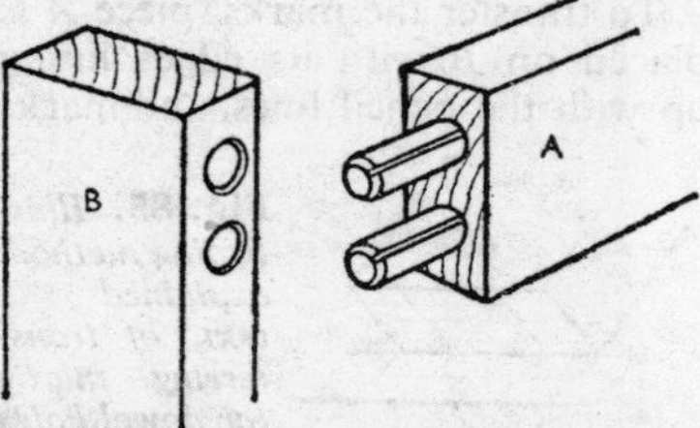

Fig. 83. *The dowel joint should have at least two dowels, to prevent twisting; the holes must be bored square and straight.*

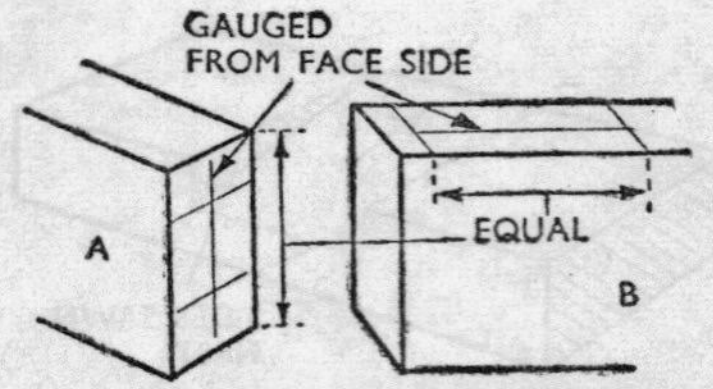

Fig. 84. *Setting out a dowel joint. The dowels come at the intersections of the marked lines on* A.

joint to prevent any twisting tendency, though they should not be crowded unduly, as this makes the wood between them likely to crumble, so weakening the joint. The usual size of dowel for $\frac{7}{8}$-in. or 1-in. wood is $\frac{3}{8}$ in. Fig. 83 shows a typical joint, and it is at once obvious that the holes must be bored square and straight. An auger bit should always be used.

There are various ways of setting out, and perhaps the simplest when only one or two joints have to be made is that shown here. The end of *A* is cut off square, preferably halfway through from each side. A gauge is set to half the thickness and a mark made as in Fig. 84. Two other lines are gauged or squared across, the intersections being the positions of the dowels. In the case of piece *B*, two lines representing the width of *A* are squared across (see Fig. 84) and a gauge-mark made between them from the face side, with the gauge at the same setting as before.

To transfer the marks, piece *A* is placed on *B* with its edges lining up with the pencil lines, and marks are made on *B*, as in Fig. 85. The holes can then be bored, and it is a good plan to countersink the holes a trifle as in Fig. 86. This allows for any accumulation of dried-up glue. Cut up the dowel rod into lengths, and make a saw-cut along the length of each. This allows glue to squeeze out when the dowels are driven in. If this is not done, the imprisoned glue, being unable to get away, may burst open the wood. It is also as well to round over the ends of the dowels (Fig. 86).

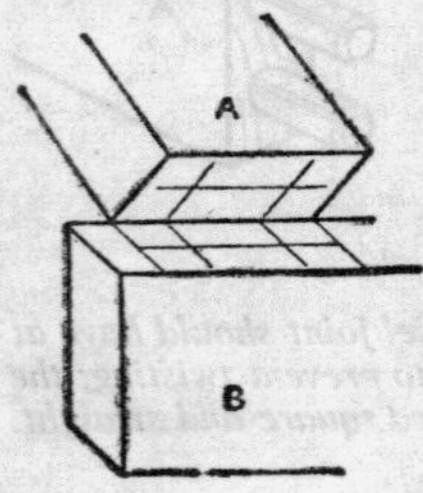

Fig. 85. *Illustrating method, explained in text, of transferring marks for dowel holes from one piece to the other.*

When assembling, glue the dowels into piece *A*. It is then regarded as a tenon, and glued up normally. Make sure that the dowels are not too long for the holes. Both holes and dowels should be glued.

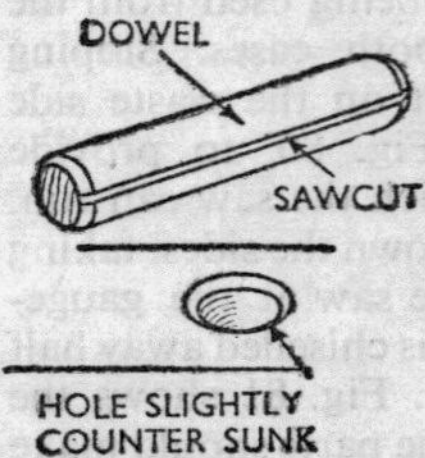

Fig. 86. *Dowel holes* (below) *should be slightly countersunk and dowel edges rounded over; dowels* (above) *need a saw-cut to allow for escaping glue.*

There are various kinds of glue nowadays, but Scotch glue largely remains the favourite, and if properly used it has tremendous strength. It is obtained in flat cakes and is sold by the pound. A glue-kettle is necessary, this having an inner container for the glue and an outer one for water. Thus, when heated, the glue-container is never in direct contact with the flame.

Prepare your glue the day before you need it. Break up the glue into small pieces with a hammer, wrapping up the glue in a bit of old material to prevent splinters from flying about. Put the pieces in the glue-container and cover them with water, leaving them overnight. The next day half-fill the outer container and heat it. The glue will have settled into a mass below the water and it should be stirred with a stick. When thoroughly mixed (and this can only happen when hot) dip in the brush and raise it a few inches from the pot. The glue should run down in an even, unbroken stream without lumps. Lumpiness usually indicates that the glue is too thick. Too thin a glue breaks up into drops. The latter can be corrected by continuing the heating. When finished with, the brush should be removed and washed out in hot water.

One of the reasons for heating the glue (apart from liquefying it) is that it enables it to run into the pores of the wood and so form innumerable little "dovetails." It is obvious then that, if applied to a piece of cold wood, the glue will at once be chilled, and will lose a high percentage of its strength. You see the remedy; always heat the joints before using the glue. It gives time for the parts to be assembled before the glue chills. One precaution is that you must not hold the joints too near a flame, as the edges, shoulders, etc., may be singed and given an unsightly black mark.

Casein Glue

Another form of glue is casein glue, which is used cold. No heating of joints is required for this. It is in the form of a powder which is mixed with water, the exact amount depending on the make. Instructions are supplied by the manufacturers. Sufficient for the work in hand only is made up, because after so many hours it becomes useless. As this glue is of an alkaline nature, a reaction is set up with the acid contained in some hardwoods—oak, mahogany, walnut, and so on. This turns the wood dark, and it is therefore advisable to avoid it for these woods. A non-staining casein is obtainable, but this is not waterproof, like ordinary casein (in any case a certain amount of staining is inevitable). For softwoods casein can be used freely, as no staining takes place.

Certain joints do not need cramping, but when they are used everything should be prepared in advance

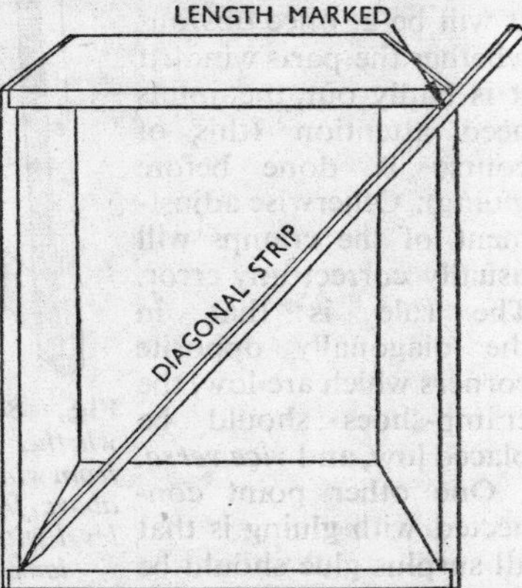

Fig. 87. *For testing squareness of work a diagonal strip should be placed from corner to corner across each diagonal.*

so that the gluing process can be carried out quickly. Cramps should be opened the right amount, blocks to put beneath the shoes should be prepared, and the square and other testing apparatus got ready. This enables the whole job to be gone through without delay.

Testing the work is important. For a small item such as a box the bench-square is suitable, but for larger items a diagonal strip is more satisfactory. This is a thin strip of wood sharpened to a flat point at one end. It is used as shown in Fig. 87. It is placed diagonally across the job and the length marked with a pencil. When put into the opposite corners it will show the same length if square. The same method can be used for large doors, etc.

A second test is that of whether the work is free from winding. For instance, in Fig. 88 the door may be square, but the opposite parts are out of alignment. To test for this, hold the work level with the eye and look across it. It will be at once obvious whether the parts wind. If it is badly out, the joints need attention (this of course is done before gluing). Otherwise adjustment of the cramps will usually correct any error. The rule is that in the diagonally opposite corners which are low, the cramp-shoes should be placed low, and *vice versa*.

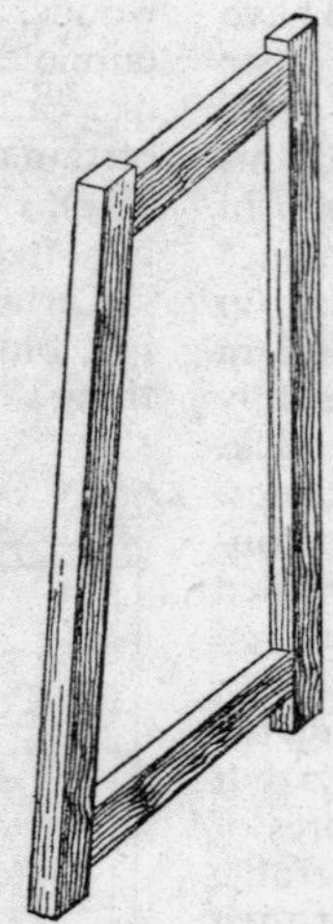

Fig. 88. *To test whether work is free from winding, as is the above frame, hold it level with the eye and look across it.*

One other point connected with gluing is that all surplus glue should be removed before it hardens. It can mostly be washed off with the glue-brush dipped into clean hot water. Sometimes scraping with the chisel is necessary. Five minutes spent at this stage may save an hour's work later.

Self Testing Questions

(1) *If you buy unplaned wood how would you proceed to bring it to an even thickness?*

(2) *How can you remove tears left by the plane?*

(3) *If a joint is out of alignment how would you correct it when planing?*

(4) *How long should a glued joint be allowed to set?*

(5) *What determines the exact thickness of the tenon?*

(6) *Why should a tenon not fit very tightly?*

(7) *Why must the mortise gauge be used from the face side in both mortise and tenon?*

(8) *What is the purpose of the sloping cut made at the gauge-line before chopping dovetails?*

(9) *What is the angle for the slope of dovetails?*

(10) *Why must the lapped joint be nailed as well as glued?*

(11) *Why is the tongue in Fig.* 71 *comparatively narrow?*

(12) *How are shelves fixed in the housed joint?*

(13) *If two mouldings meet at an angle of* 70 *deg., what is the mitreing angle?*

(14) *Is there any general rule to be observed when sawing the mitres of a moulding to avoid a rough edge?*

(15) *Why is the saw held on the waste side when sawing a halved joint?*

(16) *If one part of a joint is set in from the other, how do you allow for this when marking out?*

(17) *Can you assemble a rubbed joint with casein glue without cramps?*

(18) *Would you glue up the whole framework of, say, a table in one operation?*

(19) *What is the object of heating a joint before assembling?*

THE ANSWERS ARE ON PAGE 179

LESSON 5

Fitting Metal-Work

THE type of hinge most commonly used in furniture-making is the butt-hinge. This requires to be let into the wood so that it is flush. There are various ways of doing this, but the simplest from the beginner's point of view is that shown in Fig. 89. Note that the pin or centre of the knuckle projects to the extent of half its thickness and enables the door to open to the extent of 180 deg.

Two gauges are handy when marking out, because it saves re-setting, but they are not essential. Set the first gauge as shown at *A*, Fig. 90, so that the marker points to the centre of the knuckle. The second one is set as shown at *B*. Never set it to the thickness of the flange or leaf. It is the centre of the knuckle that counts. Fix the door in the bench-vice and decide the position of the hinge. Its own length from the end is a general indication. Mark the length and square pencil lines across as in Fig. 91. You can then make gauge-marks between the lines.

To cut the recesses make a saw-cut at each end, holding the saw at an angle. Two or three additional saw-cuts are made to cut up the grain as in Fig. 92. Stop the saw short of the gauge-marks. With a keen chisel cut vertically down the sides and back (Fig. 93), and then pare away the waste wood evenly. Fix the hinge with two screws only.

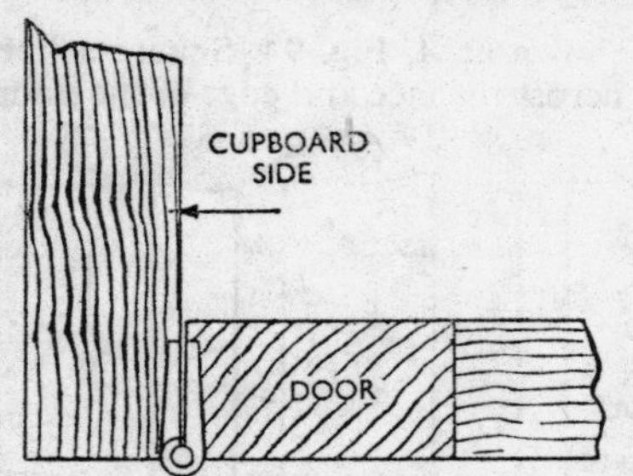

Fig. 89. *This is the simplest way of letting in a butt-hinge, the hinge most commonly used in furniture-making.*

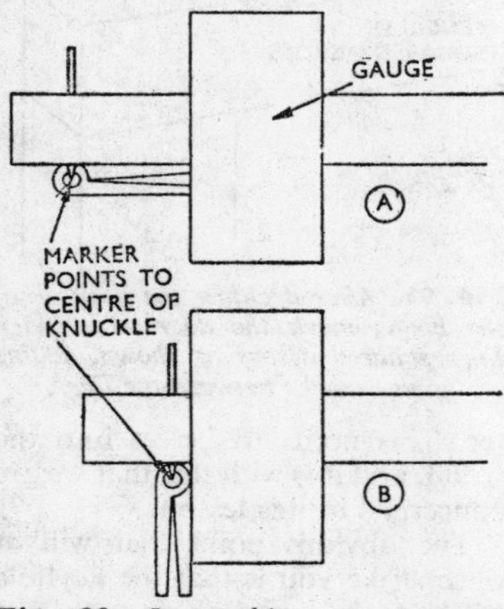

Fig. 90. *In marking out, use two gauges, setting one as at* A, *the second as at* B, *the markers in each case pointing to the centre of the knuckles.*

You now have to find the position of the recesses to be cut in the cupboard side. Place the door in the position it is to occupy, and make a mark at each side of the hinge with a marking awl. Remove the door and square in the marks with the pencil. It is then merely a matter of repeating the process. Use a single screw to each hinge and test the door to see that it opens satisfactorily. Make any necessary adjustments and drive in the remaining screws.

A lock may be needed for a drawer or a door (in the latter case for one which closes right- or left-hand), and it is necessary to state which when ordering, because the keyhole is another way round in the one case. For simple work the screw-on type is used, but in the best furniture the flush-lock is better. This needs to be let into the wood, and it is with this that we are concerned in this lesson.

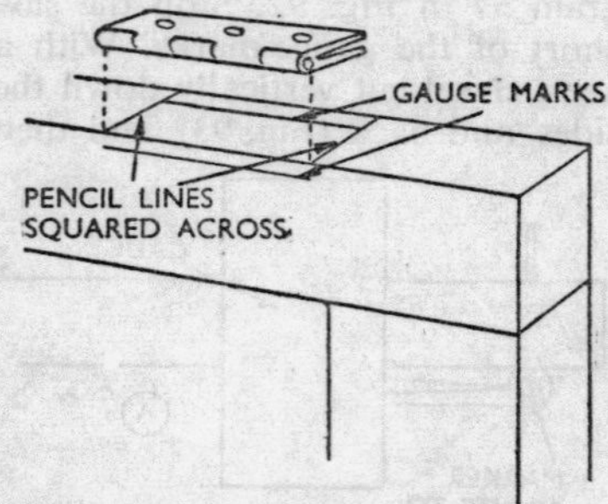

Fig. 91. *After deciding the position of the hinge, mark the door with pencil lines squared across as shown, adding gauge-marks between the lines.*

The obvious point that will at once strike you is that the keyhole in the lock must line up with that cut in the wood. Since the keyhole is invariably in the centre of the door or drawer, this is cut first, and the recess for the body of the lock made afterwards. The example chosen is a door lock. It is to be fitted to the left-hand side of the door.

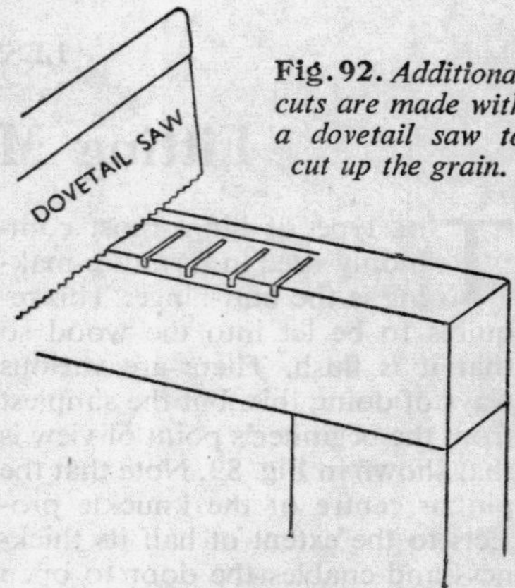

Fig. 92. *Additional cuts are made with a dovetail saw to cut up the grain.*

Set a gauge so that the marker points to the centre of the pin (this is in the middle of the keyhole) as

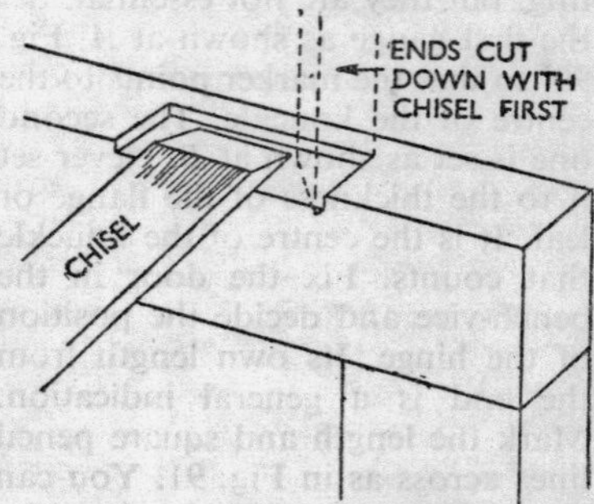

Fig. 93. *The sides and back of the recess are cut down with a chisel, and the waste is pared away evenly.*

shown at *A*, Fig. 94. Square a line across the face and edge of the door

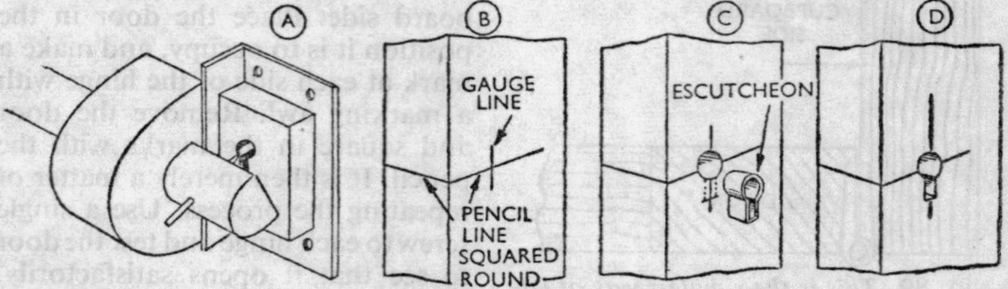

Fig. 94. *Stages of cutting a keyhole.* **A, B** *show the marking;* **C,** *the hole bored for the escutcheon, which must be of a size to make a tight fit;* **D,** *the completed hole.*

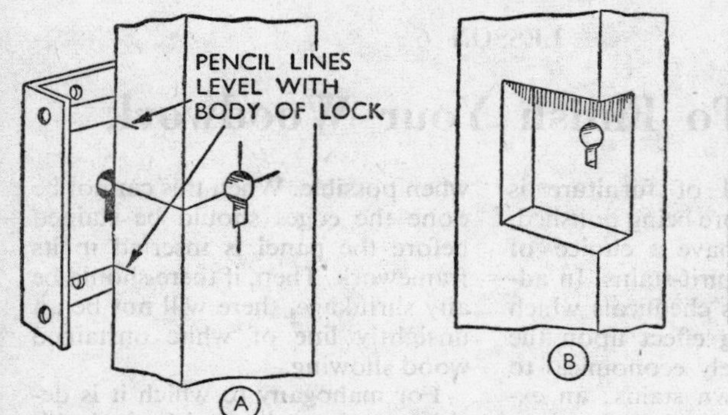

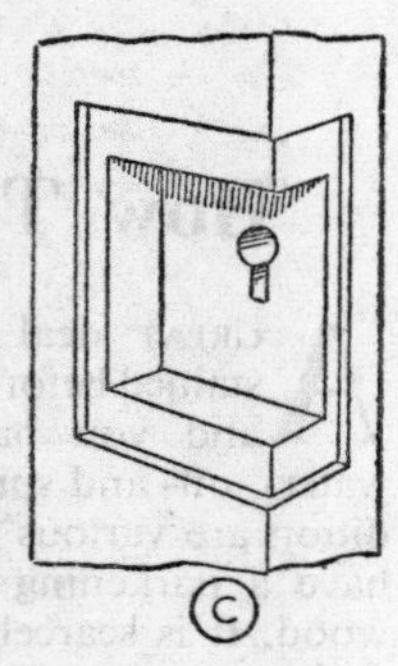

Fig. 95. *Stages of cutting a lock recess.* A, *marking out lines level with the body of the lock;* B, *lock recess cut;* C, *shallow recess for plate chiselled.*

in the middle, and mark the face from the edge with the gauge (see *B*). The hole for the key can then be bored right through as at *C*. If there is to be a brass escutcheon the hole must be of such a size that this will make a tight fit. Otherwise it can be made to give generous allowance for the key. In the case of the escutcheon the latter is placed in position and tapped with the hammer to make an indentation of its shape. Cut down the sides with the keyhole saw and chisel out the wood. *D* shows the completed hole (minus the escutcheon).

To find the position for the recess hold the lock so that the pin lines up with pencil line on the edge of the door, and make pencil marks level with the body of the lock as at *A*, Fig. 95. Square the marks across the back, and gauge the depth and thickness, allowing for the thickness of the plate. The recess can then be cut out as at *B*. The sides can be partly sawn, and the rest chopped out with the chisel. Put the lock in position and mark where the plate comes. A shallow recess for this is chiselled as at *C*, and the lock can be screwed in position.

You will have to cut a little mortise in the cupboard side into which the bolt can shoot. To find its position shoot out the bolt and smear the top with a dark liquid (such as the dirty oil from the oilstone), and turn the bolt in again. Shut the door and turn the key so that a mark is left on the cupboard side. The mortise can be cut with a small chisel.

Self Testing Questions

(1) *Why is the gauge-marker set to the centre of the knuckle rather than to the thickness of the flange?*

(2) *Why must the butt-hinge be let into the wood?*

(3) *Locks are made to fit on either the left- or right-hand side of a door. They are known as left- or right-hand. How do you know which to order?*

(4) *How can you tell which size of flush escutcheon to order for a lock?*

THE ANSWERS ARE ON PAGE 180.

LESSON 6

How To Finish Your Woodwork

A GREAT deal of furniture is stained before being polished, and you have a choice of water-, oil- and spirit-stains. In addition are various chemicals which have a darkening effect upon the wood. It is scarcely economical to make up your own stains; an excellent and reliable range of various shades is available from most polish suppliers. Water-stains have the advantage of cheapness, but are liable to raise the grain. The work should therefore be damped first and be glass-papered down when dry before the stain is applied. Both spirit- and oil-stains are largely free from this trouble and can be applied straightway. In all cases, however, a better result is obtained by giving two light coats rather than one strong one. In the second coat it is frequently an advantage to miss any end grain parts, because this soaks up the stain and is liable to turn darker than the rest, especially in the case of soft-woods.

Fuming Oak

A brush is usually used to apply the stain. Keep the edge alive so that there are no joining-up marks, and proceed in long streaks *with* the grain. When the whole surface has been covered, go over the whole thing with a rag damped with the stain to take out any brush-marks. If the work is panelled, do the panels first, follow with the rails as far as the shoulders, and then the stiles or uprights. Any mouldings can be picked in finally. You will realise, of course, that it is always an advantage to stain the panels separately when possible. When this cannot be done the edges should be stained before the panel is inserted in its framework. Then, if there should be any shrinkage, there will not be an unsightly line of white unstained wood showing.

For mahogany to which it is desired to give a brownish shade bichromate of potash can be used. The crystals are placed in water, which will gradually assume an orange tone. It is applied in daylight, and when dry the yellowish dust which is left on the surface is dusted off.

Oak can be darkened by fuming with ammonia. Ask for point eight-eighty ammonia. The work is placed in any airproof cupboard, the ammonia being poured out into a saucer. Fix a glass panel in the cupboard so that progress can be noted. All the oak must be of the same kind: some kinds darken readily, whilst others are scarcely affected. American oak does not fume well. Never stoop over the ammonia, as the fumes are powerful.

Any form of stain can be used regardless of the polish to be used, but if wax polish is to be used it is essential that a coat of french polish should be given over oil-stain. Otherwise the stain may become lighter in patches. Between each coat of stain rub down the surface with fine glass-paper.

Wax Polishing

You can apply wax to either a stained surface or to the bare wood. If, however, an oil-stain has been used, it is important to give first a single coat of french polish to fix the stain. In any case the surface should be rubbed down to remove any roughness and any grease (the latter is often left by oil-stain). Use a No. 0 grade of glass-paper. There are many proprietary brands of wax polish which can be used successfully, or you can make up your own. Obtain some beeswax, light if it is desired to keep the tone light, or dark if the work has been stained. Shred it into a tin and cover with turpentine. It will take several hours to dissolve. You can speed up the process by heating the mixture in a saucepan of hot water, but never heat it over a flame, as it is most inflammable. It should form a fairly thin paste.

Scrub it well into the surface with a boot brush, using the polish quite freely, and allow about 24 hours for the turpentine to evaporate. No polish is possible until all the turpentine has gone. Polish with another boot brush and finish off with a dry duster. The first application will produce only a dull shine, but the advantage of the process is that it can be renewed at any time and every fresh application improves the finish. The secret is to use plenty of elbow-grease.

Oak is usually the wood to be waxed, though nowadays there is a tendency to apply it to other hardwoods such as walnut and some of the Empire timbers.

French Polishing

This is a finish which requires considerable experience before a satisfactory result can be obtained. You are therefore advised to practise on pieces of spare wood before attempting to polish a job on which you may have spent considerable time. Let us assume that you have a mahogany cabinet to french polish. You have stained it and are ready to begin polishing. The first step is to fill in the grain, and a reliable and inexpensive filler is plaster of Paris. Get the superfine grade, shake it out into a saucer, and have ready a pot of water. Wet a rag, dip it into the plaster, and go over the whole surface with a circular movement. Incidentally, it is advisable in the case of mahogany and other dark-reddish woods to add some powder rose-pink to the plaster before starting. It will set rapidly, but before it does so, rub the surface with a piece of canvas to take off the surplus.

Fig. 96. *The rubber* (above) *used in french polishing is held with the first and second fingers astride the pointed end and the thumb and the other fingers are grouped towards the rear.*

Take care also that there is no accumulation at the corners. These and other awkward parts can usually be picked out cleanly with a matchstick.

When dry the surface will appear white. Now soak a piece of cotton wool in linseed oil and rub over the surface sparingly. This will kill the whiteness and will cause the plaster to form into a paste which can be cleaned off with fine glass-paper.

Now comes the first polishing stage, known as fadding. You can use either button polish, which produces a golden tone, or garnet, which is a darker and warmer brown. One method is to begin with button and finish with garnet, but never reverse the order. You will realise that it is always an advantage to polish several pieces of work at the same time, because time has to be allowed for the surface to harden, and there is otherwise considerable delay. The rubber with which the polish is applied is approximately oval-shaped, with one end pointed. Unbleached wadding covered with fine linen is used. Fig. 96 shows the shape of the rubber. It is held so that the first and second fingers are astride the pointed end and the thumb and remaining fingers grouped towards the rear.

In this initial stage the polish can be used fairly freely. Soak the wadding in polish, and wrap the rag around it. When the finger is pressed on the sole a *little* polish should exude. Work the rubber with a cir-

Fig. 97. *The rubber is worked with a circular movement, following the lines shown in the illustration.*

cular movement as in Fig. 97. When the rubber dries add more polish and repeat the process. Go from part to part, so as to allow time to dry. Before going over the work again rub down with worn No. 0 glass-paper. This will produce a faint shine, and the work should then be set aside for an hour or so to harden.

In the next stage a little linseed oil is used to lubricate the rubber. Charge the rubber with polish and put a spot of oil on the sole with the finger. After rubbing down with glass-paper continue with the circular movement. Take special care with the corners and edges. The effect of the oil will be to produce a smear. This will have to be got rid

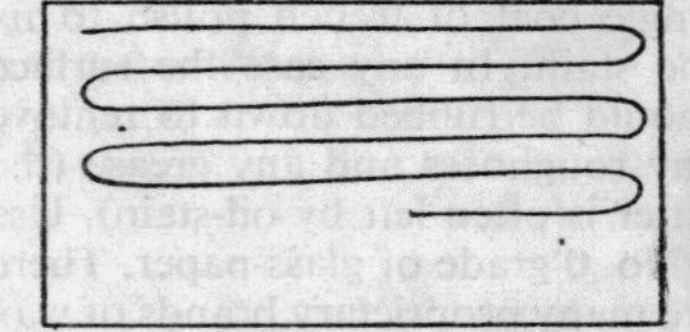

Fig. 98. *In the next stage long sweeps of the rubber, lubricated by a little linseed oil, replace the circular movements.*

of later, but at present it enables the rubber to travel over the surface and produce a shine by friction. Remember that it is the work put into the polishing which produces the result, not the quantity of polish applied. Allow time to harden, and repeat the process until a good body of shine is produced. Finally, the rounded movement can be changed for long sweeps as shown in Fig. 98. Remember to attend to the edges at the same time. Work out the rubber in every case until it is almost dry before re-charging.

A quite bright polish should now appear on the surface, but still with traces of oil showing in the form of light smears. Remember that, although a little oil is necessary for lubricating the rubber, no oil must appear in the finished work. The rule then is to use no more oil than is essential.

To finish off, prepare a fresh rubber and put a drop or two of methylated spirits on the wadding. On no account soak it. Press the rubber so that the spirit is distributed evenly. Go over the surface as in Fig. 99,

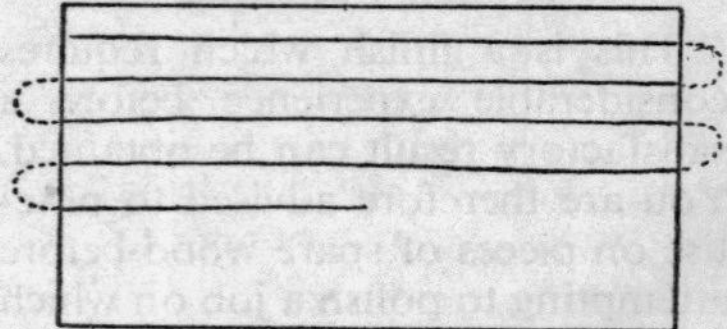

Fig. 99. *In finishing off, the rubber should be worked right across the job, and should be taken off at the edges.*

taking the rubber off at the edges. No liquid should exude from the rubber. Its sole purpose is to pick up the oil and burnish the surface. After a while it will be found that the sole of the rubber has become greasy with oil, and the position of the rag should be altered so that a clean piece is presented. The rubber will soon become practically dry, when the pressure can be increased. Remember that too much spirits will simply pull off the existing polish instead of just burnishing the surface. Finally, don't attempt to spirit off until a good body of polish has been built up.

Self Testing Questions

(1) *Can you darken with stain a surface which has been already polished?*

(2) *What is the advantage of fuming?*

(3) *What is the object of using turpentine with wax?*

(4) *How would you polish the recessed portions of carved work?*

(5) *What is the purpose of using a filler?*

(6) *Should oil be used in the first stages of fadding in after the grain has been filled?*

THE ANSWERS ARE ON PAGE 180.

LESSON 7

Things You Can Make Yourself

Electric Table Standard

In making a standard of this kind one of the difficulties frequently experienced by the beginner is that of boring the hole through the middle for the flex. Of course, it is necessary to bore perfectly in line with the work, but there is no special difficulty if a couple of battens are fixed to adjacent sides as a guide for holding the brace. In any case, the hole is bored half-way through from each end.

Alternatively, you can make the standard of two pieces glued together, the groove being cut first. This can either be done with a small gouge or be worked with the grooving plane. But the solid piece is the better.

Cut out the piece for the pillar, allowing for the tenon at the bottom, and plane it square to size. Then bore the $\frac{1}{4}$-in. hole from end to end. The base is also prepared as a square piece. Mark out and cut the mortise-and-tenon joint, afterwards fitting the joint (Fig. 101).

You will see that the pillar has parallel sides for a distance of 3 in. above the shoulders, but is tapered from this point up to the top. This tapering is now planed, an equal amount being taken from all four sides. When you work the chamfered corners the bulk of the waste is removed with the spokeshave. The lower end where it is stopped you can chisel. Incidentally, remember to mark the depth with the pencil; a gauge would leave marks. A small round file is handy for working the decorative stops. At the top a piece of $\frac{1}{8}$-in. stuff is cut to shape, its edges rounded, and glued and pinned on.

You can now take off the corners of the base to an extent of $1\frac{1}{8}$ in., measuring along each side. When you work the top chamfer, deal with the end-grain first. When all is satisfactory, glue the parts together.

Allow to set, and cut a small groove in the under-side of the base to allow the flex to be fitted in flush as in Fig. 102. A thin covering piece can be screwed on afterwards (Fig. 100).

The addition of the small feet (screwed on) and the brass fitting at the top completes the standard.

Oak should be used preferably.

Cutting List

	Length	Width	Thickness (finished)
1 Pillar . .	1 ft. ½ in.	1⅜ in sq.	
1 Base . .	5¼ in.	5⅛ in.	⅞ in.
4 Feet . .	2½ in.	1⅛ in.	¼ in.
1 Capping . .	1½ in.	1½ in.	⅛ in.

In this cutting list and those given throughout the rest of this course allowance for cutting joints and for trimming has been made in lengths and widths. Thicknesses are the finished sizes.

Tray

You will notice (Fig. 106) that the edgings of this tray are made of plain strips dovetailed together at the corners. There is no need to conceal a well-cut joint, but the work must be neatly done, of course. Almost any hardwood can be used: oak, walnut or mahogany. Plane up the four strips to the finished section and cut off the ends to length. Make sure that the opposite pieces are exactly the same length. Cut the dovetails and glue up the parts, making sure that they are square and free from winding.

The base follows. It can be in solid wood (in which case it may be necessary to joint two pieces together), or it can be of veneered plywood or lamin-board. The last two would need to have a thin lipping applied all round to conceal the layers.

Note from Fig. 103 how the base stands in about ⅛ in. all round. Trim it so that it lines up nicely with the sides and bore screw-holes all round. Countersink the holes and drive in the screws.

Details of the handles are given in Figs. 104–105. A rebate is cut at the inner edge so that it fits over the top of the sides. Underneath, it is scooped out to form a convenient grip for the fingers. To fix the handles, brass screws can be driven from the inside of the edgings through into the ends of the handles where they are not scooped out. When polishing the tray the handles and edgings should be removed.

Cutting List

	Length	Width	Thickness
1 Base . .	1 ft. 10 in.	14 in.	⅜ in.
2 Edgings .	1 ft. 10½ in.	1⅛ in.	⅝ in.
2 ,, .	1 ft. 2½ in.	1⅛ in.	⅝ in.
2 Handles .	3½ in.	1⅝ in.	¾ in.

Cigarette Box

This makes an attractive little box when the work is carried out in oak. As it is a small item it is advisable to select wood with small figure. The sides are through dovetailed, and if neatly cut they form a decorative feature. The lid lifts off and is provided with a lining piece beneath to keep it in position. You will realise that the width is calculated so that the box holds cigarettes comfortably with a little to spare.

Cut out the four sides to the sizes given in Fig. 107, taking care to make the opposite pieces exactly alike. The edges are best planed on the shooting-board. Set the cutting gauge to the thickness of the wood and mark the ends of all four pieces on both sides. Space out the dovetails on the short sides and cut them without, however, chopping away the waste. Mark out the pins on the long sides from them, and complete the cutting. Having cleaned up the inner surfaces, glue the parts together and allow them to set. The outer surfaces can then be cleaned up; also the top and bottom edges.

Notice from Fig. 107 that the bottom stands in a bare ⅛ in. all round.

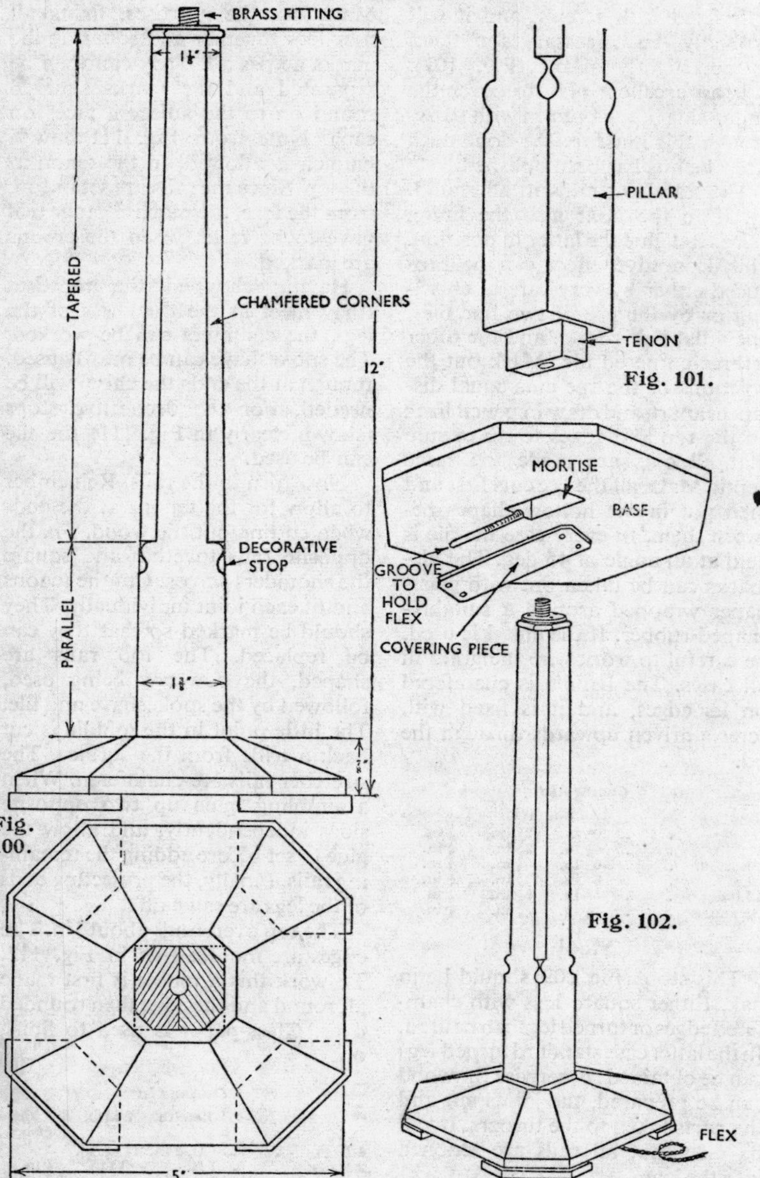

Figs. 100–102. *Electric table standard. Fig.* 100 (left), *the complete job; Fig.* 101 (top right), *joint and flex groove at base. Fig.* 102 (bottom right), *base and pillar.*

It is fixed with screws, and it will probably be necessary for them to be slightly aslant (Fig. 107). It is an excellent plan to cover the under-side of the bottom with baize, though this must not be done until after the box has been polished.

The lid also stands in all round. Fit it to the box; also the lining piece, and glue the latter in position. The decorative effect can be produced either by very careful chiselling or by the use of two fine files, one a flat half-round, and the other a three-cornered file. Mark out the positions of the vee cuts equal distances apart, and draw in pencil lines on the top and edges to make sure that all cuts are made the same depth. Make all the vee cuts first and then put in the hollow shapes between them. In every case the file is held at an angle of 45 deg. The file-marks can be taken out with glass-paper wrapped around a suitably-shaped rubber. If the chisel is used, be careful to work *with* the grain in all cases. The handle is chamfered on its edges, and it is fixed with screws driven upwards through the lid.

Cutting List

	Length	Width	Thickness
2 Sides . .	6¼ in.	2½ in.	⅜ in.
2 ,, . .	4⅛ in.	2½ in.	⅜ in.
1 Bottom . .	6 in.	3⅞ in.	⅜ in.
1 Lid . . .	6 in.	3⅞ in.	¼ in.
1 Lining . .	5½ in.	3¼ in.	⅛ in.
1 Handle . .	2⅛ in.	¾ in.	¼ in.

Stool

This stool (Fig. 109) should be in oak. Either square legs with chamfered edges or turned legs can be used. In the latter case standard turned legs can be obtained; otherwise the wood can be prepared, the joints cut and the parts taken to the turners. It will be seen that all rails are tenoned into the legs.

Cut out the stuff for the legs, allowing about ¼ in. extra at the top. Mark out the mortises, fixing all four legs together and squaring the marks across all. They can then be separated and the marks squared round on to the adjacent faces on each. Note from Fig. 111 how a haunch is allowed on the tenon at the top. Since the rails are set in ⅛ in. from the face, the mortise gauge will have to be re-set when the tenons are marked.

Having chopped the mortises (they meet in the thickness of the leg), the chamfers can be worked. The spokeshave can be mostly used, though at the ends the chisel will be needed. For the decorative stops (shown clearly in Fig. 111) the file can be used.

Now turn to the rails. Remember to allow for the tenons at the ends when cutting out the wood. Fix the opposite rails together and square the shoulders across. Cut the tenons and fit each joint individually. They should be marked so that they can be replaced. The top rails are shaped, the bow-saw being used, followed by the spokeshave and file. The little point in the middle is cut back a trifle from the surface. The stretcher rails are chamfered. When assembling, glue up two opposite sides independently, and allow the glue to set before adding the remaining rails. Finally, the projecting ends of the legs are sawn off.

The top overhangs about ¾ in. The edges are moulded as in Fig. 112. To work this a rebate is first made all round and the edge then rounded over. Glass-paper is used to finish off.

Cutting List

	Length	Width	Thickness (finished)
4 Legs . .	1 ft. 2 in.	1⅜ in. sq.	
2 Rails . .	1 ft.	1⅞ in.	⅞ in.
2 ,, . .	1 ft. 3 in.	1⅞ in.	⅞ in.
2 Stretchers .	1 ft.	1⅛ in.	⅞ in.
2 ,, . .	1 ft. 3 in.	1⅛ in.	⅞ in.
1 Top . .	1 ft. 5 in.	14 in.	⅝ in

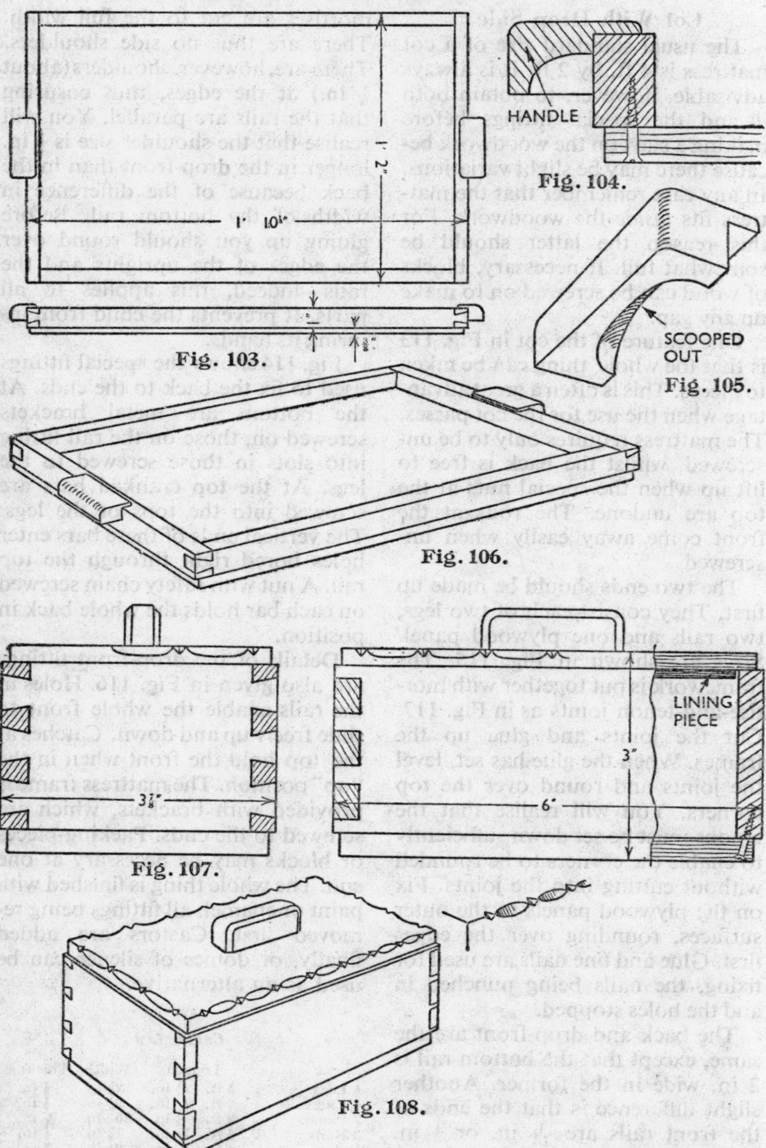

Figs. 103–108. Above (*Figs.* 103–106), *tray, with details of marking out and measurements and showing method of making and attaching the handles;* below (*Figs.* 107 *and* 108), *cigarette box, with marking out details.*

Cot With Drop Side

The usual standard size of a cot mattress is 4 ft. by 2 ft. It is always advisable, however, to obtain both it and the special fittings before making a start on the woodwork because there may be slight variations. In any case remember that the mattress fits *inside* the woodwork. For this reason the latter should be somewhat full. If necessary, blocks of wood can be screwed on to make up any gap.

One feature of the cot in Fig. 113 is that the whole thing can be taken to pieces. This is often a great advantage when the use for the cot passes. The mattress requires only to be unscrewed, whilst the back is free to lift up when the special nuts at the top are undone. The rods at the front come away easily when unscrewed.

The two ends should be made up first. They consist each of two legs, two rails and one plywood panel. Sizes are shown in Fig. 115. The framework is put together with mortise-and-tenon joints as in Fig. 117. Cut the joints and glue up the frames. When the glue has set, level the joints and round over the top corners. You will realise that the tenons must be set down sufficiently to enable the corners to be rounded without cutting into the joints. Fix on the plywood panels to the outer surfaces, rounding over the edges first. Glue and fine nails are used for fixing, the nails being punched in and the holes stopped.

The back and drop-front are the same, except that the bottom rail is 2 in. wide in the former. Another slight difference is that the ends of the front rails are $\frac{1}{16}$ in. or $\frac{1}{8}$ in. shorter to allow clearance. All the uprights are tenoned in as in Fig. 117. They are $\frac{3}{8}$ in. thick, and the mortises are cut to the full width. There are thus no side shoulders. There are, however, shoulders (about $\frac{1}{8}$ in.) at the edges, thus ensuring that the rails are parallel. You will realise that the shoulder size is $\frac{1}{2}$ in. longer in the drop-front than in the back because of the difference in width of the bottom rail. Before gluing up you should round over the edges of the uprights and the rails—indeed, this applies to all parts. It prevents the child from injuring its hands.

Fig. 114 shows the special fittings used to fix the back to the ends. At the bottom are metal brackets screwed on, those on the rail fitting into slots in those screwed to the legs. At the top cranked bars are screwed into the tops of the legs. The vertical ends of these bars enter holes bored right through the top rail. A nut with safety chain screwed on each bar holds the whole back in position.

Details of the drop-front fittings are also given in Fig. 116. Holes in the rails enable the whole front to slide freely up and down. Catches at the top hold the front when in the "up" position. The mattress frame is provided with brackets, which are screwed to the ends. Packing-pieces or blocks may be necessary at one end. The whole thing is finished with paint or enamel, all fittings being removed first. Castors are added finally, or domes of silence can be used as an alternative.

Cutting List

	Length	Width	Thickness
4 Legs . .	3 ft. $2\frac{1}{2}$ in.	$2\frac{1}{8}$ in.	$\frac{7}{8}$ in.
4 End rails .	2 ft. 2 in.	$2\frac{1}{8}$ in.	$\frac{7}{8}$ in.
2 Panels .	2 ft. $\frac{1}{4}$ in.	25 in.	$\frac{3}{16}$ in.
3 Rails . .	4 ft. 1 in.	$1\frac{5}{8}$ in.	$\frac{7}{8}$ in.
1 ,, . .	4 ft. 1 in.	$2\frac{1}{8}$ in.	$\frac{7}{8}$ in.
3 Uprights .	1 ft. 11 in.	$4\frac{1}{8}$ in.	$\frac{3}{8}$ in.
3 ,, .	1 ft. $10\frac{1}{2}$ in.	$4\frac{1}{8}$ in.	$\frac{3}{8}$ in.
4 ,, .	1 ft. 11 in.	$1\frac{5}{8}$ in.	$\frac{3}{8}$ in.
4 ,, .	1 ft. $10\frac{1}{2}$ in.	$1\frac{5}{8}$ in.	$\frac{3}{8}$ in.

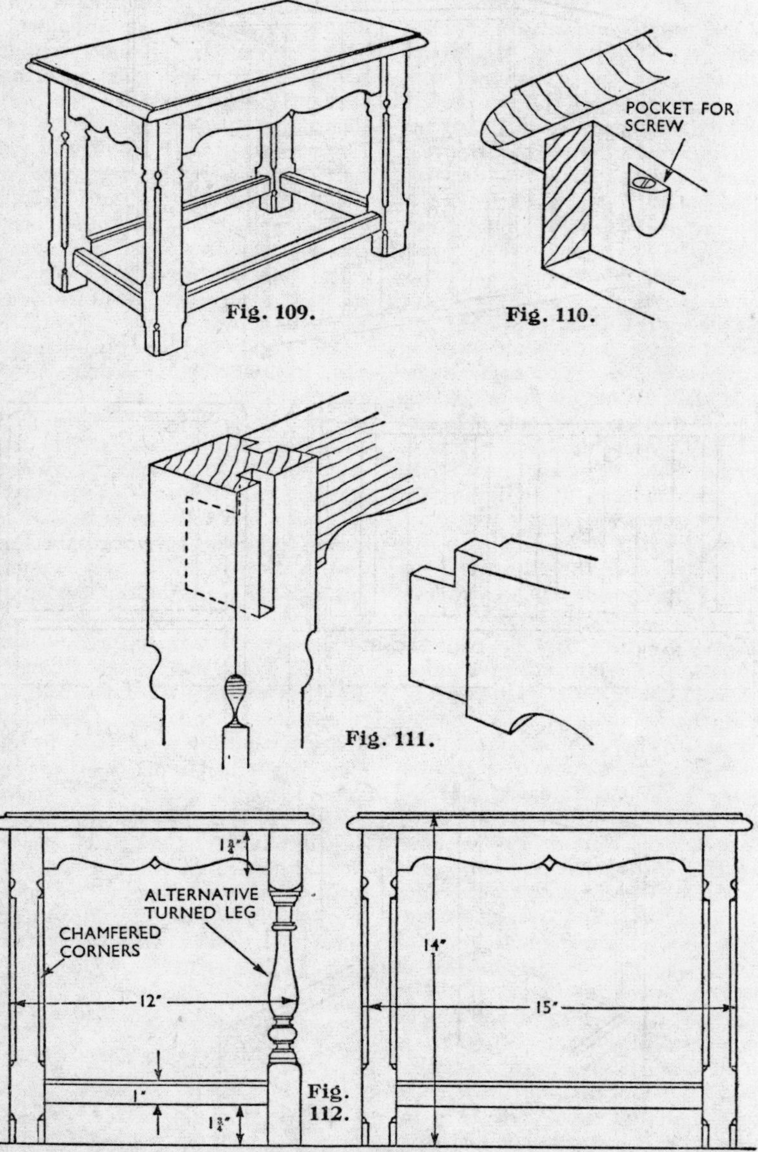

Figs. 109–112. *Drawings for stool. Fig.* 109 *shows the complete job; Fig.* 110 (top right), *the moulded edges and screw pocket; Fig.* 111 (centre), *the leg joints and stops; Fig.* 112 (bottom), *details and measurements with alternative leg shapes.*

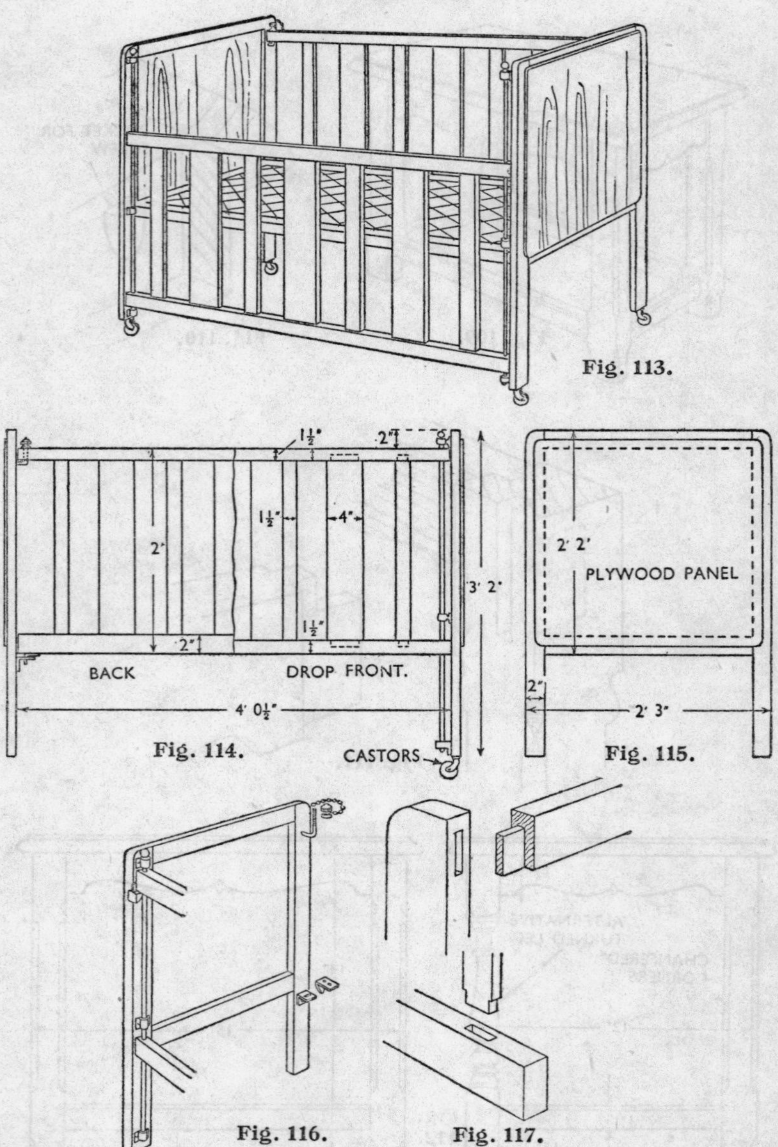

Figs. 113–117. *Drop-sided cot. Fig.* 113, *the finished cot; Fig.* 114, *details of back and front, showing sizes and method of attachment of back and ends; Fig.* 115 *end panel; Fig.* 116, *attachment of runner rails; Fig.* 117 *details of joints.*

Figs. 118–120. *Occasional table. Fig.* 118, *the completed table; Fig.* 119, *plan and method of joining, with* (inset) *details of rails; Fig.* 120, *details of joints and method of fitting rails.*

Fig. 118.

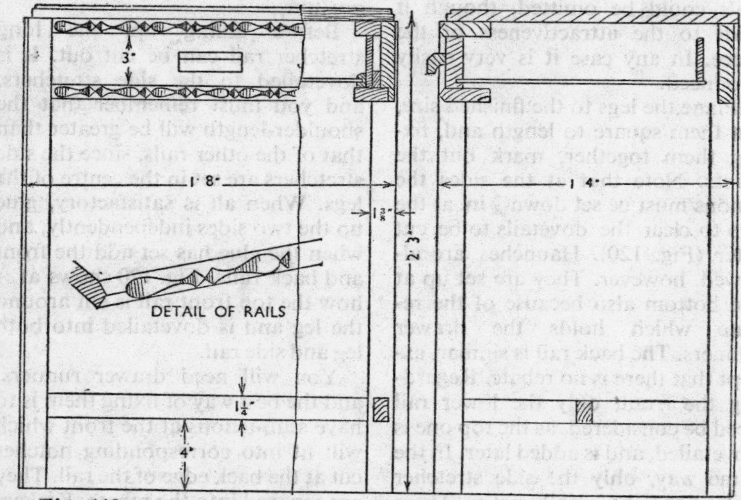

Fig. 119.

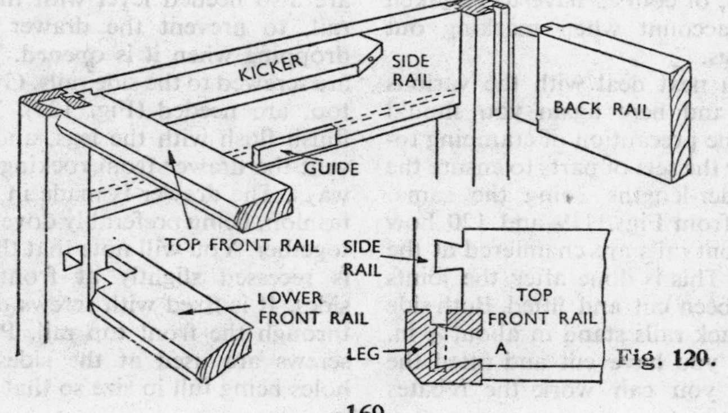

Fig. 120.

Occasional Table

A table of this kind is handy for the bedside, for the hall, or to stand in the window. Its size will prove about right for most purposes, though an inch or so will not affect the design if the table is required to fit a special size. A handy drawer is fitted beneath the top (Fig. 118).

The construction is straightforward, the mortise-and-tenon joint being used for the greater part. If desired, the decoration in the top rails could be omitted, though it adds to the attractiveness of the piece. In any case it is very easily produced.

Plane the legs to the finished size, cut them square to length and, fixing them together, mark out the joints. Note that at the sides the tenons must be set down $\frac{7}{8}$ in. at the top to clear the dovetails to be cut later (Fig. 120). Haunches are allowed, however. They are set up at the bottom also because of the rebate which holds the drawer runners. The back rail is similar, except that there is no rebate. Regarding the front, only the lower rail need be considered, as the top one is dovetailed, and is added later. In the same way, only the side stretcher rails need be dealt with. These points, of course, have to be taken into account when marking out the legs.

You next deal with the various rails, and here again you should take the precaution of cramping together the sets of parts to ensure the shoulder-lengths being the same. Note from Figs. 119 and 120 how the front rails are chamfered at the front. This is done after the joints have been cut and fitted. Both side and back rails stand in about $\frac{1}{8}$ in. When you have cut and fitted the joints you can work the rebates and chamfers. The inset sketch in Fig. 119 shows how the decoration on the rails is formed. It could be chiselled, though the simplest plan is to use the rasp and file, finishing off with glass-paper wrapped around a suitably-shaped wooden rubber. The file is worked straight across the work at right angles. To ensure regularity, space out the design with dividers and cut in the small depressions with a triangular file. The half-round file is used for smoothing off the other portions.

Before gluing up, the long stretcher rail can be cut out. It is dovetailed to the side stretchers, and you must remember that the shoulder-length will be greater than that of the other rails, since the side stretchers are set in the centre of the legs. When all is satisfactory, glue up the two sides independently, and when the glue has set add the front and back rails. Fig. 120 shows at *A* how the top front rail is cut around the leg and is dovetailed into both leg and side rail.

You will need drawer runners, and the best way of fixing them is to have stub-tenons at the front which will fit into corresponding notches cut at the back edge of the rail. They are screwed into the rebate. Kickers are also needed level with the top rail, to prevent the drawer from dropping when it is opened. These are screwed to the side rails. Guides, too, are needed (Fig. 120). These finish flush with the legs, and prevent the drawer from rocking sideways. The drawer is made in usual fashion, being preferably dovetailed together. You will note that the top is recessed slightly at front and sides. It is fixed with screws driven through the front top rail. Pocket screws are used at the sides, the holes being full in size so that there is slight give in the event of shrinkage.

Cutting List

	Length	Width	Thickness (finished)
4 Legs . .	2 ft. 3 in.	$1\frac{3}{8}$ in. sq.	
2 Rails . .	1 ft. 8 in.	$2\frac{3}{4}$ in.	$\frac{7}{8}$ in.
1 ,, . .	1 ft. 8 in.	5 in.	$\frac{7}{8}$ in.
2 ,, . .	1 ft. 4 in.	5 in.	$\frac{7}{8}$ in.
1 Stretcher .	1 ft. 8 in.	$1\frac{3}{8}$ in.	$\frac{7}{8}$ in.
2 Stretchers .	1 ft. 4 in.	$1\frac{3}{8}$ in.	$\frac{7}{8}$ in.
1 Top . .	1 ft. 8 in.	16 in.	$\frac{1}{2}$ in.
2 Runners .	1 ft. 1 in.	2 in.	$\frac{7}{8}$ in.
1 Drawer front	1 ft. $5\frac{1}{2}$ in.	$3\frac{1}{8}$ in.	$\frac{7}{8}$ in.
2 ,, sides	1 ft. 2 in.	$3\frac{1}{8}$ in.	$\frac{3}{8}$ in.
1 ,, back	1 ft. $5\frac{1}{2}$ in.	$2\frac{7}{8}$ in.	$\frac{3}{8}$ in.
1 ,, bottom	1 ft. $4\frac{1}{2}$ in.	14 in.	$\frac{3}{16}$ in.

Small parts needed in addition.

Firescreen

This screen consists in the main of a simple framework, the uprights of which are continued down and are tenoned into feet. A rebated moulding is mitred around the opening, this forming a rebate in which the plywood panel fits. A head at the back secures it in position. The brackets above the feet are not purely decorative; they serve to strengthen the joint considerably.

Prepare the four pieces for the framework, remembering to make the uprights long enough for the tenons which pass through the feet. Fix the opposite parts together when marking out so that they are the same length. Note from the dotted lines in Fig. 121 how the tenons are set down at the top. The feet can either be cut from a piece of $1\frac{1}{2}$-in. wood, or they can be bought ready made, in which case the standard pattern will have to be accepted.

When the joints have been cut and fitted, the whole can be glued up. The joints are then levelled and the feet fitted. Note how the tenons here are wedged from beneath to strengthen them. Before gluing cut a notch at each side as shown by the dotted lines in Fig. 124. These are to hold the brackets. The brackets should be a fairly tight fit in the notches. When the feet have been glued on the brackets are glued in and a screw driven in near the top. A hole large enough to take the head is bored half-way through first, and then a smaller one for the shank. In this way the screw is recessed and a plug can be inserted as shown in Fig. 122.

The rebated moulding is mitred around the opening and fixed with glue and fine nails. Plywood is used for the panel, a bead being nailed around the back to hold it.

Cutting List

	Length	Width	Thickness
2 Uprights .	2 ft. 6 in.	$1\frac{3}{8}$ in.	$\frac{7}{8}$ in.
2 Rails . .	1 ft. 9 in.	$1\frac{3}{8}$ in.	$\frac{7}{8}$ in.
2 Feet . .	$10\frac{1}{2}$ in.	$3\frac{1}{4}$ in.	$1\frac{1}{2}$ in.
4 Brackets .	$4\frac{3}{4}$ in.	$2\frac{3}{4}$ in.	$\frac{5}{8}$ in.
1 Panel . .	1 ft. $9\frac{3}{4}$ in.	$18\frac{3}{4}$ in.	$\frac{1}{4}$ in.

Moulding and beads extra.

Bedside Pedestal

If you prefer it, you can adapt the height of this pedestal a little to suit the particular bedstead against which it is to be placed. Modern beds are frequently considerably lower than older ones. It can be carried out in practically any hardwood. A particularly attractive effect can be produced by veneering the door as shown in Figs. 125 and 127, though this is not essential.

Fig. 126 shows the construction. The bottom is lap-dovetailed to the sides. At the top two rails are also lap-dovetailed in. The drawer rail is tenoned in. Prepare the two sides, if necessary glue-jointing two pieces together. Trim them to size, making sure that both are alike. Fix them together temporarily so that the mortises for the drawer-rail can be squared across both. When dovetailing note that the front rail is level at the front edge. The back one, however, is set in flush with the rebate which holds the back ($\frac{1}{4}$ in.). A similar idea applies at the bottom, the latter being narrower than the

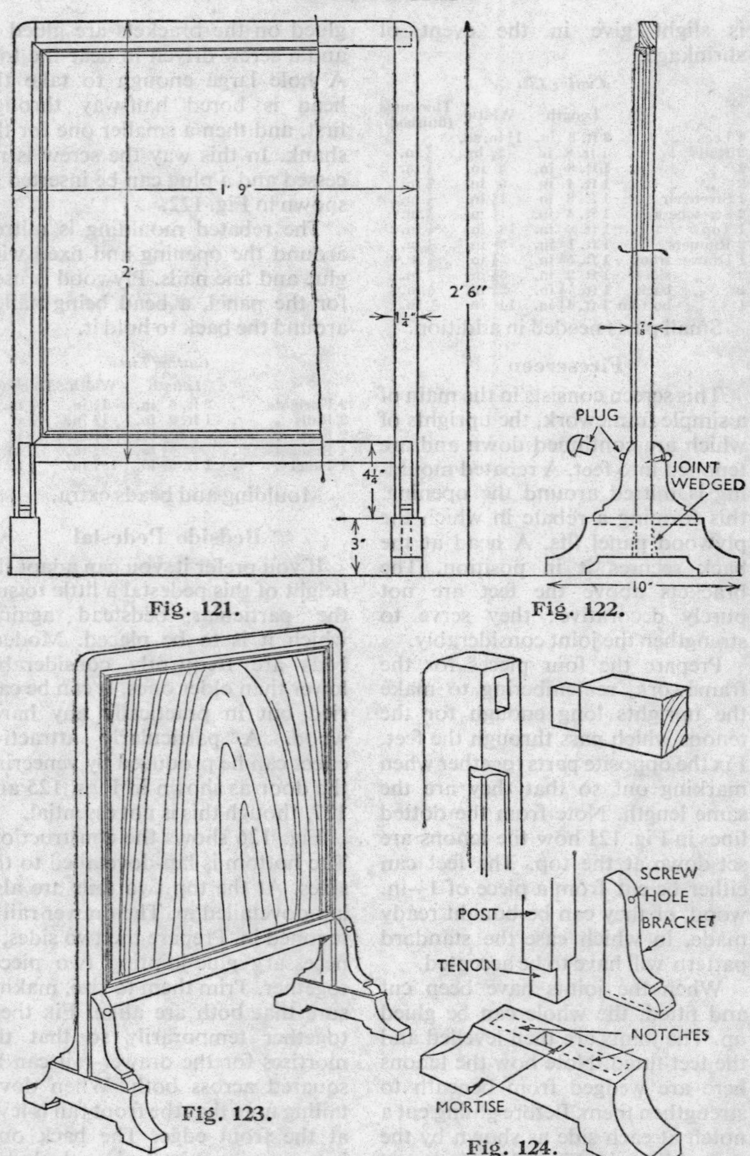

Figs. 121–124. *Firescreen. Fig.* 121, *plan giving details of measurements and positions of joints; Fig.* 122, *how a plug conceals screw fitting screen to feet; Fig.* 123, *the complete screen; Fig.* 124, *details of joints and fitting of feet.*

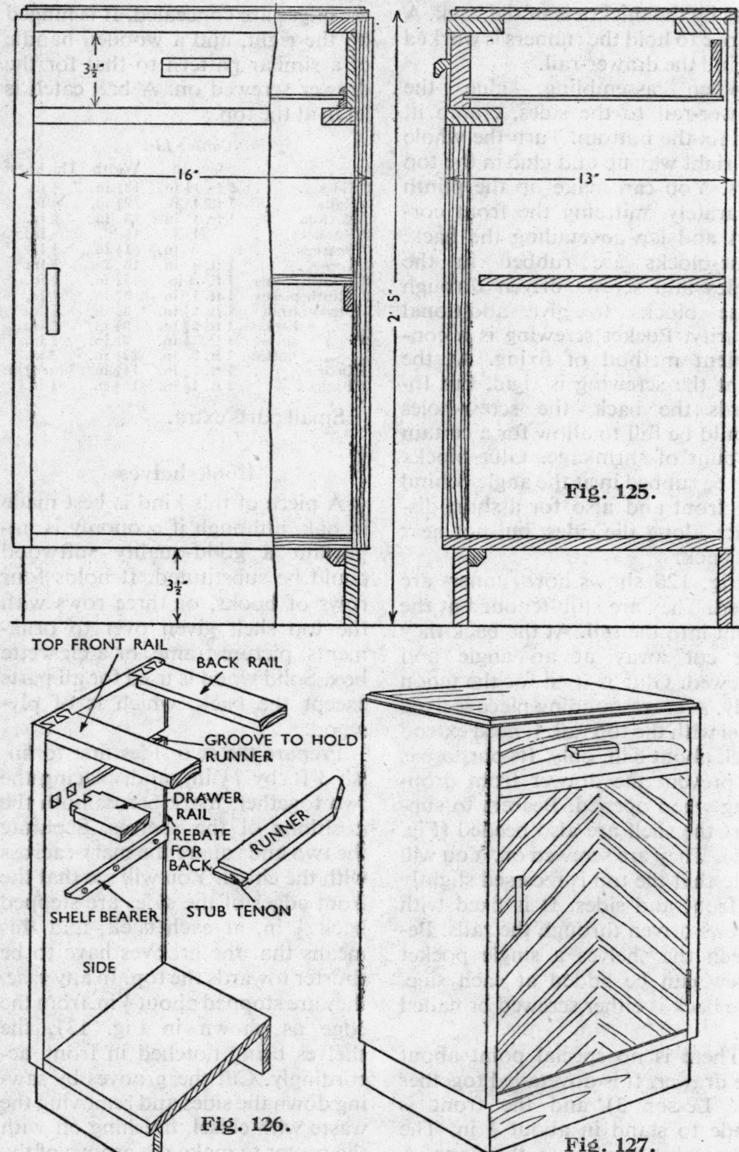

Figs. 125–127. *Bedside pedestal. Fig.* 125, *plan and elevation, showing veneering and giving details of measurements; Fig.* 126, *construction, showing how runners and shelf-bearers are fitted; Fig.* 127, *the completed pedestal.*

sides by the thickness of the back. A groove to hold the runners is worked behind the drawer-rail.

When assembling, glue the drawer-rail to the sides, cramp it, and fix the bottom. Turn the whole the right way up and glue in the top rails. You can make up the plinth separately, mitreing the front corners and lap-dovetailing the back. Glue-blocks are rubbed in the angles and screws driven through these blocks to give additional security. Pocket screwing is a convenient method of fixing. At the front the screwing is rigid, but towards the back the screw-holes should be full to allow for a certain amount of shrinkage. Glue-blocks can be rubbed in at the angle behind the front and also for a short distance along the sides, but not near the back.

Fig. 126 shows how runners are fitted. They are stub-tenoned at the front into the rail. At the back they are cut away at an angle and screwed. Glue is used for the tenon only. A corresponding piece is fixed level with the top rail. It need extend back about 6 in. only. Its purpose is to prevent the drawer from dropping when opened. Bearers to support the shelf are also needed (Fig. 126). They are screwed on. You will note that the top is recessed slightly at front and sides. It is fixed with screws driven through the rails. Between the shelves a single pocket screw can be added at each side. The back is either screwed or nailed on.

There is no special point about the drawer. It is dovetailed together (see Lesson 3) and the front is made to stand in about ⅛ in. The same thing applies to the door. A piece of laminated board veneered on both sides is the best material to use. It should be lipped first so that the edges are concealed. It is hinged on the right, and a wooden handle of a similar pattern to that for the drawer screwed on. A ball catch is let in at the top.

Cutting List

	Length	Width	Thickness
2 Sides . .	2 ft. 1½ in.	13¼ in.	¾ in.
3 Rails . .	1 ft. 4 in.	2¾ in.	⅝ in.
1 Bottom .	1 ft. 4 in.	13 in.	⅝ in.
2 Runners .	11 in.	1¾ in.	⅝ in.
2 Bearers .	9 in.	1½ in.	¼ in.
1 Top . .	1 ft. 4 in.	13 in.	½ in.
2 Plinth pieces	1 ft 3½ in.	3¾ in.	⅝ in.
2 Plinth pieces	1 ft. 1 in	3¾ in.	⅝ in.
1 Drawer front	1 ft. 2¾ in.	3⅝ in.	⅞ in.
1 ,, back	1 ft. 2¾ in.	3⅜ in.	⅜ in.
2 ,, sides	1 ft. ½ in.	3⅝ in.	⅜ in.
1 ,, bottom	1 ft. 2 in.	12¼ in.	3/16 in.
1 Door . .	1 ft. 7¾ in.	14¾ in.	⅞ (or ¾) in.
1 Back . .	2 ft. 1½ in.	15¾ in.	¼ in.

Small parts extra.

Bookshelves

A piece of this kind is best made in oak, although if economy is important a good-quality softwood could be substituted. It holds four rows of books, or three rows with the top shelf given over to ornaments, picture-frame, or a cigarette box. Solid wood is used for all parts except the back, which is of plywood.

Prepare the two sides first to finish 3 ft. by 7½ in., and, placing the two together, mark across both the positions of the shelves. Separate the two and square the marks across with the chisel. You will see that the front edges of the sides are stepped back ½ in. at each shelf, and this means that the grooves have to be shorter towards the top. In any case, they are stopped about ½ in. from the edge as shown in Fig. 131, the shelves being notched in front accordingly. Cut the grooves by sawing down the sides and removing the waste with chisel, finishing off with the router to make the groove of the same depth throughout. The lesson on the housed joint (page 148) shows how to cut this up to the stop.

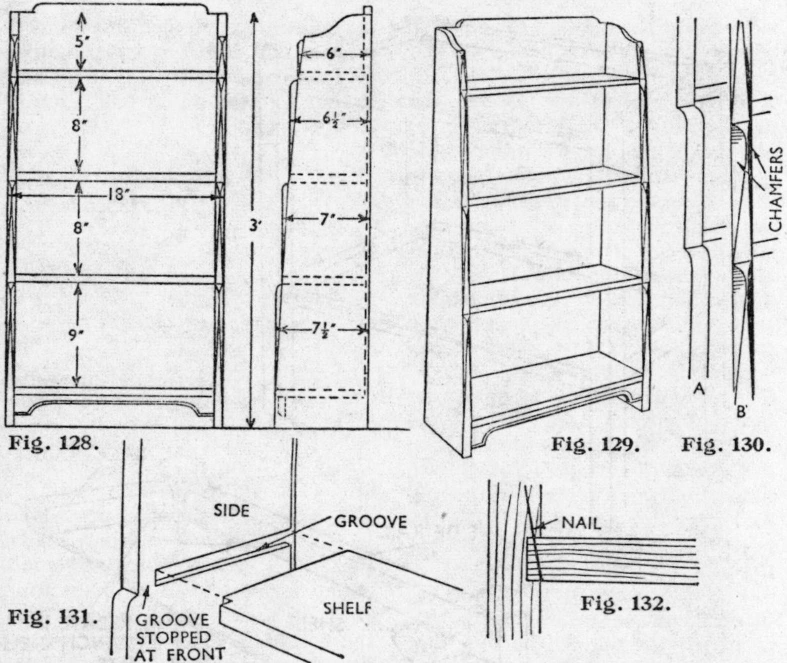

Fig. 128. Fig. 129. Fig. 130. Fig. 131. Fig. 132.

Figs. 128–132. *Drawings for oak bookshelves. Fig.* 128, *plan and elevation; Fig.* 129, *completed shelves; Fig.* 130, *plain edge and chamfers; Fig.* 131, *stopped groove; Fig.* 132, *method of nailing corners.*

Having finished the grooves, the rebate for the ¼-in. back can be worked along the back edges. It can be of the same depth as the grooves, or a little deeper. At the top it is made wider to hold the ½-in. shaped back-piece fixed above the top shelf. You can now cut the shaping of the front edges. Cut with the saw and finish off as far as possible with the plane. The corners can be chiselled or finished with the file and glass-paper. If you prefer a simple job you can leave the edges as they are, but a much more attractive result is obtained by working the chamfers as shown in Fig. 130. *A* shows the plain edge, and *B* the chamfers. They can be worked with the plane, and are so arranged as to run out at the bottom and reach to nearly half-way across the thickness at the top.

One point you must remember when preparing the shelves is that they finish at the back level with the rebate. When you have cut the notches at the front you can round over the front edges slightly. The shaped piece beneath the bottom shelf can be either fitted into notches cut in the sides or it can be just held with glue-blocks.

When assembling glue the ends of the shelves and the grooves, and cramp the whole together. Test for squareness and, turning the whole up-side down, drive in nails askew at the corners as shown in Fig. 132. The top back-rail is held with glue and nails; the back is either nailed or screwed.

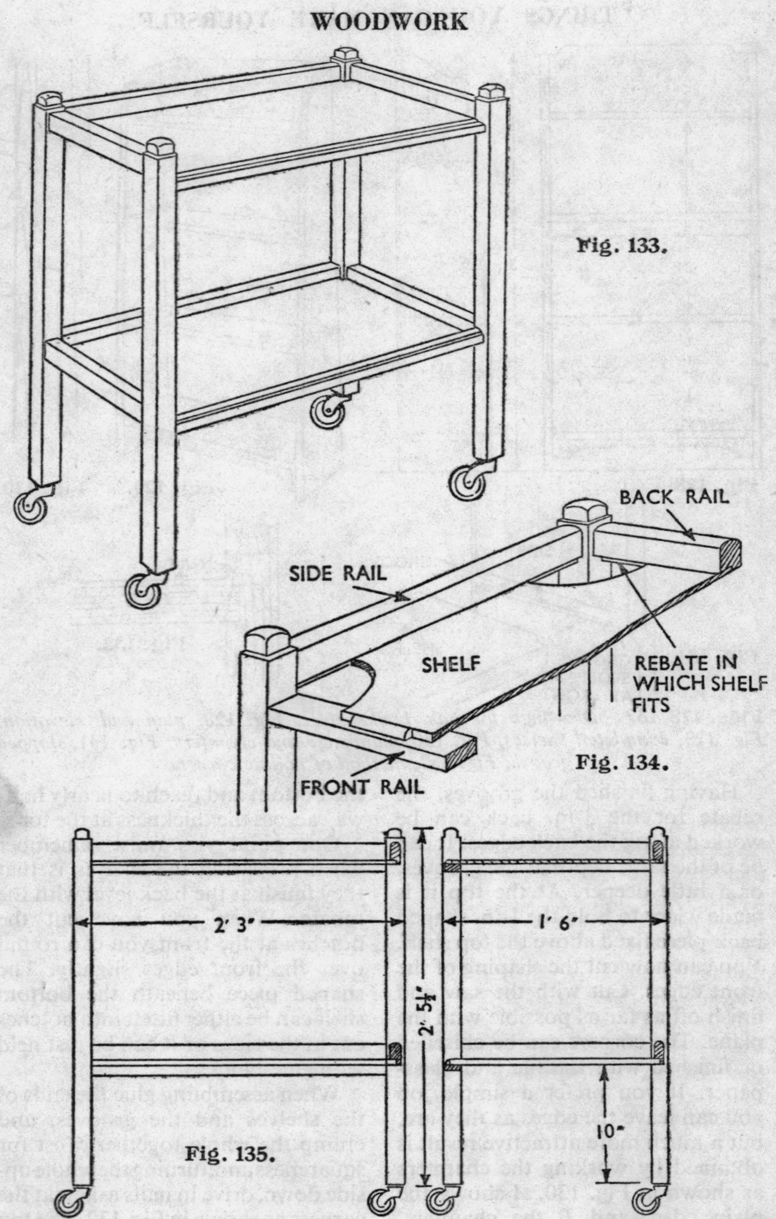

Figs. 133–135. *Tea Trolley; Fig.* 133, *complete job; Figs.* 134–135, *details of construction.*

Cutting List

	Length	Width	Thickness
2 Sides . .	3 ft. ½ in.	7⅝ in.	¾ in.
1 Shelf . .	1 ft. 5½ in.	6 in.	¾ in.
1 ,, . .	1 ft. 5½ in.	6½ in.	¾ in.
1 ,, . .	1 ft. 5½ in.	7 in.	¾ in.
1 ,, . .	1 ft. 5½ in.	7½ in.	¾ in.
1 Top back .	1 ft. 5¾ in.	6 in.	½ in.
1 Bottom rail .	1 ft. 5¾ in.	2⅝ in.	¾ in.
1 Back . .	2 ft. 4½ in.	18 in.	¼ in. (ply)

Tea Trolley

The chief essentials of a trolley are that it must be light, able to travel easily over carpets, have plenty of room between the shelves, and have an open edge across which trays and plates can be drawn easily.

That shown in Fig. 133 has quite good accommodation, and yet does not occupy much space. It could be made in practically any hardwood, though oak is the first choice. The shelves should preferably be of plywood or laminated board, as these materials are practically as strong *across* the grain as *with* it, and there is no liability to shrink.

Cut off the legs to the over-all size (2 ft. 5½ in.) and fix them together with a cramp. This enables all to be marked out alike, since the marks can be squared across. You will see from the illustrations that at the back and sides the shelves fit in rebates worked *beneath* the rails. At the front, however, they rest *upon* rails which lie flat, so enabling plates, etc., to be drawn off easily. Thus, the bottom edges of the side and back rails are level with the top edges of the front rails. At the same time, since the rebates cut away the wood of the back and side rails, it is obvious that the mortises must be set up by the thickness of the shelves (⅜ in.). This, of course, must be done in the marking out. After separating the rails, square round the marks on to the adjacent faces where required. Note from Fig. 135 that the joints are set down at the top also.

After chopping the mortises, work the decorative tops and prepare the rails. These again are cramped together in sets to ensure the shoulder-length being the same. Cut the tenons, but before sawing the shoulders work the rebates of the side and back rails. When this is completed, fit the joints and round over the top corners. You can now put together the two opposite sides independently.

At this stage the shelves can be fitted. It will be a help if the front and back rails are inserted dry. At the front the shelves are set back about ½ in., to allow a quarter-round lipping to be fixed, so hiding the layers of the plywood. When all is satisfactory glue up the whole job, inserting the shelves in the process. When dry, drive in screws all round up into the rails.

It might be possible to insert the shelves after gluing up, but it would probably necessitate a fairly loose fit where they are cut around the legs. This can be tried out when the job is cramped together dry.

This completes the woodwork, and it remains only to add the castors, which should be of the large rubber-tyred variety. The fixing depends upon the particular castor used; most need only a hole to take the spindle.

Cutting List

	Length	Width	Thickness (finished)
4 Legs . .	2 ft. 6 in.	1⅜ in. sq.	
2 Front rails .	2 ft. 2½ in.	1½ in.	½ in.
2 Back rails .	2 ft. 2½ in.	1⅞ in.	⅞ in.
4 Side rails .	1 ft. 5½ in.	1⅞ in.	⅞ in.
2 Shelves .	2 ft. 2½ in.	17¼ in.	⅜ in.
2 Lippings .	2 ft. 1 in.	½ in.	⅜ in.

Answers to Self Testing Questions

LESSON 1

(1) A cross-cut is best as it can be used for cutting with the grain as well as cross-cutting.

(2) Linseed oil is the best, though any good machine oil applied with a lightly soaked rag can be used.

(3) It steadies the saw and gives good control.

(4) No. Move the plane over towards the higher edge. The curvature of the cutter will then remove a thicker shaving at that edge.

(5) By chiselling off the far corner.

(6) If the plane is of wood, tap the back of the cutter sideways. If it is of metal, use the lateral lever.

(7) The medullary rays should be as nearly upright as possible. These can be seen at the end of the plane.

(8) Not for chopping out, but it is handy for the final cleaning out.

(9) Yes, when the sharpened bevel has become so wide that it takes a long time to sharpen.

(10) Always stand at the end of the wood, because it is easier to tell whether the brace leans to the right or left than whether it bears away from or toward you.

(11) The auger bit, because it is not liable to wander with the grain.

(12) The corners of the shank should fit in the vee notches in the jaws within the chuck.

(13) For making marks parallel with the edge, and for cutting strips in thin wood. In the latter case the wood is cut half-way through from each side.

(14) Always keep the butt of the square against either the face side or face edge.

(15) Make point marks from one side of the wood and then hold the gauge from the other side. The two sets of marks should agree. Always use the gauge from the face side, however.

(16) Only for rough carpentry work.

(17) Yes, by driving in the nails at an angle right in the corners.

(18) Vaseline or candle-grease is suitable. All screws should be lubricated to prevent rust, especially in oak, the acid in which is likely to cause corrosion.

(19) Because it dubs over the edges and will not take out inequalities.

(20) As a rule it is an advantage to hold it at a slight angle so that it has a slightly slicing cut.

(21) It is used for trimming mitres after they are sawn.

(22) The best lubricant is black lead.

LESSON 2

(1) Multiply the price by the length in feet.

(2) $2\frac{1}{4}$-ft. super.

(3) They are formed one each year on the outside of the tree. The outer ones make the sapwood.

(4) It must run radially from the centre.

(5) Its freedom from shrinkage, and the great widths in which it can be obtained.

(6) For veneered work.

LESSON 3

(1) Chiefly the mortise and tenon. For cheaper work the dowelled and halved joints are sometimes used, but neither is so satisfactory.

(2) Either in a groove or a rebate. In the latter case a bead is nailed or glued to the framework at the back.

(3) No, though it would not matter in the case of a plywood or laminated board panel, because neither of these shrinks.

(4) One which is perfectly flat at the front. It may have no framework, or there may be one which is concealed.

(5) Because the slips save weakening the sides by grooving and increase the width of the wearing surface.

(6) For the front $\frac{7}{8}$-in. stuff; sides and back $\frac{3}{8}$ in.; bottom $\frac{3}{16}$ in. These thicknesses could be less for quite small drawers.

(7) At the front lapped dovetails, and through dovetails at the back.

(8) They help to prevent the sides from curling outwards in the event of warping.

(9) It necessitates a haunch at the top to fill in the groove, and makes it essential to reduce the mortise length by an amount equal to the groove depth.

(10) Legs between 2 and 3 in. square; top rails 4 to 5 in. by $\frac{7}{8}$ in.; stretchers about 2 in. by $\frac{7}{8}$ in.

(11) Not entirely. They stiffen the legs at the bottom.

(12) Because the weakest parts of a joint are the ends and, being cramped in the middle, the ends are forced tightly together by the spring of the wood.

(13) A $\frac{3}{8}$-in. dowel about $1\frac{1}{2}$ in. long over-all.

(14) It should be just hand-tight. If too tight it will tend to force out the sides of the groove.

(15) The top dovetail should be arranged to be within the edging when the latter is cut off.

(16) Because a gap will appear at the ends if the rebate is deeper. If it is less there will not be enough room for the fixing-screws.

(17) Because they are liable to show through to the surface of the veneer in the event of shrinkage.

(18) Because they conceal the end-grain of the ends of the frieze.

(19) It simply rests on the carcase, and is held in position by blocks, which engage the corners. The blocks are fixed to the carcase top.

(20) It can either be screwed from beneath, or can remain loose, being held in the same way as the loose cornice.

LESSON 4

(1) First plane one side true, first traversing then planing *with* the grain. Set a gauge to the finished thickness and plane the other side down to this.

(2) You can minimise tearing by setting the back-iron close to the cutting edge. Afterwards the scraper is used to take out unavoidable tears.

(3) Hold the plane towards the side needing the thickest shaving. Do not rock the plane.

(4) At least 12 hours when Scotch glue is used.

(5) The width of the chisel used for mortising. This should be as nearly as possible one-third the thickness of the wood.

(6) Because it is apt to split out the mortise.

(7) Because this ensures their being level when assembled.

(8) It makes a convenient channel in which the chisel can rest when chopping downwards.

(9) It slopes to the extent of $\frac{5}{8}$ in. in 3 in.

(10) Because there is no friction fit to hold the parts together when being glued.

(11) Because it allows the cross grain at the outer end of piece *A* to be as wide as possible.

(12) In rough work nails can be driven right through the side into the shelf. In better work the whole is cramped and nails are driven in upwards askew at the inner corner from beneath.

(13) The mitreing angle is 35 deg.

(14) Always work the saw *towards* the moulding, so that any roughness occurs at the back instead of on the face.

(15) Because otherwise too much wood will be removed and the parts will not be flush when put together.

(16) It is necessary merely to reset the gauge by an amount equal to the set-in of the joint.

(17) No. This should be done only with Scotch glue, because there is no tackiness in casein glue.

(18) No. Glue up the opposite ends independently, and add the remaining rails when the glue has set. This applies to all similar work. It saves having to deal with many joints in one operation.

(19) It prevents the glue from chilling, giving the glue maximum efficiency, and giving more time for the operation.

LESSON 5

(1) Because the flanges of most hinges taper towards the edge, and it is about the centre of the knuckle that all pivoting takes place.

(2) Because otherwise there would be a gap between the door and the side of the cupboard.

(3) Stand in front of the door. If the bolt has to shoot to the left to lock the door, you need a left-hand lock, and *vice versa*.

(4) It should fit over the key with a fairly generous allowance.

LESSON 6

(1) No. You must either remove the polish and stain afresh, or use a dark polish over the existing polish.

(2) No liquid touches the wood. The grain is therefore not raised.

(3) It thins out the wax, enabling it to be spread evenly over the work.

(4) Use a boot-brush. The bristles will reach into the recesses and polish them.

(5) It fills in the grain, so producing a surface free from pores.

(6) No. It is necessary to seal the wood with polish so that no oil is trapped under the surface.

ELECTRICITY

By Barnard Way

LESSON 1

What Is Electricity?

From the very start it must be admitted quite frankly that we do not know what electricity really is, but as the same may be said about almost everything else, it does not matter a great deal. We do know how to set it in motion—not how to *make* it—and we know how to control it. We also know what it will do for us, and in this respect it is about the most useful thing we have, if electricity can be described as a thing. True, many people live comfortably without using it in their homes directly, and only a generation ago its use was very limited; but with the steady extension of its use the amenities of life have been improved for almost everyone. And so it will go on. The next ten years will see an enormous increase in the employment of electricity in the homes of the people. Consequently, it is up to everyone to learn as much as possible about it, and about what it can do for them.

The Nature of Matter

Electricity is not such a difficult subject as some people think. In the advanced stages of its study it becomes a highly complicated science, but an elementary knowledge, sufficient to give the average man confidence in his ability to tackle household repairs and such like, is not hard to attain. Like everything else, it is based upon a number of simple principles that can soon be mastered.

Let us see first what science has discovered about the nature of matter—the material substances, visible and invisible, of which this universe is composed. Everything is reducible to a tiny unit called an atom, and each atom of one substance differs from that of another substance in a particular way. The atoms are by no means the final division, for we believe them to be composed of varying numbers of much smaller particles, the nature of which it is impossible to do more than guess at. We are sure, however, that two of these particles consist of electrical energy, and so it may be said that everything in existence is made up of electricity—electricity in violent motion, for the particles in their respective atoms are all moving in tiny orbits about a central core at velocities incredibly great (Fig. 1).

These particles are known as electrons, protons and neutrons; for our purpose the electron is the most important. The central core of the atom is made up of a proton, and it is surrounded by a certain number of the flying electrons; the difference in the number makes the difference between one substance and another. It is not our business here to go into further details as to the numbers of these electrons, but it may be of interest to note that the three metals that have magnetic properties—iron, cobalt and nickel—have twenty-six, twenty-seven and twenty-eight electrons respectively. The metal with the second best power of conducting an electric current—copper—has twenty-nine, but it has no magnetic properties.

Electrons in Motion

Electrons repel each other strongly, but all are attracted strongly by the proton core. Neutrons do not concern us at all, or so we believe. We say that electrons are negative charges and protons positive charges of electricity, and that is the first important thing to bear in mind.

In the whirling system of electrons a certain number may be detached from the parent atom without immediately altering the nature of that atom. They may attach themselves to a neighbouring atom. They will almost certainly do so if that one has been similarly deprived of some of its electrons. One of nature's most striking displays—lightning—is, of course, an electric discharge on a huge scale. The breaking up of drops of water by the action of a strong wind releases electrons, and these accumulate until there are enough of them to make a discharge in the form of a flash between the clouds in which they have gathered, or into the earth.

Later on, we shall see that electricity in one form "flows" along wires that are called conductors, and it is believed that what happens is just this movement of electrons, from atom to atom, along the length of the wire. It is, perhaps, not of very great importance to know this, and it is by no means certain that this does indeed occur, but it *is* certain that an electric current entails the movement of vast quantities of electrons.

Electricity, Light and Heat

The speed at which a current of electricity travels is exactly the same as that of light; it is the highest speed possible in this universe—186,000 miles a second! This equality of speed between electric currents and light rays is not the only similarity, for just as light can cross any open space, so can electricity in certain forms. The broadcast waves that your radio set picks up have travelled to your aerial across the intervening space. They do so in a form that we call waves, though there is no particular evidence of their existence. Light, and heat too, travel in exactly the same way as this, and it is the rate of motion of the waves that distinguishes light, heat and electricity, as well as other things. The interesting point about electric waves—known as electro-magnetic waves—is that they are all set up by the movement of electrons. This movement is extremely rapid, and is called oscillation. The *frequency* of a wave is the number of oscillations in a second; figures can convey but little, but it is interesting to note that four thousand million million oscillations a second produce the sensation your eyes record as red.

Self Testing Questions

(1) *What is the most important part of an atom?*

(2) *What is the nature of an electron?*

(3) *Name two other things similar in character to electricity.*

THE ANSWERS ARE ON PAGE 247.

LESSON 2

How Is Electricity Made?

ELECTRICITY consists of a movement of electrons from one place to another—so much we have seen. Free electrons—that is, electrons that have been parted from their parent atoms—seize the first opportunity of getting re-attached to an atom that is short of its proper number. Consequently an accumulation, or charge, of electrons is in a highly unstable state. The quantity of electricity is measured by the number of electrons in the charge, and as each one of them is repelling its neighbour vigorously, the charge has a lively nature described as its *potential*. This character may perhaps be compared to the pressure of a quantity of gas; we shall look into that presently.

Some Simple Experiments

The simplest way of producing a charge of electricity is to rub the body of your fountain-pen on the sleeve of your coat. This, in effect, removes electrons from the atoms that go to make up the material

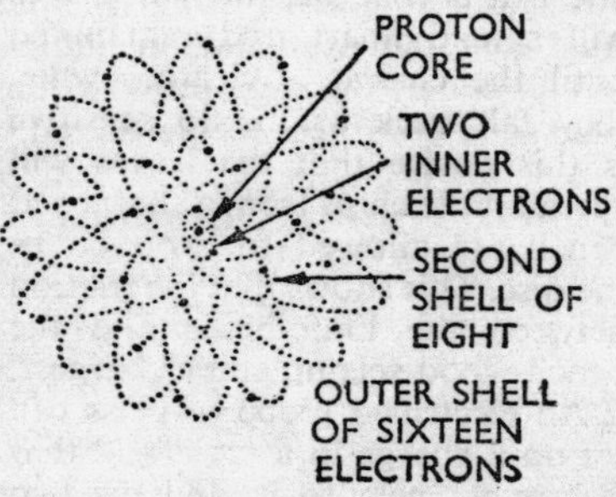

Fig. 1. *A diagram to show the orbits followed by electrons in a copper atom.*

of the coat as well as the pen, and they gather on the vulcanite, preferring that to the coat. Why, we cannot tell.

Here we can make a practical experiment. A stick of sealing-wax serves best; rub this vigorously on your coat-sleeve, so long as they are both dry. The wax is now charged with negative particles, all anxious to get away from each other and to return to an association with a positive particle.

If you bring the end of the stick of wax close to some small bits of tissue-paper that you have previously torn up, these will fly up and stick to the wax (Fig 2). Why is this? The charge of negative particles is strong enough to attract the positive particles—or protons—in the atoms that make up the paper,

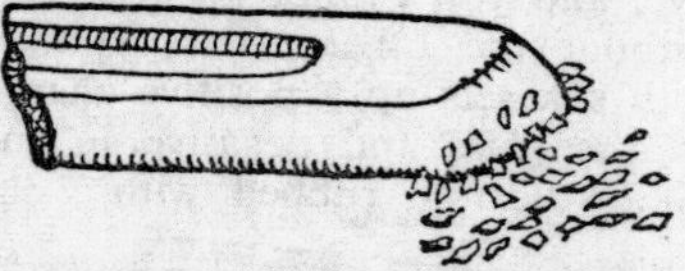

Fig. 2. *The sealing-wax experiment.*

and so the little pieces are held until the electrons have all found homes in those various atoms. Then the paper drops away.

From this simple experiment we discover one of the first great laws governing the science of electricity, which may be set down thus: *Like particles repel, and unlike particles attract, each other.* In various forms we shall meet this law very frequently.

The ancient Greek philosopher, Thales, made the discovery that

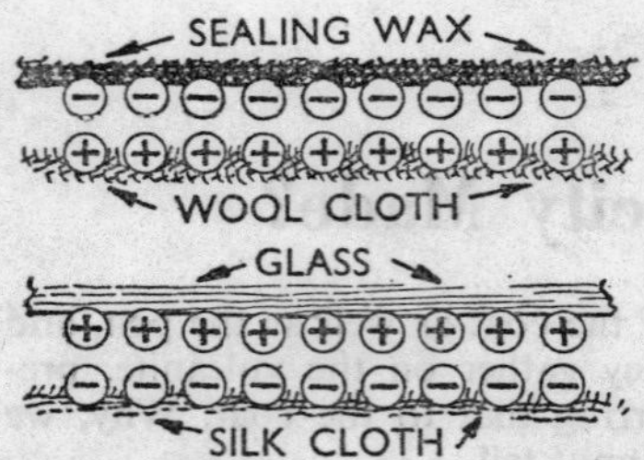

Fig. 3. *Static charges, produced chiefly by friction, are opposite in character.*

amber, rubbed with a silken cloth, would thus attract small pieces of stuff, hairs, and so on. The Greek name for amber, elektron, gave the name to the great science we are about to study, but its original discoverer considered it as nothing more than an entertaining experiment.

Positive and Negative Charges

Many other pairs of substances produce this effect, but some produce it in a different form from that we have just seen. There are two kinds of charges, positive and negative, and you cannot produce one without the other. Glass rubbed with silk sets up a positive charge on the glass and negative in the silk. Vulcanite rubbed with wool

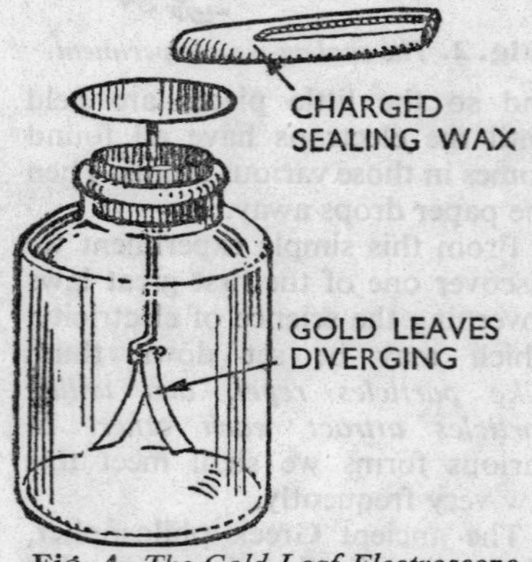

Fig. 4. *The Gold-Leaf Electroscope.*

(your coat-sleeve) results in a negative charge on the vulcanite and a positive on the wool. In diagram form, charges are indicated by a row of + (plus) signs for positive and — (minus) signs for negative.

Friction is one principal source of this form of electricity, which is known as *static* from its ability to keep still (Fig. 3).

Note that positively charged bodies attract those negatively charged, and repel those charged in the same way. The Gold-Leaf Electroscope (Fig. 4) is a sensitive device that tells if a static charge is

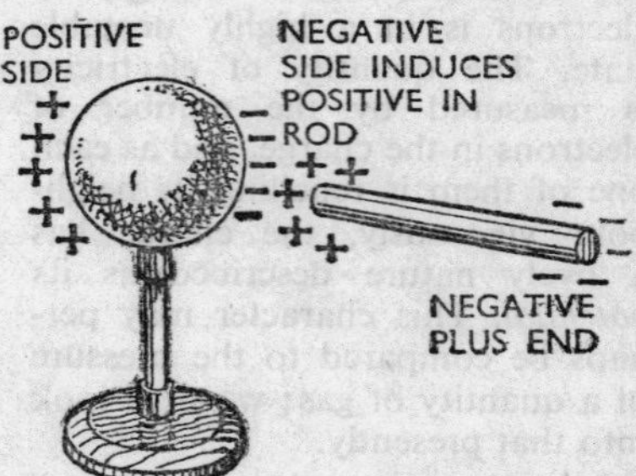

Fig. 5. *The rod receives a charge from the electrified globe by influence.*

present. Hanging from a brass rod in a glass jar is a pair of gold leaves, and on the top end of the brass rod is a disc of the same metal. Bring the electrified rod near to the disc, and if it is charged, the gold leaves will spread apart and remain so until the charge is cleared, when they fall back again. So sensitive is this device that the leaves will spread if the chips from a sharpened pencil are allowed to drop on to the disc. This shows that the friction between the knife-blade and the pencil-wood sets up static charges.

An electrified globe of glass can set up a charge in a brass rod that is brought near to it, and the two ends of the rod will be oppositely charged, though the middle of the rod has none. This charge vanishes as soon as the rod is taken away, but the glass globe will not have lost any of its charge (Fig. 5). Influence is the name given to this effect.

Wimshurst Machine and Leyden Jar

In order to produce powerful charges of this character a machine is used, in which static effects are set up and passed out by this influence effect. The Wimshurst machine is the best known of these. It consists of two glass discs spun in opposite directions by belt-and-pulley gear. On each disc a number of sector strips of tinfoil are cemented. Brass rods with tufts of tinsel at their ends are fixed so that the tinsel touches each sector plate as it passes. The rods are fixed at right angles to each other; hence the tinsel tufts divide the plates into four quadrants (Fig. 6).

A slight positive charge in one of the metal sectors is sufficient to build up considerable quantities of charge, which can be accumulated

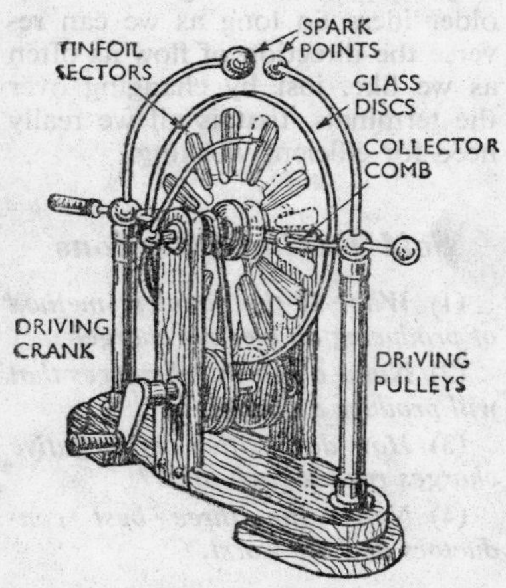

Fig. 6. *The Wimshurst machine.*

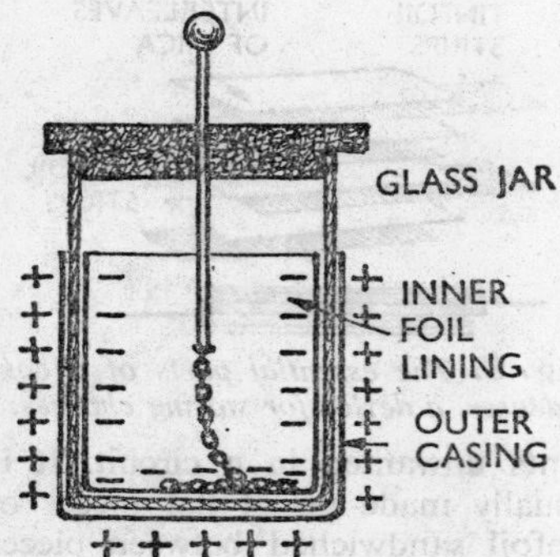

Fig. 7. *A Leyden jar in section.*

and stored in a device called a Leyden jar. This consists of a glass jar coated with tinfoil half-way up, both inside and outside, as shown in the sketch. A brass rod with a knob set in a stopper connects with the inner lining by a short piece of chain. The jar can be charged by connecting the positive terminal of the Wimshurst machine to the knob, holding the outer coating of foil in the hand, or connecting it to the earth. A considerable charge can be put into the jar, and it will remain there for a long time, but it can be discharged by means of a pair of tongs, with insulating handle for preference. If one end of the tongs is brought near the brass knob while the other end touches the outer coating, a good spark will result. You can try it with your knuckle, while holding the jar, but the shock can be rather unpleasant, so look out!

The Wimshurst machine will produce a stream of sparks continuously between the two prime conductors, as the adjustable knobs are called.

The Leyden jar is a form of condenser, a most valuable device for the storage of charges, and for blocking the path of certain cur-

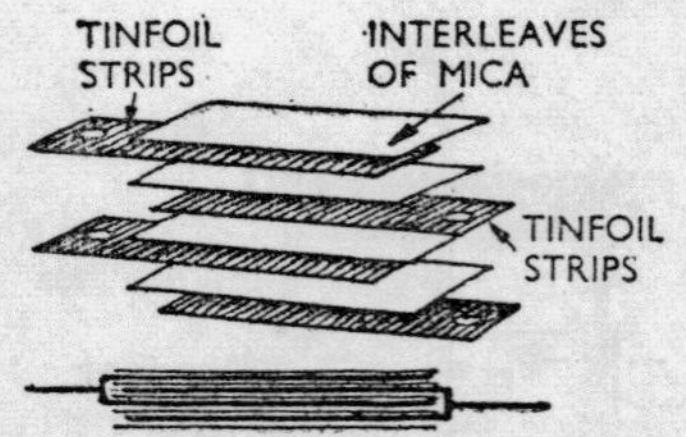

Fig. 8. *The essential parts of a condenser, a device for storing charges.*

rents unwanted in a circuit. It is usually made up of flat pieces of tinfoil sandwiched between pieces of mica, a mineral substance that resists the passage of electricity (Fig. 8).

Conductors and Insulators

This brings us to an important consideration, that of conductors and non-conductors or insulators. Some substances, mostly metals, have the power to pass electricity freely, others cannot do so at all, or only to a very small extent. Between the two extremes there is a wide variation. Here is a list, showing the approximate order from the best conductors to the worst:

CONDUCTORS: silver; copper; aluminium; other metals; carbon; water.

PARTIAL CONDUCTORS: cotton; wood; paper.

INSULATORS: oil; wool; silk; porcelain; rubber; glass; air.

There are many manufactured substances, based on resin and similar natural products, that are very bad conductors, or good insulators, but we have not room to detail these in full. No metal is a perfect conductor, nor is air a perfect insulator, though it is adequate for most electrical work, as we shall see.

The second, and more important form in which electricity exists is the current, or flowing state. We have seen how the positive charge will flow away from an electrified body; now, if by any means that charge could be kept up, then the flow would be continuous. There are various means by which this can be done, the best known, and the simplest, being by the chemical action that takes place in a battery. Fuller details of this action will be found in a later lesson.

Continuous current is generated in the machines we call dynamos; these also will be described in due course. There is one feature about all currents that we have met already, and that is the *polarity*, positive or negative. Current supplied by a battery always flows one way through the conducting wires joining the terminals, but there is very little evidence to prove which way it does flow. Up to a few years ago it was always assumed that it flowed from positive to negative, but modern ideas suggest that the flow is opposite to this. Fortunately it does not really matter very much, because all our electrical devices work for us quite well, and they have been designed on the older idea. So long as we can reverse the direction of flow as often as we like, just by changing over the terminals, that is all we really need for efficient working.

Self Testing Questions

(1) *What is the simplest method of producing an electric charge?*

(2) *Name a pair of substances that will produce a charge.*

(3) *How do positive and negative charges regard each other?*

(4) *Name the three best conductors and the worst.*

THE ANSWERS ARE ON PAGE 247.

LESSON 3

Electricity and Magnetism

EVERYONE knows what a magnet is, and what it can do. Magnets were known to the ancients; the name is derived from Magnesia, a province in Asia Minor, where an ore of iron with strong magnetic properties is found. The Chinese are believed to have been the first to discover that if a bar of this ore were hung by a strand of silk it would take up a position along a line pointing north and south. They are reputed to have used these lodestones in their navigation, and the Phœnicians may have done the same.

For centuries men were satisfied to know just this much about the magnet, just as they were with the amber and static electricity. When scientific men got to work, having available some knowledge of electric currents, it was discovered that there was more than a connection between electricity and magnetism; they were, in fact, part of the same science.

A piece of steel, rubbed with a lodestone, was given similar powers, but the lodestone lost nothing; this is one of the remarkable points about it all. One small magnet is sufficient to magnetise all the steel in the world, without loss to itself.

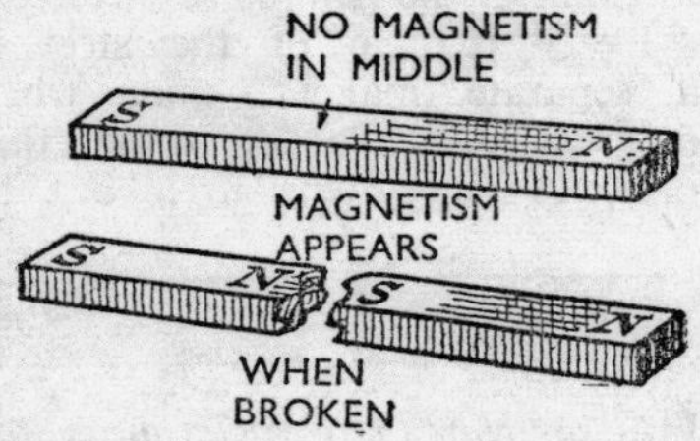

Fig. 9. *Two complete magnets result where one magnet is broken in half.*

The power of a magnet lies at its two ends, with none at all in the middle. Break it, and you have two complete magnets (Fig. 9). These ends are called its poles, and they are referred to, for convenience, as north and south, the north being the one that points in the direction of the north pole of the earth. The very first experiments show that, with two magnets at work, north poles repel each other, but north attracts south. Most magnets have a letter "N" stamped upon the north-seeking pole, which is really its south pole.

The first law of magnetism lays it down thus: *Like poles repel, unlike poles attract.* This is suggestive of the behaviour of positive and negative charges of electricity.

Demonstration of this law can be made by magnetising strips of steel—tinplate will do, though it is not very good—and floating them on corks (Fig. 10). To make a magnet of this sort, the steel strip should be laid on the table, and one pole of a magnet drawn along it from one end to the other several times, lifting the magnet clear every time. The metal must be

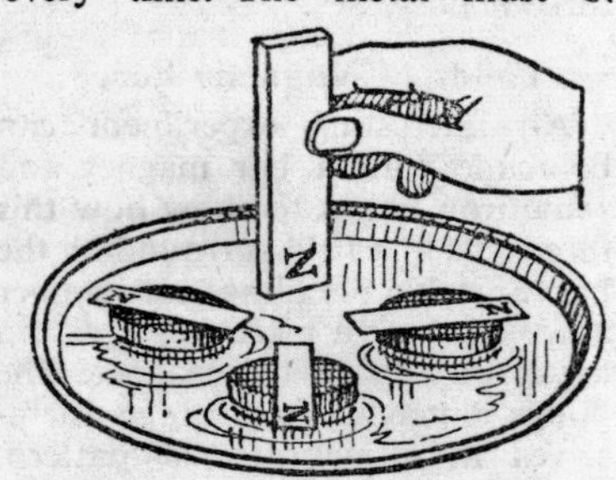

Fig. 10. *Demonstrating the first law of magnetism—attraction and repulsion.*

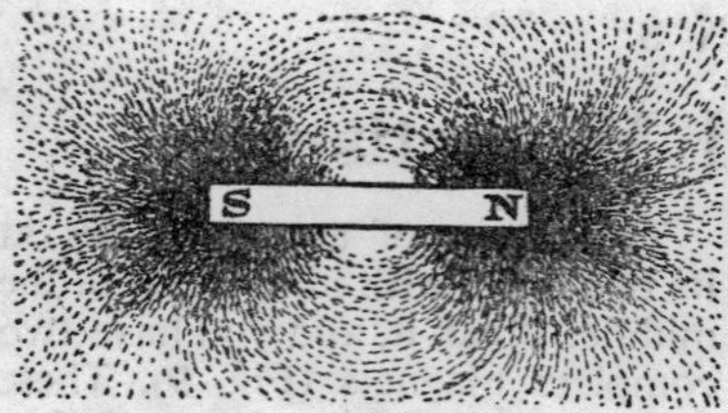

Fig. 11. *The magnetic field of a bar magnet, shown by iron filings.*

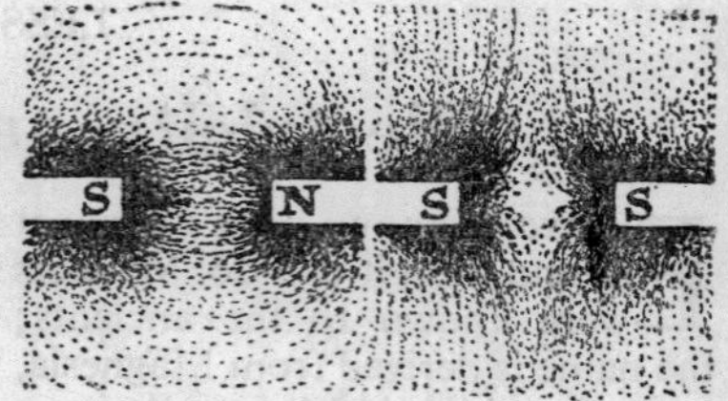

Fig. 12. *The fields between* (left) *unlike, and* (right) *like, poles.*

steel and not iron, for though iron is attracted and held by a magnet, it does not retain the magnetism as steel does. Actually this property of iron is extremely valuable; it is the basis of all our great dynamos, motors and other necessary apparatus.

The earth is a huge magnet, and the poles are very close to the imaginary poles that we call north and south, about which it rotates. It is this fact that makes the mariner's compass possible.

The attraction of a magnet can only be cut off in one way; it will act through any substance or metal except iron. You can wrap a magnet in as many layers of different things as you like, but it still acts on iron or steel through them all. Put it into an iron box, however, and all its power is gone, because the iron conducts away all the magnetic force it possesses.

Fields of Magnetic Force

An interesting experiment can be made with a bar magnet and some iron filings to show how this force acts in a field surrounding the bar. Sprinkle the filings evenly over a postcard, or a piece of glass, and lay it on top of the magnet. The filings immediately arrange themselves in a symmetrical pattern, which can be improved by tapping the card lightly (Fig. 11).

The experiment can be repeated with a horseshoe magnet, or two magnets laid first with both north poles toward each other, but not touching, and then with north and south poles similarly arranged (Fig. 12).

Now, if a wire carrying an electric current is surrounded by a piece of card on which iron filings are dusted, it will be found that the filings sort themselves out into rings, suggestive of magnetic action of some sort. The fact is that an electric current does set up a magnetic field outside the wire along which it travels (Fig. 14).

The lines drawn out by the filings in the pattern suggest lines of force, and this name has been applied to imaginary lines, indicating by their closeness the strength of the magnet. When we refer later to the magnetic lines, it is these that will be meant; there are no such actual lines, of course, but it helps the imagination to think of the field as so covered.

Every particle of the steel is a separate magnet, and, when magnetised, each of these tiny particles straightens itself out to

Fig. 13. *How the particles in an iron bar may be arranged* (left) *before, and* (right) *after, magnetising.*

point along the line of the whole magnet (Fig. 13). The harder the steel, the more difficult to make a magnet of it, but once it is done it will hold its power tenaciously and will be difficult to de-magnetise again. To remove magnetism is not easy without spoiling the steel. It can be done only by hammering or by heating to red heat.

The metals cobalt and nickel are slightly magnetic, and all alloy steel containing either of these is able to take more magnetism and hold it better than a simple steel. Other metals, such as manganese, alloyed into the steel make it non-magnetic altogether.

Peculiarities of Magnets

There are some odd things about magnets that are not easy to account for. Hang a horseshoe magnet with its poles pointing downward and load it with pieces of iron to the limit. After a day like this, a further load can be added, and later on still more, showing that an increased power has come from somewhere. When the limit is finally reached and the whole load is pulled off, the power has gone back to what it was in the beginning.

The magnets to which we have been referring are what is known as permanent, and in that form they do not show any immediate connection between magnetism and electricity. If a coil of insulated wire is wound around a bar of iron, and a current of electricity is run through the coil, then the iron is at once magnetised (Fig. 15). Changing the direction of the current changes the poles of the magnet. Cut off the current, and the magnetism is gone at once—so long as the bar was iron and not steel. If it had been steel, then some magnetism would have remained, though not so much as when the current was on.

This is the electro-magnet, a much more powerful form than the permanent magnet. It is used in every kind of electrical machine and for hundreds of other duties besides. Some of these we shall see.

How to Make an Electro-Magnet

It is a good exercise to make an electro-magnet. A small one is sufficient, and can be used for many experiments and for working models. Instead of using a bar of iron, take a quantity of soft iron wire; bend this to horseshoe shape and tie it into as tight a bundle as possible. Make the bundle about half an inch in diameter, and trim the ends square and sharp with a

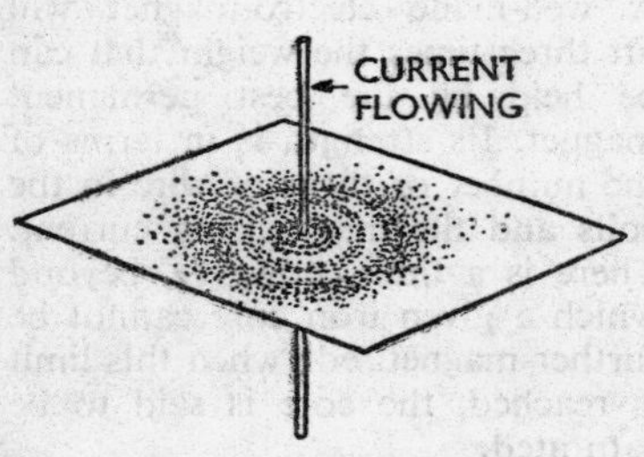

Fig. 14. *A magnetic field surrounds the wire carrying a current.*

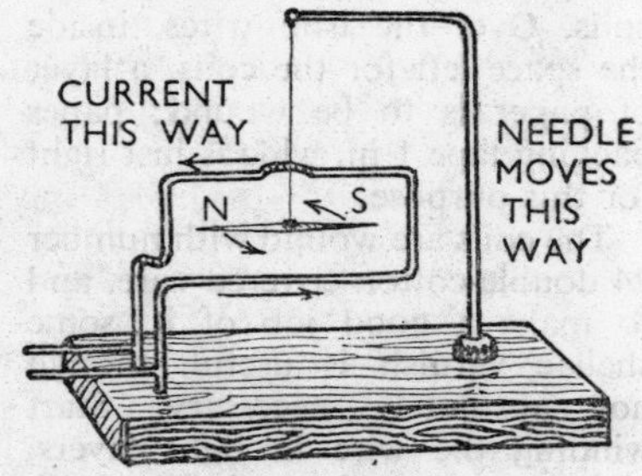

Fig. 15. *Demonstrating the magnetic effect of a flowing current.*

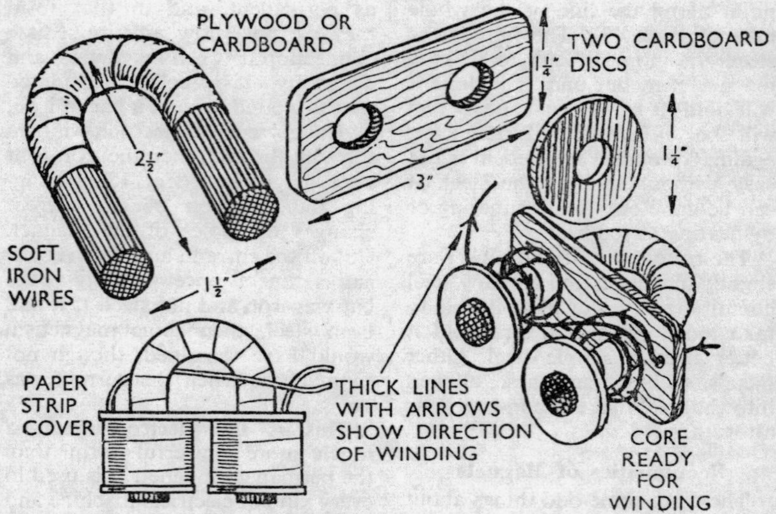

Fig. 16. *Sketches to show the parts of a home-made electro-magnet.*

fine file. The centres of the poles should be 1½ in. apart. Now take an oblong piece of plywood or thick cardboard, 3 in. long and 1½ in. broad. Through it cut two holes spaced 1½ in. apart; through these force the pole legs, packing them tightly with extra wires if necessary. Push this down until the legs stand clear by 1¼ in. (Fig. 16).

Now put on each pole-end a disc of thick cardboard, also wedged tightly, 1½ in. in diameter, and you are ready for winding the coils. Over the iron wires, inside the space left for the coils, a layer of paper is to be wound; paper packing tape 1 in. wide is just right for this purpose.

The coils are wound with number 24 double-cotton-covered wire, and to make a good job of it, some shellac varnish is useful, though not absolutely necessary. Start winding the wire in tight layers, giving a coat of varnish to each layer as soon as it is complete. Finish one coil completely first, counting the number of turns put on, then cross over as shown in the diagram and start winding the other coil *in the opposite direction*. When an equal number of turns has been put on this second coil, it is ready. Wind a layer of the packing-tape round the outside of each coil and your magnet is complete.

The free ends of the wire can now be joined to the poles of a flash-lamp battery, and the power of your magnet will astonish you. A well-made electro-magnet will lift three times the weight that can be held by the best permanent magnet. Its strength is in terms of the number of turns of wire in the coils and the magnetising current. There is a limit, however, beyond which a given iron core cannot be further magnetised; when this limit is reached, the core is said to be saturated.

Magnets of great power are made for many industrial purposes. Two extremes may be quoted; the first a device in use in eye hospitals for removing small splinters of iron or steel from the eyes of workmen who have been injured in factory work. In this, the magnetism is concentrated into a core with a sharp conical point, and the patient's eye being brought up close to this, the splinter is gently drawn out. The other type of electro-magnet is used in steel works for lifting heavy steel plates and girders. A magnet, slung from the hook of a crane, can be lowered on to the material that has to be lifted, and, current being switched on, the steel is held by the magnet so that it can be lifted by the crane. Such work is often awkward and difficult where ordinary cranes have to be used, but the lifting magnet makes light of it. Hot steel from the forge can be lifted, long before men can put slings round it; scrap steel—nasty jagged stuff that tears the stoutest leather gloves—can be handled easily. The current consumed by the eye-magnet would lift about 4

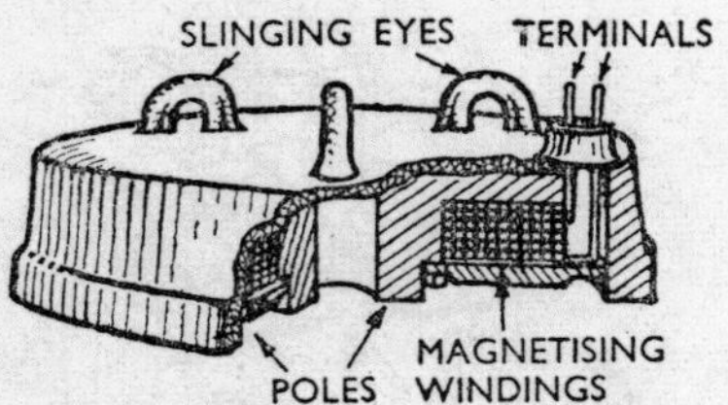

Fig. 17. *Part section of a lifting magnet for a crane.*

tons of steel if applied in this way! The biggest crane-magnets can lift about 30 tons, and the current they use represents about 16 horse-power.

Self Testing Questions

(1) *Which pole of a suspended magnet points North?*

(2) *What is the First Law of Magnetism?*

(3) *What is the connection between electricity and magnetism?*

(4) *What metals compose permanent and electro-magnets?*

THE ANSWERS ARE ON PAGE 247.

LESSON 4

Electricity By Chemical Action

In the science of chemistry we learn that many pairs of substances, when mixed together, will act upon each other, the result in the end being a pair of entirely different substances from those we started from. In addition to this change, other action takes place; it may be that heat is given off, or else the product is much colder. The heat may be intense enough to produce fire, or even light, but the effect that interests us most is the production of electricity.

The simplest possible example of this can be demonstrated if you have a sensitive tongue. Take a shilling and a halfpenny and hold them apart, but in contact with your tongue, one on top and one below. Now bring their outer edges in contact while they still touch your tongue, and you should experience what can only be called an effect; it is hardly a flavour. It is a very small electric current due to the slightly acid nature of the moisture on your tongue, acting upon a pair of different metals.

Two plates, of zinc and of copper,

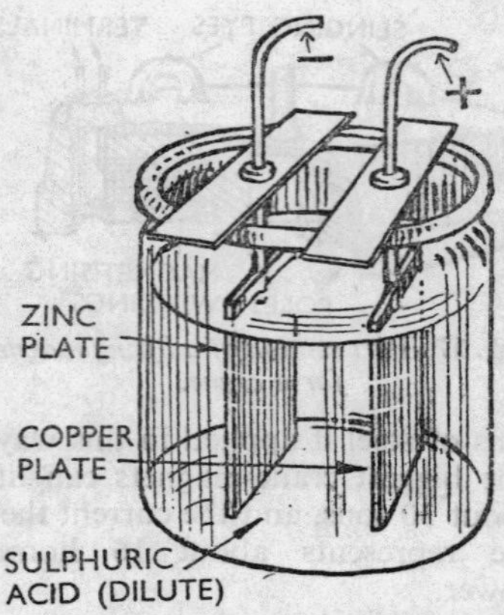

Fig. 18. *The simple electric cell.*

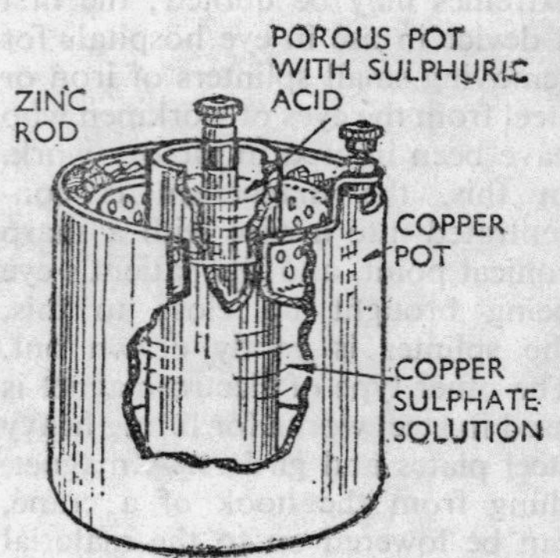

Fig. 19. *The Post Office Daniell cell gives a steady current of* 1·1 *volts.*

suspended in a jar of dilute sulphuric acid resist the action of the acid, so long as they are in a pure form. If the plates are connected by a length of wire, then the acid gets to work at once, and bubbles of hydrogen gather on the copper. The zinc plate will be slowly consumed, turning what was the weak acid into a solution of zinc sulphate. What is interesting to us is the fact that a current of electricity flows through the connecting wire, and this can be made to do work of some sort (Fig. 18).

Electric Cells

This work is not something for nothing, it is a conversion of one form of energy into another; the change of state in the zinc and the acid releases energy in the form of current, which, as we have seen, entails the setting in motion of a quantity of free electrons. Cut the connecting wire between the two plates and all action stops at once.

We call this arrangement a *cell*; it is of a simple type, and, considered as a source of electricity, extremely wasteful. At one time the chemical battery of this sort was the principal source of current, though there were numerous variations in the component material. The Post Office telegraphists used a cell in which a saturated solution of copper sulphate was held in a copper jar. Immersed in this was a porous pot holding weak sulphuric acid, in which a stick of zinc stood. The current flowed in a wire joining the zinc stick and the copper pot. It was a useful type of cell, and

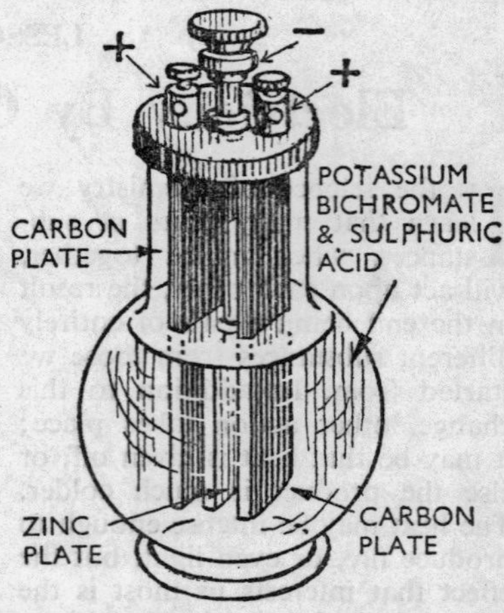

Fig. 20. *The bichromate of potash cell will give a current of* 2 *volts.*

would give a steady current continuously (Fig. 19). Several of them would be joined together to form a battery of cells.

Another cell used a zinc plate suspended between two carbon plates in a strong solution of bichromate of potash and sulphuric acid. When not in use, the zinc plate had to be lifted out of the solution because the acid would eat it away quickly, whether the cell was giving current or not (Fig. 20).

The Leclanché Cell

The trouble with chemical cells is that relatively short use finds them choked with bubbles of hydrogen; this is particularly true of the simple acid and metal type. Some way had to be found of getting rid of this effect, and the two latter types of cells are much more satisfactory, though continuous action brings about a gradual falling off in the current. This choking effect is called polarisation.

The Leclanché cell uses a plate of carbon, packed in black oxide of manganese in a porous jar, immersed in a strong solution of sal-ammoniac, in which a zinc stick stands. Current flows as soon as the zinc and carbon are joined, but it cannot maintain a constant flow very long. The good feature of such a cell is its ability to recover quickly in readiness for the next call; for this reason batteries of these cells were formerly used to ring electric bells (Fig. 21).

The so-called dry batteries used for portable lamps and torches, for bells, radio sets and other purposes, are all based upon this cell. The sal-ammoniac, instead of being in solution, is in the form of a moist paste, enclosed in a small cylinder of sheet zinc. Unlike the wet Leclanché cell, they cannot be revived once their life is ended. With the wet cell, all that is required is a fresh solution of sal-ammoniac—2 oz. in a pint of water, a clean up, and it will be as good as ever.

You should know the names given to the various parts of these batteries, and be able to distinguish between the positive and negative

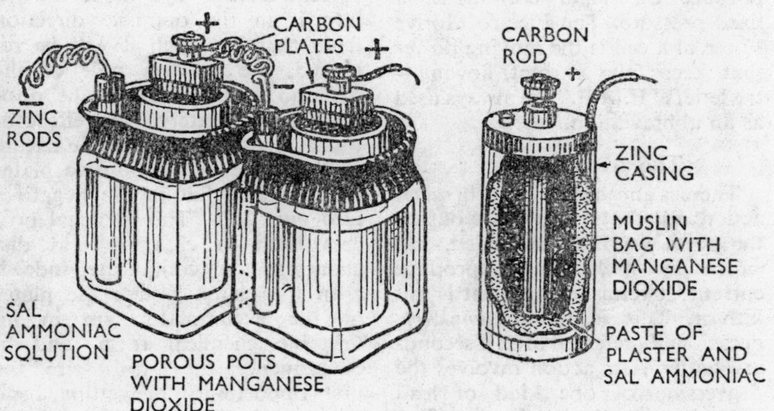

Fig. 21. *On the left is a Leclanché wet battery of two cells; on the right, a dry cell of the same sort. A single cell will give* 1·4 *volts. This is a widely-used type.*

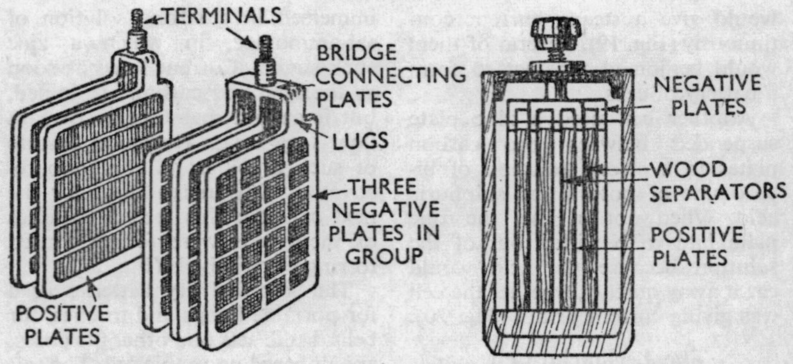

Fig. 22. *The plates of an accumulator,* (left) *separated, and* (right) *assembled.*

poles. The drawings indicate these. The solutions, whether of acid or of other substances, are the electrolyte; the oxide of manganese, or the bichromate of potash, or other chemical forms, the depolariser, for getting rid of the choking hydrogen bubbles. The carbon or copper plates form the positive pole, or anode, and the zinc is the negative or cathode. Which way the current really flows is immaterial.

Different cells, when in a good active state, can be relied upon to produce a certain current at a fixed pressure. The Electro-Motive Force of a cell is the moving power that keeps the current flowing—the letters "E.M.F." are always used as an abbreviation.

The Accumulator

There is another form of chemical action cell that has almost ousted the types we have discussed, but which by itself cannot produce current; it returns only what is put into it. This is the *accumulator,* occasionally referred to as a secondary battery. Its action involves the conversion of one kind of lead oxide into another under the effect of the action of sulphuric acid and an electric current.

There is, as a rule, a number of positive plates interleaved with negative plates, both kinds being made of lead in a honeycomb or grid form. This grid is packed with red oxide of lead for the positive plates and another oxide of lead called letharge for the negatives, and the whole group is immersed in sulphuric acid in a glass or celluloid jar (Fig. 22).

Charging an Accumulator

To charge an accumulator, direct current from a dynamo is turned into it in the opposite direction from that in which it will be returned, the positive pole of the dynamo being joined to the positive of the battery. The effect of this current is to change the nature of the oxide in the positive plates and to turn that in the negatives into pure lead. The chemical process both in charging and discharging is very complicated indeed.

In the charged state the plates of the accumulator are in an unstable chemical form, and in consequence they will seize the first opportunity of getting back to normal. This comes when the terminals are joined together by way of a working circuit such as a lamp, or a motor. When this is done, the material in the plates begins to return to its original form, giving out current in a very steady flow which is maintained practically undiminished until the charge is quite expended. An interesting point about this is that the state of the electrolyte gives exact information about the charge still remaining.

Using the Hydrometer

To find out about this, the device called a hydrometer is used. This consists of a glass tube with a bulb in it, into which a quantity of the electrolyte can be drawn by means of a rubber bulb at the top. Inside the tube is a little weighted float, marked with graduations, and the depth at which this will float in the acid is a measure of the gravity of the electrolyte. Fully charged, the gravity should be about 1·200, and in the discharged state it will drop to about 1·100.

Accumulators are rated in ampère-hours capacity. A 60-ampère-hour battery can be discharged at a rate of 2 amps. and will continue this for practically 30 hours, or 1 amp. for nearly 60 hours. Each cell will give a steady 2 volts. Batteries for motor-car starting and lighting are made to withstand very heavy discharges for short periods, at rates that would quickly destroy ordinary types.

Self Testing Questions

(1) *Name the parts of a simple cell.*

(2) *What is the purpose of the depolariser?*

(3) *Name the electrolyte and depolariser of a Leclanché cell.*

(4) *What does E.M.F. mean?*

THE ANSWERS ARE ON PAGE 247.

LESSON 5

Measurement and Units

We have already suggested that electricity is measurable in point of quantity flowing, and it is so, but with such an indefinite thing it is not simple to establish any basis of measurement. What we have to do is to consider what the electric current will do to something else, that we *can* measure, if we allow it to flow. In some respects, electricity flowing along a wire is like water flowing in a pipe. With the latter, the volume of water that passes through the pipe in a minute can be measured, and so we could get the rate of flow in a fixed time.

The electro-motive force has already been mentioned, and this can quite reasonably be compared to the pressure that pushes the current along. The electrical unit is the *volt*, and you can think of volts in terms of pressure; the more volts, then the greater will be the current flow. The rate of flow is the voltage.

Now we have also seen that some substances allow a current to pass more easily than others. Some

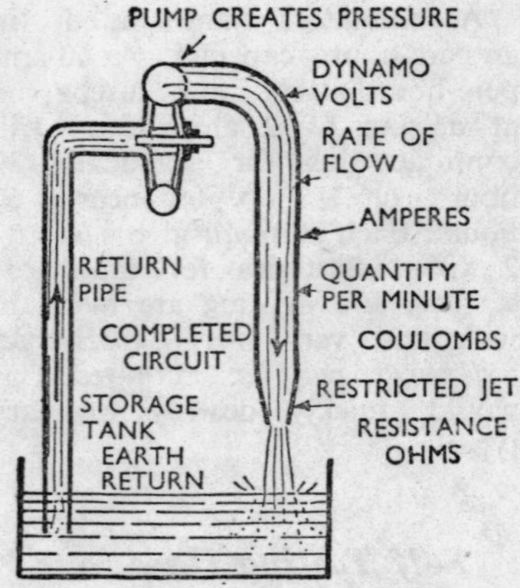

Fig. 23. *The flow of water and of electricity compared.*

metals conduct the current very well, and some other substances do their utmost to resist. No metal, however, is a perfect conductor; they all offer some resistance, and this is measured in units called *ohms.* If our current has to flow through a group of various pieces of apparatus, then we speak of the resistance of the circuit. The amount of this resistance is always the same, no matter how much current we get through.

The Ampère

Let us now consider another unit, the one known as an *ampère*, which represents the rate at which the flow is maintained. Going back to our comparison with water in a pipe, we can think of a continuous flow of so much water every minute, so long as the pipe remains clear and a constant supply of water at a steady pressure is available at the entrance to the pipe. If the delivery end of the pipe is partly closed, as it might be by a tap, then the rate of flow will be checked, but this rate can be brought back to the original quantity by increasing the pressure at the supply end. Also, the rate of flow can be reduced, and will be reduced, if an additional length of pipe with a rough bore be added. Friction in the bore will always check the flow of water, and this, as well as the partial closing of the outlet, can be compared to the resistance of an electric circuit.

Ohm's Law

In this comparison we have the same three essential items that appear in the electric circuit, all acting in precisely the same way. These are Rate of Flow (ampères), Resistance of Circuit (ohms), and Pressure of Supply (volts). The simple law governing their relationship is called Ohm's Law, and is set down thus as an equation:

$$E = I \times R, \text{ or } I = \frac{E}{R},$$

where E is the E.M.F. in volts, I is the current in ampères (amps. for short), R is the resistance in ohms. We shall return to this law again shortly, but a brief study of it will show that a pressure of one volt will see to it that a current of 1 ampère gets past a resistance amounting to 1 ohm.

Combinations of these primary units are met with when we consider the rating of electrical machinery or power-using apparatus.

Measuring Electric Power and Consumption

The ampère-hour represents a current of 1 ampère in continuous flow for 1 hour. The watt is a unit of power, representing a current of 1 ampère at a pressure of 1 volt; thus, a 40-watt lamp is able to deal with various combinations of current and pressure amounting to 40. A kilowatt is the more convenient form to consider where big machines are concerned; it amounts to 1000 watts, and is usually abbreviated as K.W. The kilowatt is equal to about one and one-third engine horse-power.

Now 1 kilowatt flowing for an hour would seem to be a clear basis for a power unit, and this is exactly what the electricity meter in your house sets out to record. Kilowatt-hours (k.w.h.) are the units you pay for, whatever your demands on the supply may be required to do. Let us see what we can make out of these units in terms of, say, electric light.

The pressure at which current is supplied for domestic use in this country varies from 220 to 250 volts, let us say 240. If we have four sizes of lamps in use in our house, and these are rated at 5, 40, 60 and 100 watts, what can we get out of each one by the time one unit of electricity is recorded on the meter?

One unit equals one k.w.h., that is 1000 watts flowing for 1 hour, so clearly all we have to do is to divide 1000 by the wattage of the lamp, and the result gives us the number of hours of light that can be expected. The 5-watt lamp will give 200 hours, and the 100-watt, 10 hours. Alternatively, 200 lamps of 5 watts rating will consume a steady 1 k.w. every hour, as will twenty-five lamps of 40 watts, or ten of 100 watts. Two each of the four sizes of lamps mentioned, all lit up together, will take 2 hours 26½ minutes to consume one unit.

Measuring Resistance

What resistance does the incandescent wire inside the lamp offer to the passage of the current? This is easily discovered by the use of Ohm's Law. The 5-watt lamp allows a current equal to $\frac{5}{240}$ amps. to pass—remember that 5 watts represents 5 amps. × volts. Now $I \times R = E$, so $R = \frac{E}{I}$.

$$E = 240, \text{ and } I = \frac{5}{240}.$$

$$\text{So } R = \frac{240 \times 240}{5} = 11{,}520 \text{ ohms.}$$

In the same way, the 100-watt lamp can be shown to pass 0·41 amps. and to have a resistance amounting to 576 ohms.

Electricity Bills

This rule applies equally well in all cases, so that you can get a fair idea of what your electricity bills ought to be; and when considering the purchase of domestic appliances, you can soon discover for how many hours it will be possible to run them on one unit.

The unit of electrical quantity is not often used outside scientific circles. It is the coulomb, and represents that quantity of electricity that passes when a current of 1 ampère flows for 1 minute. It need not really trouble us again, but it is as well to know what it means.

Self Testing Questions

(1) *What are the factors that govern the flow of a current in a circuit?*

(2) *In a shop there are ten lamps, each with a resistance of* 1440 *ohms; the voltage is* 240. *The bill at the end of one quarter is* £1 11*s.* 6*d.; this includes a fixed charge of* 15*s.* *and* ½*d. per unit. Find the wattage of the lamps, and the number of hours they have been used.*

THE ANSWERS ARE ON PAGE 247.

LESSON 6

Electrical Symbols and Circuits

It is of the greatest assistance in describing an electrical circuit —that is, an arrangement of apparatus, batteries and so on— to be able to make a clearly understood diagram of it all. In order to do this, a system of symbols has been devised, in which every piece of apparatus is represented by its own mark, and this mark or symbol always means just that and nothing else. It is necessary to understand the system at this point in our studies, but it will be necessary at the same time to mention a good many items of equipment that we have not yet come across. We shall give full details of these in due course.

Learn These Electrical Symbols

The page opposite shows these symbols. Some of them suggest, by their form, the actual thing themselves; batteries, for instance, coils, switches, lamps. A line represents a conductor. Note that these are always drawn as straight, with bends at right angles, never curved, as you often find them in actual apparatus. Where one line crosses over another, without touching it so as to make electrical connection, it is shown either with a little arch over, or else without the arch. If lines do make electrical connection, then a round spot is put at that point.

A single cell is represented by a thin line and a shorter, thick one; the first indicates the positive pole and the second the negative. A battery, which, you will remember, is a number of cells joined together, is shown by a repetition of this symbol.

Here we meet another important matter: the two ways of connecting electrical apparatus in a circuit. If the current from a battery goes through everything in a line and then returns to the battery, the circuit is described as being in *series*. Consider a simple arrangement of a battery, a switch and two lamps. If the current pushes its way through one lamp, and then in its somewhat depleted state has to push through the second one, the result would be a very poor sort of light. In Fig. 25 compare top and bottom.

Now consider the re-arrangement of the circuit, where the two lamps bridge across two lines, one coming away from the switch and the other returning to the battery. In this arrangement, described as in *parallel*, each lamp receives full pressure from the battery, and, in consequence, gives full light.

Batteries in Series and in Parallel

The same arrangement can be used where more than one cell is joined up into a battery. If the cells are joined up positive to negative throughout, they are in series, and the result is a multiplication of volts, each cell adding its extra quota. But we do not get a heavier current, and actually, owing to the internal resistance of each cell, we do not really get the full voltage that we should have. Now, if the battery is made up in parallel, all positives being joined and all negatives also, we get no increase in

ELECTRICAL SYMBOLS AND CIRCUITS

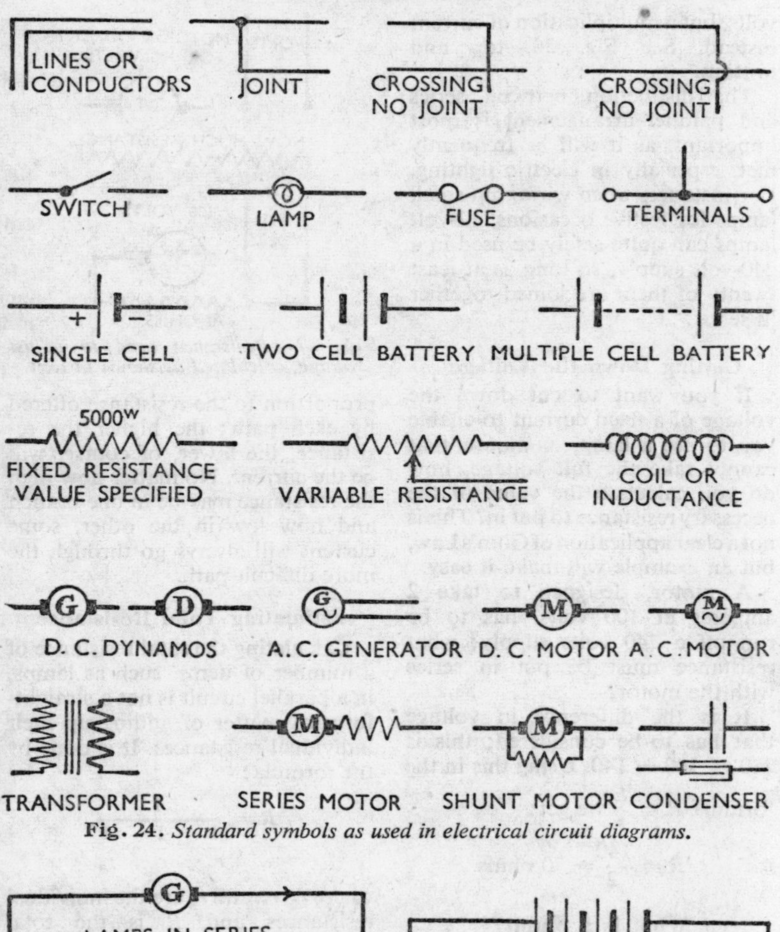

Fig. 24. *Standard symbols as used in electrical circuit diagrams.*

G
LAMPS IN SERIES
G
LAMPS IN PARALLEL

CELLS IN SERIES
GIVE MORE VOLTS
CELLS IN PARALLEL
GIVE MORE CURRENT

Figs. 25 and 26. (Left) *Fig. 25, circuit diagrams of a dynamo and lamps in series and in parallel.* (Right) *Fig. 26, a battery of cells in series and in parallel.*

volts, but a multiplication of current instead. See Fig. 26, top and bottom.

The distinction between series and parallel arrangement is most important, as it will be frequently met, especially in electric lighting. For instance, when wiring up small lamps for festive occasions, 12-volt lamps can quite safely be used in a 240-volt supply, so long as at least twenty of them are joined together in series.

Cutting Down the Voltage

If you want to cut down the voltage of a fixed current to enable you to use a lamp, or motor, that cannot take the full voltage, how do you calculate the value of the necessary resistance to put in? This is not a clear application of Ohm's Law, but an example will make it easy.

A motor, designed to take 2 ampères at 100 volts, has to be run off a 240 volts supply; what resistance must be put in series with the motor?

It is the difference in voltage that has to be considered; this is 240 — 100 = 140. Using this in the formula $R = \frac{E}{I}$ we get:

$$R = \frac{140}{2} = 70 \text{ ohms.}$$

What is a Shunt?

A *shunt* gives an alternative path or a side-track through which a part of the current can flow. It is formed by dividing the circuit into two branches, which rejoin after passing through the items in the circuit they were designed to supply. This system is much used in electrical engineering.

You should note that the current does not necessarily divide equally at the branch; the division is in

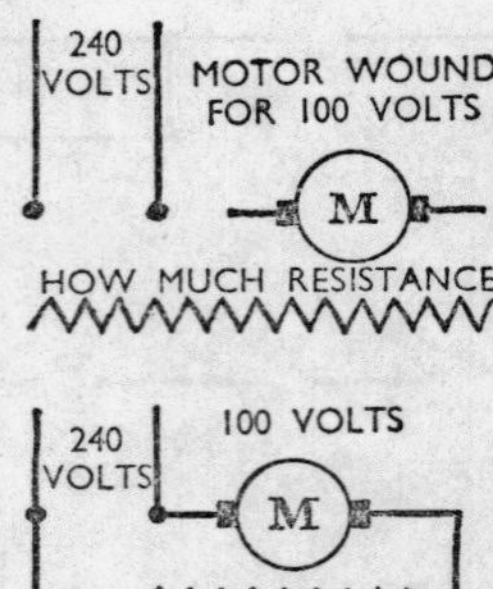

Fig. 27. *Resistance used to adjust voltage, calculated as shown in text.*

proportion to the resistance offered by each path: the higher the resistance, the lower, of course, will be the current. No matter how high the resistance may be in one branch and how low in the other, some current will always go through the more difficult path.

Estimating Total Resistance

Calculating the total resistance of a number of items, such as lamps, in a parallel circuit is not a straightforward matter of adding up their individual resistances. It is done by the formula:

$$R = \frac{1}{\frac{1}{r_1} + \frac{1}{r_2} + \frac{1}{r_3}},$$

where r_1, r_2, and r_3 are the individual resistances and R is the total wanted. As an example, if we connect four lamps, each having a resistance of 1,000 ohms, in parallel, then the total resistance will be found thus:

$$R = \frac{1}{\frac{1}{1000} + \frac{1}{1000} + \frac{1}{1000} + \frac{1}{1000}}$$
$$= 250 \text{ ohms.}$$

This result seems somewhat surprising by comparison with the total of 4,000 ohms that results from joining in series, but when the lamps are considered as each offering a path, four of them in all, the reason becomes more plain.

There is one more symbol that needs a word of explanation, and that is the little wavy mark used to indicate an alternating-current supply, or piece of apparatus designed to work such current. A full explanation of alternating current follows in Lesson 8, but it is necessary to show the symbol here for the sake of completeness.

Self Testing Questions

(1) *In the symbol for a cell, which is the positive pole?*

(2) *You have two 12-volt lamps. How would you wire them to get full light in a 12-volt circuit, and in a 24-volt circuit?*

(3) *You have a 100-volt 60-watt lamp to wire into a 220-volt circuit, and a quantity of wire leaving a resistance of 25 ohms to the foot. How would you arrange this?*

THE ANSWERS ARE ON PAGE 247,

LESSON 7

Generating Electricity

In our first lesson we mentioned the chief methods by means of which electricity could be made to flow, the principal method being the mechanical one. Before we go into fuller details of the machines used, it will be necessary to understand one or two principles, the discovery of which led up to the invention of the dynamo.

The first of these was made by the great Michael Faraday, who found that a magnet moved in and out of the loops of a coil of wire of many turns set up impulses of current in the coil, and these could be measured by a galvanometer—a sensitive instrument for recording currents (Fig. 28). He found, too, that a coil of wire, moved through the field of a fixed magnet, produced the same result. An old scientific experiment is the one in which you move a sheet of copper or aluminium between the poles of a magnet. Neither of these two metals is magnetic, but moving the sheet is like stirring treacle—there is resistance to the movement.

Faraday's first experiment resulted in the discovery of what we call *induction*, and we say that the movement of a closed circuit in a magnetic field sets up currents by induction. Later on he found that if a steady current through one coil was changed in any way, a current pulse would be set up in another coil set close to the first one, but not otherwise connected. This change of current can be made by switching on and off, or by

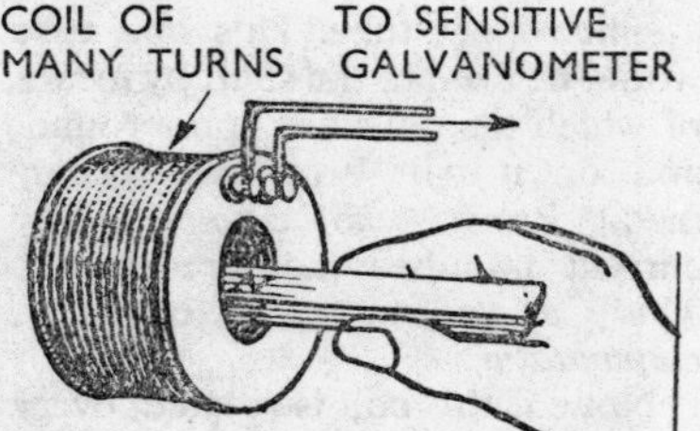

Fig. 28. *Faraday's experiment.*

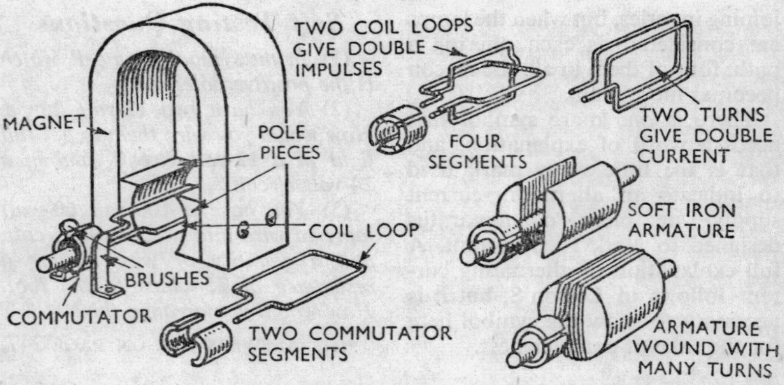

Fig. 29. *The simplest form of dynamo, based on Faraday's discoveries.*

quick increases or decreases; whatever they are, the result is the same. Now let us see how these principles have been worked into the generation of electricity.

The Commutator

First of all we had better think of a permanent magnet machine in which we have a ready-made magnetic field. Fig. 29, above, shows this, with the poles set downward; iron shoes fixed to their ends form a tunnel in which the wire coils can be spun round. Imagine the lines of magnetic force crossing this tunnel, as we saw in the lesson on magnets (page 188).

To make the diagram clearer, instead of a thick coil of wire, one loop only is shown, its two ends being fastened to the two halves of a split copper tube. This split tube would be fixed to the shaft by means of which the coils are spun round, and on it will bear two springy metal brushes to take off any current impulses that are set up. This arrangement is called a *commutator*.

Now, if this coil is rotated, every time it cuts across those lines of force an impulse will be passed on, and if the ends of wire from the brushes are connected to a sensitive instrument, then those pulses will be recorded. Such an apparatus would, however, produce but little electricity. We must see in what way it can be improved. One improvement would be to add to the number of the wire loops, giving each loop a pair of commutator segments of its own, but, even so, very little useful current could be expected to be produced.

Arriving at the Dynamo

A better way to set about it is to wind the coils of wire upon a soft iron block, shaped so that it will turn round freely between the pole shoes of the magnet, yet be as near to them as possible. This iron gives a very free passage for the lines of force, so that the coils have a concentrated field in which to work. In this way much stronger impulses are generated. A machine constructed on this principle is called a dynamo.

Now, some people wrongly suppose that power is given away for nothing in the dynamo. But it is only necessary to turn the shaft of a quite small dynamo to discover that a good deal of power is needed to pull the armature round before electrical energy can be generated. This comes from the engine used to drive the shaft of the dynamo. In brief, the force required to drive the dynamo is transformed by the dynamo into electrical power.

This permanent-magnet type of machine would not be much good for big outputs of current, so we shall have to look round for further improvements. We have already seen how magnets of greater power are easily made, magnets that will give several times as strong a field as the best permanent magnet. We refer, of course, to the electro-magnet. There is no reason why the field magnet of our dynamo should not be of this sort. Further, it can be magnetised by the current generated from its own field. Let us see how it can be done.

Using the Electro-Magnet

First of all we start off with a soft iron horseshoe with the pole-pieces shaped as before, but above these we wind the magnetising coils as we did with the experimental electro-magnet. Next we put in an armature, starting with the simplest kind with one coil and a commutator that has just two segments. Connecting up the magnet coils has to be done in series with the circuit that our dynamo is going to supply; we may imagine here that it is a lamp. Fig. 30 shows the order in which it is all done; you will note from this that the current set up in the coil passes by way of the commutator brush to the magnet coils, then to the lamp, and back to the armature coil by the other brush of the commutator.

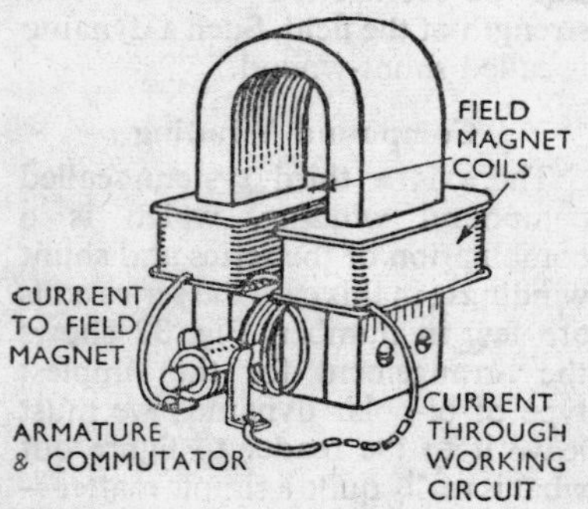

Fig. 30. *A simple type of dynamo with an electro-magnet as its basis.*

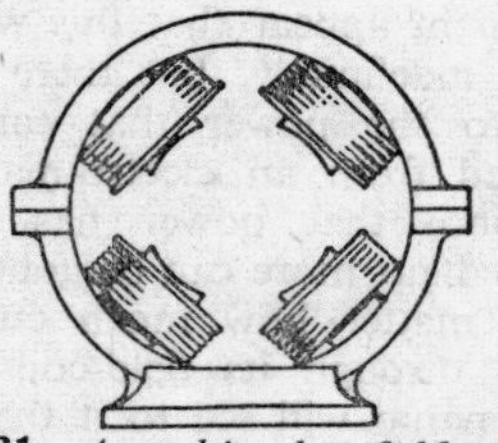

Fig. 31. *A multi-polar field magnet, with armature removed.*

Perhaps the careful student may have noted a weak point somewhere in the sequence. He may ask where the magnet is that provides the necessary field to start with, if our magnet is of the soft iron sort that, as we pointed out previously, retains no magnetism. That would certainly be a very proper question indeed. The answer to it is that the metal used for such a magnet is always able to retain a very small amount of magnetism, once it has been subjected to a strong current through its field-coils. This is called residual magnetism, and it provides a weak field for the armature coils to cut through, but all the same a slight current is set up, and this goes through the field-coil, increasing the power of the magnets. Thus the field strengthens, and with it the generated pulses of current. As these increase, so does the power of the field, and so again does the generated current in its turn.

It might appear that this would go on indefinitely, but there is a limit to the power that can be expected from an electro-magnet, and once that power has been achieved no more can be got from it, no matter how much current is run through its field-coils. So our dynamo will see to it that no more than a definite output can be had from it, however fast its armature may be spun round. When its full speed has been attained it can be run at that speed, and any increase will be wasted on it.

Armature Coils

An armature with only one coil would be a poor affair, however, and the light from an ordinary lamp would be of a flickering description. This is because the current would be in the form of two impulses, rising from nothing to a maximum twice in each revolution, at the moments when the armature coils were cutting across the maximum number of lines of force. If we multiply the number of coils, we increase the number of impulses to each revolution, so reducing the flicker effect of the light on our eyes.

Multi-Polar Dynamo

There is another way by which the current output can be improved, and that is to abandon the horse-shoe type of field magnet. Instead of this, an arrangement of magnets, with four, six, eight or even more poles, is built up to give a cylinder-shaped field in which an armature with many coils can work. Such a dynamo is called multi-polar, and all machines would be constructed on this principle today. The action is exactly as we have described it, occurring every time a coil passes through a set of lines of force, so the more coils and magnets there are the greater will be the number of current impulses to every revolution of the armature, and, in consequence, the smoother will be the output of current (Fig. 31).

Controlling the Output

Now, it must always be remembered that you cannot *make* electricity, but you can set it in motion. You cannot do this unless you give it a complete circuit through which to travel; it does not matter how far it may be, but the current must be able to go out of one terminal and return by the other. Your dynamo will not generate unless the circuit is complete.

Our simple series-wound dynamo is all very well for some purposes, but there are times when we want to be able to control the output. This can be done only by varying the speed when all the output goes through the field magnet coils, and that is not always convenient. We have already explained what a shunt is, and this idea has been applied to the winding of the field-coils. Only a part of the generated current goes through these coils, and that can be controlled to vary the strength of the field. Such a dynamo is called shunt-wound.

Compound Winding

There is a third system, called compound winding, which is a combination of the series and shunt windings; in this case the series coils are few in number. Fig. 32 shows the arrangement for the simplest type of bi-polar dynamo; we must leave it to the reader to figure out what is really quite a simple matter—how three or more sets of magnet poles are similarly wound.

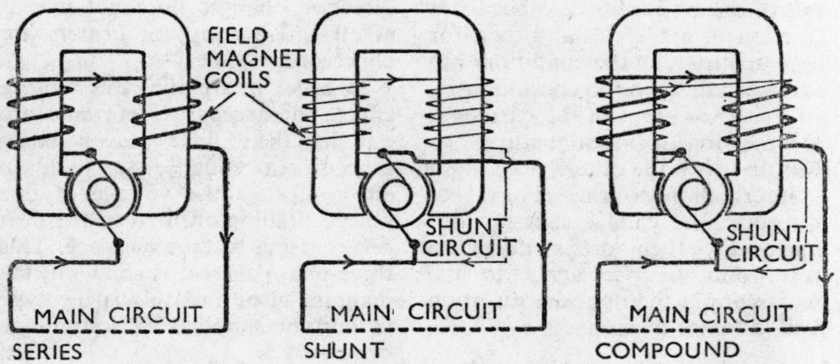

Fig. 32. *Three arrangements for winding the field coils of a dynamo.*

An important point to note about the output of current from this type of generator is that it always flows one way, out of one terminal and back by the other. In this respect it is like the output of the battery: we have positive and negative. Presently we shall meet a form of machine-generated current that is not of this description.

Self Testing Questions

(1) *What is the principle on which the dynamo works?*

(2) *If a dynamo armature has four coils, how many segments will there be on the commutator?*

(3) *What is the difference between series and shunt winding?*

THE ANSWERS ARE ON PAGE 247.

LESSON 8

Alternating Currents

So far we have considered the type of current known as Direct, or Continuous, because it flows one way only, leaving one terminal of the battery or dynamo —and always the same terminal— returning by way of the other. We now have to look into another sort, that known as Alternating, in which there is no positive or negative.

Alternating current—which we might occasionally abbreviate as A.C., as distinct from Direct, which may similarly be termed D.C.—will do very nearly all the things that direct current will. What is more important is that it will do many things, essential to our industrial life, that D.C. will *not* do. By its aid, we can have a lavish supply of cheap current generated in the most economical manner in large power-stations.

The basis of the A.C. generator is the same as that of the D.C. machine in principle—we will examine one in the next lesson—but the output terminals are not positive and negative. The current flows out of one and into the other for a fraction of a second, and then for an equal fraction the conditions are reversed; this goes on continuously, so that the output of the current is a succession of pulsations first one way and then the other.

In addition to this reversal of direction, the voltage rises up to a maximum, then drops down to zero, only to rise again to the maximum in the opposite direction and fall once more.

The Frequency of Alternation

You can follow this from the graph shown in Fig. 33. The horizontal line indicates zero, and the wavy line indicates the rise and fall of the pressure as it is generated, above the line in one direction, positive if you like, and below the line in the opposite direction, similarly negative. These changes take place at perfectly regular intervals once the generator is running at its proper speed.

One complete wave—that is, one above and one below the zero line—makes up a period, or phase, and there are fifty repetitions of this to the second, on the British National Grid system. This number of phases is called the frequency; it will be marked on the front of your electricity supply-meter, and it is necessary to know it before buying some kinds of domestic apparatus, radio sets in particular.

Getting Rid of the Flicker

It is clear that if the voltage rises and falls in this way we should have a very unsteady, flickering sort of current. Supposing the maximum to be 100, then we only get this 100 times in every second, but we also get no volts at all 100 times. Actually the average voltage is about 70, but the fact that the direction changes does not matter at all where lamps or heaters are concerned.

In order to smother this pulsing effect, three separate currents are put together, their phases being spaced out equally, so that, in effect, just as the voltage of one phase is falling off, that of the next one is rising to take its place. This three-phase current is shown in the diagram also, and this is the type of current supplied to your home or factory.

The principal value of A.C. is actually in its pulsing nature, for Michael Faraday's discovery of the principles of induction serve us very well in one or two ways here. Changes in the flow of current in one coil induce currents in another coil set close to the first, and these induced currents are much stronger if the two coils are wound upon an iron frame or ring.

Advantages of Alternating Current

Few discoveries had a more far-reaching effect than this in the electrical world, for upon it we depend for our whole system of electrical distribution, and much of the apparatus we use besides. It is from this discovery that the transformer has been produced. The reader may wonder what value there is in being able to induce a current in a second coil on an iron frame by means of a pulsing current in a first coil. The answer is this: if the second coil has twice as many loops in it as the first one has, then the voltage of the induced currents will be double that in the first. The same rule holds good for any proportion in the numbers of loops in the two coils. In case the reader might think we were going to get something for nothing here, we

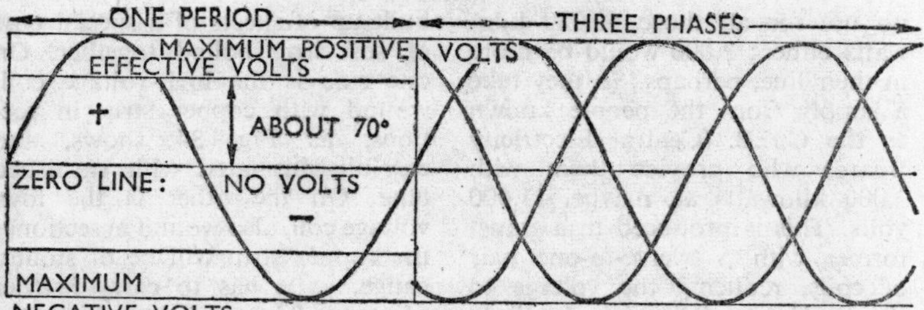

Fig. 33. *Diagram illustrating the operation of alternating current.*

hasten to say that if the volts are doubled, the current ampères are halved. If, on the other hand, the pulsing current is put into the second coil, then the current in the first coil will have half the volts and twice the ampères.

The Value of the Transformer

Before we describe the action of the transformer more fully, we ought to ask why it has proved so valuable an invention. It is always more economical to generate current in large quantities, and this is best done in very big machines. As we have seen already, there are two features about an electric current that have to be considered: its pressure (volts), and the rate of flow (ampères). High pressure forces more current along the wire, but high current flow tends to make the wire hot. The only way to counteract this heating is to provide very thick wire, and for long distances this is very expensive. In some places in Great Britain the electricity is generated more than 100 miles away, and brought in by the overhead lines that are such a feature of the landscape today. These lines, in fact, link up every power-station in the kingdom. Somehow we have to transmit power to the extent of scores of thousands of kilowatts through these lines without losing a lot in merely heating them. That means the current ampères must be kept low, but the volts can be anything within reason.

In this country the main transmission lines carry current at a voltage of 132,000, but no user of it can think of taking in a supply at such a pressure. Neither can the power companies produce it in their generators at that figure, though they now do it at 33,000 volts in some stations.

Long-Distance Transmission

Let us consider, say, 50,000 kilowatts coming out of a generator, at a voltage of 33,000. Now, 50,000 kilowatts means 50 million watts, so we have $\frac{50,000,000}{33,000}$ ampères to reckon with; we can call this 1,500—rather a heavy current to send a long way. Here we find our transformer idea comes in, for by putting this current into one winding, and taking the current induced in a coil with four times the number of loops, wound on the same frame as the first, we have 375 ampères at 132,000 volts. This we can send over the lines to the distant user.

Unfortunately, if you are the user, along with thousands of other householders, your ideas about voltage run no higher than 250. Your local supply company have no use for all those 50,000 kilowatts either; 2,000 would be more in their line, perhaps. So they take a supply from the people known as the C.E.B. (Central Electricity Board) who provide them with 2,000 kilowatts at, maybe, 11,000 volts. This is produced in a transformer with a twelve-to-one pair of coils, reducing the voltage to one-twelfth of the original supply pressure. But it does not increase the ampères twelve times, for the first coil is designed so that no more than 2,000 kilowatts can circulate through it. How this is done we will see in a moment.

Varying the Voltage Supplied

The local company may have some power users on its books who want current at 500 volts, as well as the householders who want it at 250. So they will have two transformers, one for each pressure; though this is not bound to be the case, we will assume it to be so. To reduce 11,000 volts to 250 means a proportion between the coils of 44 to 1, so it is more than likely that there will be two transformers to divide it into two stages.

However they may do it, the current will be put into the street cables, from which you draw the supply you want. Though these cables may be carrying hundreds of ampères, the apparatus in your house comes to no harm; though there is that weight of current outside, even the delicate filament of an electric lamp can take care of itself. It would immediately burn out and break if more than its rated current were forced into it.

The Parts of a Transformer

Let us look quickly at the arrangements of a transformer. First we shall find an iron frame, built up of sheets of a special type of soft iron bolted together. On one side is the high-voltage coil, wound with copper strip in sections, as Fig. 34 shows, and carefully insulated with varnished tape. On the other is the low-voltage coil, also wound in sections; the copper strip will be of stouter gauge, as it has to carry heavier currents. The coil in which the original current flows is the primary, and that in which the induced current flows is the secondary. This secondary coil may be wound with tappings—loops drawn out at various numbers of turns—so that a variety of voltages may be had, all from the same primary coil. The whole assembly will be enclosed in a steel tank filled with oil to keep it cool.

Mutual Induction

The pulses of current in the primary coil set up magnetism in the iron frame, and these produce current pulses in the secondary. But we have already seen that if you are not using electricity you cannot make it. What happens, then, if nobody wants any of the secondary current that the power company is putting into the mains? They only want to pay the C.E.B. for the current their customers use, of course, so some way has to be found to control the current entering the primary coil so that its value does not exceed what is going out to the consumers in their houses.

Fortunately this is not difficult, because there is a natural interaction between the coils, known as Mutual Induction. The current induced in the secondary coil tends to produce magnetism in the iron frame in a contrary direction to that of the primary, and this sets

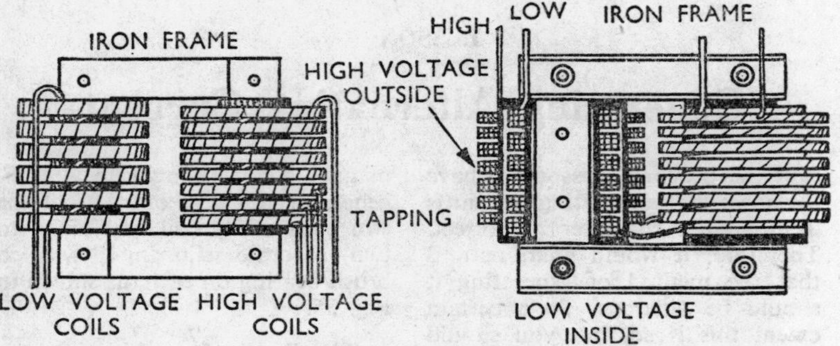

Fig. 34. *Two types of transformers removed from their casings.*

up what the engineer calls a "back voltage" in the primary coil, effectively choking down the flow. This choking effect is reduced if the secondary current can flow freely. In a well-designed transformer this works quite automatically, and when no demand is made upon the secondary current the primary flow is cut down to just the minimum necessary to magnetise the frame, ensuring an immediate response as soon as somebody wants current again.

For this reason, the user of a small transformer can always rely upon it that no current to speak of is being wasted when the secondary circuit is not working, even though the primary is switched on. This applies to such small transformers as are supplied with model electric railways.

When using these small appliances, care must be taken to avoid short-circuiting the output, because the result may well destroy the winding, either primary or secondary, whichever is wound with the finer wire. Repair is not easy, though it can be done; it means carefully unwinding the coils after dismantling the whole thing. As it is likely that a good many turns may have been destroyed, enough wire of the proper gauge will have to be put in to make up for this when it is re-wound. Details for testing the coils will be found in a later lesson. A good deal, of course, can be learned about transformer design by dismantling a damaged one.

To discover whether your electricity supply is A.C. or D.C., wave a table-knife, held by the point of the blade, below a lamp. If it is A.C., a fan-like effect can be seen, consisting of snapshot views of the handle seen during the maximum pulses of current, when the light given out is at its best, 50 times a second. With D.C. no such effect is seen.

Others matters relating to A.C. must be included in the next lesson.

Self Testing Questions

(1) *What is the main difference between A.C. and D.C.?*

(2) *What is meant by a phase?*

(3) *Why is A.C. transmitted at a high voltage?*

(4) *The proportion of coils in a transformer is* 22 *to* 1. *If the pressure in the primary is* 33,000, *what volts shall we have at the secondary?*

THE ANSWERS ARE ON PAGE 247.

LESSON 9

Generating Alternating Current

In the previous Lesson we have shown that alternating current is different in character from direct. Therefore, it would seem natural that the method of generating it should be different. To a certain extent this is so, but you should remember that the D.C. dynamo really generates A.C., but owing to the arrangement of the brushes on the commutator, the pulses of current are taken off so that they all flow in the same way. Remember the explanation of the simple dynamo working. We showed there that current was only generated as the single-coil loop cut through the lines of magnetic force, giving two impulses to each revolution.

In the A.C. generator there is no commutator; any impulses set up are allowed to flow out without any attempt to alter their direction. The design of the alternator is quite different from that of the D.C. dynamo, though both of them depend on the same simple principle—when a closed circuit coil moves through the field of force of a magnet, a current is set up. A D.C. generator will give out A.C. if the two ends of its coil are joined to two separate slip-rings, with a brush bearing on each, as shown in Fig. 35.

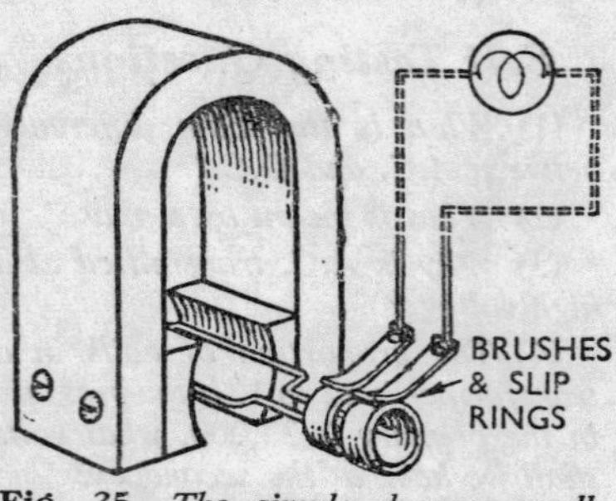

Fig. 35. *The simple dynamo really generates A.C.*

The Parts of an Alternator

As a rule, the arrangement of the parts in the alternator is reversed from that of the dynamo, though it need not be so. Instead of spinning the coils round in a tunnel formed by the poles of magnets, the magnet rotates and the coils are fixed. The spinning magnets are formed on the rim of a large wheel, or, in the largest types of alternators, a drum, and this part is called the rotor. Surrounding the rotor is a circular frame called the stator, and standing inward from this are the coils in which the current impulses are generated.

It is just as certain that a current will be set up in a fixed coil by a moving magnet, as it will be by a moving coil and a fixed magnet. In fact, our first experiment in induction consisted in pushing a bar-magnet through a closed circuit coil, which is the same sort of thing exactly.

Fig. 36 shows the idea, the coils being set in a circle, in which a magnet—for simplicity's sake, a permanent one of bar shape—is rotating. Currents are set up in these coils, which pass out by way of one connection and in by the other, the outgoing impulses using each alternately.

The arrangement of the three-phase coils is shown in a similar

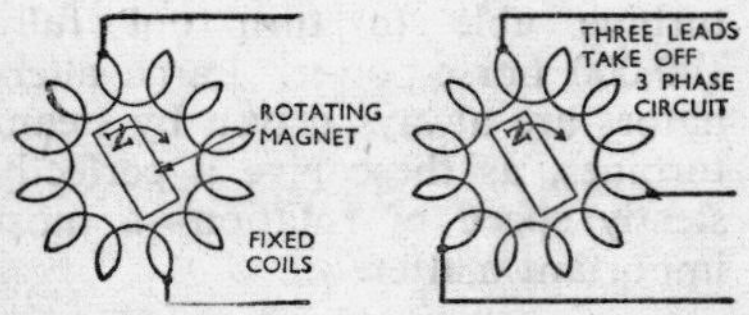

Fig. 36. *Single* (left) *and three-phase* (right) *generators in principle.*

diagram, except that there are three outgoing leads. In this case there need not be return leads, because the outgoing current in any one lead will always be equal to that returning by way of the other two.

Multi-Polar Alternator

The magnet wheel has a number of poles set round the rim; these are all poles of electro-magnets—in pairs, of course. Current to magnetise them is supplied by a small D.C. dynamo fixed at the end of the driving-shaft; this is called the exciter. Sometimes the exciter is separate from the main machine, then the current will be passed to the magnet coils through two brass rings, called slip rings, on which brushes bear.

The coils in which the current is set up may be connected in series or in parallel, according to whether high voltage or high current is required. In Fig. 37, we see the arrangement of an alternator with a six-pole magnet wheel. There will be six coils on the stator to correspond. Notice that the terminals by which the current passes out of the machine are fixed, so there are no moving commutator segments and brushes to consider, not a very good system of collecting heavy currents.

The six poles of the magnet wheel are made up of three magnets, each of which may be considered as of horseshoe type. This arrangement would produce three periods to every revolution, but almost any number of poles and coils can be used. As many as 72 can be seen in some big machines of this wheel type. Many more would be provided in alternators designed to generate three-phase current, where the three phases are produced in a single machine.

When the magnet poles and the coils are in line, as in Fig. 37, the voltage and current are at zero; the maximum voltage occurs when they are midway. As each magnet pole passes the coil, a flow of magnetism passes into the coil; this may be from an "N" pole, we will assume. When the pole has passed on, and has reached the midway position, the polarity in the coil is about to change, as the next magnet pole to approach it will be "S." This change marks the moment when the voltage reaches its maximum.

Maximum Volts and Maximum Amps

Now, it is a curious thing about A.C. that the maximum volts and the maximum ampères do not occur at the same moment, as they must do with D.C. The pressure wave comes first, followed by the current wave. The separation be-

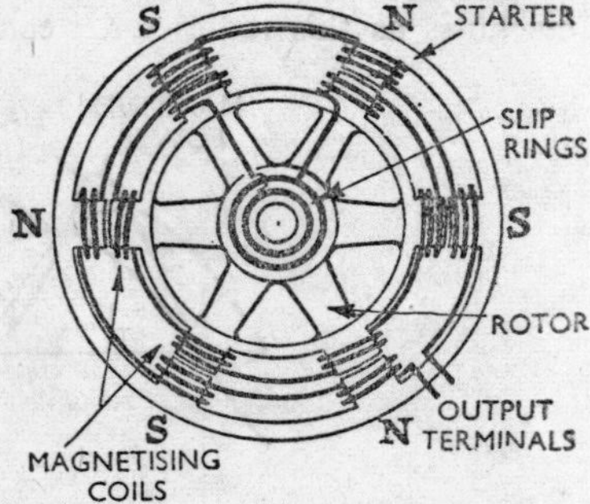

Fig. 37. *Arrangement of magnet wheel and stator coils of a simple alternator.*

tween them depends on how well-designed the machine may be. The point about this is that though the alternator may generate, say, 500 volts and 100 ampères, we cannot multiply these together and call them watts, as we can where D.C. is concerned, because their peaks do not happen at the same moment. The loss of power—for loss it certainly is—may be anything up to about 30 per cent. The proportion of power obtained is called the power factor, and this can be as high as 90 per cent.

Volt-Ampères

Because of this failing, we cannot use the expression watt to describe the output of power from the alternator, as it would be quite misleading. Instead, we multiply volts and ampères together and call the result volt-ampères. If there are enough of these to amount to a thousand (or more), then the prefix kilo is added, so 1,000 A.C. watts would be one kilo-volt-ampère, or K.V.A. for short.

Some very big alternators have been constructed generating current at voltages as high as 33,000. One reason for this high pressure is seen in the enormous power output, which may amount to more than 100,000 K.V.A. To drive such machines as this requires a steam turbine able to turn out fully 140,000 horse-power. Large alternators are always driven by steam turbines, as these give a perfectly steady speed of rotation—a most important matter.

Synchronising

If we are to have several alternators working together in a power-station, all supplying the same system of cables, then they must all be sending out the waves, or periods, exactly in step. Further, if we have a number of power-stations at a distance from each other, but all putting their quotas of current into linked-up transmission lines, then every one of the machines at work must also be in exact step. This is called synchronising. Perfect synchronism provides us with a very useful time-keeping device, which we shall look into presently.

Self Testing Questions

(1) *What, once more, is the principle on which all generators work?*

(2) *Why do we speak of K.V.A. and not K.W. output from an alternator?*

(3) *Could you adapt a simple D.C. generator to give out A.C., and how?*

THE ANSWERS ARE ON PAGE 247.

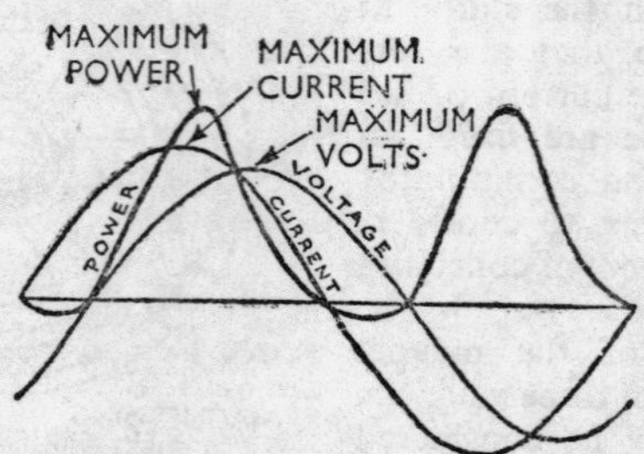

Fig. 38. *Graph to show variation in A.C. power output.*

LESSON 10

What Electricity Will Do: Heat

All metals, even silver, copper and aluminium, offer some resistance to the passage of a current, and by most of them obstruction is considerable. Even the best conductor will resist, according to its size, as compared with the quantity of current we wish to put through. If we consider a fixed size of conductor and a fixed current, the conductor being thick enough to carry what we want, the table given below will give an idea of the resistance different metals offer. Silver is taken as the basis, because it is the best we have, though copper is the most practical, owing to its comparative cheapness:

Silver 1.	Iron 6·2.
Copper 1·08.	Platinum 7·5.
Gold 1·50.	Nickel 8·4.
Aluminium 1·8.	Tin 8·4.
Zinc 3·9.	Lead 13·9.

How Electricity Heats: Fuse Wire and Short Circuits

When a current is put into a conductor that is not able to carry it freely, then the conductor replies by getting hot. If the current is maintained at a steady rate, then the conductor will heat up to a certain temperature and remain at that. On the other hand, if the conducting wire is of too small a size to carry the current indefinitely, it will get hotter and hotter until its melting point is reached; it will then fuse, and the circuit will be broken. This heating effect of electricity is an extremely valuable one, and we are able to make considerable use of it in many directions.

The wire that fuses is a simple device that can be employed to safeguard valuable apparatus, or circuits such as the wiring system in your house, or in a factory. The fuse wire is of such a size that it will bear the normal current that would be quite safe in the circuit, but if for any reason, such as a short circuit, a sudden heavy rush of current pours in, then the fuse wire will melt and cut the circuit clear of the mains. The melting of the fuse gives certain indication that something is wrong with the circuit that must be discovered and rectified before a new piece of fuse wire is put in. This wire, usually made of tin, is to be had in several thicknesses, able to carry currents of 5, 10, 20 amps. safely. For this reason it is important to know what current is normally passing through the circircuit.

At this point, perhaps, we should explain that it is dangerous in the extreme to join the two opposite poles of any electric circuit—positive to negative, for instance—without some kind of working device to control the flow of the current. A lamp, a resistance or a motor—any of these will be able to look after themselves, permitting only a limited current to flow. When the two wires are allowed to touch, or make connection by some mischance, as by a screwdriver, if only for a moment, a "short circuit" occurs with a great rush of current that will probably burn out the wires, just as the fuse wire does.

This ability to produce heat is a most useful thing, because it is so easy to control. Various metallic alloys have been produced that can be drawn into wire and that offer great resistance to the flow of current, with very little risk of fusion. When such metal is used, its behaviour is well understood and the temperature to which it will rise in certain conditions is known.

Length of Resistance Wire for Heater

Suppose we want to make a heater for use as a domestic radiator. Knowing the resistance of a foot length of wire, and the voltage of the supply, we can calculate what length of wire will be necessary to keep the current flow down to 1 amp or more, according to our requirements.

Ohm's Law, $I = \frac{E}{R}$, that we have already met, comes to our aid here; for as we know the pressure or voltage of the supply, and the current we want to pass, the resistance in ohms of the length of wire is quickly found. A glance is sufficient to show that with a pressure of 250 volts, 250 ohms will pass 1 amp, and half of this 2 amps, and so on.

Electric Fires and Toasters

There are various forms of domestic heaters. Perhaps the most familiar is the electric fire, or radiator, where the resistance wire is coiled into a spiral and wound along a fire-clay rod, called the clinker. Alternatively, it may be clipped into zig-zag grooves in a fire-clay block, the idea being to provide some reserve of heat when the block is warmed up.

Another arrangement is that of the electric toaster, where a straight length of wire is wound upon sheets of mica, a convenient mineral substance that withstands fierce heat and is amongst the best non-conductors of electricity.

Heating units of this sort are usually known as elements, and are made up to pass a certain definite current. When they have deteriorated in course of time and have broken, repairs are not worth while. If you try joining together the broken wires of such an element you will find that the twisted joint gets hotter, and offers more resistance, than the rest of the wire. It will quickly burn out and break again, if it does not do so at once.

The domestic laundry iron has an element in which the heater wires are laid, in a pattern resembling the veining of a leaf, between two heavy cast-iron plates that give the necessary weight and heat storage (Fig. 39).

Irons and Cookers

These, and other similar appliances, such as kettles, grills and cookers, are examples of moderate heat producers. Electricity will do more than this for us, however, for we find that it is used in industry to an enormous extent, even for melting steel. The finest grades of alloy steel are made in electric furnaces of various sorts.

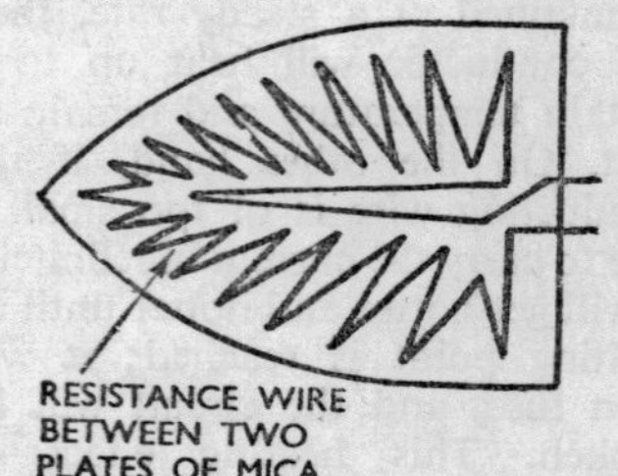

Fig. 39. *The heater element of a laundry iron, formed of wires and plates.*

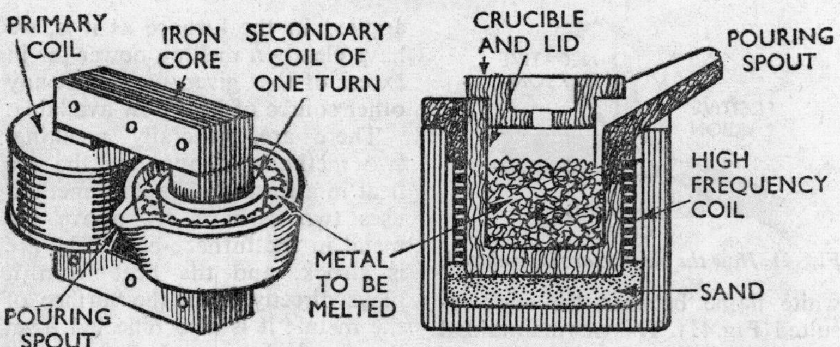

Fig. 40. *Two types of induction furnace. That on the left is used for alloy melting.*

As in the domestic type of heater, there are heating elements in the Resistance furnace, though they are of much greater power.

Types of Electric Furnace

The crucible in which the metal is contained is surrounded by these elements, and their heat passed into the metal. This may be considered a moderate temperature furnace. Muffle furnaces for tempering tools or heat-treatment would be of this sort, because the degree of heat can be so easily controlled by varying the amount of resistance wire in the circuit.

A much more interesting type is the Induction furnace. We already know a little about the principle of the transformer. This furnace is, in effect, a transformer. We have the iron frame; on one side of this the primary coil will be wound, and in this coil the alternating current is circulated. Round the other side of the iron frame the crucible containing the metal to be melted is formed, in the shape of a ring. So we have a secondary coil consisting of one turn only, and that short-circuited. When the A.C. is switched into the primary, a heavy current is set up by induction in the secondary, and this circulates in the metal. The result of this is to start an effect called an eddy current. These currents have considerable heating power, so the metal is very quickly melted. Further, it is cleanly melted, because it has had no contact with fumes from burning fuel. Such furnaces as these are much used in melting brass and similar alloy metals (Fig. 40, *left*).

Another form of Induction furnace has the crucible of the usual cylindrical form, enclosed in a casing round which the windings are formed (Fig. 40, *right*). Through the windings an A.C. of high frequency, oscillating 20,000 times a second, is passed. Vigorous eddy currents are set up, which effectively stir the molten metal. But only metals would be heated in such a furnace as this. No heat would be produced in any non-conducting substances, and the furnace would remain cold unless the crucible contained metal of some sort.

The third form of furnace employs the intense heat of the electric arc.

Many years ago it was discovered that, if carbon sticks were connected to the poles of a battery able to give at least 45 volts, and if the sticks were first brought into contact, then drawn apart, a brilliant

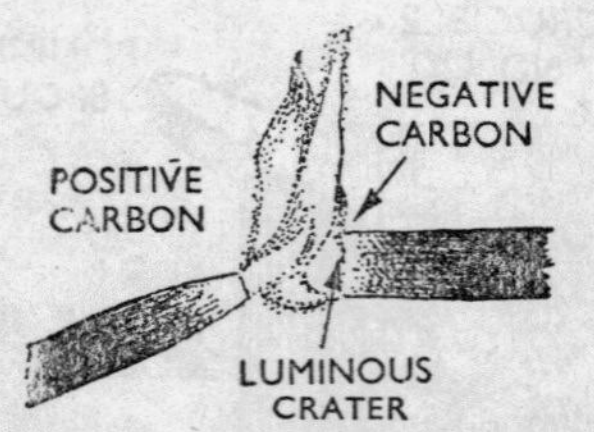

Fig. 41. *How the electric arc is produced.*

white flame between the ends resulted (Fig. 41). This was maintained as long as the gap between the sticks did not exceed a certain amount, and also as long as the battery could keep up the supply of current. As this demand is very heavy, the early arc lamps could not have been very serviceable, as they were fed from batteries only. Today we have practically unlimited supplies of current available, and so the arc can be freely employed.

A low pressure is all that is necessary, but a high current is essential. An arc can be struck with 45 volts, but about 100 volts is usual where furnaces are concerned. For lighting purposes, the current may amount to 120 amps, but a big furnace will use anything up to 12,000 amps.

The Electric Arc

The brilliant flame is caused by the actual vaporising of the carbon at a temperature of over 5000° Fahrenheit. If this heat could be applied in the furnace as it is, we have clearly a melting power far in excess of that given by almost any other source of heat now available.

There are, generally speaking, two methods of applying the arc heat in a furnace. The first method uses two carbons set above the metal in the furnace-bath. The arc is struck, and the heat from it plays directly upon the surface of the metal; it is also reflected from the roof downward. This is the indirect arc (Fig. 42, *left*).

The Direct Arc

More interesting in a way is the direct arc. Here the metal to be melted forms one pole of the circuit. The carbon is embedded in this to start with; and, the current being turned on, the carbon is withdrawn enough to start the arc going. So we have the arc playing between a carbon rod and the metal that is being melted (Fig. 42, *left*).

The carbons used in furnace work may be as much as 18 in. in diameter. These, using 12,000 amps at 100 volts, represent a consumption of power amounting to 1,600 horsepower continuously.

We shall meet the electric arc again presently. In the meantime, a few notes on what can be expected in the way of heating service for the consumption of one unit of electricity may be of interest.

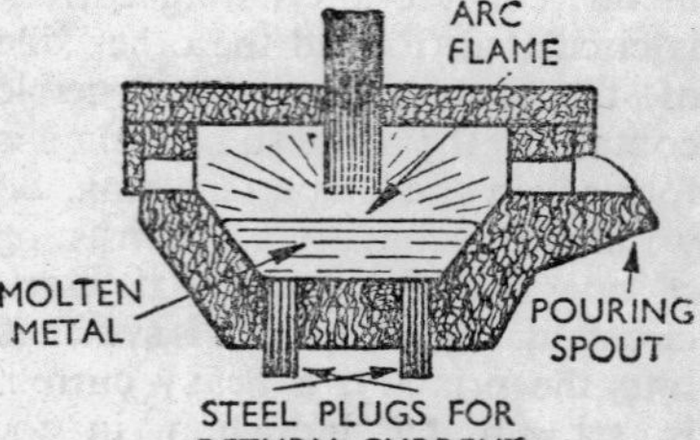

Figs. 42 and 43. (Left) *Fig.* 42, *The indirect arc furnace in section.* (Right) *Fig.* 43, *The direct arc furnace. The metal being melted forms one pole.*

One unit, as we have already explained, amounts to 1,000 watt-hours, 1,000 watts for 1 hour, 500 watts for 2 hours, or however it may be. A small bowl-fire may consume 500 watts, so this will give 2 hours' service for one unit. If the voltage is 250, then it is taking 2 amps. A larger type of two-element fire will probably take 1,000 watts; clearly this will run 1 hour on a unit; if units cost $\frac{1}{2}$*d.*, then a fair day's service can be had for no more than 6*d.*, comparing favourably with coal at the present price of 3*s.* a hundredweight.

It should be emphasised that such appliances ought never to be run from lighting sockets, but only through properly laid circuits. The currents they consume are much in excess of what is safely carried by lighting-switches; these will get unduly hot when a heating appliance is run off their circuits.

Self Testing Questions

(1) *Using wire with resistance of* 1 *ohm to the foot, how much will be wanted to replace the coil of a radiator taking* 2 *units per hour on* 250 *volts?*

(2) *What gauge of fuse wire should be used in this circuit?*

(3) *A laundry iron takes* 800 *watts; how much does it add to your bill every hour it is run continuously? Current is at* $\frac{5}{8}$*d. per unit.*

THE ANSWERS ARE ON PAGE 247.

LESSON 11

Light

The subject of electric light is bound up with that of heat, for much of our lighting depends on the intense heating of short lengths of fine wire to such an extent that they glow with brilliant light.

The light most familiar to the householder is the ordinary incandescent-bulb lamp. In this, a very fine spiral of tungsten wire is subjected to the current, and its resistance being extremely high it is heated to a brilliant whiteness. Its melting point is also very high, so it is able to withstand this degree of heat without damage (Fig. 44).

The resistance of the filament is great because it is sealed up in an air-tight glass bulb, from which all air has been extracted and a small quantity of an inert gas called argon put in. The oxygen in the air would quickly burn up the metal filament if this extraction process were not thoroughly done. But although the gas-filled type of bulb is admittedly the best source of light so far developed for general use, it has to be admitted that it is extremely inefficient as a job of work, considering it on the basis of the power it uses. Not much more than a sixtieth part of the energy put into the lamp comes out in the form of light, the remainder being lost in radiated heat.

There are other forms of lighting that are more efficient than the gas-filled incandescent kind, and these we shall consider presently.

The arc lamp is a source of light employed where great intensity of illumination is wanted,

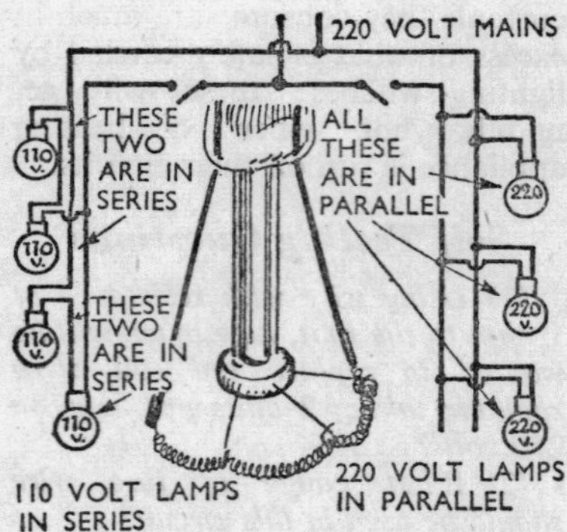

Fig. 44. *This shows the modern coiled filament of a gas-filled lamp. On the* left *is shown the way to wire* 110-*volt lamps into a* 220-*volt circuit, and on the* right 220-*volt lamps arranged in parallel.*

such as n searchlights and cinematograph projectors. As a street-lighting unit it was formerly common, but it is not now used, we believe. The principle of the arc was briefly explained in our section dealing with heat, but the manner of its employment in a furnace is a far cry from the modern arc lamp of a powerful searchlight or cinema projector, a drawing of each of which is in Fig. 45.

Some of these lamps are made automatic in their action, others require occasional attention. Direct current is almost invariably used, though alternating can be worked. Positive and negative carbons are of different sizes with D.C., because the positive carbon is consumed much more quickly and thicker ones are usually provided.

How the Arc Lamp Works

You may remember that the carbon sticks are joined up to the positive and negative terminals of the source of current, and as soon as the current is turned on, they are drawn apart. A brilliant white flame results across the gap, and this continues as long as that gap does not exceed a certain limit that can be found by trial. As the carbons gradually burn away and the gap gets wider, the current begins to fall off, and would soon stop altogether if they were not moved up closer again. This can be done automatically by a device sensitive to the current flowing. If all this current is passed through this device, it responds at once, moving the carbons farther apart if the current is too high, or closing them up if it is too low.

In addition to this arrangement, an adjusting screw is provided so

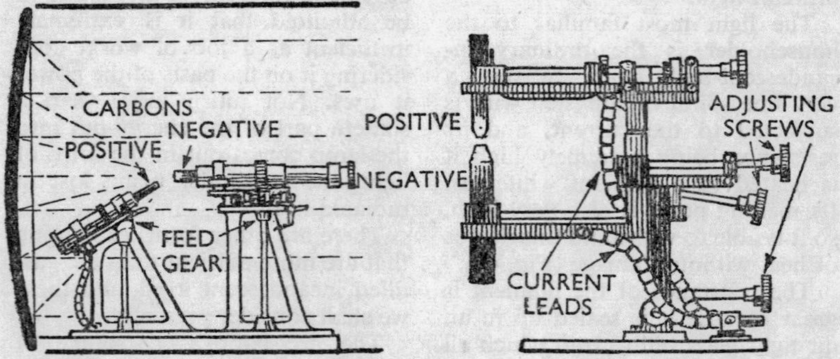

Fig. 45. Left, *a searchlight arc; and* right, *a kinema projector arc with hand adjustment for setting the carbons at the most effective distance apart.*

that the operator can make the setting if he prefers it. Some types of arc lamps are not automatic at all, being maintained constantly by hand. As soon as the current is cut off the carbons are immediately returned to make contact, and so they remain until current is switched on once more.

Arc lamps work at low voltages—40 is enough—but they consume heavy currents: a large one will, as we have seen, need 120 amps. As far as illumination is concerned, 1,000 watts will produce 1,000 candle-power. Searchlights have been made with arc lamps giving candle-powers reckoned by the thousand million. Some of these have to be provided with cooling arrangements for the carbon-holders, as the heat emitted is sufficient to melt the metal of which they are made.

When the arc is working, a crater is formed in the end of the positive carbon, and there will be a spot in the pit of this that compares in brilliance of illumination with the surface of the sun. Modern arc-light carbons are often cored out with a hollow bore, filled with a rare earth called thorium. This, when subjected to the intense heat, glows even more brilliantly than the carbon itself. Trial has also been made with cores of other substances, giving a bright colour such as yellow, green or violet to the rays emitted, the idea being that these rays might have greater penetrating power when used in searchlights.

The Mercury Vapour Lamp

Many years ago it was discovered that an electric discharge put into a tube filled with neon—a rare gas found in the atmosphere—caused the gas to glow brightly with a

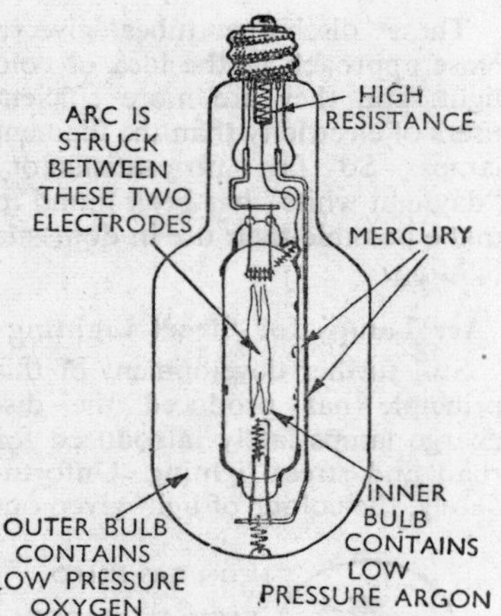

Fig. 46. *A mercury vapour low-pressure electric discharge lamp.*

flaming red colour. Further experiments with other gases showed that mercury vapour glowed with a cold blue; nitrogen, an apricot colour; carbon dioxide, white; and helium, a pale heliotrope. The gases are sealed into the tubes and are at a very low pressure—less than one-hundredth part of that of the atmosphere—and, of course, all air is previously drawn out. At each end of the tube is a plate of iron. To start up the glow, a pressure of about 10,000 volts has to be put on to these electrodes, but once the glow begins it can be kept up with about 3,000 volts. Very little current is used, and transformers supply the high voltage easily (Fig. 46).

They are relatively cheap to make and keep running, but they do not last indefinitely. It is believed that the action of the electrical discharge is to "ionise" the atoms of the gas—that is, to knock some of the electrons off—and as there is very little gas in the tube, a year or so sees a good deal less, so it has to be replaced from time to time.

These discharge tubes give a close approach to the idea of cold light, and they are more efficient users of electricity than the filament lamps. So far, no satisfactory "daylight white" has been found to make possible their use in domestic lighting.

Arc Lamps for Street Lighting

Still further development of this principle has produced the discharge lamps lately introduced for road and street lighting. Unfortunately, the colour of light given out

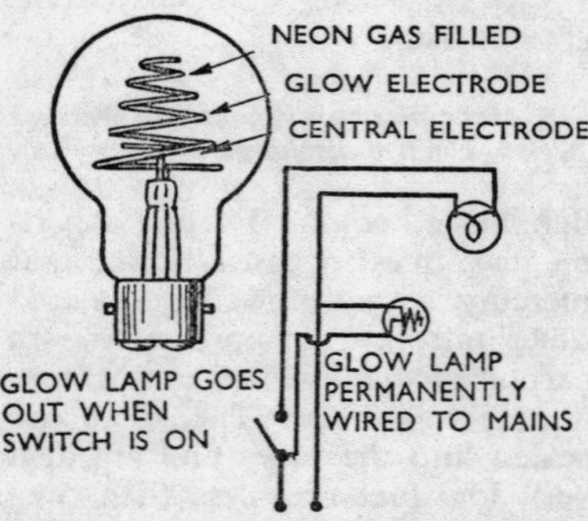

Fig. 47. *The Beehive lamp and how to wire it into circuit as a switch indicator.*

is horrible. Its effect is to make everything appear to be in tones of one colour, and it imparts a ghastly pallor to the human face. Their chief advantage is that they illuminate roads with some sort of bright light, and that they do not cost very much to run.

Glow Lamps

Small discharge lamps can be had for use in the home; these, known as Beehive lamps, from the shape of the electrode inside, are often used to provide a faint glow that just kills complete darkness, or as a switch-indicator in dark places. The bulb has a small quantity of neon gas in it, and a pressure of only 200 volts is sufficient to start the glow, which plays in the form of a rosy light around the electrodes. They are very economical of current, using no more than 5 watts, and when employed as switch-indicators they can be wired up so that their light is extinguished as soon as the main light is switched on. Fig. 47 shows the wiring for this.

Cost of Consumption

The question of cost is one that affects everyone, including the householder, who is often tempted to buy very cheap lamps that seem to give a better light for the current they are supposed to consume. Any filament can be made to glow more brightly if it is overloaded; try putting a lamp designed for 220 volts on a 250-volt circuit. The result is, for the time being, at least 12 per cent. better light. But it will not be for long. Because of that overload the filament of even the best lamp will fail much sooner. A series of calculations with the Ohm's Law formula shows that a lamp designed for 40 watts at 220 volts is consuming nearly 52 watts when put on a 250-volt circuit. Where, then, is the economy in this, even if, as is often not the case, the lamps stand up to it?

Self Testing Questions

(1) *Why is electric light inefficient?*

(2) *Why are incandescent lamps gas-filled?*

(3) *Why cannot arc lamps be used for domestic lighting?*

(4) *Why not discharge lamps for lighting the home?*

THE ANSWERS ARE ON PAGE 247.

LESSON 12

Power

GENERATED electricity is simply a form of power or, rather, energy, converted from some other source, such as burning coal or oil, or falling water. It is in a convenient form for transmission over long distances, but in itself it has no value. We must provide apparatus to use it in whatever direction we want. So far we have seen how heat and light can be had by its use; now we shall see in what way we can make it turn wheels for us.

Electric Motors

Just as electricity comes to us from a machine with a set of coils rotating on a shaft, so we can put it back into a similar machine and make a set of coils rotate the shaft upon which they are fixed. In its essential parts the electric motor is practically the same machine as the dynamo, the driving current being put in in a reverse direction from that in which it came out of the dynamo. A little thought will show that if some of the current applied to the motor goes to the field magnet and some to the armature windings, then the armature on its shaft will be pulled round.

This applies to the D.C. motor, and, as we shall see, to a certain extent to the A.C., but as some details need a fuller explanation, we will examine a typical motor adapted for variable-speed working, as well as reversing.

First of all we must see how the current supplied to a motor can be varied, for clearly it is only by doing this that we can control the speed of rotation. Our supply of current is limited, and comes in at a fixed voltage. Full speed is attained when the motor is given the whole weight of this, but to check the speed, resistances are put in series with the windings, thus absorbing some of the energy and wasting it in heat. This is unavoidable. To start up a motor, especially if it is loaded as a railway or tramway motor would be, a small current must first be applied. The resistance of a motor of this sort—a Series motor—is very low, and a heavy current might easily burn out the windings, unless the armature was able to jump to it quickly.

Starting a Heavy Motor

The controller handle moves across a set of contacts, between each of which a resistance is fixed, the last of them being connected directly to the motor supply lead. Fig. 48 shows a simple arrangement, with four contact studs, and at the side is shown the actual circuit with each stud used in succession.

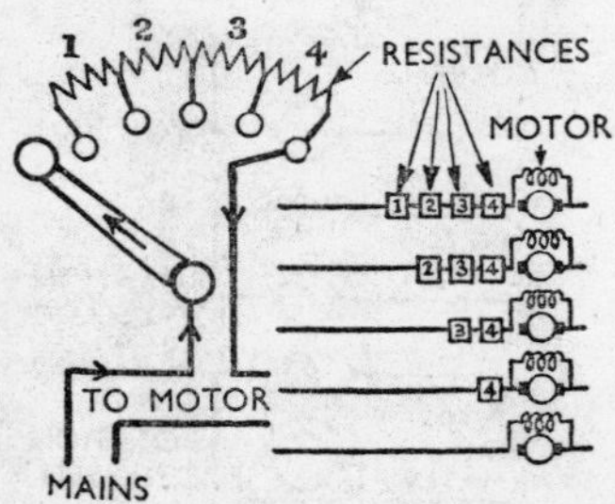

Fig. 48. *The circuit arrangement for a simple four-stud motor starter.*

Motors are of two kinds for use with D.C., Series and Shunt. Our section on the dynamo showed what these expressions mean, and their field magnets are wound in the same way. A series motor is a variable-speed machine; its armature runs just as fast as its load will allow, subject to the driving-current, of course. A shunt-motor—of the sort that would be used in a workshop—sets out to run at a fixed speed whatever the load.

Reversing

Reversing a motor is a simple process. It does not matter which direction you put the current through, the motor will always run in the same direction; but if the direction of the current is reversed through the field windings or the armature, *but not through both*, the direction of rotation will likewise be reversed (Fig. 49).

Making a Model Electric Motor

Making a model motor is a good exercise. Much can be learned from it, and even though it is a more or less flimsy affair, it works. It is a series motor, so that the reversing process can be tried, as well as the controlled starting. It will work equally well with D.C. or A.C. In the latter case a 6- or 20-volt transformer will provide the current.

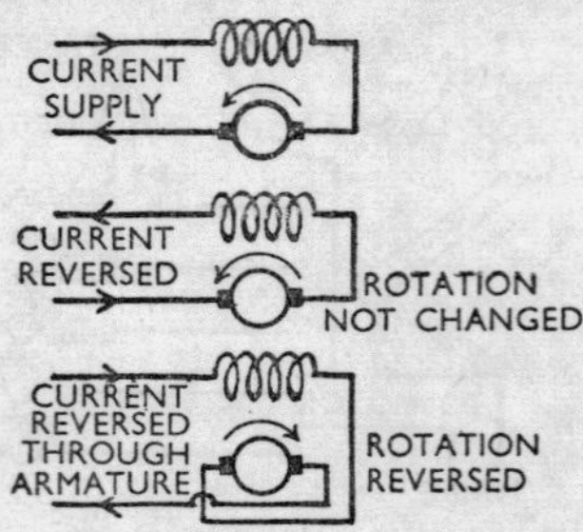

Fig. 49. *Reversing arrangements of current for a D.C. series motor.*

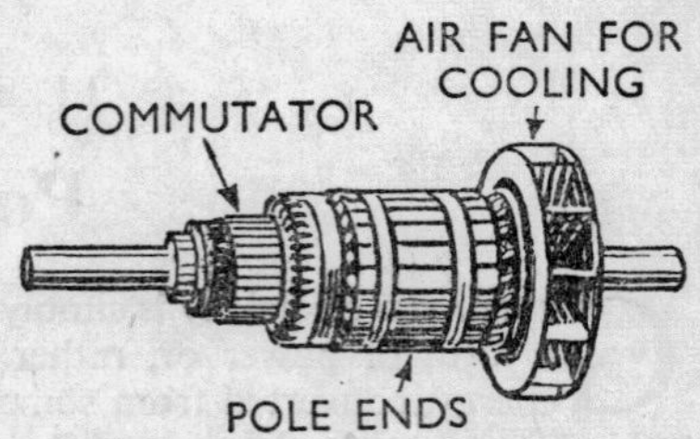

Fig. 50. *The armature of a direct current motor; note the cooling fan.*

Fig. 51 gives the dimensions of the various pieces, which can be cut out of ordinary tinplate, but better still would be thick sheet iron. The field magnet and armature are both cut out of a strip 1 in. wide. The first is a piece 7½ in. long, and the second is made up of two pieces each 1½ in. long. They must be bent carefully to the shapes shown, bearing in mind that the armature is to spin round in the magnet tunnel that you have formed, and the nearer the two parts are without touching, the better the motor will be.

Cut two pieces of card, and make a slit in each so they can be run on to the magnet. These are to keep the coil in place; when they are there, wind on one or two turns of thin paper over the iron, and you are ready to wind the field-coil. A small quantity of no. 24 enamelled copper wire is the best for the purpose, and about 250 turns will be sufficient. Try this with a pocket flash-lamp battery when wound; it should support a steel ruler easily.

The Armature

The armature must be formed so as to clip the shaft tightly. Before winding these coils you must wind on a layer or two of thin paper as before, then the coils can be put on. A length of the same wire, 40 ft. long, is taken and its half-way point

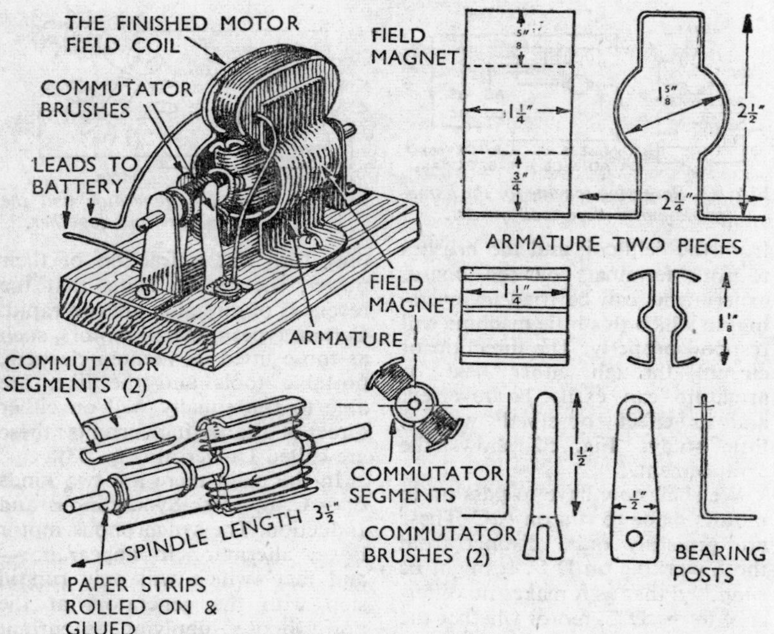

Fig. 51. *Sketches for making a simple D.C. motor, with dimensions of parts.*

found. Each half is to be wound on a half of the armature, taking care to cross over and wind each half in the opposite direction. There should be about 100 turns on each side. To bind the free ends it is a good idea to wind some gummed paper around each half; this will hold the coils in place. The diagram shows the direction of winding, and if you have made a good job of bending the iron to the spindle, then tight winding will lock the armature well on to it.

Spindle and Commutator

The spindle is a good straight length of stout wire—a knitting needle is as good as anything—and its bearings are as shown, made out of the same iron as the magnet. To make the commutator, a length of glued paper $\frac{3}{4}$ in. wide is wound on tightly until it is $\frac{3}{8}$ in. diameter; glue it well. The segments are two pieces of tinplate, or, if you can get it, thin brass, bound in place by thread at each end. On no account must they touch. Each one occupies 90°, or a quarter of the circumference, so the gap between them should be about $\frac{1}{4}$ in. Set them at right angles to the armature coils, but before binding them down slip under each one an end of the armature winding, previously cleaned of its insulation.

The brushes are two strips of tinplate; under one of them fix one end of the field-magnet winding. Now, if the terminals of a flashlamp battery are joined up, one to the spare brush and the other to the free end of the magnet coil, your motor will run.

By bringing out the connections

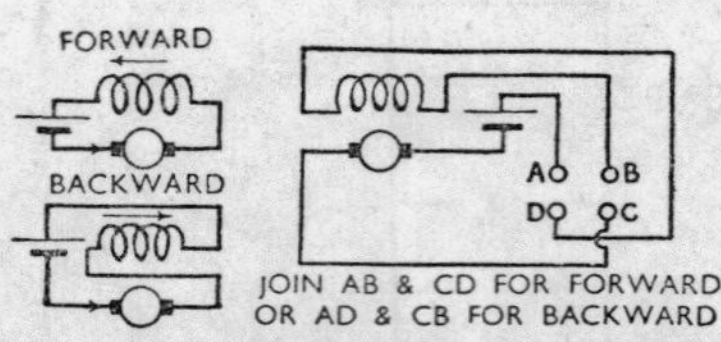

Fig. 52. *Reversing scheme for the home-made motor described in text.*

from the field-coil and the brushes to four terminals on the board, experiments can be tried in reversing, to which this little machine will respond properly. The direction of current through either field or armature can easily be reversed, and its effect observed with a little study. Fig. 52 shows the arrangement.

We shall now have to pass on to motors made to run on A.C. These are generally quite distinct from those working on D.C. It might be supposed that as it makes no difference to the D.C. motor whether the current is reversed or not through all its windings, then it should run quite well on A.C., which is simply a constantly reversing current. Most D.C. motors will, in fact, run on A.C., but inefficiently. They would

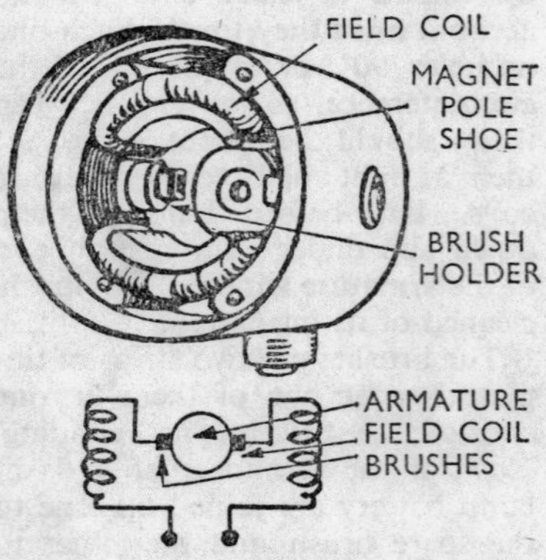

Fig. 53. *The field magnets of a universal (either A.C. or D.C.) motor. The internal circuit is shown below.*

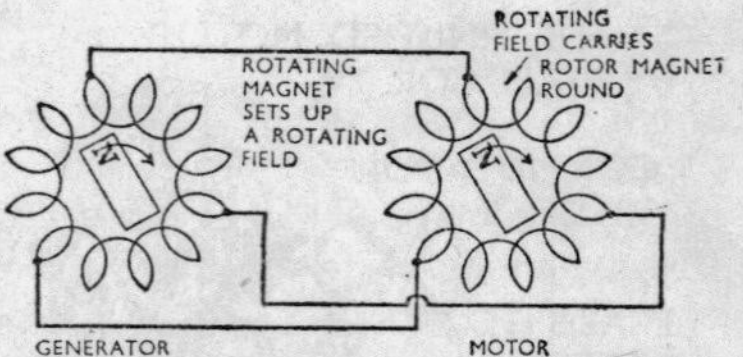

Fig. 54. *How the generator and the synchronous motor work together.*

only turn out a fraction of their power, the reason being that the reversals of direction are too rapid. Certain types of small motors, such as those fitted in vacuum cleaners, portable tools and the like, are able to run equally well on either direct or alternating currents; these are called Universal (Fig. 53).

In the main there are two kinds of A.C. motors: Synchronous and Induction. The synchronous motor is an alternator in appearance—and fact—which will only run in step with the generators at the power-house supplying its current (Fig. 54). This does not mean that it must run at the same speed—that depends on the number of its magnet poles. It cannot start itself.

The Synchronous Motor

A separate motor is coupled to its shaft, and this, when required, will spin the magnet wheel until it is running at the critical speed, when the big motor takes charge, maintaining that speed. So long as these motors are able to handle the load they will run, but if a sudden overload checks the speed only a little they will stop, and must then be re-started. Such a machine would seem to be a tiresome affair, but they are always well up to their work, and are used where really powerful motors are wanted, such as in steel rolling-mills.

An exception to this is the tiny machine at the other end of the scale, the little motor driving your electric clock. You will remember about the synchronising all over the country of current with a frequency of 50 to the second? The accuracy with which this is maintained gives us perfect timekeeping. A synchronous motor which, once started, will run at a perfectly steady speed so long as current is supplied to it only requires a train of gears to drive a pair of clock-hands, and there you have as good a timekeeper as Greenwich. Starting such a motor has to be done by means of a geared trigger arrangement, for even these little motors have to have their armatures spun up to critical speed before they will run (Fig. 55).

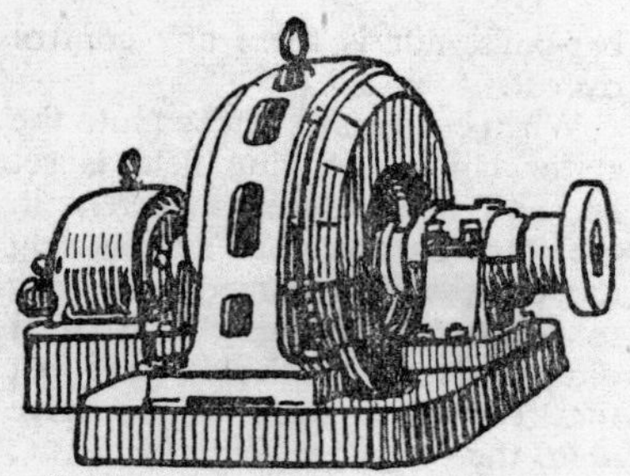

Fig. 55. *A large synchronous motor.*

The Induction Motor

The induction motor is the useful type of machine that does most of the work on A.C. in factories and elsewhere. Its working is ingenious, but not difficult to understand. An experiment was referred to in a previous lesson, in which a piece of aluminium or copper is moved about between the poles of a magnet. The observation from that experiment is to the effect that movement of a conductor in the field of a magnet is resisted. Here we have the basis of this motor (Fig. 56).

A series of coils is arranged round the inside of the motor-casing—or stator—and when A.C. is turned into these the result is a continuously rotating magnetic field. The rotors are of two sorts. There will be a core, consisting of discs of iron clamped together, with slots at their outer rim; in these slots there will be embedded copper or aluminium bars joined up at their outer ends so that they form short-circuited coils of one turn each; this is the Squirrel-Cage type. With Wound rotors wire coils are formed in the slots, and these pass out to slip-rings at their ends; brushes make contact with these, and in the starting and control switch resistances can be cut in to vary the resistance of these coils. With the Squirrel-Cage motor there is practically no resistance in the

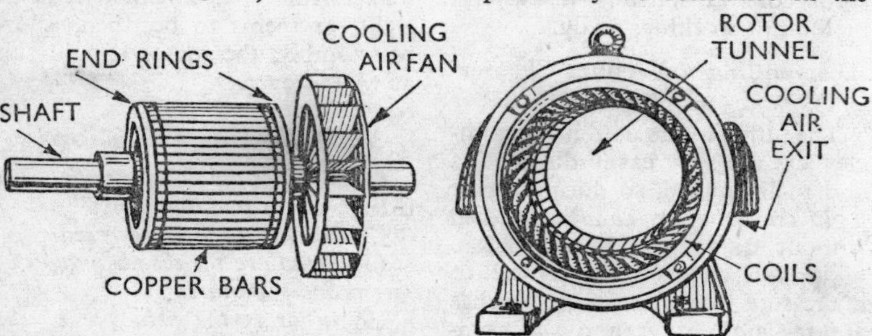

Fig. 56. A, *the rotor of an induction motor of squirrel cage type.* B, *the stator or casing of an induction motor; rotation of the coils creates a magnetic field.*

bar-coils, nor is there any control over it.

When current is switched into the stator coils a moving field is set up, and this induces a current in the rotor bars or coils magnetising the core, which immediately tries to follow the rotating field. If it did not do so, we should have just that condition that, as we have seen, the magnetic field objects to: a movement of a conductor within it. It is just the same whether the field moves and conductor stands still or *vice versa.* So the rotor begins to turn and tries to catch up with the field; it never does so, because if it did, then there would be no movement between them. True, they are both moving, but they are moving in the same direction and at the same speed, so no power would be developed. Once this idea is grasped, the principle is mastered.

Induction motors of the Squirrel-Cage type take a great rush of current at starting—maybe five times the amount needed for normal running—but they develop great power at starting: "high torque," as the engineer calls it. The wound, slip-ring type of rotor is designed to check this rush of current by controlling the current in use in the rotor coils at starting—a wasteful method of working, really.

Dismantling a Vacuum Cleaner Motor

The little motors used in vacuum-cleaners are very easily dismantled and re-assembled, so during repair their construction can be studied without doing any harm. Before taking any chances, it is as well to make sure that the carbon brushes are in good order and the commutator is clean; the brushes should slide easily in their sockets and be long enough to bear firmly on the commutator. If the latter is very black it is almost certainly necessary to get the armature out to clean it.

Having taken all to pieces, and noted the arrangement, marking with scratches any parts about which you may have doubts when re-assembling, clean the commutator first with some very soft, old, fine emery cloth, and then with a little petrol. Now examine the two field-coils. These must be tested with a cycle-lamp and battery in series, and if the lamp fails to light, then one or both of the coils has been burnt out somewhere. Testing each one individually will decide which it is. This repair is easy, for the coil at fault can quite easily be unwound till the broken turns are found, and a sufficient length of new wire spliced—and soldered—in. There is no difficulty about this, but insulate the joints with a little insulating tape, and, when re-wound, insulate the coil with more tape; as a rule the silk tape you have to remove is hard and dry and no longer of use.

Careful examination of the armature may show that to have been burnt. If this is the case, nothing can be done but to send it to the makers for replacement. If it is all right, or seems to be, then, after-re-assembly, the motor should run as well as ever.

Self Testing Questions

(1) *What is the difference between a D.C. motor and a dynamo?*

(2) *How is a motor reversed?*

(3) *What are the disadvantages of synchronous motors?*

(4) *What is the principle of the induction motor?*

THE ANSWERS ARE ON PAGE 248.

LESSON 13

A.C. and D.C.

THERE are several electrical devices that we have not yet studied, although some depend on principles that we have already discussed.

First amongst these comes the Induction, or Shocking Coil, a well-known scientific entertainment of fifty years ago. It is used in many directions now, however, other than for amusement purposes. Its purpose is to produce high voltages—much higher than the transformer is capable of: such as are wanted in X-ray work, for instance.

The Induction Coil

In principle it is a transformer, using D.C. that has been broken up into a series of rapid vibrations. On a core of soft iron wires a few layers of moderately thick wire are wound, sufficient to magnetise it thoroughly when current is put through the coil. A simple induction coil will have a vibrating spring with an iron bob on it, which is fixed so that the magnetised core attracts it. The current to the magnetising coils passes through this spring by way of contact points, so that as the bob is moved, the flow of current is broken, the magnetism fails, and the bob springs back. Contact is re-made, the core is again magnetised, the bob attracted, and so on. This sequence can be adjusted to occur with great rapidity (Fig. 57).

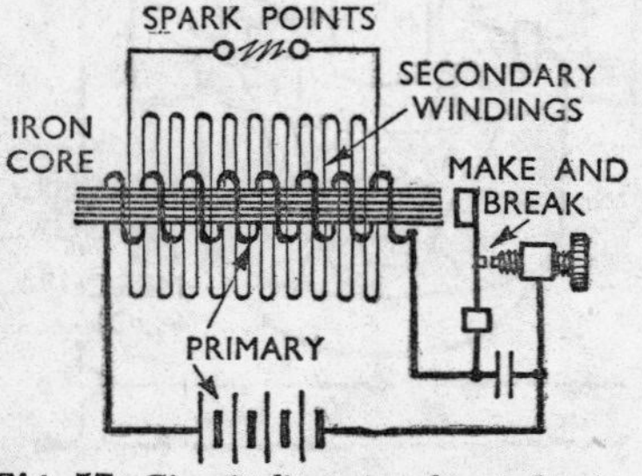

Fig. 57. *Circuit diagram of an induction coil, used for producing high voltages.*

Over the primary, or magnetising coil, the secondary coils, consisting of many thousands of turns of fine wire, are wound. These will have a considerable resistance.

Remembering what we have learned about the transformer's action, we shall expect high voltages to be set up in this secondary coil. The first impulse is small, and comes with the making of contact, when magnetism is growing in the core. The principal impulse comes with the break of contact, when magnetism is dying away.

How the Magneto Works

A large induction coil can produce a momentary surge of perhaps 200,000 volts; the E.M.F. is sufficient to throw a spark across between two points a yard apart. Such coils, however, would not have a simple make-and-break such as we have described, which would not act with sufficient speed. A little motor drives a jet of mercury at high speed against brass contacts in such a way that 10,000 interruptions a minute are set up.

We shall see some uses for this induction coil later, but we will mention one of them now. The Magneto—that clever device that has simplified ignition arrangements for motor-car and aeroplane

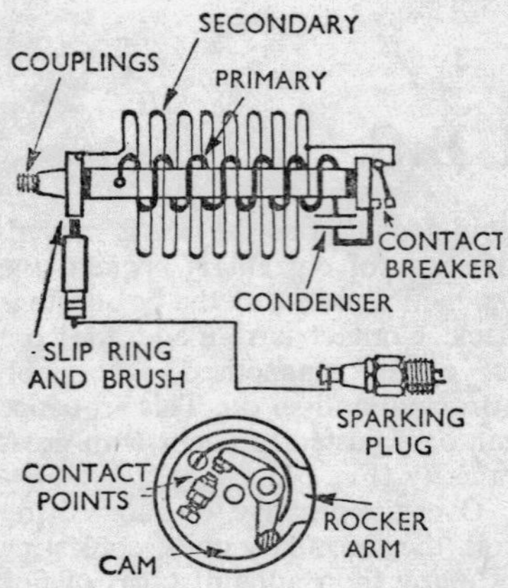

Fig. 58. *Circuit diagram and details of contact break of a magneto.*

engines—uses it in an ingenious way (Fig. 58).

First we have a simple dynamo, with an armature of H-type, just as we saw it in the lesson on D.C. dynamos, working in the field of an extremely powerful permanent magnet. The winding of this armature makes what will be the primary winding, and in series with it is a contact make-and-break, worked mechanically as the spindle is rotated, so that the currents set up in the primary are made intermittent.

Over this primary many thousand turns of fine wire are wound. These make the secondary coil, in which the high-voltage currents are induced. The contact-breaker is arranged to interrupt the primary current at the moment when the flow is at its maximum. Just as with the induction coil, an impulse is set up at the moment of making contact. This is strong enough to make a spark if it were allowed to pass out, but it is not wanted, so a condenser is put in the primary circuit to check it. This condenser holds up the impulse until the break comes, then it releases it to add to the strength of the proper impulse.

The secondary impulse passes out by way of a brass slip-ring, on which a carbon brush bears, and is led by a stoutly insulated lead to the sparking-plug in the engine cylinder. The gap across which the spark jumps is no more than $\frac{1}{60}$ in., and the E.M.F. is about 5,000 volts. By running the magneto at a certain speed relative to the engine shaft, we can supply at least eight cylinders—needing four sparks to each revolution of its shaft—from one magneto, which produces two sparks at each revolution.

Other Devices

The next devices we must look at are necessary in these days, when most public supplies of current are alternating. There are many things for which only D.C. will serve. So some method must be found to convert the one into the other, and there are several of these devices available, both small and large. If your radio set works off the A.C. mains there must be some such device in it, one of which belongs definitely to the radio section. The

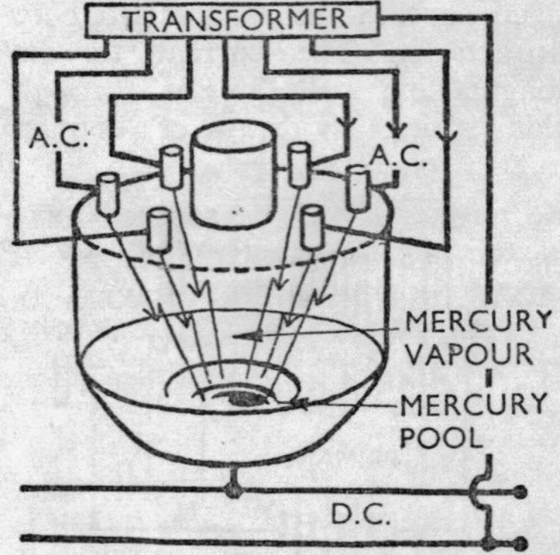

Fig. 59. *The mercury arc rectifier in diagram, showing the six anode heads.*

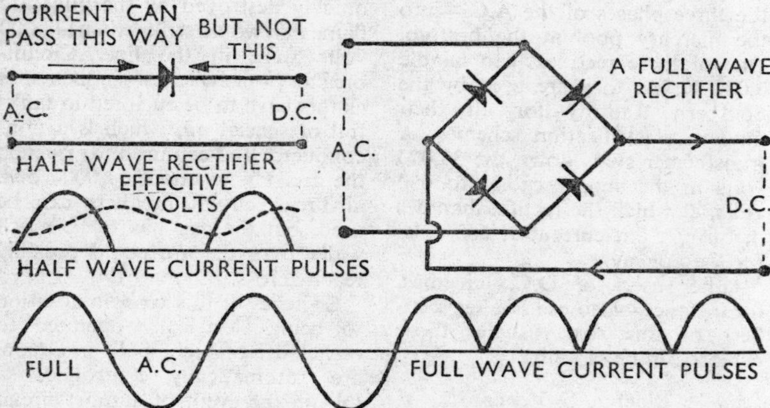

Fig. 60. *Details of the Westinghouse Metal Rectifier, with rectified current graphs.*

other is our direct concern, as it is used largely elsewhere.

Rectification

The Metal Rectifier—this conversion is often called Rectification—consists of a succession of contacts between substances that only allow an electric current to go one way. This rather odd principle is very useful because the positive and the negative impulses of A.C. can both be thus collected and joined together conveniently, though the result is a not entirely smooth-flowing current. By passing it through a coil known as a Choke, which is simply a winding of many turns of fine wire over an iron core, the pulsing effect is smoothed out, so the resulting current is good enough for most purposes.

In the case of the Westinghouse Rectifier (Fig. 60), contacts are made between successions of lead, copper and copper oxide; the current can get through the oxide to the copper, but not the other way. The diagram shows the symbol for this sort of contact, the arrow-head indicating the direction in which current can proceed. The final D.C. voltage is about three-quarters of the original A.C. volts. For charging accumulators, these are excellent, and can be had for quite considerable currents, suitable for working arc lamps. In fact, we learn that installations able to turn out 12,000 amps. are at work. One pair of contacts will rectify about 6 volts.

Formerly, the usual method of conversion was by means of the Rotary Converter, consisting, in its essential principle, of an A.C. motor driving a D.C. dynamo. Later, the windings of the two were combined, so that it appeared to be one machine. These are not so much used now, since the rectifiers came to the fore.

The Mercury Vapour Rectifier

Another form of Rectifier (Fig. 59) employs a cloud of mercury vapour in a glass bulb—or in a steel cylinder—from which all air is extracted. Again, this arrangement acts as a one-way valve. The successive pulses of current are all taken through the vapour from six anode heads—two for each of the three phases of the A.C.—into the mercury pool at the bottom. One of these rectifiers can handle 3,000 K.W.; they are used by the Southern Railway for all their modern electrification schemes. A transformer steps down the 33,000 volts in the supply cables to 690 volts, at which the rectifier handles it, turning out current at 660 volts for the railway.

Other users of D.C.—cinemas, for instance—also use smaller rectifiers of this sort, usually those enclosed in glass bulbs.

Electric Switches

A necessary item in the control of electricity is something to break the circuit, to stop the flow of current.

This is done by the switch. The usual rule is to have a spring-controlled arm that makes a quick break, but however quickly the break is made there is always something of a spark—the engineer calls it an "arc"—across the points. This is of no account with small currents of a few hundred watts, but we have already mentioned currents amounting to millions. An ordinary switch would be very quickly destroyed by the huge arc flame that would strike when132,000 volts were in the line. Circuit-breakers—or switches—in such lines as this have to be enclosed in tanks full of special oil, which is a non-conductor and can instantly quench the arc. Up to about 11,000 volts, air-break circuit breakers can be used, but the gap has to be much wider than the arc could possibly reach across.

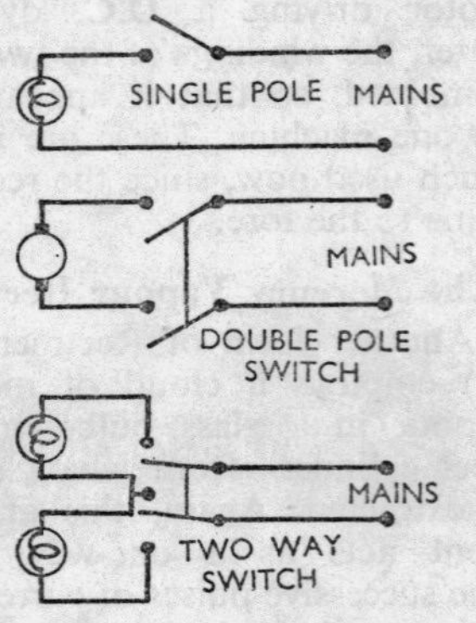

Fig. 61. *Three types of switches in common use, shown in diagram form.*

Switches of this type, in addition to being electrically operated to make sure of high speed in action, are automatically controlled, so that in the event of a short circuit that might destroy a lot of valuable gear, theycome into action instantly.

The beginner must always remember that switches are invariably put into a circuit *in series*. When installing a lamp or other apparatus, there are two wires to be connected to the points of the lamp-holder, and the switch is joined up into one of these lines, which has to be cut. In some cases, especially with A.C., a double-pole switch may be put in, and this breaks both wires, but for an ordinary lamp it is not necessary. The switch-button works both breaker arms at the same time, and a diagram shows the principle. There are several sorts of switches for various purposes. For instance, a two-way switch cuts off the current in one circuit to turn it into another, and is useful in wiring up domestic lamps. They are shown in Fig. 61.

Self Testing Questions

(1) *What is the principle of the induction coil?*

(2) *How does a magneto work?*

(3) *What is rectification?*

(4) *What is the most important point to remember about switches?*

THE ANSWERS ARE ON PAGE 248.

LESSON 14

Bells and Telephones

THE common electric bell demonstrates a very valuable point about magnetism—the rapidity with which soft iron throws off this power when the energising current is cut off. This speed of action is most important, particularly in that part of the science we are about to study.

The Electric Bell

The necessary parts of a bell, or a buzzer, consist of a magnet wound with two or three hundred turns of wire; an iron plate carried on a steel spring, fixed so that it can be attracted by the magnet poles, and a contact make-and-break worked by the moving spring. The iron plate, or armature, has a stiff wire extension with a hammer-head, which strikes a gong whenever the magnet pulls it over. The make-and-break—controlling the flow of current to the magnet coils—includes a contact stud on the spring and an adjustable screw contact point. Fig. 62 shows the action better than words.

To bring the bell into action a battery is necessary, and a switch, usually in the form of a spring contact, made by pressing a button. Any number of these switches can be wired on to the same bell, in the manner shown in the circuit diagram. Bells do not need much attention as a rule, but contact points are better for occasional cleaning, and batteries run down sometimes also.

Buzzers have a similar mechanism, but instead of a gong and hammer, a flat iron plate is used instead. When this is attracted and released rapidly by the magnet, it sets up sound waves of a high or low pitch, according to the speed of its vibration. The motor-car hooter works on this plan.

Sound Waves and Diaphragms

That brings us to the subject of sound waves. Sounds are passed from point to point by a system of waves in the air, and though you cannot feel them, yet they are strong enough to vibrate thin metal plates, called diaphragms, put in their way. The range of sound audible to the human ear lies between 16 and 10,000 vibrations or waves to the second. This is easily within the compass of an electro-magnet, so if we have a current of electricity vibrating 261 times a second, and put this into a

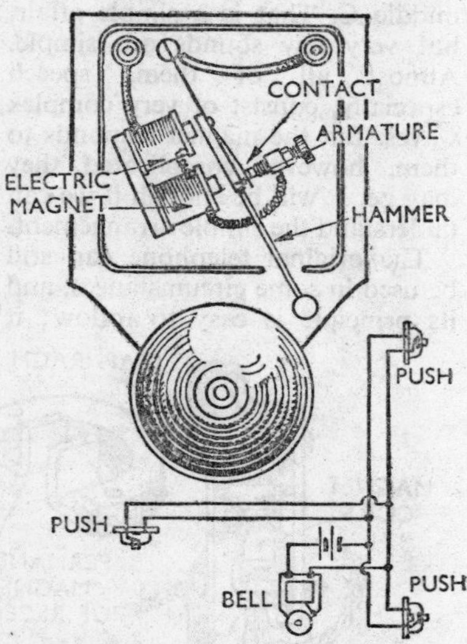

Fig. 62. *The electric bell; and* below, *circuit to show three pushes to work one bell.*

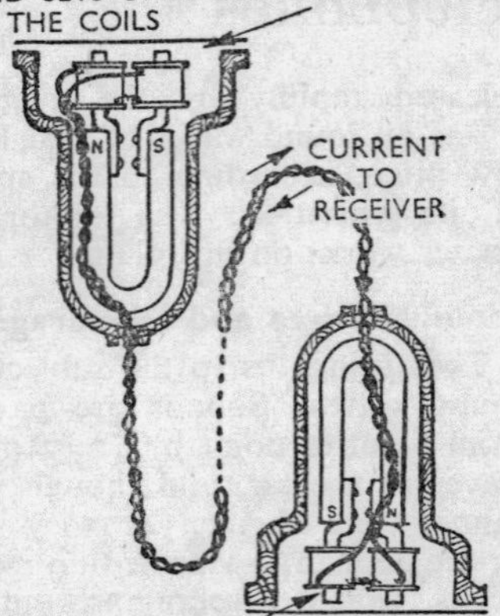

Fig. 63. *The original Bell telephone principle. It may be used in either direction.*

magnet that can vibrate a buzzer diaphragm, the sound we shall get will be what the musician calls middle C. That is a simple affair, but very few sounds are simple. Almost all of them, speech especially, consist of very complex waves. But the magnet responds to them, however complicated they may be. It will be enough if we can understand the simple arrangement.

The original telephone can still be used in some circumstances, and its principle is easy to follow; it needs no batteries. Transmitter and receiver are exactly the same, and are used in either way, according to whether you are speaking or listening (Fig. 63).

How the Early Telephone Worked

A strong permanent magnet has a coil of fine wire wound on each pole, and the ends of these two coils pass into the lines connecting the two instruments. A diaphragm —which is an iron disc clamped all round its edge—is set very close to the poles without touching them, and there is the whole apparatus. Speak at the diaphragm, and it vibrates in time with the sound-waves your vocal chords put out. Tiny currents are set up in the field-coils; these pass along the lines to the coils in the other instrument, energising them, increasing or decreasing the strength of the magnetism in that field. The diaphragm is attracted and released by the increase or decrease of strength, and every time it moves outwards it sets up a sound-wave in the air. Actually, the receiver diaphragm moves in and out just as the transmitter diaphragm moves out and in. The whole action is, in effect, the dynamo and the motor, working on the basis of the *movement of a conductor in a magnetic field* (Fig. 64).

The modern telephone trans-

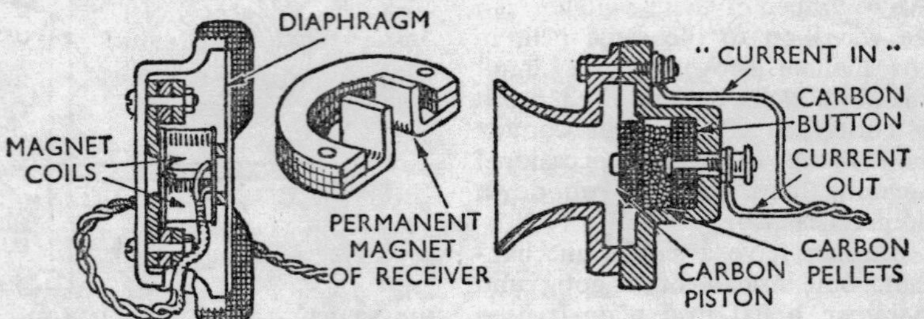

Fig. 64. *The modern telephone, as the text explains, is much more sensitive.*

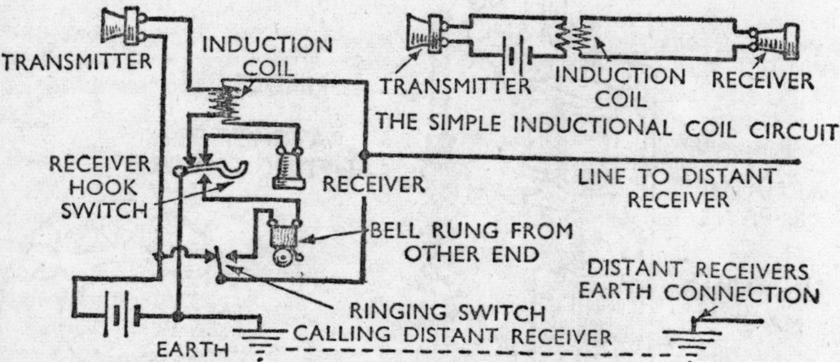

Fig. 65. *Telephone circuit for long-distance transmission as might be used at a simple exchange, showing induction coil for increasing voltage.*

mitter does not work in this way, but the receiver does. Telephone messages go long distances, so we have to provide some outside source of current from a battery to get the tiny current movements through safely.

How the Modern Telephone Works

When you speak at the diaphragm you do not drive a dynamo this time, you rattle a little box full of tiny carbon pellets through which the current is passing. When the pellets are loose, the resistance is high and not so much current gets through, but when they are packed tight, the resistance is lowered and more current can pass. The moving diaphragm does just this, for a piston fastened to it squeezes—or eases—the little pellets in their box, by only a microscopic amount, but quite enough for the resistance to be altered, and the current with it. This is the microphone, producing a vibrating current that can easily be amplified to any degree of strength.

When you have listened to the recognisable tones of your friend's voice on the modern telephone instrument, you will realise that what sounds unlikely is true. Merely altering the pressure on that little crowd of carbon pellets permits the finest adjustments of current, acting with instant speed, to pass along hundreds of miles, maybe, of copper wire to the distant receiver. There the same fine gradations of current energise the magnet coils, to vibrate the diaphragm in such a way that you know at once who is speaking.

The receiver is almost exactly as it has always been, consisting of a permanent magnet to keep up a continuous strong field, with coils on its poles to take the currents from the transmitter. This arrangement is much more sensitive than a simple electro-magnet would be.

Long-Distance Telephone Calls

When telephone messages are sent over a long distance, it is the rule to put the speech vibrations through an induction coil, a simple arrangement of primary and secondary windings on an iron core. No make-and-break is required, because the incoming current is already of a pulsing nature. The effect of the induction coil is to

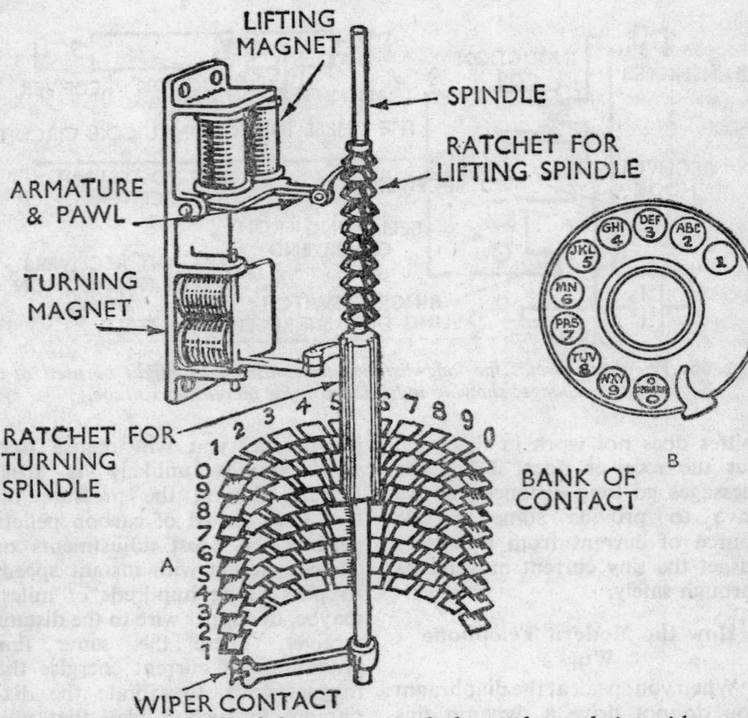

Fig. 66. A, *the principle of the automatic telephone selector device, with contact bank for* 100 *contacts;* B, *the dial of an automatic telephone.*

step up the voltage, so enabling the currents to overcome the resistance of the line, but of course a battery would be used here. A circuit (Fig. 65), showing the connections at a simple telephone exchange is given; this must be imagined as duplicated one between the other, so that both can speak or listen at will, using the same single line and one earth return. This is not done with Post Office telephones, however; an all-metal circuit, giving much clearer speech, is always provided, so instead of an earth, we should have two lines.

There are many remarkable devices at the telephone exchange, where you can be connected to your friend's number either by hand—when it is a simple matter of joining up by cords and plugs—or mechanically. The modern automatic telephone is a highly complex affair, but a few words of explanation may give some idea as to its principle (Fig. 66, *A* and *B*).

Automatic Dialling

Every automatic telephone has a dial on its base, by means of which the subscriber gets in touch with his exchange, all the other exchanges, and all the other subscribers on the system. In London, where there are more than a hundred and twenty of these exchanges, all numbers are seven-figure numbers, though the first three are letters, the first three of the exchange name, thus TEM for Temple Bar. The dial shows ten holes, numbered 1 to 9; the tenth one serves both as figure and letter O. In addition, the hole marked 2 is also marked ABC, and so on, round to the ninth, which is WXY.

How the Selector Operates

The apparatus at the exchange responds to any movement of the dial, and as soon as you lift your instrument it is switched in. The work is done by a group of machines called selectors, in which groups of 100 contacts are arranged in ten rows of ten in a section of a cylinder. A spindle with a "wiper" contact is set in the centre line so that as it turns round it can make contact with any of the fixed contacts. This spindle is lifted one step at a time by a magnet, and turned round one at a time by another.

Getting Your Number

Suppose the number you want is Temple Bar 7378. Now, if you dial, the lifting magnet gives seven lifts to the spindle; then three, and the turning magnet pulls it round by three, so contact is made with the third point on the seventh row. That is the basis of the machine, though there is much more in it than that.

By the time your call is completed, you will be occupying, first a line-switch—the device that looks round to find a disengaged director for you. It is this director that takes the first three letters from your dialling and connects you to the proper exchange, and then three more selectors to get the actual number. So your call occupies five selectors in addition to the director.

Fresh Current Impulses

To send speech through a long line means providing some arrangement for refreshing the current impulses, that would naturally lose strength as the resistance of the line increases. A simple way of doing this is by means of a relay, in which the passing currents induce fresh, strong currents supplied from batteries at regular points along the line. Between London and Glasgow this refreshing process occurs eight times, but the relaying process in the modern repeater station is done in just the same way as the radio set amplifies the tiny impulses that are picked up by your aerial.

Using Telegraph Lines

Some remarkable work is now done by the telephone engineers, for by using a system that we shall discuss in the next lesson, they are able to use telegraph lines, through which messages are being sent, for telephone speech as well.

Self Testing Questions

(1) *How do you wire in extra pushes for a bell circuit?*

(2) *What is the principle of the simple telephone transmitter and receiver?*

(3) *How does the carbon microphone work?*

THE ANSWERS ARE ON PAGE 248.

LESSON 15

Telegraphy

MODERN machine telegraphy is such an intricate affair that we cannot spare much room for history if we are to get any real idea of its working. It is necessary, however, to see what were the difficulties that the early engineers encountered, in order to understand why things are done in certain ways.

Telegraphy is concerned entirely with the sending of messages over long distances, and we are interested here only in electric telegraphy. Everyone has heard of the Morse Code, that system of dots and dashes by which the letters of the alphabet, and numerals too, can be signalled.

Making a Morse Key

A knowledge of this code is often useful, and is not hard to acquire. A simple key and buzzer can be made without the use of any elaborate tools, on the lines shown in Fig. 68. Some stout sheet iron, a few screws and nuts such as are used in radio sets, some yards of insulated wire, and a little patience!

The key is made by forming a strip of sheet iron over a piece of ¼-in. bar iron, or the edge of a flat file, held in the vice. Drill it for its pivot, the contact screws, and finger knob at the points shown. Its bearing is simply a piece of the same iron bent to three sides of a square, drilled also as shown for holding-down screws and pivot; screw this on to a piece of wood for a base board. The arrangement of the contact screws —which can be brass screws, round-headed for preference, with flats filed upon the centres of their heads —is clearly drawn in the sketch. To make a neat job, run the connecting wires in grooves cut underneath, and finish off with two terminals at the end of the board. An insulated terminal nut and screw make a neat finger-knob if they can be found. So much for the key.

The buzzer is exactly the same sort of thing as was described under the heading of electric bells, using a small horseshoe magnet pulling on a flat strip of iron, with a make-and-break put together from an ordinary small screw about an inch in length and a couple of nuts.

Join up key, buzzer and a flat torch battery according to the circuit given, and you can start to practise—it is an interesting study, of immense value on occasions, as many have found recently.

Long-Distance Transmission

Originally, the telegraph engineer used the code in just this simple way, sending long and short impulses of current through his lines, and devising a variety of machines

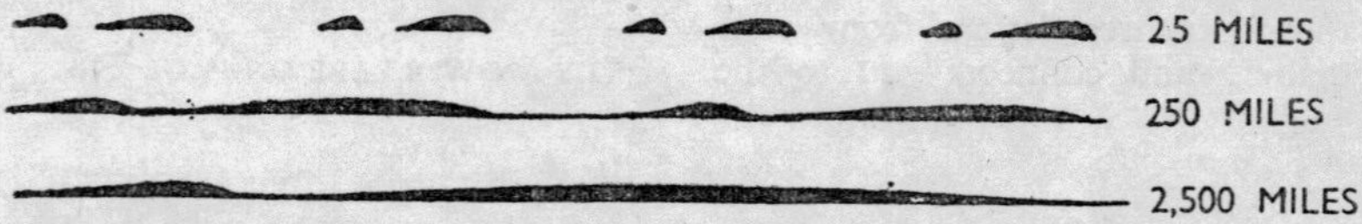

Fig. 67. *How capacity affects the number of telegraph signals that can be sent.*

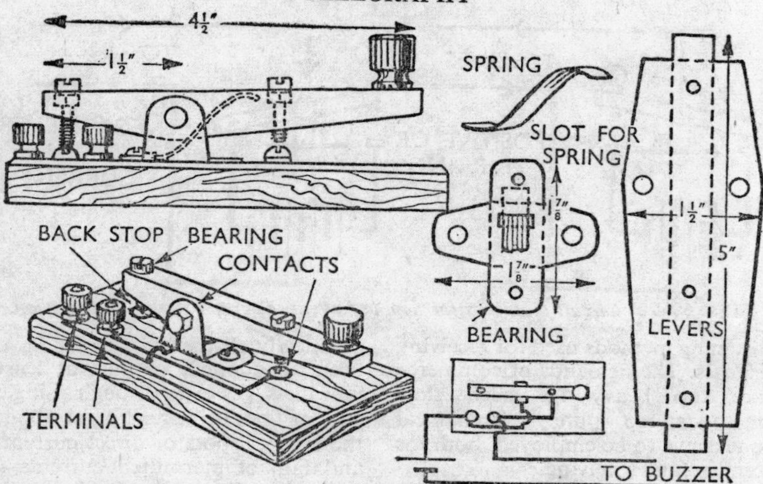

Fig. 68. *A simple Morse key. The text explains how to construct one.*

at the far end for receiving and recording the signals. This was all very well for short distances, but it broke down badly where long distances were concerned, owing to trouble number one—Capacity.

This difficulty can be better understood by thinking of a long hose-pipe that must first be filled with water before delivery can commence at the far end. If the pipe is short, quick jerks of water can be sent by sharp openings and closings of the controlling tap. If the pipe is long, the start and stop of flow are not so crisp, but with a very long one the flow does not stop at all, merely rising and falling a little later than the tap movements. What is more, the longer the pipe, the smaller must be the number of tap movements in a given time to ensure that some message will get through at the far end.

So it is with the telegraph signals. Fig. 67 will show you the idea—a series of dot and dash signals sent over various lengths of line. The character of the line shows the form of the signal as received, and the fact that the line is continuous is intended to show that the current does not stop flowing, even though the sender at the far end is working his key quite clearly. The thickening of the line indicates maximum current. Note also that the short line enables the sender to put through, say, four signals in a given time. Ten times the length of line halves the number, and a hundred times the length brings it down to an eighth at most.

To get over some of this the whole basis was changed, and a dot was sent as a spot of positive current—"marking"—and a dash as an equal spot of negative current—"spacing"—as the engineer calls it. In this way the line is filled and emptied of current every time a signal goes through. This is the Double-Current system, and it needs a differently wired key to work it; the circuit is shown in Figs. 69–70.

Hand-sending of signals by means of the Morse key is not used much today, nor are visual reading or

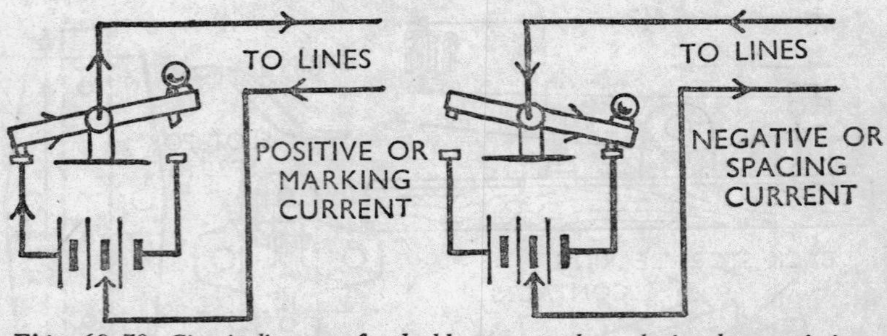

Figs. 69–70. *Circuit diagrams for double current telegraph signal transmission.*

listening methods used for receiving signals. The demands of commerce are too heavy for such slow methods, so purely mechanical ones have to be employed, both for sending and receiving.

Modern Telegraphy

The telegraph lines that cover this country, mostly buried underground now, are worked at full pressure; but if each pair of lines carried only one message conditions would be hopeless. One line only is necessary to send a message; the return line wanted to complete the circuit is made through the earth. Even so, it would be impossible to cope with the load, and systems were worked out by means of which a message could be sent one way at the same time that one was being sent the opposite way. This is the Duplex system, and another, the Diplex, allowed two messages to be sent the same way at one time. Combining these two, we get two each way, four altogether—Quadruplex as it was called. As the two latter systems are not now used to any extent, we will leave them, but Duplex *is* used.

Its working depends on the use of a group of instruments tuned to respond only to the required signals, careful balancing with resistances being necessary.

The modern method, in which practically all the old systems have been abandoned, permits at least nine messages to go through a single pair of lines at once. Forget about the idea of spots of direct current, and think of intermittent currents—A.C., if you like—currents that oscillate rapidly. Those in use by the G.P.O. vary from 420 a second up to 2,460 a second, rising by 120's. Imagine a dot as occupying perhaps one-tenth of a second; at the lowest rate this will mean 42 oscillations; a dash will run to three times this—126.

Filtering Messages

If you can imagine a device in the nature of a filter—which is what the engineer calls it—that will take the whole collection of currents coming along the line and filter out only that one with its own particular number of oscillations—or frequency—then you have the whole idea. The nature of the filter belongs to the radio division of this course, being dependent on a radio-valve to a certain extent. A bank of nine of these filters will take the whole of the signals coming along, and each will sort out its own, passing it along for strengthening and return to the line, or else for recording and despatch.

The currents, or frequencies, are generated in a single dynamo, designed to turn out eighteen different currents at once.

At the destination point the frequency, after being filtered out, is handed over to another radio-valve to be turned into D.C., in a form capable of working some sort of machine, possibly a direct printer.

On such a line as this it is possible to run a telephone conversation, though instead of using a battery current to transmit the vibrations, a current of high-frequency is used, so that the tiny vibrations, maybe at 2,700 to the second, will be split up into very much smaller ones.

The Galvanometer and its Work

So much for modern methods on the land lines; we have also to consider the submarine cables, through which the round-the-world messages are sent. Many people thought that wireless would put cables out of business, but it has not proved so, possibly on account of the lack of secrecy about wireless.

The enormous length of some stretches of cable under the sea—up to 3,500 miles in at least one case—means that we are faced with the task of magnifying signals of the tiniest nature imaginable. This was a serious matter for the early engineers, but at least one of their solutions of the difficulty—the Kelvin Galvanometer—is still in use, and can be seen in any cable-station.

Between the poles of a powerful magnet a coil of many turns of very fine wire is suspended by a strand of silk. On the coil a tiny mirror is fixed, reflecting a ray of light, thrown on to it by a lamp, on to a divided scale. The incoming cable current being led into the coil, we get the electric motor principle again—movement of a current in a magnetic field produces movement in the conductor. The coil swings, only slightly, but enough to record a tell-tale movement of the spot of light moving across the scale, and the amount of this movement is proportional to the current (Fig. 71).

Practically every instrument handling incoming cable signals works on this principle, but though they are of great interest, their working is too advanced for us here. Let it suffice that this movement of an energised coil in a strong field is employed to work relays, by means of which strong new signals, exactly similar to the original ones, are sent into the lines. These may be to pass the message on to the next station, or else to work a writer or a printing-machine to record the message for local delivery. Sending cable messages today is an entirely mechanical affair, without the intervention of hands at any point. A message from London to Melbourne may go by various routes. The usual one crosses the Atlantic to Halifax (Nova Scotia) and the Canadian continent alongside the C.P.R., down into the Pacific at Vancouver, where the long stretch of 3,500 miles to Fanning Island begins. After calls at Fiji, Auckland and Sydney, it will duly arrive at the destination, having been regenerated automatically at least eight times on the way.

The instrument that handles the

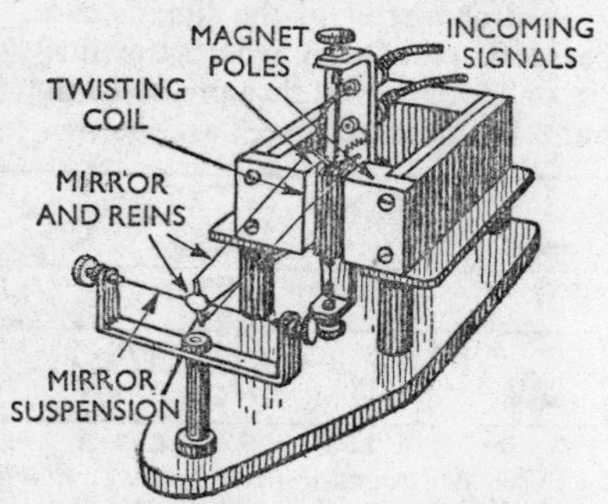

Fig. 71. *The mirror galvanometer.*

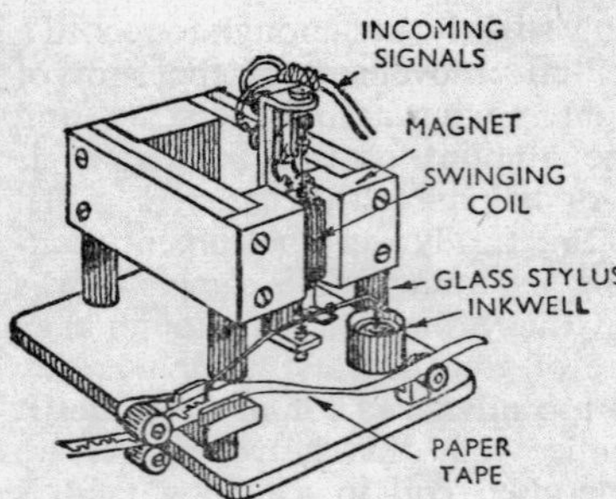

Fig. 72. *The modern telegraph inker.*

weakest signals uses radio-valves, but even when these have done their work, the currents are still of a very slight description, and at least two other machines are needed before vigorous signals are moving.

Inker Machines

The machine that records the movement of current rising and falling, by means of a glass stylus tracing an undulating line on a long strip of paper, is worth a little attention. Originally the invention of the great Lord Kelvin, it has been improved considerably to enable it to handle high-speed signals. Drawings to show sections of messages recorded by these inker machines, of the early and the modern types, are shown (Fig. 73), and a sketch of the modern inker (Fig. 72). The improved character of the signals can be seen. Note that where the line rises above the middle a positive impulse has been received, and below, a negative, bearing in mind that the first means a dot and the second a dash. Try to decipher the letters signalled in the early example—incidentally, this would be regarded as very clear by the old-time telegraphist.

Submarine Cables

The submarine cable is a remarkable thing, too, the modern form being the reliable result of many years of trial and failure, though there are some stretches still at work after 40 years' service and more. There are three types: the Inshore, Intermediate and Deep Sea.

The first is heavily armoured to resist rough seas and rocky sea-bottoms, as well as ship's anchors and fishermen's trawls, and has two layers of stout steel wire embedded in its outer casing. The second is somewhat lighter as to its armour, and the deep-sea type is less than 1 in. in diameter, but immensely strong. It may have to lie at the bottom of the sea several miles below the surface, but even there it has an implacable enemy to meet—the burrowing teredo worm. To defeat this assiduous shellfish, a brass tape has to be worked into the protective wrappings of the slender stranded copper conductor.

In Fig. 75 are shown the various layers of insulation, protection and armouring of the deep-sea cable. Its cost is enormous, so once laid it must be worked to the fullest

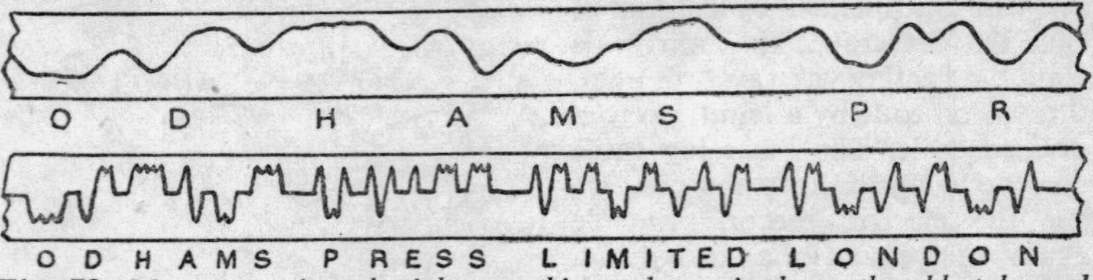

Fig. 73. *Messages written by inker machines;* above, *is shown the old style, and* below, *the modern. Lines above the middle represent dots; below, dashes.*

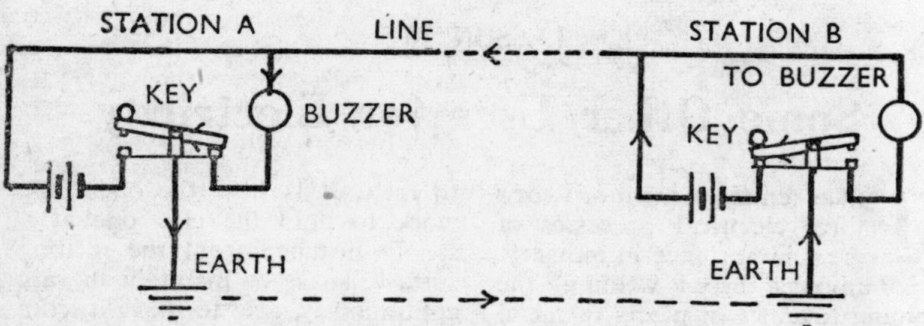

Fig. 74. *Circuit diagram for two Morse telegraph stations, each with key and buzzer.*

extent in order to make it pay. This is one reason for the introduction of the entirely mechanical methods now in use. Remember, however, that all has grown out of the simple telegraph key and buzzer that we hope you made in the beginning, or will now set out to make.

To return to this for a moment, we think it may be of interest to add a complete circuit by means of which two stations, similarly equipped with key and buzzer, can maintain communications (Fig. 74).

The back stop contacts come into use here, so an additional terminal can be put on to the base-board of the key, but this is not absolutely necessary. An earth return is quite practicable, so long as a good clean brass or aluminium plate is buried in damp soil to make the contact at each end. Remember to make some pre-arranged signal when you have finished your message, then release your key to make a return circuit for the other station's reply to pass through your buzzer.

Self Testing Questions

(1) *Why is the earth used as a return line in telegraphy?*

(2) *What is the advantage of double-current working in telegraphy?*

(3) *What is the principle of all sensitive recording devices used in cable work?*

THE ANSWERS ARE ON PAGE 248.

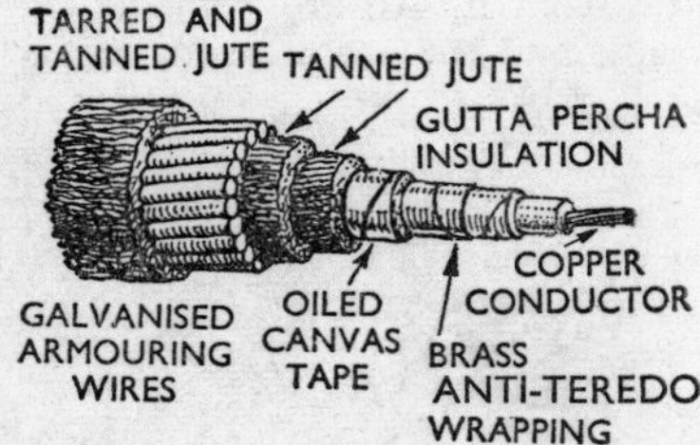

Fig. 75. *Composite insulating layers of the deep sea type of submarine cable.*

LESSON 16

Some Other Uses for Electricity

THERE remain to mention two or three electrical processes of great importance in industry. First amongst these is welding—the joining together of pieces of metal by melting. We have already seen that great heat can be set up with the electric arc, sufficient to vaporise carbon; this involves a temperature of over 7,000 deg. Fahrenheit—more than enough to melt any metal that is at present known.

Electric Welding

The process of welding begins with the careful cleaning and shaping of the metal; when it is ready it may be necessary to clamp the parts together. The metal pieces are then joined to one pole of the circuit, usually, but not invariably, the negative. The positive lead is attached to a stick of either carbon, or of the metal being welded, and, contact being made with the work, its point is withdrawn a little from it. An arc immediately forms, and the metal soon begins to melt. It is now the operator's work to hold the electrode at a steady distance from the melting surface, so as to maintain the arc continuously, also to move it from side to side in a zigzag path to ensure an extension of the weld on either side of the joint. Considerable skill is required, as well as judgment, to get sufficient depth in the melted portions, and also to avoid the oxidising of the metal (Fig. 76).

It is well known that oxygen attacks almost every metal, especially when it is hot, and as an oxidised weld would have very little strength, it is essential to keep this inquisitive gas away. In arc welding it can be done by adding a flux—some material which melts into an impervious covering that excludes the oxygen while the metal is in a sensitive state, and which can be scraped off quite easily when it is cold. Some fluxes give off a gas that is not harmful, providing a non-active shield for the molten metal.

Carbon-arc welding uses the

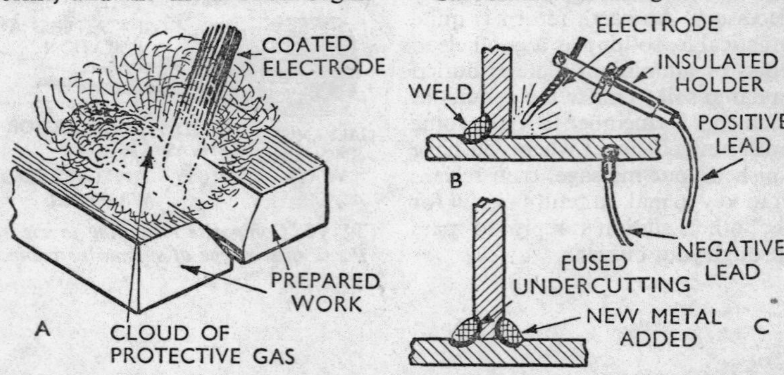

Fig. 76. A, *the arc welding process showing the protective gas cloud from the fused flux.* B, *arc welding arrangement and electrode holder.* C, *a welded joint in section.*

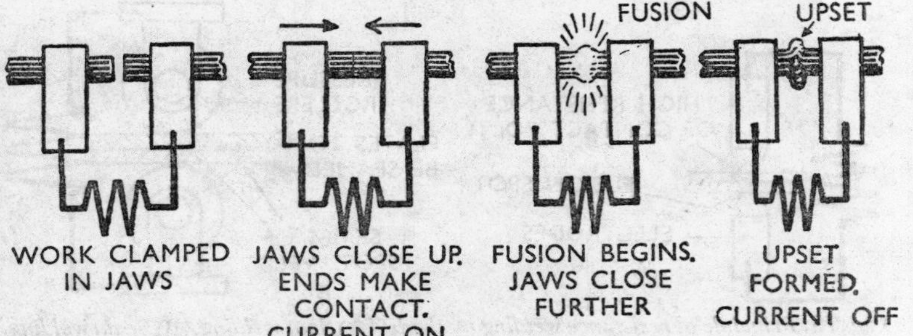

Fig. 77. *Sequence of events in simple butt welding. The joint needs only trimming.*

metal of the two pieces to be joined, but if additional metal is necessary, then a stick of it must be held in the flame so that it, too, melts, adding filling as required. A much more convenient method, almost universally employed now, is to have a stick of the metal for an electrode, using no carbon at all. This stick will be coated with a suitable flux that melts over the work. Welding engineers have an extensive selection of metal electrodes available, for there are few metals that cannot be welded; practically all those most useful in commerce can be so treated.

Welders always wear dark blue glass goggles, for the blinding white light of the arc flame would ruin the sight very quickly.

Direct current is always used for this sort of welding, and as a rule this is provided by a portable generator, driven by a petrol or similar engine. As with the arc-lamp, welding currents are heavy.

Resistance Welding

Resistance welding is much used in the factory today, providing a quick method of building up intricate metal parts for machinery that would need a great deal of careful work to machine out of the solid. The two parts to be joined are squeezed together in a press, and a heavy current passed through them across the joint. Now, as we have seen before, a joint is a bad thing, electrically speaking, and it offers considerable resistance, however firmly pressed together the parts may be. With resistance welding, the joint offers so much obstruction to the flow of current that it heats up and then melts, just to enough depth to ensure both parts being fused together. When this happens, current is cut off, and the parts are kept under pressure till they have cooled. After release, they are to all intents one solid piece, only requiring a little finishing to trim off a slight roughness. This is called Butt welding (Fig. 77); there are other modifications of the same idea in use.

Spot and Seam Welding

Spot and Seam welding (Fig. 78) are two methods of using the resistance principle, providing a cheap and effective substitute for riveting sheet-metal. The metal parts are pressed together between two copper electrodes, and a heavy current run through; this immediately fuses the sheets together. A line of these spots can be run along the seam to be joined, resulting in a firm joint that will not give way. Seam welding is done with a pair of rollers,

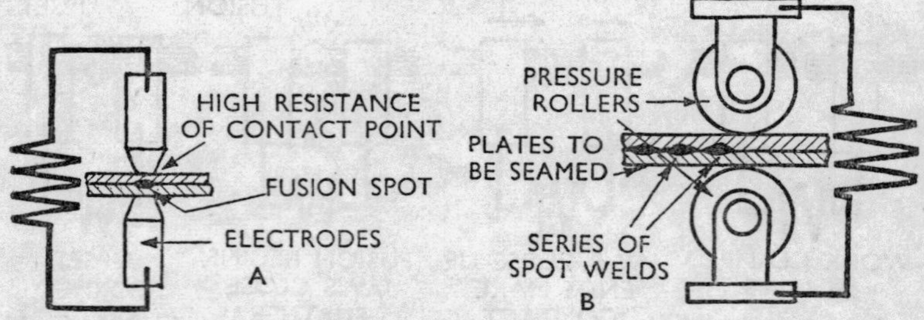

Fig.78. *Principle of resistance welding methods:* (A) *Spot welding,* (B) *Seam welding.*

producing a line of spot-welds very close together, so that the joint is gas- and liquid-proof.

Resistance welding is always done with A.C., the current used being the product of a secondary transformer winding of only two or three turns. As the time taken in producing a single weld is so short, the current consumed is relatively small, being reckoned on the basis of so many welds to each unit. With some work the current may run to 150,000 amps or even more.

Electro-Plating

Another electrical process of great interest in industry is Electroplating. This process is akin to that in which electricity is made, so to speak, chemically in the cell, for plating provides an example of the chemical effect of a current. It is simple enough in practice, for a solution of a metallic salt, such as nitrate of silver or sulphate of copper, makes a good conductor of electricity. Let us suppose that we are to deposit a layer of copper on to some metal object. The object must first be thoroughly cleaned to free it from every trace of grease. We shall want an open glass vessel, that must be filled with a solution of copper sulphate. Two rods, one for positive and the other negative, bridge the top; from the positive must be hung a plate of copper, and from the negative the object to be plated (Fig. 79).

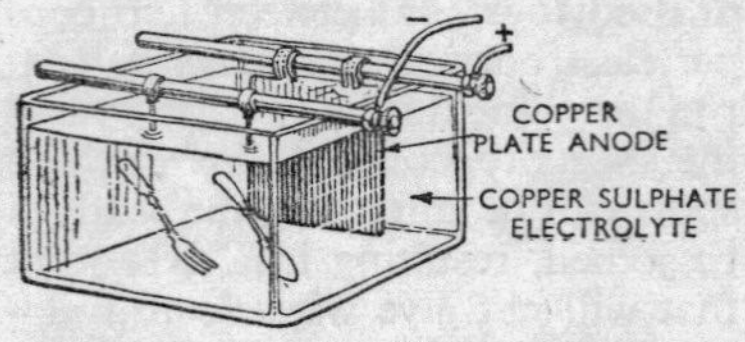

Fig. 79. *A simple electro-plating vat.*

A current of several ampères—about 5—will be needed, and it must be D.C. When this has been flowing for half an hour or so, the object will be found to have acquired quite a thick coating of copper, the thickness of which can be added to just as long as there is any copper anode left.

Any metal that can be plated goes through the same process, though the electrolyte, or solution, must be of a salt of the metal that is to be put on. For nickel, nickel sulphate is used with a little ammonium sulphate added. Silver is deposited through a solution of nitrate of silver and cyanide of potassium. An exception has to be made in the case of gold; here the solution is cyanide of potassium alone. Only pure metal is deposited, no matter what impurities there may be in the anode plate. More than half the world's copper is produced by means of electroplating from less pure metal, which it is almost impossible to refine in any other way.

Polishing

A low voltage is always used in plating, but a steady current is required if the plate is to be even in thickness. The metal, being in a crystalline form, has a dull texture, but polishing on a buffing wheel soon brings up the brilliant effect so well known.

Plating has been employed to build up worn bearings with new metal, and is regularly used to make good worn gauges in the workshop. A fixed current will add a known thickness of metal in a given time, which is valuable information where exact methods of measurement are concerned.

X-Rays

Very different from the two processes just described are the so-called X-rays. We have said that electricity exists in the form of rapid oscillations, and in this form it appears in different ways. The radiations from the wireless aerial oscillate at a comparatively low frequency, though it is rapid enough to stagger the imagination, being in the order of millions a second. Passing up the scale we find that the electrical effects seem to disappear, and that heat-rays take their place—the Infra-Red rays of the spectrum of light; following these we have the band of colours seen in the rainbow—called the spectrum—from red to violet. Then come the Ultra-Violet, or chemical action rays, again invisible to the human eye. These oscillate at the incredible rate of 10,000 million million a second—or, as the mathematician would describe it, 10^{16}. Next to these, in the still upward scale, we come to the X-rays, vibrating at least ten times as fast. Such figures as these are, of course, quite incomprehensible to the mind.

The Power of X-Rays

These rays are able to penetrate through most kinds of solid material to a depth according to their rate of oscillation. We are not able to see them, either before or after their passage through; but they will affect a photographic film, or a screen of a substance called barium platino-cyanide. This they will light up with a glow just similar to the photograph, varied in its tones ac-

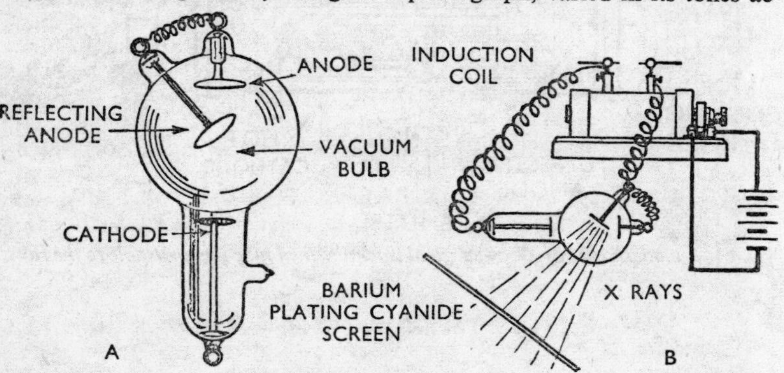

Fig. 80. A, *a simple type of X-ray tube.* B, *the X-ray tube and induction coil on circuit. The glow shows that rays are passing from the inclined anode.*

cording to the density of whatever it is they have passed through.

X-Ray Tubes

How do we set up these X-rays? They are emitted from a glass tube, shaped as shown in Fig. 80, *A*, from which all the air possible has been drawn out. One end has a platinum *cathode*, and the other end two *anodes*, one set diagonally across the bulb portion. If the terminals of an induction coil, able to produce about a 15,000-volt discharge, are connected to these two points, a greenish glow will be observed in the tube. These are not the actual X-rays, but are the visible indication that they are passing out of the tube, reflected from the inclined anode, or target (Fig. 80, *B*).

Dangers of X-Rays

At one time, cheap tubes could be bought for experimental work, but they are a danger to the unwary. Severe burns on the skin, possibly causing the loss of fingers, may result from undue exposure to the rays. Professional operators use every protection available. A section is shown (Fig. 81) of a surgical tube, using tungsten metal electrodes, with chromium-steel shields, the whole being encased in lead, through which the rays cannot penetrate.

A Wimshurst machine produces the high-voltage current necessary just as well as the induction coil. In industrial applications of X-rays used in examining machinery parts for possible flaws, transformers are often used.

Self Testing Questions

(1) *How many types of welding are there?*

(2) *Is the same type and amount of current used for all weldings?*

(3) *What steps are taken to prevent an oxidised weld?*

(4) *What are the essentials in the process of Electro-plating? Is there any variation in these requirements?*

THE ANSWERS ARE ON PAGE 248.

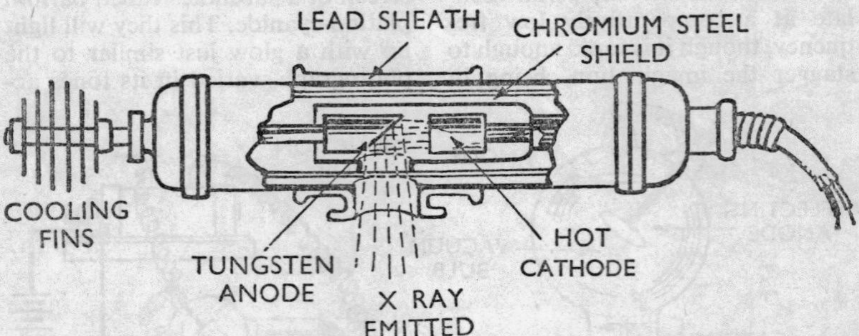

Fig.81. *A modern type of X-ray surgical lead-sheathed tube impenetrable to the rays.*

Answers to Self Testing Questions

LESSON 1

(1) Its electrons.

(2) A negative charge of electrical energy.

(3) Heat and light.

LESSON 2

(1) Friction between dissimilar substances.

(2) Sealing-wax and wool, amber and silk.

(3) They attract each other.

(4) Silver, copper, aluminium; air.

LESSON 3

(1) Its south pole—usually called the north-seeking pole.

(2) Like poles repel, unlike poles attract.

(3) Iron is magnetised by a current circulated round it.

(4) Hard steel for permanent, soft iron for electro.

LESSON 4

(1) Plates of zinc and copper in weak sulphuric acid.

(2) To prevent choking by hydrogen bubbles.

(3) Sal-ammoniac and black oxide of manganese.

(4) Electro-motive force, the power that keeps the current flowing.

LESSON 5

(1) The resistance of the circuit, and the E.M.F. of the current.

(2) 40 watts. 990 hours.

LESSON 6

(1) The long thin line.

(2) In parallel in the 12 v. and in series in the 24 v.

(3) The lamp takes 0·6 amps, so 200 ohms resistance must be put in series. Eight feet of the wire will give this.

LESSON 7

(1) If a conductor is moved in the field of a magnet a current will flow in the conductor, so long as it makes a complete circuit.

(2) Eight.

(3) All the generated current goes through a series winding, but only part of it with a shunt.

LESSON 8

(1) A.C. is a pulsing current, D.C. is continuous.

(2) One complete change from zero to zero, including a reversal of direction.

(3) To keep the ampères low.

(4) 500 volts.

LESSON 9

(1) Motion of a closed circuit coil in the field of a magnet produces a current.

(2) Maximum volts and ampères do not occur at the same moment as with D.C.

(3) Join the two ends of the coil to two separate slip-rings, with a brush for each.

LESSON 10

(1) 31¼ ft.

(2) 10 amps.

(3) ½*d.*

LESSON 11

(1) The better the light, the greater the heat, all of which is lost.

(2) To ensure the exclusion of all traces of oxygen.

(3) Too much current is required, and attention is also necessary.

(4) Too high a voltage, and no true white light is yet possible.

LESSON 12

(1) Mechanically, none. Current produces work in the motor, where work produces current in the dynamo.

(2) Reversal of direction of current through field or armature, not both.

(3) They will not start themselves, and can only run at a fixed speed.

(4) Movement of a conductor in a magnetic field is resisted.

LESSON 13

(1) Currents set up in a primary coil by changes of magnetism in an iron core are transformed in a secondary coil.

(2) A simple permanent magnet dynamo and induction coil combined.

(3) Conversion of A.C. into D.C.

(4) They are always wired in series.

LESSON 14

(1) Bell and battery in series, pushes in parallel.

(2) Dynamo and motor.

(3) Varying the resistance of a circuit by altering the packing of loose carbon pellets.

LESSON 15

(1) To save the expense of an all-metal circuit over long distances.

(2) Capacity effect is reduced by clearing the line every time a signal is sent.

(3) Current movements in a coil suspended in a magnetic field produce movements of the coil. The electric motor, in fact.

LESSON 16

(1) Six: carbon arc, metal electrode, resistance, butt, spot and seam.

(2) No. Resistance type of welding is always done with A.C., the consumption of which is relatively small.

(3) In arc welding, a flux is added. This "impervious covering . . . can be scraped off" later.

(4) Low voltage and steady current which must be D.C. Solution must be of a salt of the metal that is to be plated. The exception is gold, the solution for this being cyanide of potassium only.

RADIO

By E. M. Squire

LESSON 1

Producing the Signal

To study Radio adequately you should first have some knowledge of electricity. If you lack this knowledge, you should begin by studying the course in *Electricity*, given elsewhere in this book.

We shall start by considering how wireless signals are made.

A lady is singing in a broadcast studio. As she does so, the sound from her lips is directed toward a small object—the microphone. From the microphone the sound is changed into electricity, magnified, changed again and thrust into the transmitter aerial. From the aerial, the signal—as it now is—in the form of ether waves rushes at tremendous speed across space to the receiver aerial. Here it is picked up, changed, magnified and converted once again into a copy of the original sound, which is in due course emitted from the loudspeaker.

How the Microphone Works

Let us take a peep behind the stage, as it were, and see what takes place. As the singer directs her voice toward the microphone, a very fine ribbon is set into vibration by the sound. When the microphone plate moves, an electric current is produced which varies according to the loudness and pitch of the lady's voice. The fact that sound will cause vibration of objects is well known to everyone, for an aeroplane passing overhead will often vibrate ornaments in a house.

The varying electric currents from the microphone are passed on to apparatus that increases them. In another part of the transmitter apparatus, very rapidly fluctuating currents (called oscillations) are generated. This current as originally generated is too small for the transmitter to use effectively, so it too is magnified many times. Then the amplified oscillations are combined with the fluctuating currents due to the sound as received by the microphone. The combination is then magnified and fed into the transmitter aerial.

The Transmitter Aerial

The oscillations rush at tremendous speed up into the aerial, back to earth, up to the aerial and back again, and so on many thousands or millions of times every second. As they do so, they set up a disturbance which has the combined characteristics of the oscillating and microphone currents. This point is important, for if we remember that both currents leave their impression on the disturbance, we shall be able to understand the working of the radio receiver when we come to examine it.

Now, this disturbance goes out from the transmitter in all direc-

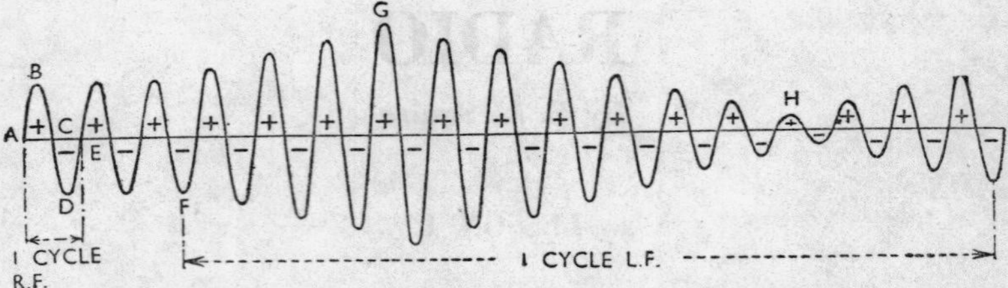

Fig. 1. *Representation of the current in the transmitter aerial.*

tions (unless, that is, the aerial is a specially designed directional one). It passes over the surface of the earth, and thus enables communication to be carried on with countries on the other side. The medium through which it travels is called the ether.

Let us examine the nature of this disturbance a little more closely. It consists of a series of waves set up round the aerial by the rapidly fluctuating signal currents. The effect of the transmitter aerial on the ether can be likened to that of a stone dropped into a pond. At the spot where the stone is dropped, a disturbance is produced. This takes the form of a wave which travels outward towards the edge of the pond. *Although the wave travels, the water remains stationary,* as can readily be proved by placing a small piece of wood near the point where the stone is dropped. The wood merely bobs up and down as the waves pass under it.

Shape of Currents

Invisible waves are similarly produced in the ether. At our broadcasting aerial the currents have the shape illustrated in Fig. 1. Starting at *A*, the current rises to a maximum or peak at *B*, then falls to *C* and to a second maximum at *D*, and so back to the starting value at *E*. As the part *ABC* is opposite in direction to the part *CDE*, it is called positive, to distinguish it from the part *CDE*, which is termed negative, as shown by the + and − signs.

It is seen from Fig. 1 that the waves at the left are equal, but then they become larger and larger, and gradually smaller again. The equal waves are those transmitted when only the oscillations produced at the transmitter are fed to the aerial, but the others are those sent out when the currents from the microphone are added. The waves are altered in height, positive and negative, *but not in length.* As the height in Fig. 1 represents the strength of the wave, it is clear that the sound-waves vary the strength of the generated wave.

The Carrier Wave

The object of generating the wave at the transmitter is to make it act as carrier for the microphone signals. For this reason it is called the carrier wave. As the microphone signal has a much lower frequency (from 25 to about 16,000 cycles per second) than the carrier wave, it is called a low-frequency wave or L.F. wave. But note carefully that the signal as sent out at the transmitter has a carrier wave, which is the wave-length of the station, and a low-frequency wave which is the real signal as shown in Fig. 1. When we come to the receiver we shall find that the carrier wave has to be discarded and the low-frequency part extracted in order to reproduce the signal.

Now, the waves that travel through space, similar to our water wave, move at a speed of 300,000,000 metres every second. The number of waves formed each second (*i.e.* the frequency) is the frequency of the transmitted carrier wave. As we know the frequency of each transmitter, we can easily find the length of the wave (the wave-length) by dividing the speed by the frequency, thus:

$$\text{wave-length} = \frac{300{,}000{,}000 \text{ metres}}{\text{carrier frequency}}.$$

For example, a station having a carrier frequency of 1,000,000 cycles per second has a wave-length of $\frac{300{,}000{,}000}{1{,}000{,}000} = 300$ metres. Instead of using such big figures, we abbreviate by using mega for one million, and kilo for one thousand. One megacycle per second is 1 million cycles per second (1 mc./s.) and one kilocycle per second is 1,000 cycles per second (1 Kc./s.).

Self Testing Questions

(1) *What is the purpose of the microphone at the transmitter?*

(2) *What does the transmitted signal consist of?*

(3) *What is the medium through which wireless waves travel?*

(4) *What is the relation existing between wave-length and frequency?*

THE ANSWERS ARE ON PAGE 311.

LESSON 2

Collecting the Signal: Aerials and Earths for Best Results

We have seen already that signal currents in the transmitter aerial produce waves that travel rapidly through space. The purpose of the receiver aerial is to collect as much of the passing signal as possible, for the more signal that is picked up by the aerial the less work is required to be done by the receiver.

How the Aerial Works

Everyone knows that an aerial is a length of wire that may be placed in almost any position and connected to the receiver at one end while the other end is left free. Now, as the wireless waves pass through the aerial wire (see Fig. 2) an electric voltage is set up which has characteristics exactly similar to those of the signal sent out from the transmitter. *All* wireless waves that pass can set up a voltage at the aerial, but obviously we want only one particular signal at a time, so we select the required one at the receiver. The aerial wire is joined to one side of the receiver, and the signals pass through the receiver to the earth.

The aerial may be considered to be a condenser (see Electricity Course, page 186), in which, as shown in Fig. 3, one plate is the earth and the other the aerial wire itself. The space between the aerial and earth is the insulation space of the condenser. During reception of a signal an electric field is produced across the condenser plates. This field is varied in strength very

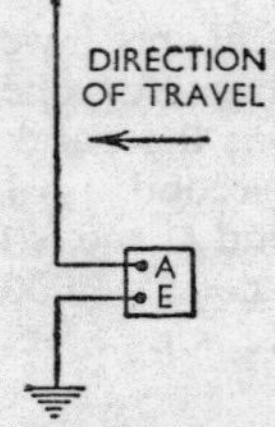

Fig. 2. *Vertical aerial.*

rapidly, in accordance with the signal-waves passing through the aerial.

It will be seen from Fig. 2 that the direction of travel of the waves is perpendicular to the down-lead. Thus the vertical part of the aerial is the most important. In a general way, therefore, the higher the aerial the better the results. But the extreme sensitivity of the modern commercial receiver makes a large outdoor aerial in general unnecessary. There may, however, be certain localities where the screening of the waves by adjacent hills causes bad reception conditions and here an outdoor aerial is still preferable.

Insulation

The aerial must be insulated from earth. If an outdoor aerial is used, porcelain insulators are required at each end. That part of the aerial which comes through a window or wall should be run in an ebonite tube to preserve its insulation when the rubber covering of the wire decays. For indoor aerials which are most commonly used, an insulated wire should be strung if possible in the attic, and as straight a lead as possible brought to the set. In

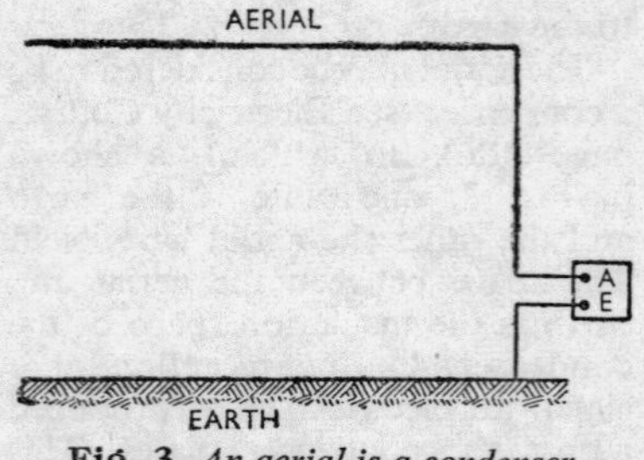

Fig. 3. *An aerial is a condenser.*

cases such as flats in urban areas where this is not practicable, a length of insulated wire strung round the picture rail will usually prove adequate. Care should be taken that where staples are used to fix the aerial, they should be of the insulated type, so that they do not damage the rubber covering.

A good plan when fixing an aerial is to try out various arrangements of the aerial wire in a temporary fashion, before fixing it perman-

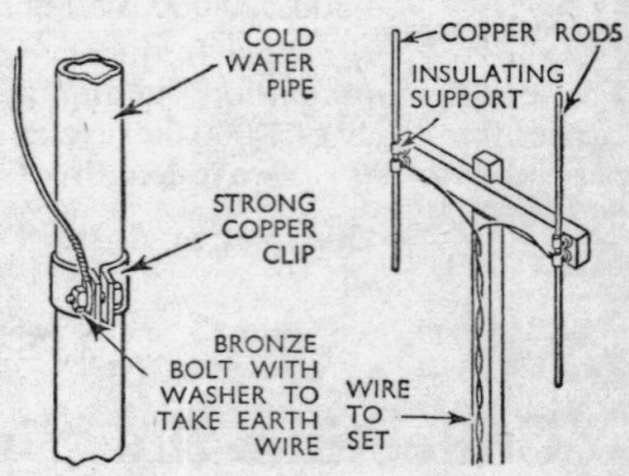

Fig. 4. *The best type of earth connection.*

Fig. 5. *The Dipole aerial.*

ently. In certain houses—particularly older premises—the electrical wiring is not all that it should be, and loud clicks are heard whenever lights and radiators are switched on and off. This is prone to happen if the aerial wire is so placed that it lies parallel to the power circuit, even though the power wires may be concealed in the plaster. This trouble cannot be entirely remedied by altering the position of the aerial, but it can be minimised by trying all possible positions until the best is found, and then fixing the aerial here permanently.

Serious interferences of a continuous nature in the form of a loud, harsh intermittent buzzing may be due to a defective mains plug, in which bad contacts inside the sockets are causing tiny arcing. No amount of experimenting with the aerial can cure this, which must be attended to at the source.

The type of wire used for an aerial is not of the utmost importance, but it should be adequately insulated. If an outdoor aerial is used, bare wire can be employed for the actual aerial itself, but a good soldered joint should be made to that portion of the wire which is to run inside.

Short-Wave Aerials

For those people who are specially interested in short-wave signals, particularly those from long distances, or for the ultra short-wave programmes associated with television, a different type of aerial is necessary. Many proprietory makes are on the market, but the amateur can construct an efficient "dipole" type of aerial array which will give him satisfactory results. A strut of wood has fixed to it at right angles two thin copper wires, each 4 feet in length. The fixing must be done by means of special insulating material, which can be purchased from any wireless dealer, and which has a low loss at the high frequencies used in short-wave circuits. The whole arrangement looks exactly like the letter H, the wood forming the cross bar. From each of the two copper rods a lead is taken in the form of a twisted flex, again of a special kind made up for the purpose and sold by wireless dealers, down to the short-wave or television set. The aerial should be fixed as high as possible, preferably on a chimney-stack, so that it is clear of screening from buildings.

Earths

It is no use making an earth connection which is not strong and permanent: otherwise, instead of ensuring safety, actual danger may arise in certain types of receivers in years to come, when the connection has corroded away. The best type of earth, and one which is usually practicable, is that which takes the form of a substantial copper or brass clip with a bronze nut and bolt securing it round a convenient water-pipe. It should be noted that only the water-pipe which is connected to the cold-water mains is suitable. Sometimes hot-water taps may, when the water is not running, be completely insulated from earth. Stout copper wire of not less than 7/22 gauge should be used, and it is always desirable that the earth wire should, if possible, be visible throughout its length.

In those cases where this method is not practicable a proper earth spike, which is usually made of copper, should be purchased, and should be driven into the ground, if possible somewhere where there is the maximum of moisture. The earth lead should be securely fixed to the screw at the top of the spike, and visible for inspection.

Self Testing Questions

(1) *Why does the aerial pick up signals?*

(2) *What are causes of inefficiency in an aerial?*

(3) *What is a dipole aerial, and what is it mainly used for?*

THE ANSWERS ARE ON PAGE 311.

LESSON 3

The Constructional Parts of a Radio Receiver

A TUNING coil is an inductance coil that has some means on it, or connected with it, of tuning it to a desired frequency, or a number of frequencies. In radio receivers we usually have coils tuned by variable condensers, but it is also practicable to vary the tuning by means of the inductance of the coil itself. This is carried out by altering the position of the iron core, and is known as permeability tuning.

Tuning coils with their variable condensers forming the tuned circuits play a fundamental part in our radio receivers, for upon them depends the ability to select the station we wish to listen to. If we had no tuned circuits, the radio set would receive all radio stations, and we should hear them from the loud-speaker all at once. The process of tuning may be likened to the playing of a note on an organ. When the organ key is depressed, a certain pipe has air passed through it and sounds a certain note. Each pipe is capable of sounding only one note, which corresponds to its natural frequency. That is why an organ has to have so many pipes.

Now, with our tuning circuit, each combination of inductance coil and condenser will tune only one frequency, which corresponds to the natural frequency of the combination, as with an organ pipe. If we wish to tune to a number of stations we must have a number of natural frequencies in our tuned circuits corresponding to the frequencies of the desired stations. With the organ a number of different pipes are used, but with our wireless receiver we use only one tuned circuit, which we vary in frequency over a wide range. For example, most radio receivers use coils that will tune over a range of 200 metres to 550 metres, with a variable condenser of ·0005 microfarad capacity. This is the medium wave-band.

Tuning coils as fitted in a radio receiver may be screened by a metal can, or they may be unscreened, depending upon the practical design adopted. In the more expensive and complicated types of receiver it is usual to screen all tuning coils.

In general construction, a tuning coil consists of a tube which holds the coils, called a former. This is shown at *F* in Fig. 6 and is seen in Fig. 7. On to the former is wound the wire coil, and the complete assembly seen in Fig. 7 is covered with wax to prevent dampness or other effects of air doing any harm

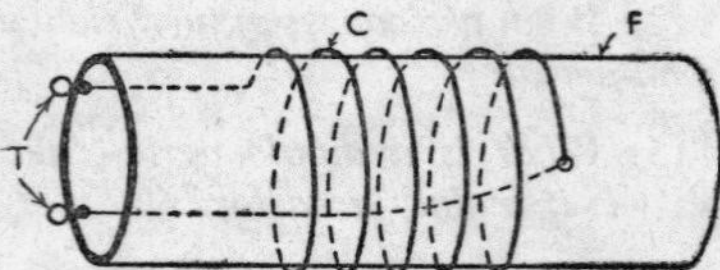

Fig. 6. *Typical short-wave coil.*

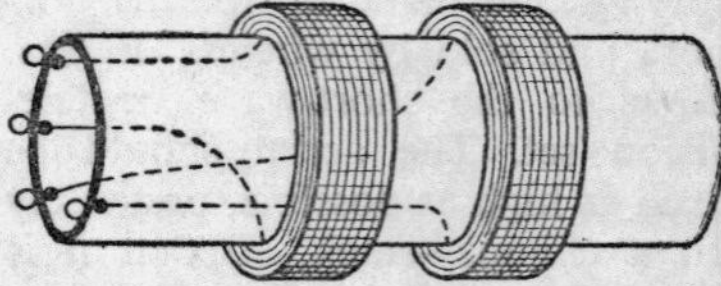

Fig. 7. *Typical long-wave double coil.*

to the properties of the coils. The size of the windings varies according to the wave-length the coil is desired to tune to. On the short waves, for example, the winding may consist of only half a dozen turns of fairly stout wire as shown in Fig. 6, whereas on the long waves, the coils made of fine wire may be a quarter of an inch deep (Fig. 7). Intermediate frequency transformers (see Lesson 6) are also constructed as shown in Fig. 7, but in this case a screening can is fitted.

Choke-coils are used wherever it is needed to keep out currents of one frequency while allowing currents of another frequency to pass. In wireless receivers we often need to use choke-coils both in high-frequency and in low-frequency circuits, as we shall see later on.

The effect of a choke-coil on electric currents is similar to that of the filter of a gas respirator. The gas filter prevents some gases from entering the respirator, but allows pure air to pass. So the choke-coil prevents unwanted currents from passing through it, but allows wanted currents through without serious hindrance. In Fig. 8 is shown the general method of working. Currents of both high and low frequencies are fed from *A*, one end of the coil, toward the choke-coil *HFC*. At the choke the high-frequency currents are stopped and sent through condenser *C*, while the low-frequency currents pass through the choke, as indicated, to the following apparatus. Some choke-coils are screened and some are unscreened. For home construction, the screened choke should be used exclusively.

We have seen already that variable condensers are used with coils for tuning the receiver to the required station. A variable condenser consists of a set of fixed metal plates, usually semi-circular in shape, in between which another similar set of plates is moved by means of a control knob. When the plates are not interleaving, there is no capacity (or rather a very small capacity) between them. As the rotatable plates are moved more and more in between the fixed plates, the capacity of the condenser increases until at last the plates are fully interleaved and the capacity is at the maximum.

There is a great tendency for the variable condensers of a radio receiver to become covered with

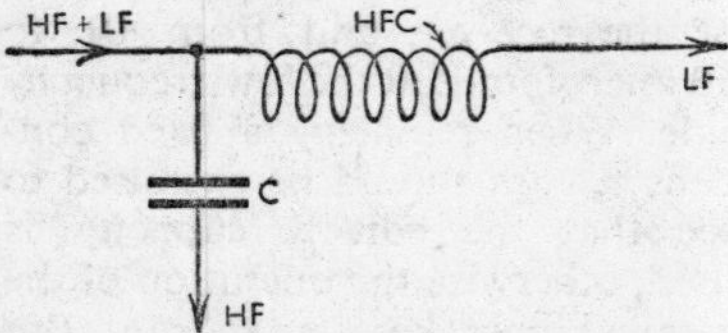

Fig. 8. *Choke* HFC *separates High Frequency from Low Frequency currents.*

dust if they are not fully screened. Such dust is likely to cause noises in a receiver and to make it work inefficiently in other ways. Be sure, therefore, to keep the condenser plates clean, either by blowing with a vacuum cleaner or even a bicycle pump, or by inserting a pipe-cleaner between the plates and removing the dirt this way. When purchasing variable condensers, it pays to obtain the best you can afford, because there is a tendency for the cheaper types to work loose at parts which spoil the electrical contact, and this may upset the working of the receiver.

Fixed condensers of various types are used in radio receivers. Most of them are of the paper or mica dielectric type, and may be housed in moulded or cardboard casings. The majority are in tubular

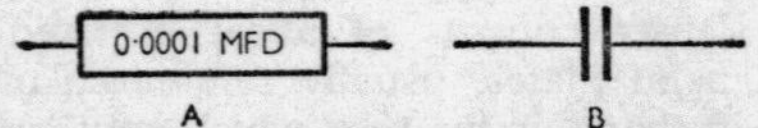

Fig. 9. *Typical tubular condenser* (A), *condenser symbol* (B).

form, as shown in Fig. 9 (*A*), with the wire connectors projecting from the ends, and the capacity marked on the body. The symbol for a fixed condenser is shown in Fig. 9 (*B*).

In the radio-frequency side of a receiver the capacity of condensers is usually much lower than capacities in the low-frequency parts. For example, capacities varying from ·00005 to ·1 microfarad are used at the radio-frequency part of the receiver, and from ·01 to 50 microfarads at the low-frequency side. When replacing a fixed condenser, care should be exercised to see that the correct capacity is used, otherwise the operation of the receiver may be thrown out. But of equal importance is the voltage at which the condenser is rated to work. Some parts of a receiver have a comparatively high voltage across them. If a low-voltage condenser is used at such parts, it will probably break down, and in doing so may damage a much more vital and expensive part of the receiver.

Electrolytic condensers are employed a great deal in modern receivers. They are manufactured by a special process which provides a high capacity within a very small space. We thus find 50-microfarad condensers within containers only a

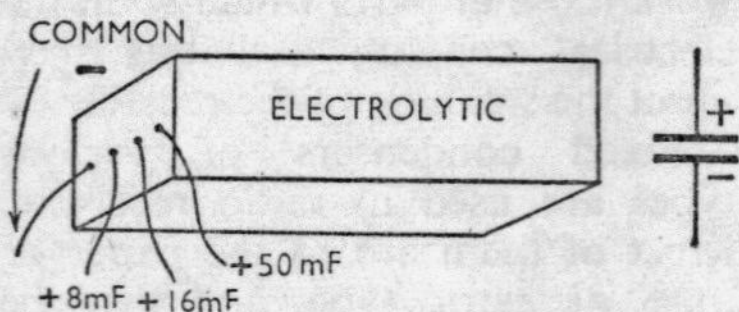

Fig. 10. *Typical electrolytic condenser. On the right is shown its symbol.*

few inches square and long. In Fig. 10 is shown a typical electrolytic condenser assembly, having one — lead and three + leads. When using, connect the — lead to chassis or the negative part of the circuit, and the + leads to the desired positive points. In most condensers of this type, the 50-microfarad condenser is of lower voltage rating than the others. So be careful!

Resistances

The most commonly used type of resistance in radio receivers consists of a tubular body with wire end connections as shown in Fig. 11. In shape they are similar to the tubular type of fixed condenser described already, but may be distinguished by the coloured markings on them. These markings indicate the value of resistance according to a colour code as follows:

Black . .	0	Green .	5
Brown . .	1	Blue . .	6
Red . .	2	Violet .	7
Orange .	3	Grey . .	8
Yellow . .	4	White .	9

The colour of the body represents the first figure of the resistance

Fig. 11. *Typical tubular resistance.*

value, the end colour the second figure, and a band or dot the number of 0's to follow. For example, 5,000 is indicated by a green body (5), black end (0) and a red band or dot (00).

Although in many parts of a radio receiver the value of resistance used is not very important, it does not pay to alter the values recommended by the designer. In some parts the resistance value is

—WWW—

Fig. 12. *Symbol for resistance.*

most important. For trouble-free operation of a receiver, the resistances should be of the required wattage. If, say, a half-watt resistance is used instead of the recommended one-watt type, the resistance will heat up excessively and trouble will be caused. To use too low a wattage resistance is like driving a 5-ton lorry over a bridge built to stand only 2½ tons—a breakdown is invited. It is safe, if wasteful, to use a higher wattage resistance than recommended. For example, to connect a 2-watt resistance in place of a 1-watt resistance is quite in order, except that it costs about twice as much as the 1-watt resistance. The symbol for resistance in diagrams is shown in Fig. 12.

Transformers

Various types of transformers are used in radio receivers. Radio frequency and intermediate frequency transformers are described elsewhere; here we will concern ourselves with the low-frequency type. Mains A.C. receivers use a mains transformer between the mains supply and the receiver, some notes on this type being given in Lesson 7. Mains transformers should be placed in the low-frequency part of the receiver so that interference will not be set up with the receiver proper. Most mains transformers are not screened, and are mounted on the upper side of the chassis. They can generally be distinguished by their size, which is larger than any other component on the chassis except the ganged variable condenser. Mains transformers are designed to operate at a certain temperature, which should not be exceeded. If they become too hot, the insulation between the windings may become damaged and the transformer spoilt.

Low-frequency transformers vary in size from little more than 1-in. cube to several inches in height, depth and breadth. They are constructed with windings in sections, the sections being mounted on an iron core in such a way that the maximum transfer of electrical energy takes place without distortion being produced in the signal passing through it. When a transformer is enclosed by a metal screen, this should be connected to the chassis or earth.

The Loudspeaker

The object of the loudspeaker is to change the electrical currents passed to it from the receiver into sound. It does this in the following way. A powerful magnet, illustrated in Fig. 13 at *M*, is shaped in such a way that circular magnetic poles are formed. Between the circular poles of the magnet a coil of wire *SC* is mounted on a former, and attached to the coil-former is a diaphragm *D*, usually in the shape of a cone, which is familiar to anyone who has seen a loudspeaker.

Currents from the receiver are passed from the output transformer through the coil *SC*, known as the speech-coil. As the signal currents pass through the speech-coil *SC* they set up a magnetic interference in the air-gap *G* between the coil and the magnet poles. This interference in the magnetic field forces the speech-coil backward and forward in the direction indicated by the arrows. The vibrations of the cone produce corresponding vibrations in the air, and in this way sound is made. The loudspeaker illustrated in Fig. 13 is known as

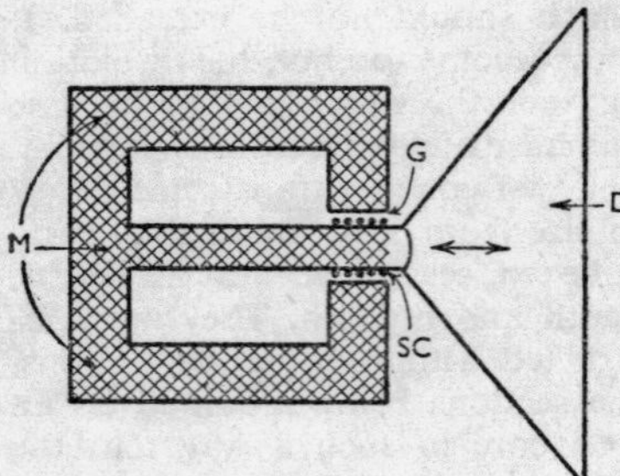

Fig. 13. *Moving coil loudspeaker.*

the permanent magnet type. There are various shapes of magnet.

Some loudspeakers, especially those used in mains receivers, have a winding fitted into a soft iron body which acts as the magnet when direct current passes through it. This current is provided by the power equipment supplying the receiver, the winding being then known as the field winding. Such a loudspeaker is referred to as the mains energised type.

Self Testing Questions

(1) *What is a tuning coil?*

(2) *What is a choke-coil?*

(3) *How can electrolytic condensers be distinguished from other types?*

(4) *Give the resistance colour code for* 750,000 *ohms.*

(5) *What type of loudspeaker is generally used* (a) *with mains receivers?* (b) *With battery receivers?*

THE ANSWERS ARE ON PAGE 311.

LESSON 4

Radio Valves: The Heart of the Receiver

THE key parts of a radio receiver are the valves. In fact, the receiver circuits are built round them. It is important, therefore, to be quite clear about the working of the valves—technically called thermionic valves—if we are to obtain a good insight into the operation of our radio receivers.

In all conductors of electricity there is a vast number of very tiny particles known as electrons. When the conductor is in its cold state of temperature, the electrons move in circular paths in the conductor. But if the conductor is placed inside some kind of envelope from which air has been pumped—that is, inside a vacuum—and its temperature then raised sufficiently high, the electrons have their speed of movement raised. At last, as the heat in the conductor goes up, a temperature is reached at which some of these electrons are moving so fast that they shoot out of the conductor. This state is illustrated in Fig. 14, where the electrons *F* are seen to leave the conductor heated by a battery *B*. The glass envelope is indicated by the circle.

Fig. 14. *Electrons shooting out of filament.*

A small boy soon learns that if he wishes to swing a stone or other object round on a piece of string, he must tie it tightly. If he does not, the stone will fly off the string as soon as he swings it round fast enough. So with our electrons. The cathode cannot hold back some of the electrons as the temperature is raised, so they shoot off.

The electrons when they leave the conductor have nowhere in particular to go, and so, unless their speed is exceptionally high, they just return to the cathode. Their speed on shooting out of the heated conductor is largely governed by the temperature to which this is raised, just as the speed of the boy's stone when it flies off the string depends on the speed at which he swings the string round.

Attracting the Electrons

Now let us place a metal plate inside the vacuum within the envelope in which our heated conductor is positioned. This arrangement is shown in Fig. 15, where the metal plate is marked *A*. To this plate we will connect the positive side of a battery B_2, the negative side of which is joined to the conductor *C* through a current-measuring instrument *M*. We know already that unlike charges attract each other; that is, a positive charge attracts a negative charge.

When the circuit shown in Fig. 15 is joined up, we find that the electrons no longer leave the heated conductor and return to it after a short journey. What happens now is that as the plate is positive and the electrons are negative a number of them pass toward the metal plate *A*. The actual number reaching the plate is dependent upon the positive voltage we connect to it; the higher the plate voltage the larger the number of electrons drawn to it. There cannot, of course, be more electrons attracted to the plate than leave the heated conductor, known as the cathode, but once *all* the electrons leaving

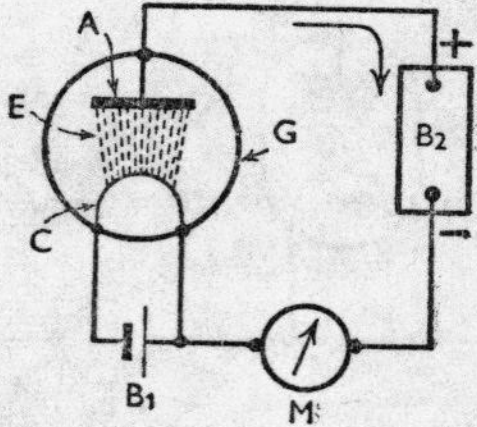

Fig. 15. *Electrons attracted from the battery* B_1 *to the anode* A.

the cathode have been collected, there is obviously nothing to gain from raising the voltage of the plate any further. If any increase in electron flow is desired, it can be obtained by heating the cathode to a higher temperature, when it will be found that more electrons will be attracted to the plate as the plate voltage is increased. There comes a time when an increase in cathode temperature and in plate voltage will not provide any additional electrons.

The electrons pass from the plate *A* through the battery B_2 and the meter *M* back to the cathode as indicated by the arrows. It is noticed that the electrons flow always in the same direction from cathode to plate inside the envelope, and from anode (as the positive plate is called) to cathode outside it. We thus have a simple valve which will pass current in one direction only. The radio valve permits only one-way traffic. The

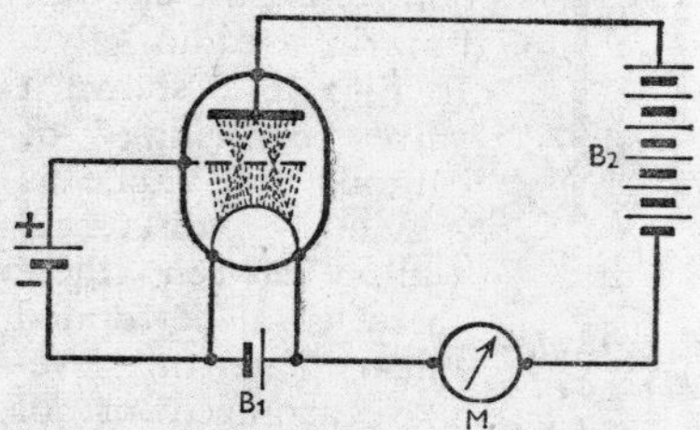

Fig. 16. *Positive grid: large current.*

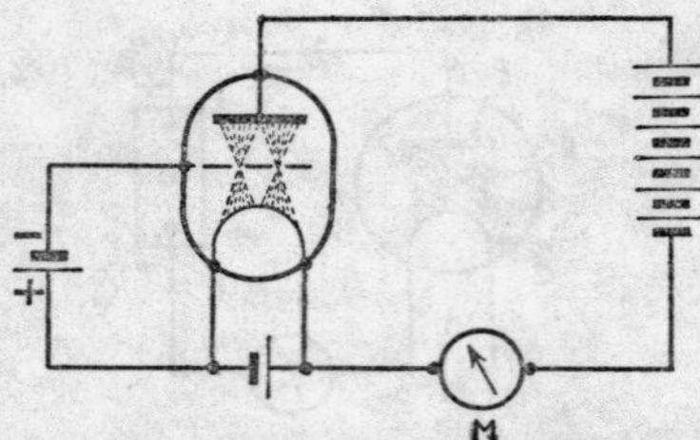

Fig. 17. *Negative grid: small current.*

device shown in Fig. 15 is very similar to the wireless diode valve that is commonly used for detection, as described in Lesson 6.

Controlling the Electrons

Since a means has been found of sending electrons from cathode to anode, it remains to show how we can control electrons. Controlling electrons in wireless valves usually means controlling the number of electrons that pass from cathode to anode, *i.e.*, the intensity of the electron flow.

We have seen already that electrons are negative. We also know that like charges repel each other. If, therefore, we put into our electron valve a wire and place it between the cathode and anode, we ought to be able to attract or repel the electrons in the stream according as we have a positive or negative voltage on it.

This is, in fact, the method employed for controlling the electron flow in a radio valve. In Fig. 16 is shown a valve consisting of cathode and anode as previously discussed, while between these there is a perforated metal plate or sieve-like arrangement of wires so placed that the electrons pass through it on the way from cathode to anode. Now, the effect of this wire, which is called the control grid, varies as the voltage applied to it is altered. In Fig. 16 is shown the effect of connecting a positive voltage to the control grid. The flow of electrons is seen to be very intense. As the positive voltage is lowered and then changed to negative, the flow of electrons to the anode is reduced, as shown by Fig. 17, which illustrates the state inside the valve when the grid is negative.

Fig. 18. *Indirectly heated cathode.*

As the voltage at the grid is made still more negative, the electrons are prevented more and more from passing to the anode. When a comparatively high negative voltage is applied to the grid, the electron flow is reduced to a very small current. Many of the electrons turn round and go back to the cathode. If the grid voltage is still further increased, a point is reached where the electron flow is stopped altogether.

A Comparison

The action of the grid is rather like that of a grid inserted in a pipe through which water is flowing.

If the grid has very large gaps, the flow of water is but little hindered. As the grid is made finer and the gaps through which water can flow are made smaller, less and less water can flow, until, if the grid is changed into a piece of solid wood to block the whole section of the pipe, no water will flow at all.

In a sense it is the same with the valve-grid. The negative bias corresponds to decreasing the gaps in the water-pipe grid, and the current flow is correspondingly reduced until it is cut off altogether. The control exercised by the grid is due to the passing electrons coming within the influence of the electric field of the grid. The negative grid repels the electrons; the more negative the grid, the greater is the repulsion.

A valve that has three electrodes, of the type illustrated in Figs. 16 and 17, is known as a triode. In general construction, the cathode consists of a fine thread of wire in battery valves, the anode being a metal cylinder, and the grid is in the form of a helix or mesh.

Indirectly Heated Cathodes

Many valves designed to be heated from the mains do not have a fine wire as cathode, but use instead an arrangement similar to that shown in Fig. 18, known as an indirectly heated cathode. The actual heating element is a wire *H* placed inside an insulator *I* on which is a metal cylinder *S* carrying the cathode layer *C*. For operating a valve, a current is passed through the heater wire *H*, which accordingly has its temperature raised. Heat generated by *H* passes across the insulator *I* and heats the cathode *C*, which then reaches the required temperature to send out electrons for the valve.

Mutual Conductance

We have seen how the size of the wire mesh of which the grid is made decides to a large extent the degree of control exercised by the grid on the electron current. It is useful, when considering the usefulness of a valve, to be able to know the amount of this control. The term "mutual conductance" expresses the change in anode current for a small change in control grid voltage. Thus, a valve having a mutual conductance of 3 milliampères per volt is one in which the anode current alters by 3 milliampères when the control grid bias is altered by 1 volt (1 milliampère is one-thousandth part of an ampère).

Amplification Factor

It has been seen how the voltage at the anode affects the flow of anode current, the higher values of voltage causing a greater attraction of electrons to it. We also know that the voltage at the control grid influences the anode current flow. The term "amplification factor" expresses the ratio of the change in anode voltage to the change in grid voltage to produce a given small change in anode current. For example, if an increase of 40 anode volts produced an increase in anode current of 1 milliampère, and then an increase in negative control grid bias of 1 volt decreased the anode current to its original value, the amplification factor of this valve would be 40. The amplification factor is not the actual amplification (see the next Lesson) that will be provided by the valve, but is the relation mentioned above. In practice it is impossible to obtain an amplification even approaching the amplification factor for many valves, although in others, such as low-frequency amplifiers, it is often practicable to do so. The amplification provided in the receiver is governed just as much by the circuit as by the valve, as we shall see later.

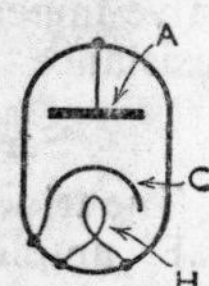

Fig. 19. *Valve with indirectly heated cathode.*

Valve Impedance

This is a term that expresses the resistance to alternating current of the anode. Its value is found by altering the anode voltage by a small amount, then dividing this by the change in anode current flow. For example, if a change of 10 anode volts brought about an alteration of 1 milliampère in anode current, the valve impedance would be :

$$\frac{10}{\frac{1}{1000}} = \frac{10 \times 1,000}{1} = 10,000 \text{ ohms.}$$

The impedance of valves varies very considerably. It may be as low as 1,000 ohms for an output triode and as high as several megohms for an R.F. pentode. Another name for valve impedance is the anode A.C. resistance.

Screen-Grid Valve

The triode is very satisfactory for L.F. amplification, detection, and as the output valve, but for R.F. amplification and frequency changing (as described later on) it is unsuitable. Owing to deficiencies that exist within the valve, the currents from the anode circuit find their way to the grid circuit and set up all kinds of trouble.

To overcome this difficulty, the screen-grid valve was developed.

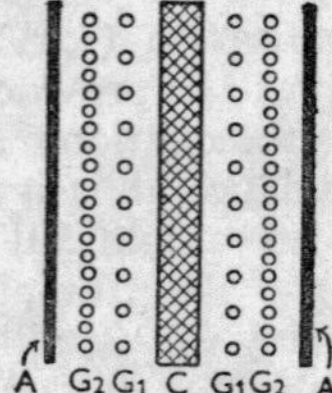

Fig. 20. *Screen-grid valve.*

This valve has a second grid situated between the control grid and the anode, as illustrated in Fig. 20. The second grid, *G* 2, shields the control-grid from the anode, and is for this reason known as the screen-grid. When the screen-grid valve is used as R.F. amplifier as shown in Fig. 21, the screen-grid is joined to H.T. + through a resistance *R*, so that it is at a positive D.C. voltage to the cathode. The screen-grid then acts like an

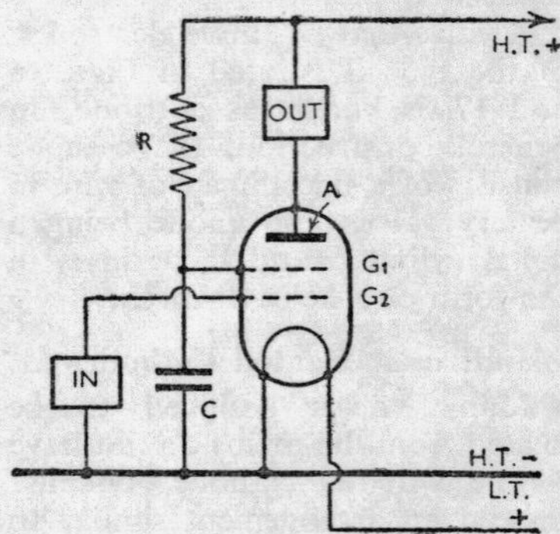

Fig. 21. *Circuit for screen-grid valve.*

anode, and attracts the electrons through the control-grid. Being a wire mesh or helical in form, the screen-grid allows many of the electrons to pass on to the anode. By adjoining the screen-grid to chassis or earth by a condenser *C* (about ·1 mfd.) the shielding effect of the screen-grid is made effective. In the operation of R.F. amplifiers, condenser *C* is important, for if it breaks down, the benefit of the screen-grid is lost, and the whole stage usually becomes unworkable.

Pentode

The screen-grid valve has certain defects that prevent it handling a large signal voltage. To improve performance, a further grid is added, this time between the screen-grid and anode, as shown in Fig. 22. This third grid, known as the suppressor-grid, is usually connected to chassis or the cathode. By this means the valve is enabled to handle a large signal voltage.

Fig. 23 shows the circuit for using the pentode as an R.F. amplifier. A screen-grid condenser *C* is still needed for the R.F. stage, but when the valve is used as the output valve (see Lesson 5) this is generally unnecessary.

Valves in General

In addition to the basic valves described above, there are a large number of others. The operation of these is based on the principles already discussed, and will be described with the suitable circuits in the following Lessons. It may be pointed out that the valve-names describe the electrodes of which they are comprised. Thus a hexode has six electrodes, a heptode seven, an octode eight. A diode-triode consists obviously of one diode and a triode, a double diode-triode of two diodes and a triode, and so on.

Valve Faults

Although modern valves are much more robust than the earlier types, there are still a fair number of defects that occur in a receiver owing to a faulty valve. Faults that arise inside the valve cannot easily be put right, but it is helpful to

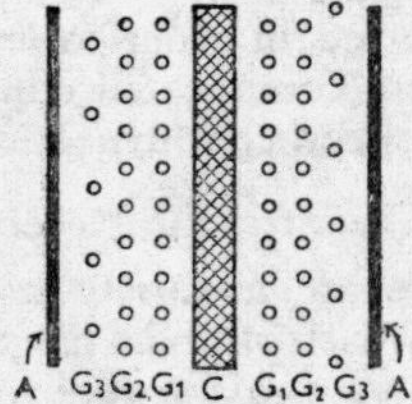

Fig. 22. *Pentode valve.*

know the possible cause of the various radio-receiver troubles.

The first thing to watch with a valve is its emission, that is, the total number of electrons passing in a giving time through the valve from the cathode. If the valve is to work properly this emission must not fall below a certain figure, depending on the type of valve used. To test a valve for emission, all that is necessary is to check the anode

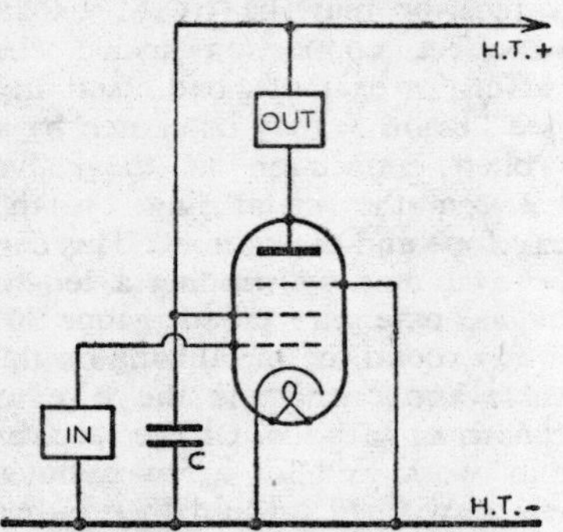

Fig. 23. *Circuit for R.F. pentode valve.*

current flow (see final Lesson). The full value of current required should be known for the grid-bias applied and *at the voltage that is actually at the anode.* If the current as indicated is much less than this figure, the emission would appear to be failing and a new valve should replace it. In the home receiver, the anode current flow for each valve should be checked while the set is in good condition, so that the required current for each valve is known.

Constructional faults occur from time to time within the valve glass bulb or the base on which the pins or contacts are fitted. A bad connection to the filament or heater which causes the heater current to flow intermittently will often cause a variation in the glow at the cathode, and this may sometimes be observable from outside the valve. In the receiver, this fault produces loud and intermittent crashing noises. But a similar noise will also occur if the contact between the valve and the valve-holder socket is intermittent: so be sure that all the valve-pins are well home in the valve-holder and making good contact.

Sometimes a mysterious fault in a receiver may be traced to an imperfect connection inside the valve. For example, bad instability (see Lesson 5) may be caused by a broken connection at the valve between the metallizing on the envelope and the cathode. This can be overcome by winding a length of fine bare wire (about gauge 30) firmly round the metallizing on the valve and connecting the wire to chassis or cathode. Or the receiver may work well for a few minutes when switched on and then either become inoperative or howl. In this case the fault may be caused by a defect within the valve which develops only when sufficient heat is produced in the valve-bulb during operation.

When handling valves, bear in mind that they are delicate articles. For example, do not pull a valve out by the bulb, but by the base or cap. If the valve is fitting rather tightly, lever it out gently with a screw-driver for a start, and then pull by the cap. When using a valve with a top cap, be careful when you are pushing home the cap connection.

Self Testing Questions

(1) *What causes the valve emission?*

(2) *What is the purpose of the screen-grid?*

(3) *Why do we use a third grid in the pentode?*

(4) *How would you test a valve for emission?*

THE ANSWERS ARE ON PAGE 311.

LESSON 5

The Straight Receiver: Its Operation and Construction

In Lesson 1 a description was given of how the radio signal is sent through space to the radio receiver aerial. When the signal passes through the aerial wire, a voltage is set up in it that is similar to that in the transmitter aerial, except that it is very much weaker. The purpose of the radio receiver is to change the signal voltage as received by the aerial to a form suitable for working the loud-speaker. The receiver is the link between the aerial and the loud-speaker.

Most modern receivers are of the superheterodyne pattern, but amateurs still construct straight receivers; and it is instructive to run through the principles of operation of such sets in order to lead up to the more complicated construction of the superheterodyne receiver.

The Straight Receiver

There are a variety of receiver circuits, each of which has particular merits. A straight receiver is one which does not use any of the special circuits, but consists of a straightforward arrangement of radio-frequency amplifier, detector, low-frequency amplifier and output valve.

In Fig. 24 is shown a diagram which illustrates the general con-

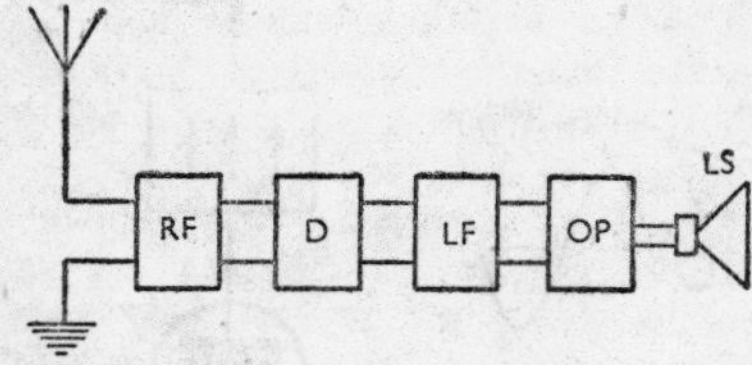

Fig. 24. *General arrangement of straight receiver. Aerial is on left.*

struction of a straight receiver. At *RF* is the radio-frequency amplifier, joined to the aerial at one side and to the detector *D* at the other. After the detector comes the low-frequency amplifier *LF* and finally the output stage *OP* with the loudspeaker *LS*.

Amplification

Straight receivers are not all arranged exactly as illustrated in Fig. 24. The receiver may have two radio-frequency amplifiers, or even none. Often the low-frequency amplifier is not a separate valve, but really forms part of the detector valve. Nevertheless, the great majority of the straight receivers sold today are of the general type illustrated in Fig. 24. Let us now see what takes place inside the straight receiver, for by so doing we can appreciate the basic principles of radio reception that are used in all types of receiver in one form or another.

The signal voltage as picked up by the aerial is much too weak to be detected and changed into power to operate the loudspeaker if a number of stations is to be received. Some means must be included in the receiver to enlarge or amplify the aerial voltage. What does the astronomer do when he wishes to find a star that is invisible to the naked eye? He uses a telescope which magnifies many times, and is thereby enabled to see clearly stars which would otherwise be invisible. So with our radio receiver, the amplifiers enable us to receive many stations which would be impossible of reception without them.

It is seen from Fig. 24 that both a radio-frequency amplifier and a low-frequency amplifier are used in the receiver. Two amplifiers are desirable, so as to increase, first the voltage from the aerial before feeding this to the detector, and then to increase the voltage provided by the detector. Most detectors do not work well unless a fairly strong signal is fed to them, so we use a radio-frequency amplifier for this purpose. The output from the detector, even when a radio-frequency amplifier is employed, is usually not enough to work the loudspeaker satisfactorily, so we must use some form of low-frequency amplification.

Its Principles

The basic principle of amplification can be best described by means of the triode circuit illustrated in Fig. 25. It does not matter how many grids the amplifier valve has, the main features are the same.

At IN is shown the input circuit

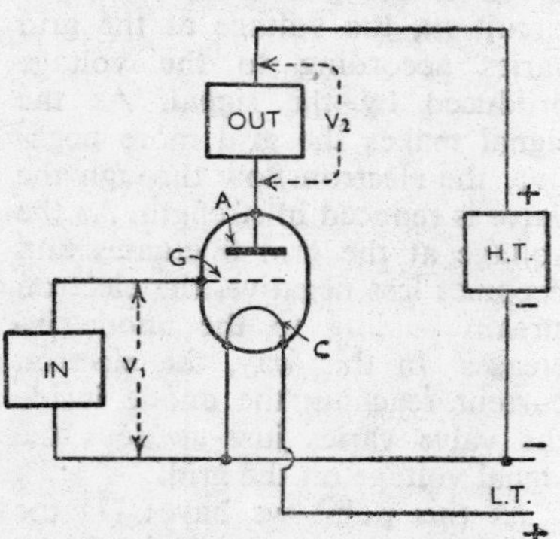

Fig. 25. *Amplifier triode circuit.*

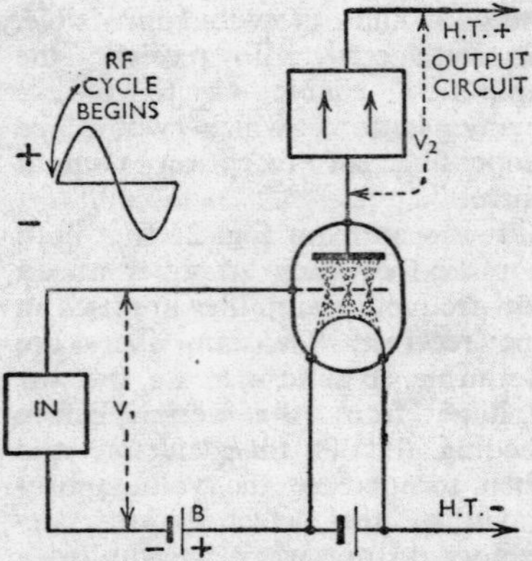

Fig. 26. *Valve condition at start of cycle.*

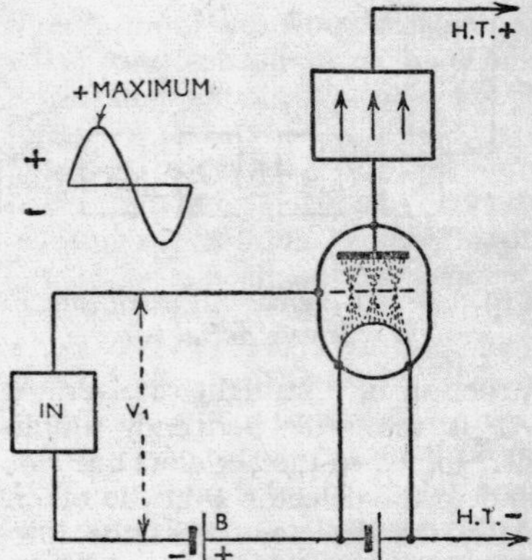

Fig. 27. *At positive peak of cycle.*

that applies the signal voltage to the grid *G* and cathode *C*. Joined to the anode *A* is another circuit, but as this feeds the voltage to the next valve, it is called the output circuit. Now, if enlargement or amplification is to take place, the working of the circuit must be such that the voltage V_2 in the output circuit OUT is greater than the voltage V_1 at the input circuit IN.

The Factors Concerned

We have seen already in Lesson 4 how the voltage at the grid controls the anode current. When the signal is fed to the grid from the input circuit IN, the voltage at the grid varies according to the voltage produced by the signal. As the signal makes the grid more negative, the electron flow through the valve is reduced in strength. As the voltage at the grid fluctuates and becomes less negative, the electron stream passing to the anode increases. In this way, the electron current reaching the anode inside the valve varies just as does the signal voltage on the grid.

At this point we have: (1) the signal voltage at the grid, (2) an electron stream that is controlled in strength by the grid voltage, and, as a result of this, (3) a varying electron current at the anode of the valve. In order to obtain amplification we have to use this varying anode current in such a way that a voltage is produced at the output circuit which is larger than that at the grid.

The effect of the signal alternating voltage as fed to the grid of the valve can be seen from Figs. 26 to 30. The signal wave itself is repre-

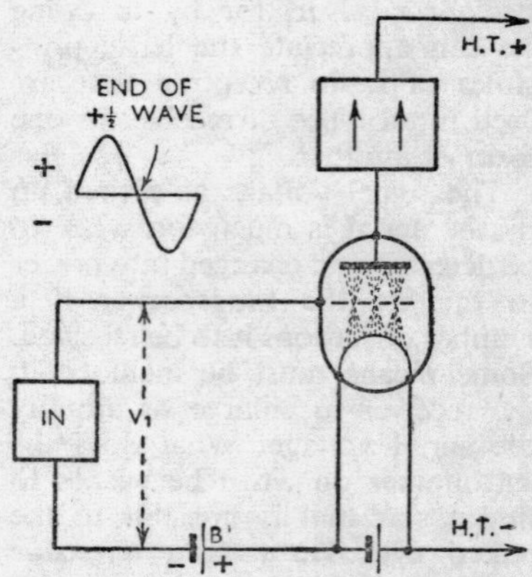

Fig. 28. *At end of positive half cycle.*

sented just above the input circuit, and is similar to that described in the first lesson. When the signal wave starts (Fig. 26) there is a fair number of electrons passing through the valve and the output circuit, this number being dependent on the fixed grid bias *B* with which the valve is working. The positive part of the signal reduces the negative bias at the control-grid until at the maximum or peak of the positive part the electron flow is at maximum (Fig. 27). At this point the current in the output circuit is largest. As the positive voltage from the signal then falls, the negative bias at the grid increases and the electron current becomes less and less. At the end of the positive part of the wave (Fig. 28) the state inside the valve is the same as at the beginning. But now the negative part of the wave forces the grid even more negative until, at the maximum point (Fig. 29) the electron flow is least of all, and the output current is the smallest. After that, the signal wave returns to the starting-point and the current through the valve increases up to the end of the wave (Fig. 30) to begin all over again.

This series of events takes place at the frequency of the input signal voltage—it may be at many millions of times in a second during R.F. amplification, or at a mere 20 times per second in L.F. amplifiers. The process, no matter what the frequency, is the same.

When the electron stream reaches the anode it passes outside the valve into the output circuit, and in so doing sets up a voltage. The radio-receiver designer's job is to choose the components in the output circuit so that at the frequency of the anode current a voltage is produced in it which is as high as practicable, at the same time bearing in mind other important points that we shall discuss later. This output voltage is larger than the input voltage—in some cases hundreds of times larger—because the grid input voltage acts as a control to a comparatively intense electron stream. Amplification is not effected by putting into the valve so many volts and then multiplying

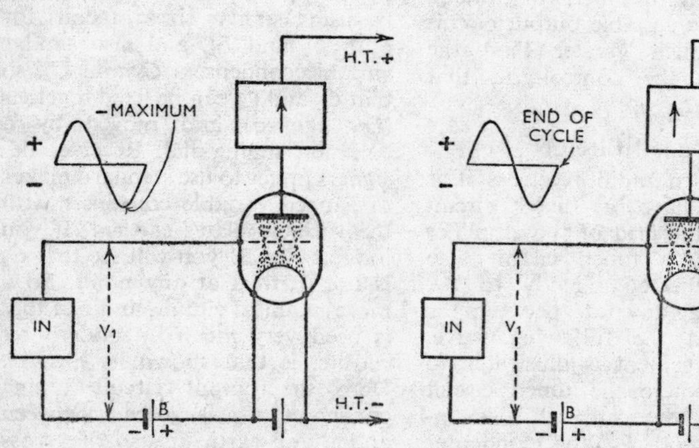

Fig. 29. *At negative peak.*

Fig. 30. *At end of cycle.*

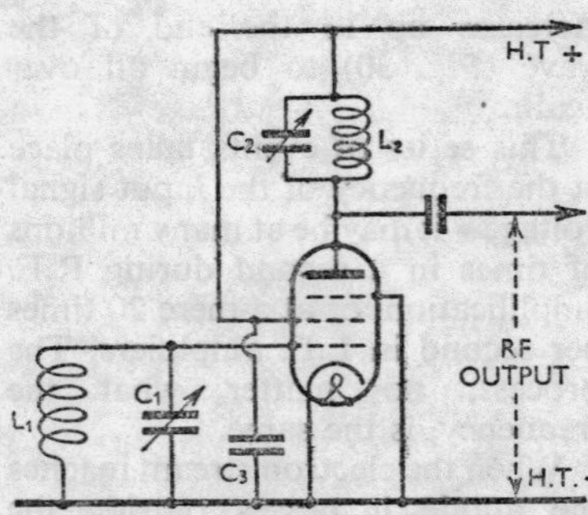

Fig. 31. *Tuned anode R.F. amplifier.*

these to get so many more volts. The amplifying effect is rather like the power control exerted by sluice- or water-gates on a rushing stream of water. As the gates close, the water-flow lessens; as they open, the flow increases. The gates are operated with comparatively small power, but the flood of water moving past them may have a mighty power. So it is with the amplifying valve. An alteration in grid voltage has a considerable influence on the large stream of electrons passing through the valve, with the result that the voltage produced by the fluctuating anode current in a suitable output circuit is very much greater than the voltage at the control-grid that caused it.

Tuned Circuits

In modern radio receivers it is usual to have a tuned circuit joined to the grid of the amplifier valve, and a tuned circuit also either connected directly to the anode or at any rate between the anode and the following valve. This arrangement is illustrated in Fig. 31, where the tuned circuit joined to the valve-grid is inductance coil L_1 and condenser C_1, while the tuned circuit L_2C_2 is connected to the anode. It will be noticed that the amplifier valve is a pentode. A condenser, value ·1 microfarad, should always be joined as shown at C_3. Both screen-grid valves (tetrodes) and pentodes are used for R.F. amplification, but triodes are not so used, as they are found to be very inefficient, for various reasons.

The circuit shown in Fig. 31 is a practical one where it is desired to use a fixed-tuned output circuit. But in a straight receiver we require to have circuits that will tune over a band of wave-lengths, such as the medium wave-band or the long wave-band. In order to tune over a band of wave-lengths, it is necessary to have one of the two parts of our tuned circuit—inductance or capacity—made variable. In most receivers the capacity is variable by means of a condenser whose movable plates may be rotated. If the R.F. amplifier is to work properly, it is important that at any point in the wave-band covered by the tuning condenser both the input circuit L_1C_1 and the output circuit L_2C_2 should be tuned to the same wave-length. This can be done by using similar sizes of coils for both L_1 and L_2, and also similar variable condensers C_1 and C_2, so that C_1 and C_2 can be fixed together (*i.e.* ganged) and moved by a common tuning-dial. Receiver designers prefer to use standard makes of ganged variable condenser with the variable plates earthed. If you look at Fig. 31 you will see that C_2 is not earthed at any point. So a more practical circuit, and one that is used very much in modern receivers, is that shown in Fig. 32. Here the output circuit tuning condenser C_2 is joined between anode and earth instead of across L_2 as in Fig. 31. The practical effect of connecting C_2 from anode to earth is just the same as joining it across L_2, but it has the big advantage that the rotatable plates are earthed and the normal type of mass-produced ganged variable condenser may be used. The circuit illustrated in Figs. 31 and 32 is the tuned anode R.F. amplifier.

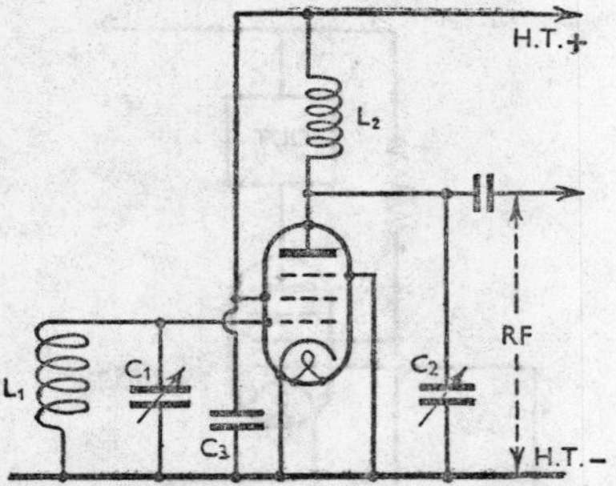

Fig. 32. *Alternative tuned anode radio-frequency amplifier.*

Instability

Probably the greatest difficulty with R.F. amplifier construction is the operation of the amplifier valve without unwanted oscillation. This oscillation is produced by a number of causes, each perhaps small enough by itself, but the total effect is sufficient to spoil completely the operation of the amplifier. The technical term used to describe this condition is instability, and the amplifier itself is referred to as being unstable.

The main cause of amplifier instability is some kind of feedback between the output circuit and the input circuit. Pentode and screen-grid valves are especially designed to reduce the capacity inside the valve to the minimum, but, even so, there still remains a certain amount of internal feedback due to the capacity that exists between the different parts of the valve. The design of our amplifier must be such, however, that this very small valve capacity is not added to. Any arrangement of the circuit components or wiring which causes a capacity to exist between the anode circuit and the grid circuit is to be avoided.

Stray capacities in a radio receiver are like holes in a water-tank. If there were holes in the storage tank in the loft of your house, water would run all over the place where it was not wanted. In a similar way, stray capacities allow the high-frequency currents to pass into different parts of the receiver, and in so doing cause a lot of trouble. So see that all the wiring in the grid and anode circuits is separated as much as possible, and in particular that no grid and anode wires run parallel.

Other Causes of Instability

Although mass-produced receivers often use unscreened coils, the home mechanic would be well advised to employ only screened coils in his R.F. amplifier, for in this way a stable circuit is most easily constructed. For the same reason metallised valves are preferred to unmetallised ones, even for the detector. Screening, however, is not much use unless it is thorough. For example, if the screening can of an R.F. coil does not make good contact all round the joint, leakage will occur, with possibly very bad results for the amplifier in whose circuit it happens to be connected. All coils and components should also be fixed very firmly, so that no movement can take place either from an accidental knock during testing or from the vibrations set up by the loudspeaker.

Instability is often caused by incorrect choice of voltage for the

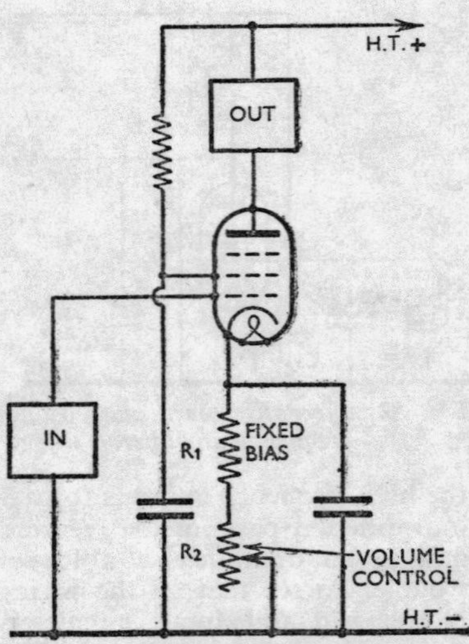

Fig. 33. *Radio-frequency amplifier with grid-bias resistances.*

amplifier valve. In a manufactured receiver, the designer will have already calculated the proper voltages to be used with the valve, but it sometimes happens that when a replacement is required the exact type of valve is not easily obtainable. The point to bear in mind with regard to voltages is that if the anode or screen-grid voltages are too high, instability is more likely to occur. One simple remedy for instability is thus to reduce the screen-grid and anode voltages. In doing so, the amplification produced by the stage is likely to be lessened, but this is usually preferable to instability.

An alternative cure for this trouble is to increase the control grid-bias of the valve. Where mains valves are concerned, the fixed cathode resistance, as shown in Fig. 33, should be increased. For example, if the trouble occurred with a fixed cathode resistance of 250 ohms, a resistance of 500 ohms should be tried. Here again the net result will be a reduced maximum amplification from the stage.

The Detector

The radio signal as provided at the output circuit of the R.F. amplifier is quite incapable of producing sound from the loudspeaker. We have already seen (in Lesson 1) that the radio signal as transmitted consists of a high-frequency wave and a low-frequency wave. It is the low-frequency portion which represents the actual signal, the high-frequency wave being for the purpose of carrying the low-frequency signal. It is the job of the detector to separate the low-frequency signal from the carrier wave, and to form it into a signal that will be able to produce sound from the loudspeaker when further amplified and passed through the output stage. With straight receivers, the type of detector employed is nearly always the grid detector.

What Detection Does

In a rather simple way, the process of detection may be likened to a corn-thrashing machine. The wheat in the field as cut is fed into the thrashing-machine, which separates the corn, throws out the straw at one side and collects the corn into a sack. The complete wheat plant is like the radio signal fed to the detector stage, the straw resembling the carrier wave which is thrown out, and the corn the low-frequency signal which is required for operating the loudspeaker after being separated from the carrier wave.

The working of the grid detector can be seen from Figs. 34, 35 and 36. When the working voltages are connected to the valve before any signal arrives at the detector, a number of electrons on their way to the anode hit against the grid wires inside the valve as shown in Fig. 34. These electrons form a grid current which passes back to the cathode along the grid leak *R*. The flow of grid current along *R* sets up a voltage which biases the grid negatively. This steady condition is shown by the — sign over the grid wire.

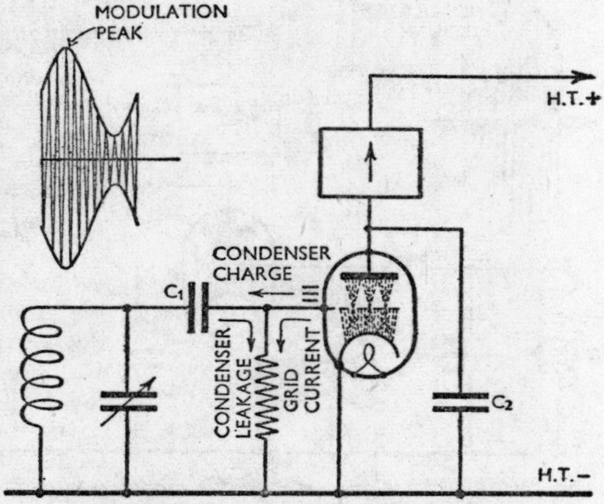

A number of electrons pass through the grid-wire spacing as indicated and reach the anode, there to form a current which passes through the output circuit. This current has a value represented by the three arrows drawn within the output circuit. Thus we find that before a signal reaches the detector there is: (1) a negative bias on the grid provided by the valve itself, and (2) a steady flow of anode current through the output circuit.

When the carrier signal arrives at the grid, the steady bias that had previously been formed there is increased according to the strength of the carrier wave. This bias is again varied according to the L.F. signal on the carrier. What happens is that alternative (positive) tips of the carrier wave make the grid slightly positive. As soon as the grid becomes positive, more electrons are caught by it from the electron stream within the valve and rush into the grid condenser C_1 to charge it. This increases the negative bias at the grid until, at the L.F. signal peak (Fig. 35), the anode current is much less than it was before the signal arrived. The increase in bias is represented by the three — signs placed near the grid, the reduced anode current being represented by only one arrow in the output circuit. The charge on the grid

Fig. 35. *Carrier signal at positive modulation peak.*

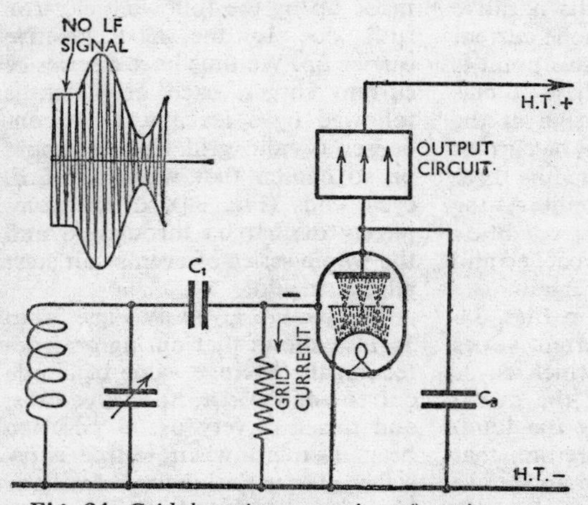

Fig. 34. *Grid detection: reception of carrier wave.*

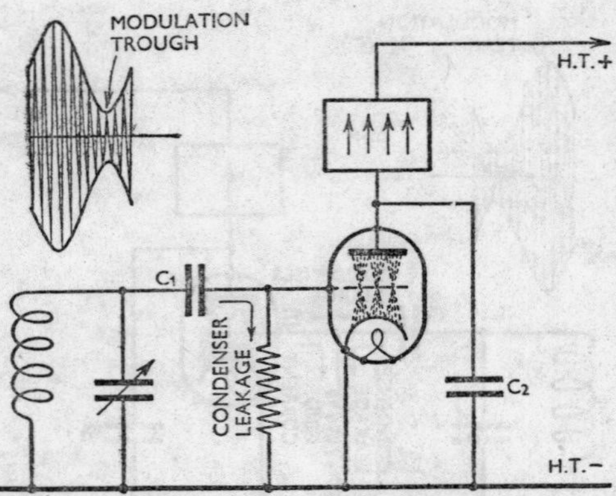

Fig. 36. *Carrier signal at negative modulation peak.*

condenser leaks gradually away between each rush of current from the grid.

Once the L.F. signal peak has passed, the alternative tips of the carrier wave make the grid less positive, so that it attracts fewer and fewer electrons from the stream inside the valve until, by the time the lower peak in the L.F. signal is received (Fig. 36) we find that the condenser discharge through the grid leak cannot be replenished. In this way, the grid has its negative bias reduced and the anode current increases. The state at this point is illustrated in Fig. 36, where no bias is indicated by no — sign at the grid, and the large flow of current to the anode is represented by three arrows in the output circuit. As the signal continues, the condition shown by Fig. 34 is approached and the series starts all over again.

It will be noted that in Figs. 34, 35 and 36 the anode current varies with the modulation, which is, as described in Lesson 1, the actual L.F. signal required by the loudspeaker. It is seen, therefore, that by the process described above, we have been able to extract the L.F. signal from the modulated carrier wave passed to the detector from the R.F. amplifier. Actually there will also be present in the anode circuit a certain amount of carrier frequency current, but this is prevented from interfering with the L.F. signal by connecting a condenser C_2 between anode and earth. This condenser offers an easy path for the R.F. currents, which are thus by-passed from the L.F. circuit. The L.F. currents do not pass through C_2 because to these lower frequencies C_2 offers a much more difficult path, so the L.F. currents find it far easier to go through the output circuit as shown. The R.F. currents at the anode may be used for reaction, as described later on.

Between each rush of electron current into C_1 the charge on this condenser leaks away gradually. As the modulation increases up to the peak, this leakage is more than made up by the following electron rush due to the next positive carrier tip. We thus have a series of current surges, each of which is followed by a leakage. Grid condenser C_1 and grid leak R should be so chosen that when the L.F. cycle ends (Fig. 34), C has completely discharged through R, and the whole series of events can start all over again.

The picture given by Figs. 34 to 36 also shows that during grid detection the average value of anode current of the detector valve falls, and this is a very useful point to bear in mind when testing a receiver. The variation in grid voltage is amplified in the valve, and appears in its amplified form in the output circuit, being then suitable for application to the output valve or a low-frequency amplifier. Note that the grid detector is in reality a detector and low-frequency amplifier.

Value of Grid Detector

The working of the grid detector is greatly influenced by the choice of grid condenser C_1 and grid leak R_1 (see Fig. 37). If a detector is required to be sensitive to weak signals, then the grid condenser should have a value of about ·00025 microfarad and R_1 about 2 megohms. The point to bear in mind about this circuit is that if the value of the grid leak R_1 is lowered, the receiver becomes less sensitive to weak signals and less capable of receiving the desired station clear of interfering ones. Also, as R_1 is lowered in resistance, C_1 should be also reduced in value correspondingly.

For better-quality reception it is advisable to use smaller values for both the grid condenser and the grid leak. A notable improvement in quality of reproduction is obtained by using as C_1 a condenser of ·0001 microfarad and for R_1 a resistance of half a megohm.

Anode Resistance

It is seen from Fig. 37 that the output circuit consists of a resistance R_2. This resistance is known as the anode resistance, and across it the output voltage is produced, and may be applied to the following valve *via* the coupling condenser C_3. The anode resistance R_2 should not be too high in value, because it reduces the voltage actually reaching the anode. When the higher values of grid condenser and leak resistance are used (·00025 microfarad and 2 megohms) the valve does not need such a high anode voltage as when the lower values (·0001 microfarad and ·5 megohm) are employed. A battery valve as grid detector will often work quite satisfactorily with an anode voltage of 40 or even less. Mains valves need a rather higher anode voltage.

When the small values are chosen for the grid condenser and leak, a much higher anode voltage should be used if the best results are to be obtained. For example, with battery valves, 80 volts should be aimed at, and with mains valves not less than 100 volts. One difficulty that arises is that the voltage dropped in the anode resistance limits the practicable anode voltage. By using a lower anode resistance, this voltage is raised. It will generally be found that 30,000 ohms is about the lowest that can be used as anode resistance, whilst at the same time providing a good amount of amplification. Where anode voltage is not of im-

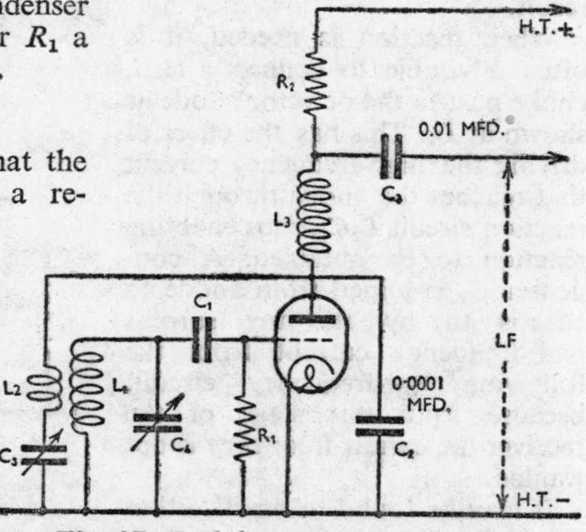

Fig. 37. *Grid detector with reaction.*

portance, up to 250,000 ohms may be used for *R*. Alternatively, transformer coupling (see later on) may be used with a very small voltage drop.

Fed-Back Voltage

One very valuable feature of the grid detector is its ability to feed back a voltage to the grid circuit from the anode circuit. This fed-back voltage is added to the signal voltage in the grid circuit if the feed-back coil is properly arranged with respect to the grid-coil. The increased total voltage is then amplified, and so we obtain greater amplification in the valve. At the same time selectivity is improved and the whole circuit operates much more satisfactorily. In Fig. 37 is shown the circuit for providing feed-back. A coil L_2 is placed near the grid-coil L_1 so that sufficient feed-back takes place. By means of a variable condenser C_5 (the reaction condenser) the amount of feed-back or reaction is controlled, most reaction taking place when condenser C_5 is set at maximum. Too much reaction should not be used, or distortion and oscillation result.

When reaction is needed, it is often advisable to connect a H.F. choke next to the detector anode as shown at L_3. This has the effect of driving the high-frequency current that reaches the anode through the reaction circuit L_2C_5, thus enabling reaction to be obtained. A condenser C_2 is joined from anode to chassis to by-pass any surplus high-frequency current from the following low-frequency circuit, because from this stage of the receiver the carrier frequency is not wanted.

It may be found in practice that the H.F. choke L_3 is not needed. If this is the case, so much the better, but if squeals occur in the receiver, the choke should be used in an attempt to cure the trouble.

The principles of amplification already described cover both high- and low-frequency amplification, so we will now go straight to the low-frequency circuits.

Resistance Capacity Amplifiers

This type of amplifier is very popular in modern receivers on account of its simplicity and the good-quality reproduction that is obtainable from its use. The circuit is given in Fig. 38, from which it is seen that the circuit components comprise two resistances and two condensers. Low-frequency voltage is fed to the input electrodes *via* grid condenser C_1 and grid leak R_1.

A suitable value for C_1 and C_2 is ·01 microfarads, but this is not critical. It should be noted, though, that a condenser of lower value than this will tend to reduce the strength of the low notes in the reproduction, and a condenser of higher value will improve low note reproduction. The highest useful

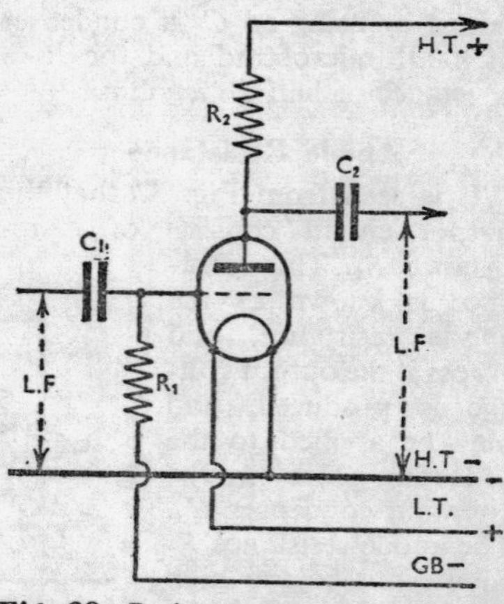

Fig. 38. *Resistance capacity amplifier.*

value for C_1 and C_2 is ·1 microfarad.

The best value for R_1 is not very critical, and in general it will be found that a resistance of from ·25 megohm to 1 megohm gives good results. A resistance higher than a certain value must not be connected in the grid circuit of some valves, and this value is usually given in the leaflet accompanying the valve. A resistance of ·5 megohm is a safe value. R_2 should be from 3 to 5 times the impedance of the valve.

With this arrangement an L.F. transformer is used to apply the voltage in the output circuit to the following valve, as shown in Fig. 39. Connected between the anode of the valve and H.T.+ is the primary *P* of the L.F. transformer, the secondary *S* being joined to the following valve.

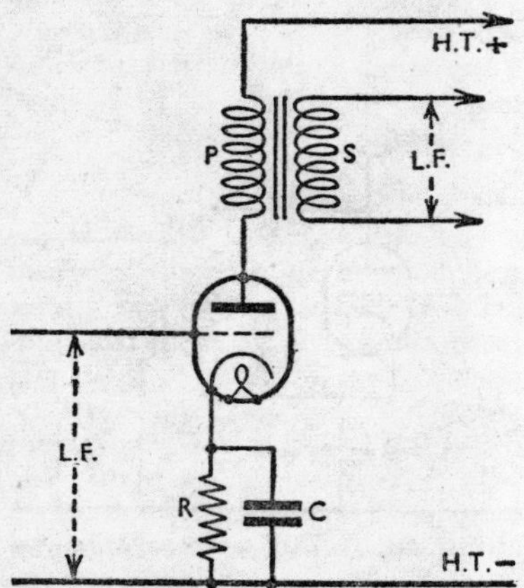

Fig. 39. *Transformer-coupled amplifier.*

Transformer-Coupled Amplifier

One advantage of the transformer-coupled L.F. amplifier is the gain that is obtained from the transformer. Often this is about 3 to 1, and may be more. This transformer gain is added to that obtained from the valve when reckoning the total amplification of the complete stage. As the transformer primary winding has usually a resistance of only 2,000 or 3,000 ohms, the voltage drop along it is small. As a result, the anode voltage is much higher than that generally used at the anode of a resistance-capacity coupled valve, and this assists further in providing a higher amplification.

Grid bias is of course needed. In Fig. 40 this is shown as being provided from a resistance *R* in the cathode lead. Speaking generally, the grid bias required for a transformer-coupled L.F. amplifier is rather higher than that for a resistance-capacity coupled amplifier, owing to the anode voltage being usually higher. The operation and choice of *R* and *C* for biasing are discussed in Lesson 7.

There is one important precaution to take when constructing a transformer-coupled L.F. amplifier. This is to see that the flow of anode direct current through its primary winding is not greater than that stated by the transformer manufacturer to be the maximum allowable. If this current is exceeded, distortion will take place. It may be as low as 1 milliampère for a small transformer or 10 milliampères when a large transformer is used. It is advisable to connect the transformer as in Fig. 40, to prevent any flow of direct current through the primary. Instead of joining the transformer primary between anode and H.T.+, a resistance *R* is joined in this position. The transformer primary is joined to the anode through a condenser *C*. What takes place is that the direct current flows through the resistance *R*, but, owing to the presence of con-

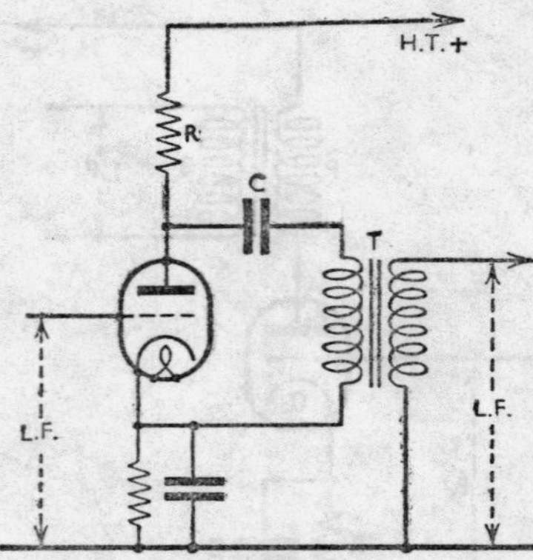

Fig. 40. *Parallel-fed transformer.*

denser *C*, the direct current is prevented from going through the transformer. The signal voltage, however, being alternating current, passes across the condenser *C* into the transformer primary to produce the signal voltage in the secondary. This type of circuit is known as parallel-feed or resistance-feed, because the anode-feed resistance *R* is effectively in parallel with the transformer primary.

Operating the Loudspeaker

Having by now received our wireless signal, amplified it, detected and again amplified it, we come to the final stage of preparing the signal for the loudspeaker which will transform the electrical current fluctuations into sound-waves. In order to operate the loudspeaker we must have *power*. Further, the moving-coil loudspeaker used almost exclusively is current-operated, in the sense that it requires as much current as practicable up to the limit of power it is designed to handle. Thus, we can appreciate that the first requirement of the output stage is to change the voltage applied to the input of the valve into a comparatively large current to operate the loudspeaker.

A triode output circuit is shown in Fig. 41. Connected between output valve anode and H.T.+ is the output transformer primary *P*, while joined across the secondary winding *S* is the speech-coil *SC* of the loudspeaker. Now, the speech-coil has a very low resistance —from 3 to 15 ohms. In order to enable the output valve to work efficiently, the primary *P* must have an impedance of several thousand ohms, but for operating the loudspeaker the secondary *S* must have an impedance of only a few ohms. The output transformer *T* is therefore of the step-down type. By stepping down the voltage, the current is increased proportionately so as to move the speech-coil in the way that has been already described in Lesson 3.

Pentode Valves

In Fig. 41 the valve shown as the output valve is a triode. This type of output valve is very satisfactory for many receivers, but a more popular valve in this part of the receiver is the pentode. The reason for the popularity of the pentode is that it gives a much louder signal

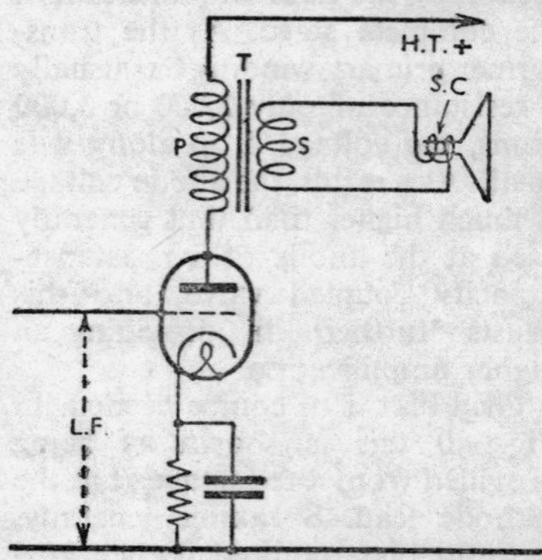

Fig. 41. *Triode output circuit.*

from the loudspeaker for a given voltage from the detector or L.F. amplifier. In other words, it is more sensitive. In most straight receivers it is an advantage to use a pentode as output valve because of this increased amplification. On the other hand, the quality of the reproduction is not usually up to the level provided by a triode. These two considerations—sensitivity *versus* quality—are the major ones that decide the choice of a pentode or triode as output valve.

Battery Connections

In Fig. 42 are shown the connections for a battery pentode. The input is applied in the usual way to the grid *via* L.F. coupling condenser C_1 (about ·01 microfarad). Grid leak R_1 (about ·5 megohm) is joined to the grid-bias battery, and care should be taken to see that the valve has the correct bias, because this is rather important for good results. Across the primary of the output transformer T is connected a tone-control circuit con-

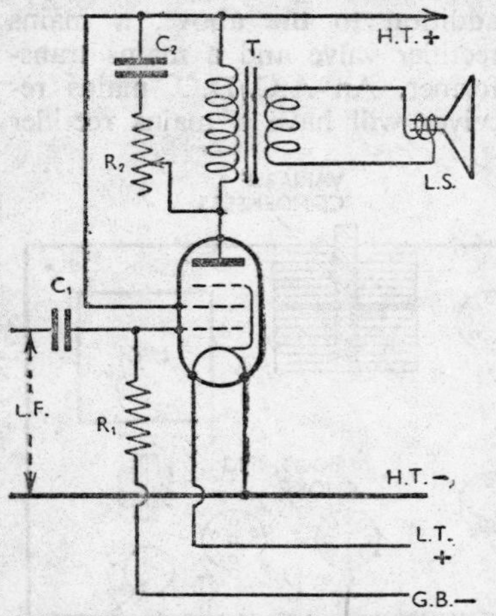

Fig. 42. *Pentode output circuit for battery valves. The input is applied to the grid* via *coupling condenser* C_1.

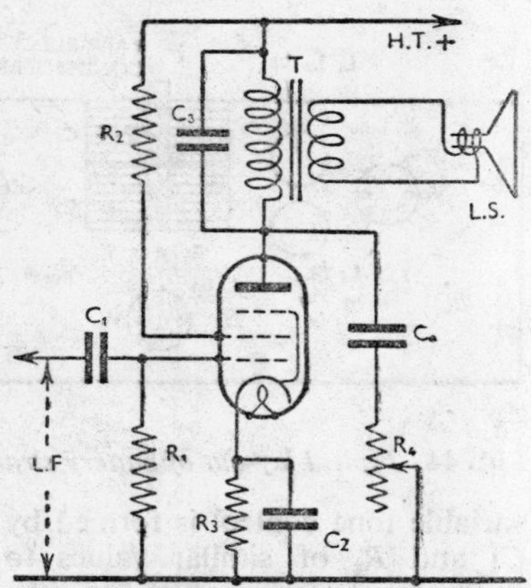

Fig. 43. *Mains pentode output circuit.*

sisting of R_2 and C_2. The values of these are dependent upon the valve and circuit, but often values of 5,000–15,000 ohms and ·01 to ·03 microfarad are suitable. Although C_2R_2 form a tone-control circuit, they should not be disconnected if considered to be unnecessary for tone, because they are needed for the satisfactory operation of the pentode valve itself. By altering the amount of resistance R_2 in circuit, the response to high notes may be varied.

With mains valves, the circuit shown in Fig. 43 is in general use. Here the input circuit is similar to that of Fig. 42. A resistance R_2 is joined between the screen-grid of the valve and H.T.+. This is not always required, but serves to equalise screen-grid and anode voltages. It should have a value of only a few hundred ohms. The grid-bias is provided by resistance R_3, which is by-passed by condenser C_2. The operation of R_3C_2 is described in Lesson 7, but it may be mentioned here that C_2 should have a value of about 50 microfarads, so as to ensure that reproduction of the low notes does not suffer. A

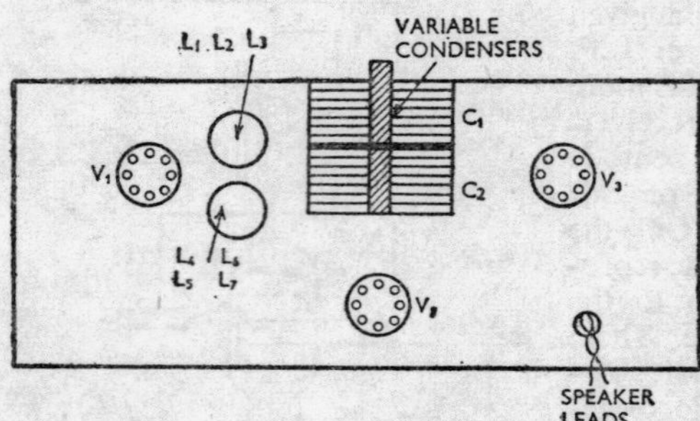

Fig. 44. *Typical lay-out of battery straight receiver.*

variable tone control is formed by C_4 and R_4 of similar values to those stated in respect of Fig. 42.

Voltage of H.T. Supply

In order to provide sufficient power to the loudspeaker, it is important that the H.T. supply to the output valve should be as high as practicable up to the rated maximum for the valve in use. Where a triode is in use, this is especially so, owing to its comparatively low sensitivity. With pentodes and output tetrodes adequate anode and screen-grid voltage is necessary. It is for this reason that the screen-grid resistance, if one is used, should be of a low value, so as not to drop too much voltage.

A modern receiver is built on to a chassis, which generally holds the entire receiver except the loudspeaker and the output transformer. Receiver chassis are usually made of metal and this is likely to remain the best medium for their construction. The chassis construction enables a compact and neat assembly of the receiver to be carried out, and when a metal chassis is used, provides a ready means of screening some of the components and valves from other components.

In the general design of straight receiver all the valves, in addition to some or all the tuning-coils, the variable tuning condensers and, if a mains set, the mains transformer, are mounted on the upper part of the chassis. Fig. 44 shows a typical lay-out for the upper part of the chassis of a three-valve battery receiver. In one screening can are L_1, L_2, L_3, these coils being the aerial coil and the two coils (L_2, L_3) to be tuned by the variable condenser C_1. The second screening can contains the detector tuning-coils L_4, L_5, tuned by variable condenser C_2, and the reaction coils L_6, L_7. The R.F. amplifier is V_1, the detector is V_2, and the output valve is V_3.

An A.C. mains straight receiver will have mounted on the chassis, in addition to the above, a mains rectifier valve and a mains transformer. An A.C./D.C. mains receiver will have a mains rectifier

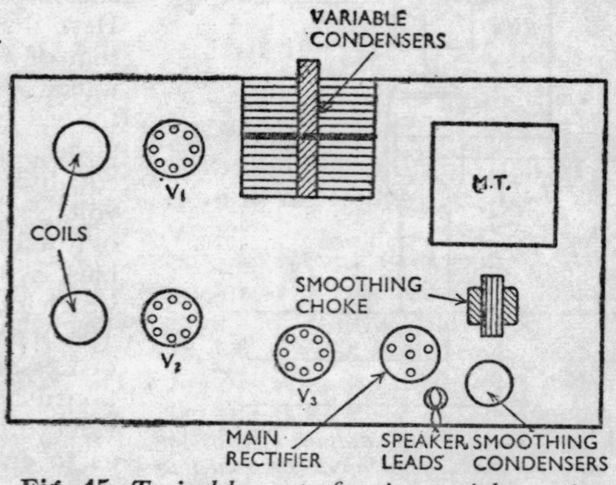

Fig. 45. *Typical lay-out of mains straight receiver.*

valve in addition to the components shown in Fig. 44, a mains transformer in this case being unnecessary. If a separate choke for smoothing the H.T. supply from the rectifier is used, this would also be mounted on top of the chassis, and if the metal-container type of electrolytic condenser is used for smoothing, this would also be mounted on top of the chassis. The upper-side of a typical A.C. mains chassis is illustrated in Fig. 45.

The under-side of the chassis contains the rest of the components required to complete the receiver. These include the R.F. choke, L.F. transformer if one is used, smoothing condensers if of the cardboard container type for a mains receiver, volume control resistance and reaction condenser. In the case of an all-wave receiver, it is usual to mount the short-wave tuning-coils under the chassis and the medium- and long-wave coils on the upper side of the chassis. Although these coils below the chassis need not be individually screened, it is advisable to arrange one set—say the short-wave R.F. coils—at right angles to the nearest other coils, such as the detector tuning-coils.

The general lay-out of receivers described above is, of course, subject to considerable modification in the various models of receivers as marketed by different manufacturers. Nevertheless, the notes given above will serve as an introduction to what may be expected by anyone approaching a straight receiver chassis for the first time.

Self Testing Questions

(1) *What do you understand by the term "amplifier"?*

(2) *Does amplification depend solely upon the valve?*

(3) *What is a detector?*

(4) *In radio work, what are understood by "low frequencies"?*

(5) *Describe the main purpose of the output stage.*

(6) *Compare the main points of triodes and pentodes as output valves.*

THE ANSWERS ARE ON PAGE 311.

LESSON 6

The Superheterodyne Receiver

WHAT is a Superheterodyne? The word "superheterodyne" is short for "supersonic heterodyne." The "heterodyne" part of the title refers to the oscillator that is used in this type of receiver, and which we shall discuss later. "Supersonic" means higher than an audible or sound frequency, and refers to the intermediate frequency.

The general arrangement of the circuits in a superheterodyne receiver is shown in Fig. 46. At *RF* we have a radio-frequency circuit or amplifier to which the aerial is connected. The voltage from *RF* is passed to a stage known as the mixer *MX*, to which a voltage from the oscillator *OSC* is also fed. These two frequencies are so combined at *MX* that there is produced a third frequency, which is known as the intermediate frequency. This

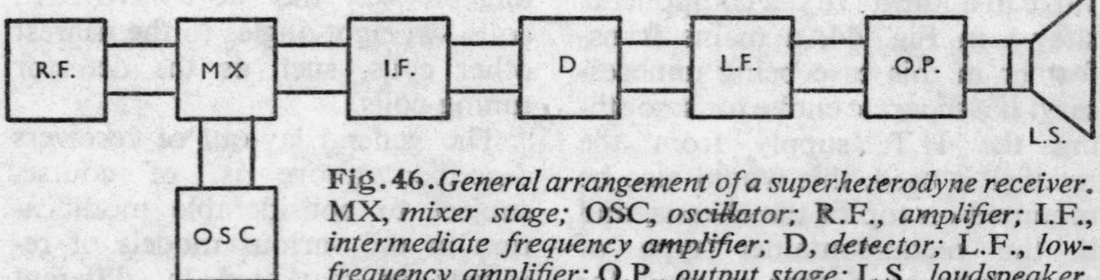

Fig. 46. *General arrangement of a superheterodyne receiver.* MX, *mixer stage;* OSC, *oscillator;* R.F., *amplifier;* I.F., *intermediate frequency amplifier;* D, *detector;* L.F., *low-frequency amplifier;* O.P., *output stage;* L.S., *loudspeaker.*

is passed to the intermediate frequency amplifier *IF*, the output of which is applied to the detector *D*, and then to the low-frequency amplifier *LF* and output stage *OP*.

An intermediate frequency amplifier works in a very similar manner to an R.F. amplifier. This being so, we can see from Fig. 46 that a superheterodyne receiver differs from a straight receiver by having a mixer stage *MX* and oscillator *OSC*. The other parts of the receiver are similar in many respects to the corresponding parts of a straight receiver. The object of having the mixer and oscillator is to form the intermediate frequency. This intermediate frequency (*IF*) contains the L.F. signal just the same as the R.F. received from the aerial, the only difference between the two being that the carrier frequency has been changed to a lower one. The process by which the I.F. is formed is known as frequency changing, and the circuit in which this process is carried out as the frequency changer.

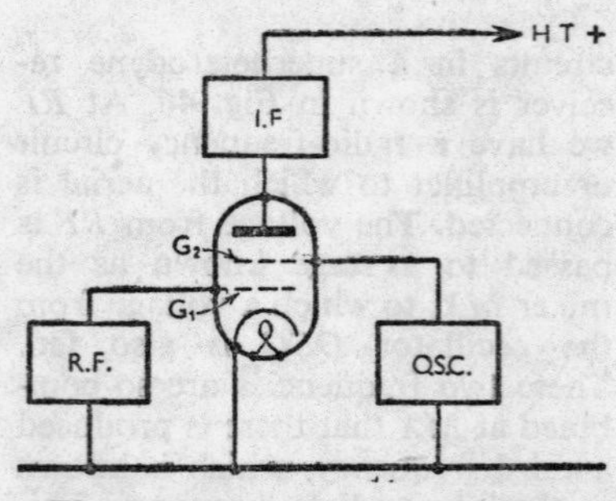

Fig. 47. *Basic method of mixing.*

Superheterodyne receivers are very popular today because they amplify the signals so much that a large variety of stations is receivable. With a superheterodyne receiver we can receive the same stations as with a straight receiver, but more clearly and free from interference, and many stations are receivable that with a straight receiver will be unheard.

The Frequency Changer

Some receivers use one valve as mixer and another as oscillator, but most broadcast receivers employ one valve to do the two jobs, the valve then being known as the frequency changer.

Let us see how the carrier frequency is changed. In Fig. 47 is shown a valve with two grids, to one of which is connected the radio-frequency circuit *RF*, and to the other of which is fed the oscillator voltage from *OSC*.

Now, the electron stream coming away from the cathode and passing through the valve toward the anode meets first of all grid G_1, to which the signal voltage is applied. The signal impresses itself on the electron stream, which then moves along toward the second grid G_2. Here it is influenced by the voltage at this grid, the oscillator voltage from *OSC*. So we see that by the time the electrons reach the anode they have been influenced by both the incoming signal and the oscillator.

It will be noticed that the actual mixing takes place inside the valve's electron stream. This mixing of two separate frequencies results in the formation of a third frequency, which is equal to the difference between the oscillator and signal (R.F.) frequencies. For example, suppose our signal carrier wave was 1,000 kilocycles and the oscillator was 1,465 kilocycles. The third or intermediate frequency would then be 1,465 − 1,000 = 465 kilocycles. The advantages of having a lower frequency to deal with in the receiver will be described later. First let us discuss some practical circuits that are very popular in modern receivers.

In some respects, frequency changing in the superheterodyne may be likened to the gearing in a watch. Here we have cog wheels arranged to reduce the rotation speed so as to move the hour-hand at only one-sixtieth the speed of the minute-hand, and $\frac{1}{3600}$th the speed of the second-hand. The oscillator frequency may be regarded as one cog wheel, the signal frequency as another, and the intermediate frequency as a third wheel whose rotation speed is due to the working of the other two.

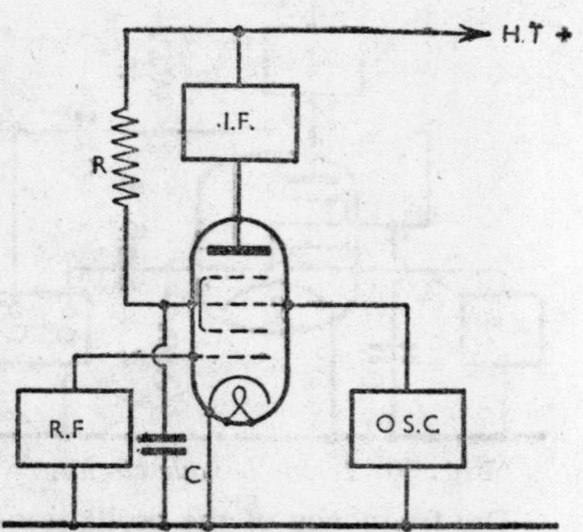

Fig. 48. *Hexode mixer circuit.*

Generating the Oscillations

In Fig. 49 is shown a circuit commonly used for producing oscillations. It is seen to be very similar to the detector circuit described in the previous lesson (see Fig. 37), in which reaction is employed. It was mentioned there that if reaction is used too much, the valve goes into oscillations. Now, with the circuit shown in Fig. 49, we simply arrange the grid-coil L_1 and the reaction-coil L_2 to be so close together and connected the proper way that these oscillations are produced and maintained.

The actual process is that when the valve is connected to its supply voltages, current flows in the anode circuit in the usual way. Owing to the closeness of the grid and anode-coils a voltage is set up in the grid-coil by the flow of current in the anode-coil. This grid voltage is amplified in the valve and appears in the anode circuit, which sets up a further and increased voltage at the grid. This is again amplified, and the whole thing goes on until a state is reached at which a steady feed-back of voltage from anode to grid occurs and oscillatory voltage is generated continuously.

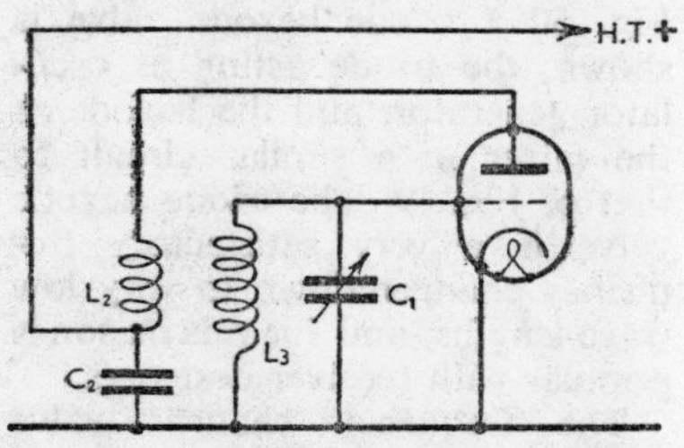

Fig. 49. *Basic oscillator circuit.*

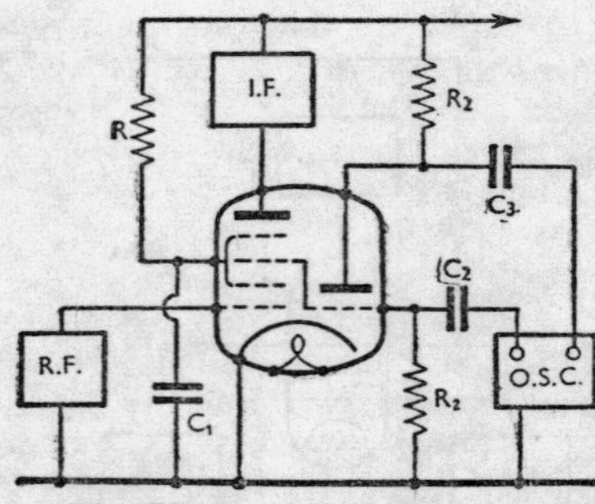

Fig. 50. *Triode hexode circuit.*

The frequency of the oscillations is dependent on the tuning of the grid circuit L_1C_1. The condenser C_1 is variable so that the frequency of the oscillations can be altered to tune the receiver to the various stations required to be received.

The arrangement shown in Fig. 47 is purely theoretical. For a practical frequency changer we must have screen-grids to shield the signal-grid from the oscillator-grid. It is better, too, if the anode is shielded from the grids.

In Figs. 49, 50 and 51 are shown practical circuits commonly used in modern broadcast receivers for frequency changing. Fig. 49 shows a hexode valve, with four grids, in which the signals are fed to the first grid and the oscillator voltage to the third grid. For shielding these, the second and fourth grids are used. With this valve, a separate oscillator valve is employed. In Fig. 50 a triode hexode valve is shown, the triode acting as oscillator generator, and the hexode as the mixer in a similar circuit to that of Fig. 49. The triode hexode valve is a very satisfactory frequency changer down to very low wave-lengths, and for this reason is popular with receiver designers.

The frequency changer valve shown in Fig. 51 is the heptode, which is seen to have five grids. In this valve the signals are fed to the fourth grid, which has a screen-grid either side of it. Oscillations are generated by the first two grids, which, with the cathode, act as a triode and may be connected as illustrated in Fig. 48. An octode, with six grids, works similarly to the heptode, the additional grid being connected to the cathode inside the valve envelope.

Now the reason that we go to all this trouble to change the frequency is that by producing an intermediate frequency we can

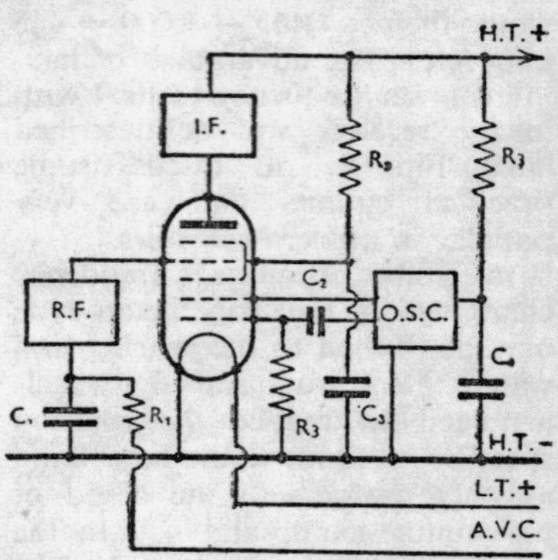

Fig. 51. *Heptode frequency changer circuit. The octode is similarly arranged.*

design a receiver to provide greater gain and selectivity. At the fixed intermediate frequency it is much easier to operate an amplifier without a risk of instability troubles outlined in the previous lesson. We can still have an R.F. amplifier in addition to our I.F. and L.F. amplifiers, so that the total gain of a superheterodyne can be made much higher than that of a straight receiver. Owing to the lower and fixed intermediate frequency it is easier to construct a two-valve I.F. amplifier than a two-valve R.F. amplifier. Most broadcast receivers employ only one I.F. amplifier, as this is found in practice to be sufficient.

Some receivers use 110 kilocycles or thereabouts as the I.F., but many use a much higher frequency—about 460 kilocycles. As the I.F. amplifier is required to be tuned to only one frequency, its design is much simpler and more efficient than in the case of the straight receiver, which has its circuit tunable over a comparatively wide band of frequencies.

Intermediate Frequency Amplifier

For the I.F. amplifier it is usual to employ two I.F. transformers arranged in the manner shown in Fig. 52. The secondary of the transformer IFT_1 whose primary is connected to the anode of the frequency changer valve V_1, is joined to the grid of the I.F. valve V_2 as shown, the condenser C being part of the A.V.C. filter. The primary of the second transformer IFT_2 is joined between the amplifier anode and H.T.+, and the secondary is connected to the following valve, which in most receivers is a diode detector.

These transformers are adjusted by means of the present condensers shown connected across each winding to tune to the required intermediate frequency. In the normal life of the receiver no further adjustment is required, although, of course, readjustment may be needed during servicing. Some I.F. transformers have the parallel condenser fixed in capacity, but the iron cores of the transformer windings adjustable. In either case only a slight variation is normally necessary to trim the circuits.

In order to enable the superheterodyne receiver to operate to best advantage, it is important that certain adjustments be carried out well. Some of these can only be done with expensive servicing equipment, but others can be effectively carried out by a home mechanic without his needing to procure special apparatus.

Best Results From a Superheterodyne

Probably the most important adjustment is that which enables the oscillator circuit to be tuned always to a certain frequency higher than the signal frequency. Some receivers use specially shaped condenser plates for the oscillator tuning condenser for this purpose. These condenser plates are so shaped that at any point in the tuning-band just the correct amount of capacity is added to the oscillator circuit to maintain its frequency at the fixed amount above the signal frequency.

Such a simple arrangement is not very practicable where more than one wave-band is required to be tuned over. For this purpose a condenser is added in series with the oscillator tuning condenser which has the desired effect, this being known as the padding condenser. Each circuit for tuning over one wave-band has a separate padding condenser, although in

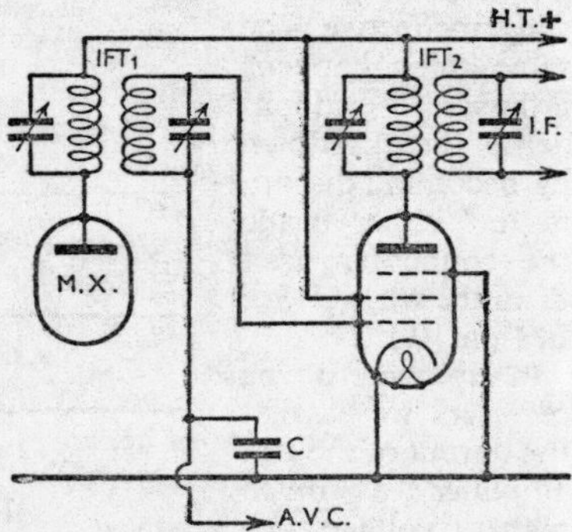

Fig. 52. *Typical I.F. amplifier circuit.*

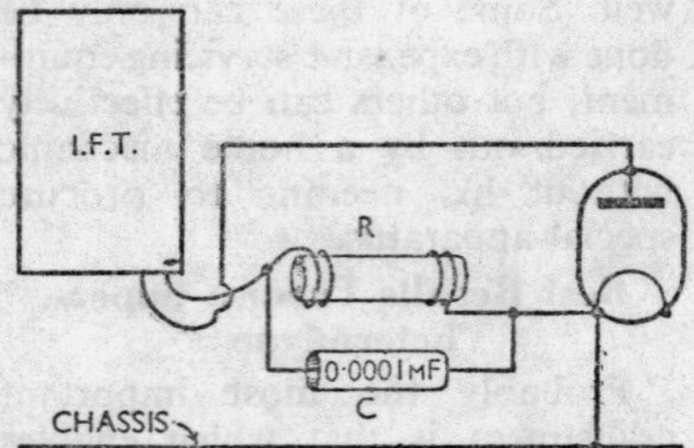

Fig. 53. *Diode detector circuit.*

some short wave-bands a padding condenser is not used.

With the frequency changer it is important that the correct operating voltages are not departed from too much. With the oscillator, for example, if the anode voltage is allowed to fall too much, the oscillations will not be strong enough to operate the mixing process properly. With mains valves, a reduced oscillator voltage would be brought about by the oscillator feed resistance to the anode going high. Where a battery set is being examined, this defect would be produced, of course, by the H.T. battery running down.

At the same time, the screen-grid voltage should not be too high, for, if it is, the mixer valve itself may oscillate and make the whole frequency changer stage ineffective. The same thing happens if the screen-grid condenser breaks down by becoming disconnected either inside the condenser itself or in the wiring. (See Lesson 10.)

In superheterodyne receivers we have at the output of the I.F. amplifier a much higher voltage for detection than is usually provided by the R.F. amplifier of a straight receiver. Grid detection is sometimes used in small superheterodynes, but most set designers prefer the diode valve as a detector, because of its ability to handle a much higher voltage. For working a diode detector with the least distortion it is best to apply to it a high signal voltage, and this requirement rather rules out the diode from use with many straight receivers. With our superheterodyne, however, we have the necessary voltage for good-quality detection, owing to the high gain that the receiver provides.

How a Diode Detector Works

In Fig. 53 is shown a diode detector circuit. In operation it works in a similar manner to the grid detector described in the previous lesson. That is to say, if the anode of the diode is considered in place of the grid of the grid detector, the general theory of detection is similar, although there is no triode to amplify the detected signal.

Referring to Fig. 53, we find that the secondary of the I.F. transformer is connected between diode anode and leak resistance *R* to cathode. Across the leak resistance is con-

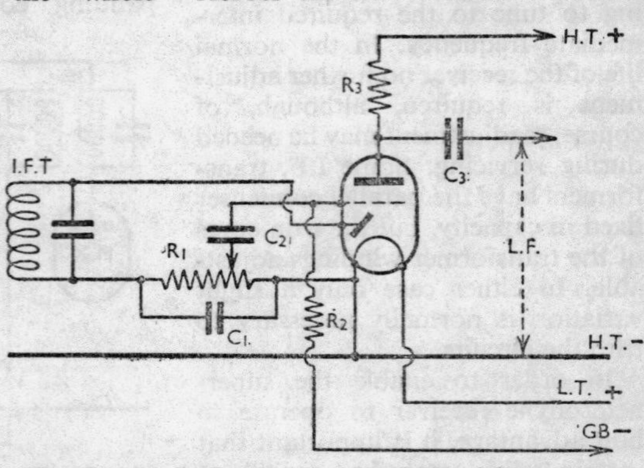

Fig. 54. *Diode detector and triode amplifier circuit.*

denser C, known as the reservoir condenser. From R the L.F. signal may be taken to an L.F. amplifier or the output stage direct. An L.F. amplifier is not always needed because, as we have already seen, there is a high signal voltage at the diode detector. Nevertheless, it is usual to employ one stage of L.F. amplification between the diode detector and the output stage.

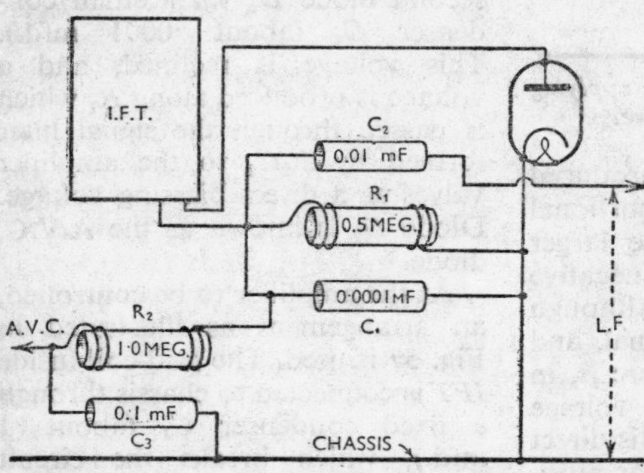

Fig. 55. *Diode valve circuit for producing A.V.C. voltage and also for detection.*

Diode Triode Circuit

Instead of using a separate valve for amplifying the detected signal provided by the diode, we may use one of the combined diode detector and triode amplifier valves.

In Fig. 54 is shown a diagram of such a valve, known as a diode triode. The diode detector circuit will be recognised, R_1 being the diode resistance and C_1 the reservoir condenser. The L.F. signal is taken from the diode resistance *via* condenser C_2 (·01 mfd.) and fed to the triode grid. A grid resistance R_2 is joined to the grid-bias battery —notice that the valve is battery-driven. The triode is connected as a resistance capacity coupled amplifier, in which the anode resistance is R_3 and the coupling condenser to the output valve is C_3 (·01 mfd.).

Automatic Volume Control

Automatic volume control is the governor of the radio receiver. It varies the sensitiveness of the receiver, depending on the signal strength. It prevents the very loud signal overloading the output stage, but makes the receiver very sensitive for weak signals. In this way, fading of signals is largely overcome.

The amplification of the receiver is controlled by varying the grid-bias that is applied to the various amplifiers (R.F. and I.F.) and also to the frequency changer. The negative bias is produced by a diode detector which may be either the signal detector for the receiver or a separate diode.

In Fig. 55 is shown the diagram of a diode detector which is also used for A.V.C. The circuit of the detector is similar to that of Fig. 53, but there is an additional resistance R_2 and condenser C_3. We know from the working of the diode detector that the anode goes negative during reception of a signal.

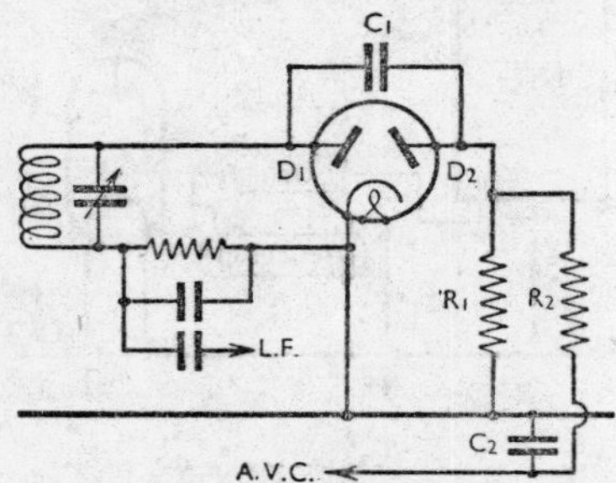

Fig. 56. *Detection and A.V.C. by two separate diodes. D_2 is the A.V.C. diode.*

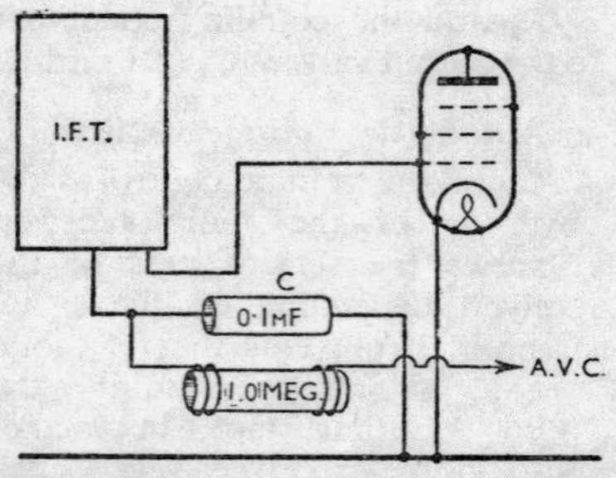

Fig. 57. *One method of applying A.V.C. to amplifier valve.*

Now, the negative voltage produced at the diode anode is proportional to the signal voltage—the larger the signal, the more negative becomes the diode anode. Although this voltage is the L.F. signal, and is therefore alternating, there is, in addition to that, a direct voltage produced across R_1. It is this direct voltage that is employed for automatically biassing the amplifier control grids, for the direct voltage also varies with the strength of the signal applied to the diode.

A.V.C. voltage is taken from the diode anode end of R_1 and the alternating signal voltage is filtered away by means of R_2 and C_3. The value of these depends upon design, but commonly used values are ·5 megohm or 1 megohm for R_2 and ·1 mfd. for C_3.

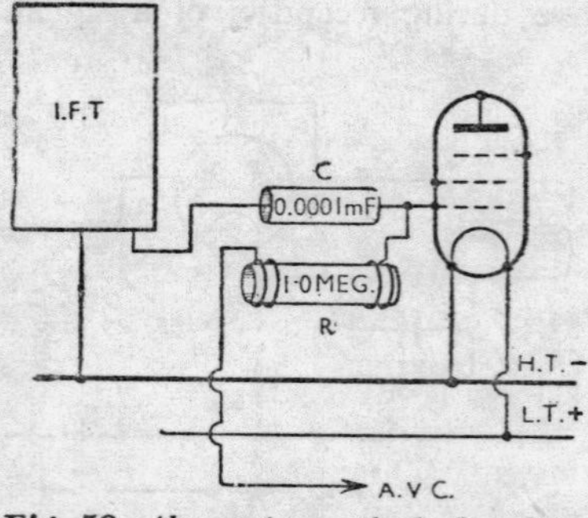

Fig. 58. *Alternative method of applying A.V.C. to the amplifier valve.*

A separate valve is often used for providing A.V.C., one circuit for this being shown in Fig. 56. Signal voltage is applied to diode anode D_1 for detection in the usual way, but, in addition, a certain amount of signal voltage is applied to a second diode D_2 *via* a small condenser C_1 (about ·0001 mfd.). This voltage is rectified, and a voltage is produced along R_1 which is passed through the signal filter formed by R_2C_2 to the amplifier valves as a direct biassing voltage. Diode D_2 is known as the A.V.C. diode.

At the amplifier to be controlled, an arrangement as illustrated in Fig. 57 is used. The grid-coil inside *IFT* is connected to chassis through a fixed condenser C_1 (about ·1 mfd.), which breaks the circuit for direct voltage. A.V.C. is applied *via* R_1 (about 1 megohm), C_1 and R_1 forming another filter for signal currents. R_1 is not always needed. An alternative method of applying A.V.C. is shown in Fig. 58, *C* being about ·0001 mfd. and *R* about 1 megohm.

Owing to the higher voltage available in the superheterodyne, we have a much larger power to handle at the output. For this reason an output circuit specially designed to provide a large power without distortion is often used. The principal circuit for this purpose is the push-pull amplifier.

Push-Pull Amplifier

The circuit of the push-pull amplifier is shown in Fig. 59. Input voltage from the secondary of L.F. transformer T_1 is applied to the control grids of two valves, the centre point of this winding being tapped and bias applied from *B*.

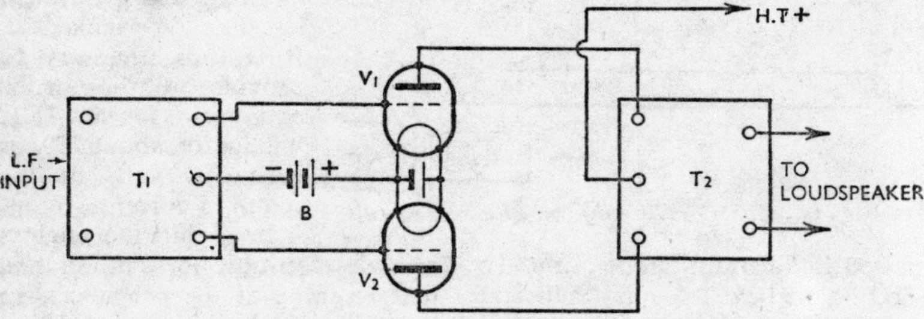

Fig. 59. *Basic push-pull amplifier, which supplies large power without distortion.*

The anodes of the valves are joined to opposite ends of the primary of the output transformer T_2, which is also centre-tapped to the H.T.+ line.

Push-pull valves work in such a way that a great deal of distortion is balanced out, with the result that the reproduction from the loudspeaker is of much better quality than that usually obtainable from a single valve. By proper design, the push-pull output stage is capable of handling large power, and it is for these two reasons (*i.e.* quality of reproduction and power handling ability) that this type of output circuit is often used in superheterodyne receivers.

Self Testing Questions

(1) *What is a superheterodyne receiver?*

(2) *How is the carrier frequency changed?*

(3) *What features distinguish the superheterodyne from a straight receiver?*

(4) *Why are diodes used as detectors in superheterodynes?*

(5) *What is automatic volume control?*

THE ANSWERS ARE ON PAGE 312.

LESSON 7

Supplying Power to Mains Receivers

RECEIVERS that are designed to work from the domestic electricity supply mains must include some apparatus for providing all the power that is required by the valves. So far we have discussed the receiver itself, quite apart from the power supply. This is because the circuits given have been suitable for either battery valves or mains valves. The supply equipment for mains valves is fitted to the receiver chassis as an essential part. For the purpose of this book, however, it is best to consider the supply apparatus separately from the receiver, so as to simplify the general discussion.

Let us first of all see what the power requirements of a receiver are. In order that the valves can operate, the cathodes must be

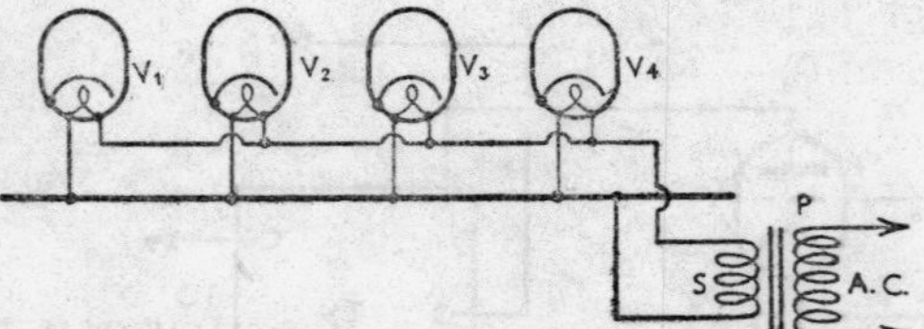

Fig. 60. *Commonly used form of heater circuit.*

raised to a certain temperature. To do this, we have to supply sufficient current through the filaments or heaters, just as an electric fire needs a certain amount of current to heat it to the desired temperature. A.C. valve-heater voltage is usually low —4 or 6·3 volts. (A.C./D.C. valves are discussed later.) The current required depends on the type of valve used, some valves, such as the Mazda A.C. 2 Pen DD and the Cossor 42 MP/Pen, needing 2 ampères each at 4 volts, while other types, such as the Mullard 904V triode, require only ·65 ampère. We thus see that the first requirement for our mains-supply equipment is a fairly heavy heater current at low voltage.

Additional Direct Voltage

In addition to heater power, we need a positive direct voltage for the valve anodes. Most valves used in the modern receiver work very well with an H.T. supply *at the anode* and screen-grid of about 200 volts. Note that this voltage should be at the anode, and not merely the voltage provided at the output of the mains-supply equipment. Many circuits, as we have already seen, include in the anode circuit of the valve a resistance. If we have a supply for H.T. of only 200 volts, by the time a voltage drop has taken place in the anode resistance, the grid-bias resistance (see later), and the smoothing choke (referred to later), the actual voltage at the anode will be much less than the original 200. It is thus necessary to provide at the mains equipment for an H.T. voltage of about 250, or even 300 volts at the required current.

In a ship the engines must develop more horse-power than that required at the propellers, so as to allow for losses in transmitting the power. So with our H.T. voltage, allowance must be made for the voltage dropped in the anode circuit between the H.T.+ line and the anodes themselves.

Grid bias has to be provided, and this is produced in the circuit of either the receiver valves themselves, or in the mains-supply equipment proper. Most grid-bias supply circuits are so arranged that the bias voltage is really subtracted from the total H.T. supply, as will be seen by the discussion on grid-bias later in this lesson. If the total H.T. voltage is 250 and the bias for the valve is 15 volts, the actual H.T. voltage available for the anode is $250 - 15 = 235$ volts.

We have now arrived at the essential requirements from our mains-supply equipment, which are:

1. Heater current for the valves,
2. H.T. voltage, due allowance being made for voltage drops in the circuits, and
3. Grid-bias voltage.

How the H.T. Supply is Obtained

As our valves require a low voltage, we must step down the mains-supply voltage. This is easily done by a transformer in which the number of turns on the secondary connected to the heaters is fewer than the number of turns in the primary joined to the A.C. supply circuit. It is usual to connect the heaters in parallel across the heater winding on the transformer, as shown in Fig. 60. In this drawing one side of each heater is joined to chassis and the other side to the heater line from the heater winding on the transformer. One side of the heater winding is, of course, joined to chassis. An alternative arrangement is to tap the heater winding at its electrical centre and join the tapping to chassis, the heaters being connected to the ends of the windings.

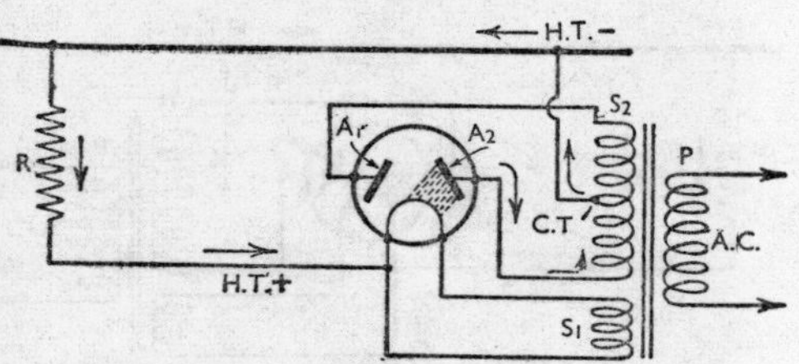

Fig. 61. *Rectification of one half cycle.*

If with this latter circuit excessive mains hum occurs, it may be due to the tap not being at the true centre. This difficulty can be overcome by fitting an adjustable resistance of about 30 ohms across the winding, after disconnecting the centre tap. The resistance should have three terminals, one of which is joined to the variable contact. The ends of the resistance are connected to the ends of the heater winding, and the variable contact arm to chassis. Now adjust the contact arm until the point of minimum hum is found. This adjustment gives the centre tap, and the arm may be fixed at that point.

The total heater consumption of the receiver is found by adding together the separate heater currents of all the valves. For example, if the receiver used four 4-volt valves, three of which consumed 1 ampère and one consumed 2 ampères, the total consumption of the set would be 5 ampères. With this in mind, it is necessary to use thick wire in the heater circuit so as to avoid voltage drop losses in the conductors.

For the anodes and screen-grids direct voltage is required. As the mains supply is alternating current in the case being discussed, some means must be provided for changing the alternating into direct current. This is done by the mains rectifier, in the following way.

Rectification

A two-anode rectifier valve is joined in the circuit shown in Fig. 61. The cathode of the valve is heated in the manner described above, from the low-voltage secondary winding S_1. The anodes of the valve are connected to the ends of the secondary winding S_2, which, because it has a high voltage across it, is referred to as the high-voltage winding. A tap from the centre of S_2 is joined to earth or chassis.

When the circuit is operating, the anodes become positive alternately. For example, in Fig. 61 is shown the course of the current during one half-wave of applied alternating voltage. The anode A_1 is made positive, and thereby attracts the electrons from the cathode. These electrons form the anode current, and pass round the circuit in the direction of the arrows. Resistance R represents the valves in the receiver. While A_1 is positive, the other anode A_2 is negative, and so passes no current.

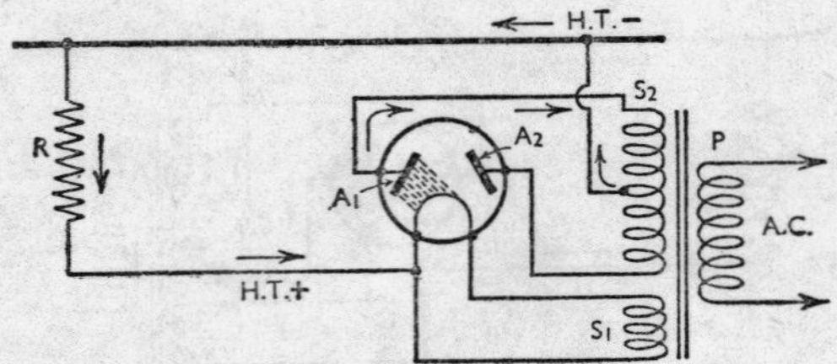

Fig. 62. *Rectification of the second half cycle.*

receiver anodes and screen grids.

The current spurts provided by the mains rectifier are not of much use to the receiver, for what we need is a *steady*, *i.e.* non-fluctuating, current. So now, having obtained a series of current spurts, all in the same direction, we must use some means to level out, or smooth, the fluctuations.

During the following half-wave, the anode A_2 becomes positive and the anode A_1 is negative. We now have the current flowing in the direction shown in Fig. 62, from cathode to anode A_2 and round the circuit as indicated by the arrows. It is seen that the flow of current

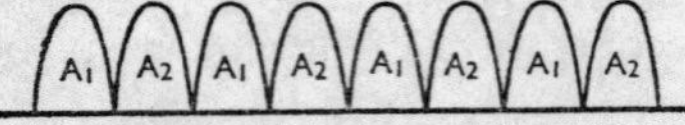

Fig. 63. *Current output of rectifier.*

through the resistance R is in the same direction during both half-waves. In other words, we have spurts of current passing through R always in the same direction, regardless of the direction of the alternating current in the secondary S_2. As long as the alternating voltage is fed to the secondary S_2 these spurts of current continue to flow, alternative spurts being passed by each anode while the other remains inoperative. This is illustrated in Fig. 63.

It will be noted that with the rectifier circuit the cathode is positive so far as the spurts of current are concerned. Although the anodes have the positive *alternating voltage* applied to them, they are negative to the cathode when these spurts of current are considered. It thus follows that for our radio receiver we must join the H.T+ lead to the cathode of the rectifier for connection to the

Smoothing the Rectifier Output

The arrangement for smoothing the rectifier output is illustrated in Fig. 64. It is seen to consist of two condensers and a smoothing choke-coil *LFC*. Joined next to the rectifier is condenser C_1. This condenser is charged up by the spurts of current from the rectifier anodes. The capacity of this condenser C_1 is chosen to be so large that it will not discharge much during the time that elapses between each spurt of current from the rectifier. Thus, the voltage across the condenser C_1, once it is charged, only falls comparatively slightly between the current spurts fed to it.

The smoothing circuit acts as a tank supplied with water in spurts. The tank acts as a reservoir from which water may be drawn steadily without any influence of the spurts, if the tank is large enough and the pipe is small in section. In our smoothing circuit the reservoir is the condenser C, which receives

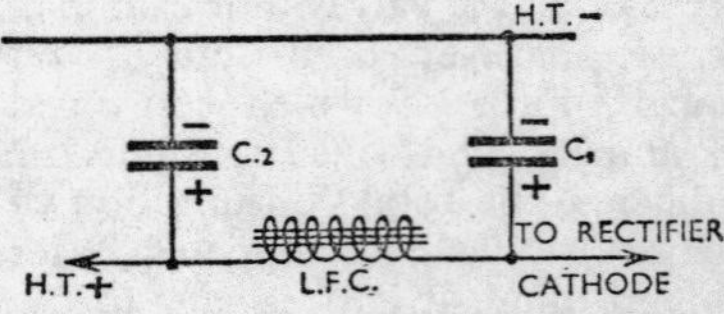

Fig. 64. *Rectifier smoothing circuit.*

the current from the rectifier in spurts and holds it just as the tank does the water, to be drawn off in a steady flow. For this reason *C* is known as the reservoir condenser.

The voltage across the reservoir condenser C_1 does, all the same, fluctuate rather too much to be completely satisfactory for our H.T.+ line, so we feed it through an iron-cored choke *LFC* to another condenser C_2. Now, we already know that a choke-coil tends to prevent any fluctuations in current passing through it. The result of connecting the choke *LFC* is, therefore, to level out still more the fluctuations in current from the rectifier. By selecting condenser C_2 of suitably large capacity, the fluctuations still remaining in the current passed through the choke *LFC* are further smoothed out. The final result is a steady direct current and voltage at the output of the smoothing circuit which may be used for the H.T. supply. Condenser C_2 is known as the smoothing condenser.

A transformer is used, as shown in the Figs. above, to step up the voltage for the rectifier. Across the complete high-voltage winding feeding the anodes is a voltage equal to twice the rectifier anode-to-cathode voltage. In many receivers this total voltage is about 700 volts. It is important, therefore, that no short circuits should occur in the transformer, because if they do, excessive heat will immediately be caused.

It should be noted that we are dealing with alternating current as far as the rectifier anodes. The parts of the circuit across which A.C. is applied are shown in Fig. 65. To test these parts of the circuit an A.C. meter is needed if the actual current or voltage is required to be known. For checking the presence of A.C., however, all that is required is a high-voltage electric lamp plugged into a lamp-holder joined to two short lengths, say 1 ft., of insulated wire, the two connector wires bared of insulation at their end. To check the A.C. parts of the mains equipment, place the bared ends of the wires *momentarily* across the following points:

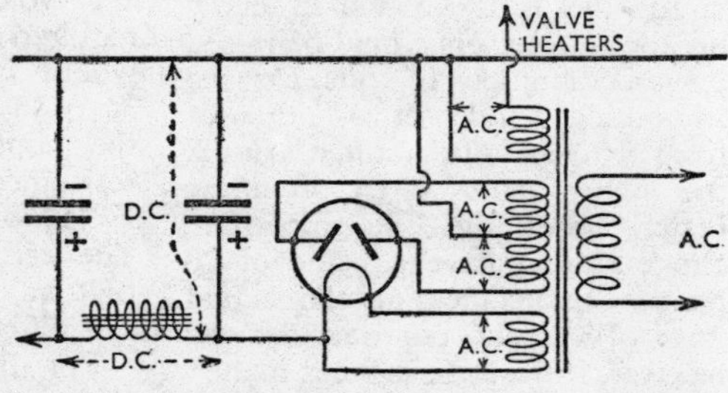

Fig. 65. *Showing points across which A.C.* (*to the rectifier anodes*) *and D.C. voltage exists.*

1. Mains transformer primary winding,
2. *Each* section of the high voltage winding,
3. Each rectifier anode to cathode.

Be careful to avoid connecting the lamp across the whole high-voltage winding, as the voltage there is enough to burn out domestic lamps. For this test, a low-wattage lamp—say up to 25 watts—may be used. If the power is in the circuit, the lamp lights up when the wire-ends are contacted as described.

The rest of the circuit has D.C. voltage across it, and may be tested with D.C. instruments as described in the final lesson.

The choice of reservoir condenser

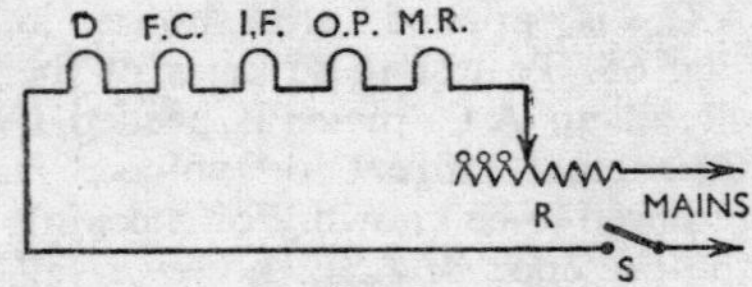

Fig. 66. *Heater circuit for A.C./D.C. four-valve superhet receiver.*

lies between a capacity of 8 microfarads and 32 microfarads. Too high a value should not be used. By increasing the size of this condenser, the H.T. voltage may be raised. For example, by increasing this condenser from 8 to 16 microfarads the H.T. voltage in many broadcast receivers would be raised by something like 15 volts. For the smoothing condenser a value of from 8 to 50 microfarads is used, the higher values often providing better smoothing. The smoothing choke should have a value of 20 henries inductance at the actual flow of current required for the receiver. If the inductance is higher, so much the better, so long as the resistance of the winding is not too high. Often the field winding of the loudspeaker is used as the choke, and this is naturally an economic arrangement.

Mains Supply for Receivers

There are some important differences between the equipment for A.C. sets and those designed to work on either A.C. or D.C. mains. A.C./D.C. valves have their heaters wired in series, as illustrated in Fig. 66, which shows a typical heater circuit for a four-valve superheterodyne receiver. It will be noted that the detector valve *D* is the last on the line.

In series with the heaters is a resistance *R* which has to be so chosen that it drops the voltage of the mains down to the value required by the valves. For example, suppose we had in the receiver two valves with 13-volt heaters, two with 26-volt heaters and one with a 35-volt heater. The total voltage required for heating the valves would be $(13 \times 2) + (26 \times 2) + 35 = 26 + 52 + 35 = 113$ volts. If the supply voltage is 230, the resistance *R* that dropped $230 - 113 = 117$ volts would have to be used. The resistance has tappings on it, so that adjustment may be made to suit different supply voltages.

For providing H.T. voltage, a mains transformer is not used. The mains voltage is applied directly to the rectifier valve, as seen from Fig. 67. Many receivers use a high-frequency choke in each mains lead, shown at HFC_1 and HFC_2, and a condenser C_1 (·01 mfd.) across the mains leads. These act as a filter to reduce interference that comes from the mains. The high-frequency chokes are not of the type used in the receiver

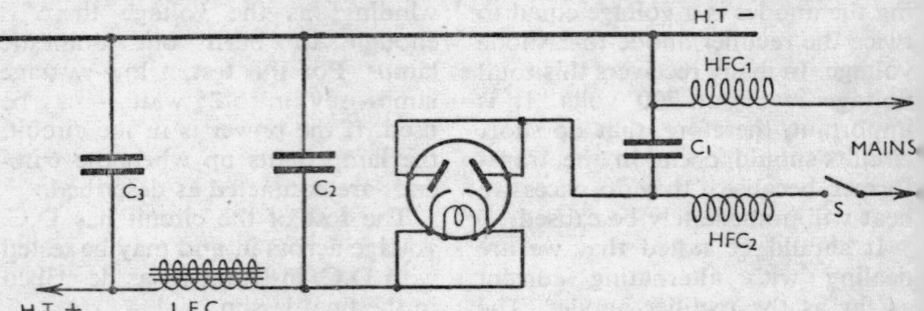

Fig. 67. *Typical H.T. supply circuit without transformer for A.C./D.C. mains.*

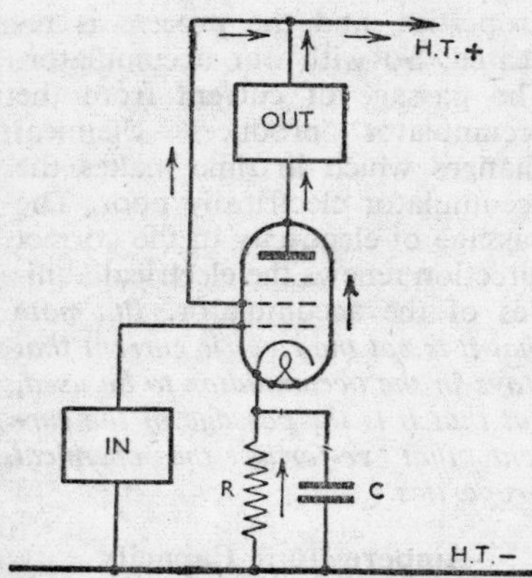

Fig. 68. *Showing flow of current through valve and grid-bias resistance* R.

circuits themselves but are wound with much thicker wire to carry the much larger current. For smoothing the H.T. supply, the usual circuit C_2, *LFC*, C_3 is used.

Automatic Grid Bias

With mains valves it is usual to provide the grid-bias voltage from a resistance connected to the cathode. In Fig. 68 this resistance is shown at *R*. It will be seen that the current from screen-grid and anode flows through *R* back to the cathode. This sets up a voltage which makes the cathode positive to chassis. As the grid is joined to chassis, it is thus negative to the cathode, and biassed.

The amount of bias is equal to the current flow multiplied by the resistance. For example, if the screen-grid current is 3 mA, anode current is 30 mA, and *R* is 500 ohms, we will have a bias of $\frac{33}{1000} \times 500 = \frac{33}{2} = 16{\cdot}5$ volts.

A condenser C_1 is needed to by-pass the signal current from *R*. It should have a capacity of ·1 mfd. for R.F. and I.F. amplifiers and frequency changers and from 20 to 50 microfarads for L.F. amplifiers and output valves. If *C* is too small in the L.F. stages, the low notes are diminished in strength.

Self Testing Questions

(1) *What are the power requirements for a receiver?*

(2) *What is the difference between heater connections for A.C. sets and A.C./D.C. sets?*

(3) *Why do we need a mains rectifier valve?*

(4) *Where does the D.C. circuit begin in the A.C. mains equipment?*

THE ANSWERS ARE ON PAGE 312.

LESSON 8

Accumulators and H.T. Batteries

ACCUMULATORS, as commonly used to heat the filaments of battery valves, consist, as is well known, of a container, usually glass, two sets of plates and some acid. The general arrangement for a two-plate accumulator, which may be called a cell, is shown in Fig. 69, where the container *C* is nearly filled with sulphuric acid *A* in which are placed two lead plates P_1 and P_2.

Now, the process by which such an accumulator provides electric current for the receiver is a chemical one. If the negative plate is made of pure lead and the positive plate of lead peroxide, while the acid has a certain strength, there will be available for a circuit across the terminals *T* a voltage of about 2. Such a voltage is suitable for heating battery valves.

As the current passes from one terminal of the accumulator to the other through the circuit connected

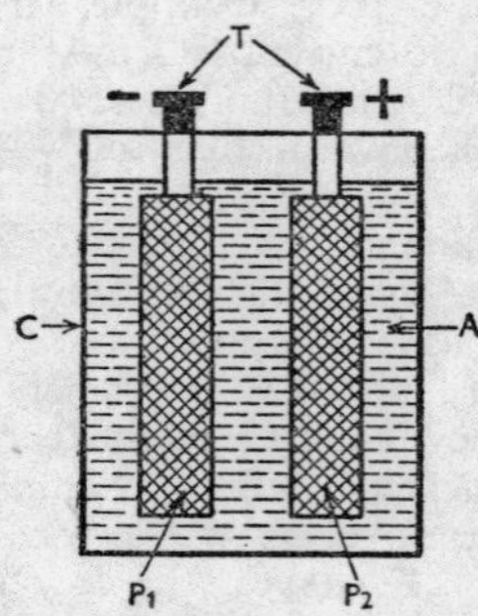

Fig. 69. *A two-plate accumulator.*

to it, the chemical make-up of the acid and the plates changes, until a point is reached where no further useful current will pass out. The accumulator is then said to be discharged, and its voltage will have dropped to about 1·75. By passing an electric current through the cell *in the opposite direction to that in which the current left it*, the chemical construction of the plates and acid can be re-formed and the original two volts made available once again.

The working of the accumulator may be likened to the time-honoured method of fertilising soil for growing crops. A farmer puts fertiliser on his ground, which is changed chemically in the earth and feeds the plants he grows. Soon the farmer finds his ground becoming poor again, so he puts more fertiliser into the ground to renew its growing properties, and the process is repeated. So with our accumulator. The passage of current from the accumulator produces chemical changes which in time makes the accumulator electrically poor. The passage of electricity in the correct direction renews the electrical abilities of the accumulator. *But note that it is not the electric current that stays in the accumulator to be used, but that it is the passage of the current that re-forms the chemical properties.*

Ampère-Hour Capacity

As accumulator cells each have the same voltage at their terminals, the deciding factor, when it comes to actual ability to do work, is the current flow from the cell. This ability of a cell to do work is known as its ampère-hour capacity, which means the number of hours a stated current can be obtained from the cell. For example, if a radio receiver accumulator has a capacity of 40 ampère-hours, it will run a set requiring half an ampère for 80 hours, or one passing 1 ampère for 40 hours. Naturally, as the discharge rate must not be too high, we could not take, say, 10 ampères for 4 hours, although, if we could, this would also give us 40 ampère-hours.

To increase the ampère-hour capacity, we can connect accumulators in parallel, as shown in Fig. 70. With parallel connections the voltage is still the same as from one cell, no matter how many we join in parallel. The ampère-hour capacity is equal to the total capacity of

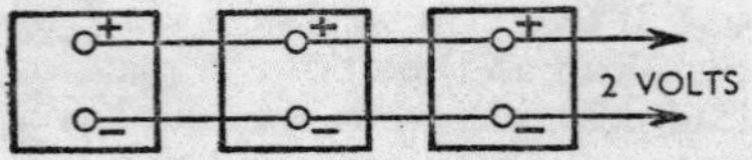

Fig. 70. *Accumulators in parallel.*

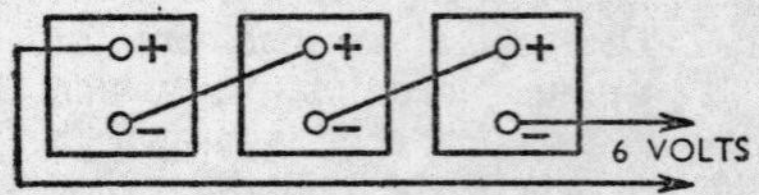

Fig. 71. *Accumulators in series.*

the cells. That is to say, if we have two cells of 40 ampère-hours in parallel, the total capacity is 80 ampère-hours. The connection of two or more cells together is known as a battery.

If we wish to increase the voltage, the cells should be joined in series, as shown in Fig. 71. In this case the total voltage of the battery is that of all the cells added together. For example, for H.T. supply accumulators are sometimes used. If a battery of 140 volts is required, then, as each cell gives 2 volts, we shall have to join 70 cells in series. Although the voltage has been increased by the series connection, the ampère-hour capacity still remains the same as that for *one* cell.

It is harmful for accumulators to be left for long in a discharged condition. As soon as an accumulator has run down, have it re-charged immediately. If you charge it yourself, do not charge it at a higher rate than that recommended by the makers. And, equally, do not discharge it too quickly, as by allowing a short circuit to occur across its terminals.

The plates should always be covered with acid. But do not add pure acid, or ordinary water. Normally, never add acid. If the level of the acid falls below the top of the plates, *fill with distilled water*, which you will be able to obtain from the chemist.

Testing the Voltage

For testing accumulator voltage, check the voltage after the set has been working for 10 minutes or so. Once the voltage falls to 1·8, have the cell or battery re-charged. Hydrometer tests are best for checking the internal condition of the accumulator, and should be used. Hydrometers cost only a few pence, and instructions are supplied with them.

We have seen already that a battery is composed of two or more cells. It will be gathered from this that an H.T. battery consists of a

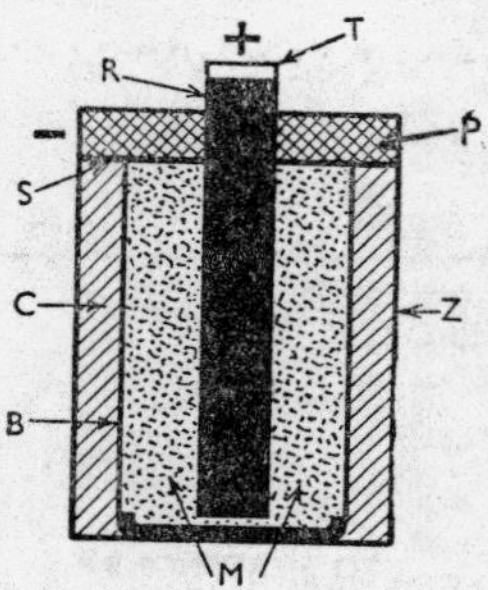

Fig. 72. *Typical dry cell.*

number of cells: just how many we shall see later.

A dry cell works by chemical action, but in a different manner from that of the accumulator. A typical dry cell is illustrated in Fig. 72. A zinc container *Z* is covered on the inside with a coating *C* surrounding a certain chemical mixture *M* held inside a cloth bag *B*. Embedded in this chemical mixture is a carbon rod *R* with a terminal *T*, and the top of the cell is filled with pitch *P*, separated from *M* by a cardboard disc *S*.

When the cell is connected to a circuit, a voltage of 1·5 volts is provided across the terminals, the carbon rod being positive and the zinc container negative. As current is drawn from the cell, chemical action takes place between the zinc and the carbon through the chemical

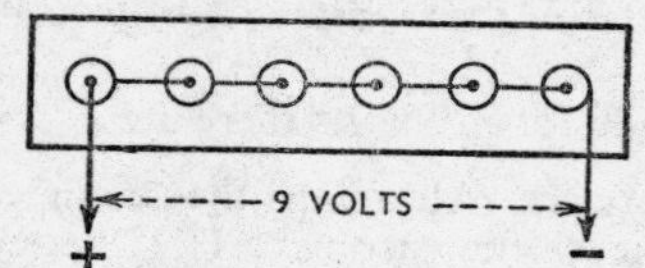

Fig. 73. *Connections of bias battery.*

mixtures. The chemical properties of the mixture *M* gradually change until in the end no useful current can pass from the cell to the circuit joined to it, and the voltage at the terminals is lowered to half a volt

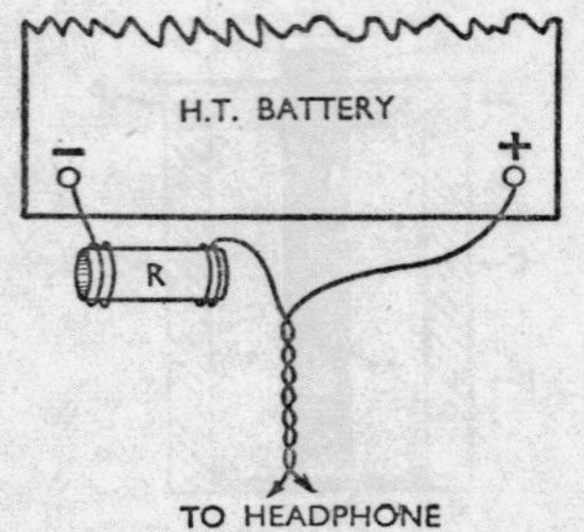

Fig. 74. *Arrangement for testing a battery for noises by using headphones.*

or less. Long before this state is reached, however, the cell has lost its usefulness to our receiver, for it will be found that when the voltage of a battery of dry cells has fallen by about a third, it will not provide a satisfactory voltage much longer, and should be renewed.

Radio Receiver Batteries

A grid-bias or high-tension battery as used in a radio receiver consists of a number of dry cells joined together in series, as shown in Fig. 73. They are housed in a cardboard box and covered with pitch. We have seen that each cell provides about 1·5 volts. The number of cells in a H.T. battery will thus depend on the maximum voltage required. For example, in the 9-volt grid-bias battery there are $\frac{9}{1{\cdot}5} = 6$ cells, while for 120 volts there are $\frac{120}{1{\cdot}5} =$ 80 cells. Although the complete unit is quite strong, a H.T. battery should not be given rough usage, in case one or more of the connections between the cells becomes broken.

Anyone who looks in the window of a shop that displays electric batteries will be struck by the large number of sizes in which the cells are manufactured. Now, a cell can be thought of, when its use is considered, as a tank which supplies energy to the apparatus connected to it. Whether this apparatus is an electric lamp or a wireless receiver does not make any difference. The larger the tank, the more energy it holds, so that if we join a wireless receiver to it, the larger tank will last longer than a small tank.

But there is a more important point to using large batteries than this. *The larger the battery, the cheaper the electricity supply.* For example, if the cheapest battery on the market were to last you three months, a larger battery at double the cost would be likely to last a good deal longer than twice the time—it may still be sound at the end of seven or eight months.

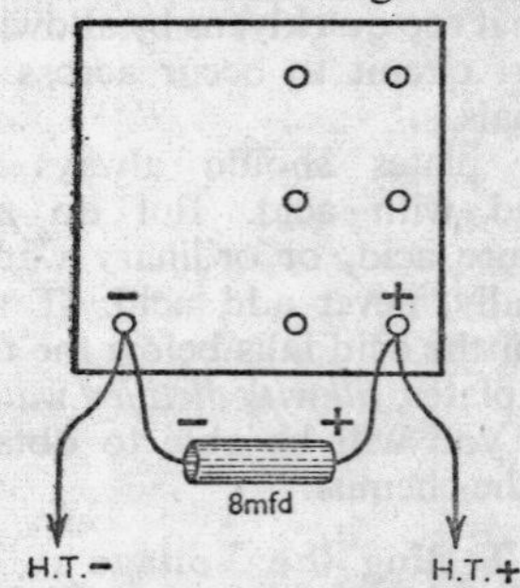

Fig. 75. *Method of connecting condenser across a H.T. battery.*

Hence the price per month will be cheaper the larger the battery used. Note that what is here considered is the actual size of the cells of the battery

Sometimes batteries develop internal weaknesses that cause noises in the receiver. If this is suspected, you can test the receiver in the following manner. Obtain a resistance value 50,000 to 100,000 ohms and join it in series with a pair of headphones or the input terminals of an output transformer connected to a loudspeaker, as shown in Fig. 74. If the battery is defective and noisy, the sound it is causing will now be reproduced in the phones or loudspeaker. A noisy battery should be thrown away.

The usefulness of a H.T. battery is improved by connecting a condenser across it. This condenser should be about 8 microfarads capacity, and is connected from H.T.— to H.T.+ as shown in Fig. 75. Be careful to join the — of an electrolytic condenser to — of battery, and the two +'s together as shown in the figure. The condenser should be joined to the highest + lead from the battery.

Self Testing Questions

(1) *What does an accumulator obtain its electric current from?*

(2) *How do you connect an accumulator for charging?*

(3) *What is the ampère-hour capacity of an accumulator?*

(4) *What are the positive and negative electrodes of a dry cell?*

(5) *What voltage is provided by* (a) *a dry cell?* (b) *An accumulator?*

THE ANSWERS ARE ON PAGE 312.

LESSON 9

Radio Servicing for the Home Mechanic

THE servicing of a radio receiver is a highly specialised job, which involves not only a deep knowledge of the working of the receiver circuits, but also the use of complicated testing and measuring equipment. Nevertheless, there are some faults that arise in practice that can be traced and often cured either with no equipment at all or with quite simple and inexpensive test instruments.

There are two parts to radio servicing. The first is examining the receiver and its external connections without unscrewing anything or taking anything to pieces beyond the back or bottom of the cabinet. The second part is getting to grips with the internal connections with meters to test the actual working of the receiver. It is surprising what a number of defects can be brought to light by the first examination, so we will consider that for a start.

In tackling a receiver, it should be appreciated that if the set has been working for some time, it is unlikely to be faulty in the lay-out of the component parts. We can, therefore, rule out the need to make any alteration in their position. It should also be realised at the beginning that it is unwise to make any alteration in the wiring or general lay-out of the receiver, for by so doing the design of the receiver may be upset and a worse fault developed. To pull a set about without specialised training is like breaking a hole in a house-roof in an attempt to find where it leaks—the last state will be worse than the first.

Let us assume that the radio re-

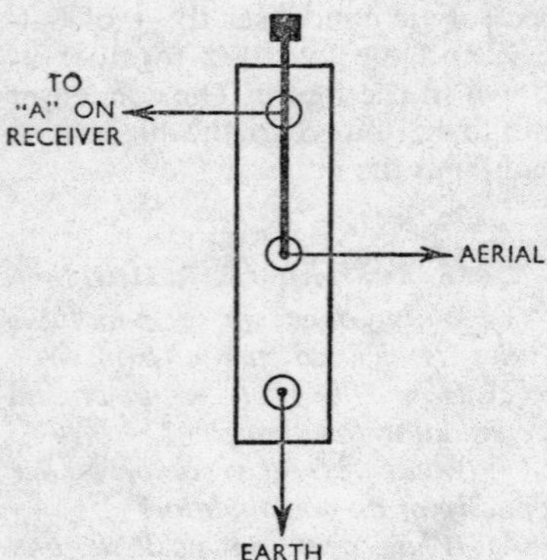

Fig. 76. *Normal arrangement of connections for aerial switch.*

ceiver is practically dead, no signals or very weak signals coming through. With a battery set, the first thing to do is to see that all connections to the batteries are in order and the plugs well pushed into the sockets. Accumulator connections should be clean and firm. With a mains set, see that the mains plug is making good contact at the pins. Perhaps the connections inside the plug are broken or loose. In the latter event, reception will be intermittent.

Now see that all the external connections to the receiver are in order. Is the aerial joined properly to the "*A*" socket and the earth to the "*E*" socket? Has the aerial broken at some point, or the earth connection become loose? The aerial switch is a cause of trouble if not watched, and should be cut out of circuit by taking the aerial wire off its terminal and connecting direct to the lead to the set's aerial socket. Normal connections for an aerial switch are shown in Fig. 76.

The external loudspeaker wiring may be defective and possibly short-circuiting the main receiver loudspeaker, so disconnect this also. Such disconnection should be done at the receiver itself, and not at the external loudspeaker.

Having satisfied ourselves that all external connections are satisfactory, we can proceed to the set itself. It is now advisable to take a look at the chassis, both top and bottom, but before doing so, work the control knobs on the panel. Sometimes a receiver is defective only on one band of wave-lengths while working satisfactorily on another. See if this is so with the receiver under examination. The volume control should be rotated to see if this is at fault—in some cases the volume cuts off in one position of the control but comes on again at another position. If this occurs, a new volume control is probably required, unless, of course, the old one can be repaired. When replacing be sure to obtain a control with the same resistance.

Scrutinising Chassis Externals

When satisfied that the controls are working normally, the back of the receiver should be taken off. This is usually done quite easily by taking out the screws holding it to the cabinet. With the back off, take a good look at the whole set above the chassis. See if anything unusual is apparent. For example, are the valves loose? Push them well down into the valve-holders. See that the top cap connections are firm on the valves. Do any wires look loose or broken? If the wire inside the insulating covering is broken, there is often a sharp and unnatural bend, which should be felt by the fingers. If a break has occurred, the ends of the wires can often be felt.

Another thing to look for is charring. This obviously indicates an overload, with consequently excessive heating. The mains transformer should be examined for this. Look for splashes near the electrolytic condensers if these are the wet type in metal containers. These splashes sometimes occur when the condenser has not been working satisfactorily, and are liable to spoil the operation of a component. The condenser itself may need replacing.

If the deposit of dust is very thick, a vacuum-cleaner should be put on the job. The dust should be blown off the components, and especially the vanes of the variable condensers. The latter may be further cleaned as described in the section dealing with condensers earlier in this course. If a vacuum cleaner is not available, the components should be carefully brushed with a small paint-brush.

Testing for Over-Heating

If the fault has not yet come to light, the set can be switched on. With the set connected, note carefully if any noises are produced, especially any crackling suggestive of burning. The mains transformer can be felt with the fingers to test if it is heating up too much, but in doing this keep well away from the connections, for some of these are at a high voltage; or, best of all, switch off before feeling. If there are any signs of burning, switch off the set immediately, so as to avoid doing any damage to the receiver. Further tests will then be needed as described later in the lesson. The valves should also be felt. These heat up, of course, if mains valves, and if after a few minutes there is no sign of heat in one valve, this may be suspected of being faulty. With A.C./D.C. sets we have seen already that the heaters are in series, so if one heater breaks down and becomes open-circuited, all the heaters are out of circuit for heater current and will, therefore, remain cold.

If no trace of the fault has yet been found, the chassis can be taken out of the cabinet. Before doing so, take a careful look at the connections. Many receivers have the loudspeaker connected to the chassis by a plug and socket which can only be inserted in one way. But in other receivers it is necessary to make certain disconnections before the set can be withdrawn. In this case, make a careful note of the connections, either on the wires themselves or on a piece of notepaper. The various wires can easily be distinguished by their differently coloured insulating sleeving. Where more than one plug and socket are to be disconnected, make a note of the proper positions for each plug.

Some receivers have a sliding bottom under the chassis. In this case it is necessary to take off only the bottom to examine the underside of the chassis. But if the bottom is fixed, the chassis will have to be taken out after all fixing screws are withdrawn. Often it will be required to take off all control knobs first. If this is done, be careful when unscrewing so as not to damage the end-slot of the grub-screw. The cabinet is easily scratched, too, and this needs to be watched.

Below the Chassis

When the under-side of the chassis can be examined, the things to look for are loose connections, broken wires, short-circuited components and charred or discoloured components. Do not pull things about unnecessarily, but if a wire looks loose or partly broken it may be given a gentle tug to see if it parts completely. If a resistance has been badly overloaded it usually provides evidence of this by an alteration in colour and irregularities in the wax covering. Any component seen to be spoilt should, of course, be replaced. Renew all defective wiring.

If after this examination no trace of the defect has been found, the receiver should be tested with instruments as outlined below.

Method

Before getting to grips with measuring gear, let us first see exactly

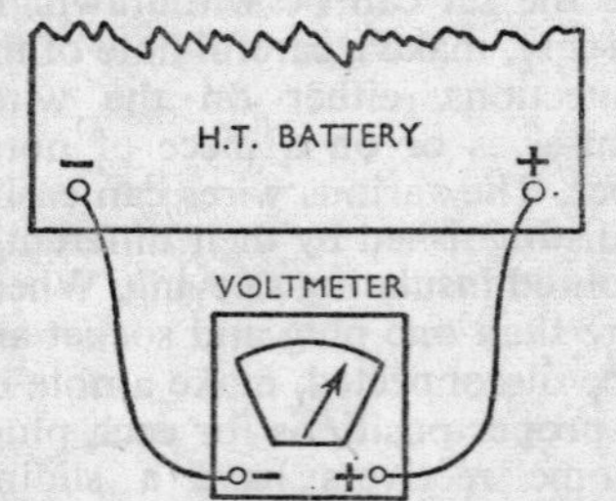

Fig. 77. *Method of testing voltage.*

the general process we are going to employ.

To be successful in your radio servicing you must adopt the method of a doctor. Just as he has to diagnose your illness, so must you diagnose the set's defects. In order to do so quickly, you should rule out all those things that are likely to be working properly, and try to acquire the habit of using logical reasoning to go to the root of the trouble. A lot of time can be wasted on tampering with things that are in perfect order.

The only testing equipment the home mechanic need have is a combined milliammeter, voltmeter and ohmmeter. One such instrument is the Avominor, but there are others on the market. This instrument enables you to check current, voltage and resistance, and to carry out all the testing described in this lesson.

Current Checking

In order to measure voltage, the negative lead from the meter is joined to the negative part of the circuit or battery and the positive lead connected to the positive part of the circuit or battery (Fig. 77).

Before making any attempt to use the meter, first examine it thoroughly to find out which are the positive and negative leads, and also which sockets or terminals are used for current tests, voltage tests and resistance tests. After becoming thoroughly acquainted with the connections, get a battery of some sort—it does not matter which type is used—and test it for voltage. But before you do so, just a word of warning. It is important, indeed it is absolutely essential, that, when measuring voltage, the meter voltage-leads or sockets be used. If you go wrong and connect the milliammeter across a source of voltage instead of the voltmeter, you will probably burn out the meter altogether and run yourself into a big bill for repairs. So whenever using the meter, pay great attention to what you are doing.

Range of the Meter

Another very important point to watch is the range of the meter to be used. For example, suppose we have a 100-volt battery. It will be useless using the meter on the 10-volt scale. The range to be used must be the one that goes *higher* than the highest reading we are likely to obtain. If we have a range of 0–120 volts, we should use this to measure a 100-volt battery. So with our 100-volt battery we proceed. Join the – terminal of the voltmeter to the – terminal on the battery. Then contact the + terminal of the voltmeter set to the 120-volt or so range to the 40-volt socket on the battery. Note the reading, then contact the + voltmeter lead with other + sockets on the battery, leaving the — lead at the — battery socket. In this way you will familiarise yourself with the general working of the voltmeter. Try out

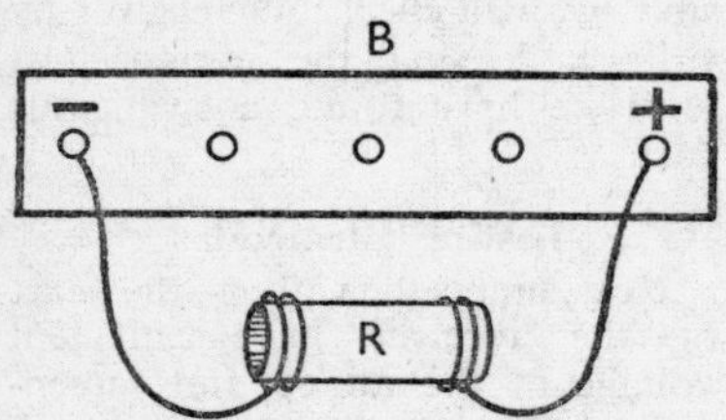

Fig. 78. *Circuit of resistance across battery for checking current flow.*

the different ranges on the various voltages available. You will note that to test voltage you connect the voltmeter across the circuit required to be checked, without disconnecting anything.

Use of Prods

For voltage testing it is advisable to use testing-prods. These can be bought for a few shillings or made for a few pence as follows. Obtain two 4-in. or 6-in. lengths of brass rod, about $\frac{3}{16}$ in. in diameter. File one end of each rod down to a blunt point. Solder a lead to the unpointed end of each rod to a lead of flexible wire about 2 ft. long, to the other end of which is connected the plug for inserting in the sockets at the meter. Now cover the rod with insulating tape, leaving the pointed end bare. When voltage testing is to be done, insert the plugs into the proper sockets at the meter and contact the bare pointed ends of the testing-prods with the parts of the circuit under examination.

In order to become acquainted with the general method of taking current readings, connect a resistance across a battery. The size of the battery does not matter, so long as you have a suitable resistance to give the required current flow. Suppose, for example, we have a $4\frac{1}{2}$-volt torch battery. Join a resistance of, say, 2,000 ohms across it, as shown in Fig. 78. Here we have a circuit consisting of battery and resistance. To check the current flow we first find out the approximate current flow through the circuit. We know this to be $\frac{\text{volts}}{\text{resistance}} = \frac{4{\cdot}5}{2{,}000}$ ampères or $\frac{4{\cdot}5}{2}$ milliampères = 2·25 milliampères. So connect the milliammeter to its 5-mA range or higher. Then disconnect the resistance at one end—say, the negative end—and connect as shown in

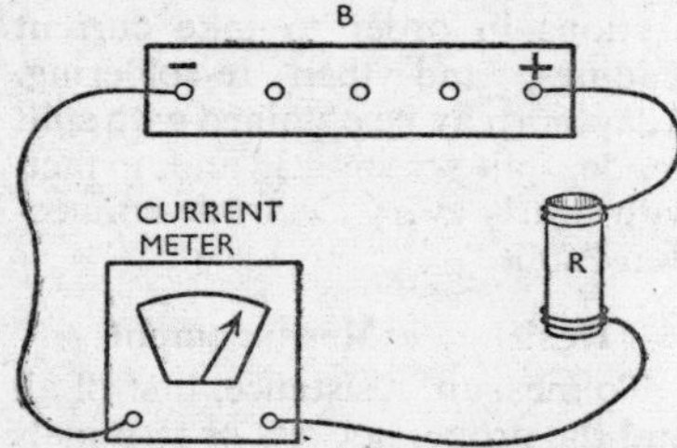

Fig. 79. *Inserting meter in circuit.*

Fig. 79 with the — meter to — of battery. A reading will be obtained at about 2·25 milliampères. Try one or two other values of resistance so as to bring the current reading on to other ranges. For example, with resistance of 500 ohms and the same 4·5-volt battery, we have a current of $\frac{4{\cdot}5}{{\cdot}5} = 9$ milliampères; with 250 ohms we obtain $\frac{4{\cdot}5}{{\cdot}25} = 18$ milliampères.

An extremely useful gadget for the home mechanic is the adapter. This consists of a suitable piece of insulating material on which are mounted pins similar to those of a valve for inserting into a valve-holder in place of the valve. The valve is then plugged into the adapter.

Adapters

At the side of the adapter is a pair, or maybe several pairs, of terminals with a short-circuiting strip. These terminals are connected inside the adapter so that the leads to the various electrodes can be broken and a milliammeter inserted. When this strip is connected across both terminals, the electrode lead is completed, but when the strip is disconnected from one terminal, the milliammeter may be connected to the terminals and a current reading taken.

The use of an adapter overcomes the need for unsoldering the connections in order to take current readings, and then re-soldering. Adapters may be obtained with split anode, split screen-grid and, in fact, with nearly every electrode connection "split."

Resistance Measurement

To measure resistance, first of all find the proper sockets or terminals at the meter. Short-circuit them by connecting the leads from the "resistance" or "ohms" sockets and adjust the "zero setter" until the point on the scale marked "zero ohms" is reached by the indicator needle. Now join a resistance of some value—say 5,000 ohms—and check the reading. Once the zero setter has been adjusted it should not need altering for other resistance tests taken soon after. So check resistances of other values, and thus see exactly what the procedure is.

By now we know just how to test voltage, current and resistance, so we can go ahead with checking the working of our receiver. The first thing to know is where to test. Shall it be a current or voltage test? For current tests we have seen that it is necessary to break the circuit to insert the meter. This takes time and is sometimes a bother, so, if possible, we will check our receiver by voltage, leaving the current test until we have found a suspicious part.

Testing Electrodes

Now, unless the valves—the heart of the receiver—have sufficient voltage at the anode and screen-grid electrodes, they cannot work well. Usually, it is fairly easy to get at the anode and screen-grid sockets at the valve-holders, so we first check the voltages there. Before doing so, we should have a very clear idea about the voltage to expect. With mains valves, the voltage normally applied to anodes is about 200; screen-grid voltage may be about the same as the anode for both R.F. pentodes and the output pentode. Some R.F. pentodes require only about 75 volts at the screen, so this should be found out before a start is made. Even so, if 75 volts is at the screen-grid, signals should be received and the valve should work. The main object in making this test is to find if voltage is reaching the electrodes. Quite likely there is a break in the circuit which will prevent the voltage reaching them, and this is immediately shown up by no voltage reading at one or more electrodes.

Making a Start on the Receiver

Before attempting to service a receiver, it is essential to have some knowledge of how the set is wired. If a diagram is available, so much the better. If it is not, have a good look at the set before you begin

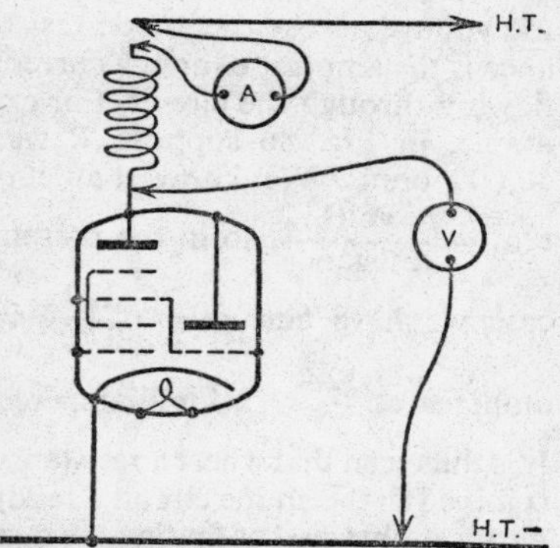

Fig. 80. *Testing anode voltage and anode current for circuit breaks.*

your checking. In particular, note the type of valve-holders. In these days of about a thousand different types of valves it is impossible for the home mechanic to remember where, say, the anode socket is located on any particular valve-holder. Yet it is necessary to know where each electrode is positioned on the valve-holder in order to carry out the tests to be described later. Many manufacturers issue charts giving the desired information, and one of these should be consulted. At any rate, before you begin your servicing, know your valve-holders.

Suppose that at the anode of the frequency changer valve (Fig. 80) there is no voltage reading, but at all the other electrodes there is the normal voltage. From this we suppose that a break in the circuit has occurred between the frequency changer anode and the H.T. supply. In considering the H.T. supply and the anode- and screen-grids, we can regard this circuit as a large tank supplying water to a number of smaller tanks through pipes. If one pipe becomes broken no flow of water takes place to the smaller tank it feeds. The valves can be regarded as the smaller tanks, the main H.T. supply as the larger tank, and the connections between H.T.+ and anode as the feed-pipe.

Having found out that there is a break in the anode circuit, we must now locate exactly where it has taken place. To do this, we connect the voltmeter negative to chassis and then go along the circuit with the positive prod. In Fig. 81 are seen the positions with which the positive lead should be contacted: first at the main H.T.+ line, then at the end of the resistance joined to H.T.+, and so on, as indicated by the numbers 1 to 6. Starting at 1 there will be the full H.T. voltage, but somewhere in this circuit the voltage will not reach, and we shall get no reading on our voltmeter. For example, suppose that at 4 we had an H.T. voltage reading but at 5 we did not. This would tell us that there was a break in the output circuit, and this would have to be examined. If the voltage is satisfactory at 2 but not at 3, we shall know a break has occurred in the resistance, so this should be replaced by a good one.

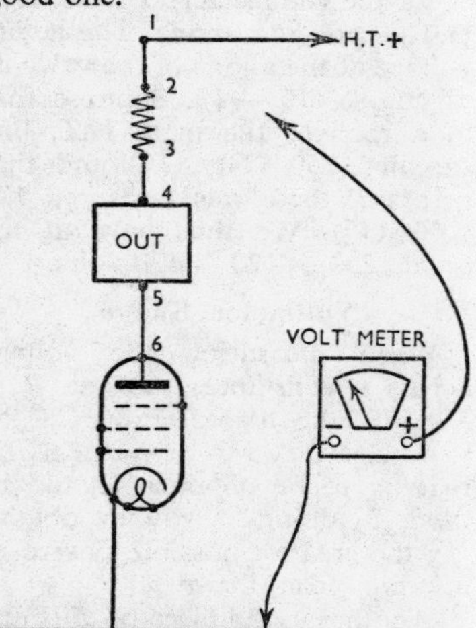

Fig. 81. *Voltage testing method.*

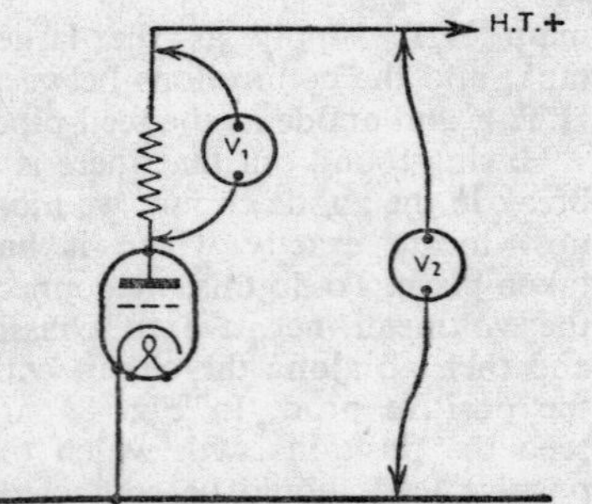

Fig. 82. *A method of using a voltmeter to test anode voltage.*

It should be appreciated right from the start that voltage testing is only approximate unless an expensive voltmeter is used. For general work a meter of the type mentioned above will be suitable, but when testing voltage across a resistance, too much reliance should not be placed on the actual reading obtained. In such circumstances the meter should be looked upon as a voltage indicator. A more accurate method of using the voltmeter is to take a reading of total H.T. voltage (shown V_1 in Fig. 82), and then to check the voltage across R between H.T.+ and the anode. The actual voltage at the anode of the valve is, of course, $V_1 - V_2$. Suppose that in a receiver the main H.T. line supplied 250 volts (V_1) and that across R there was measured 120 volts (V_2). We thus have at the anode 250 − 120 = 130 volts.

Voltmeter Range

When measuring the voltage across a resistance, such as R in Fig. 78, the highest range in the voltmeter that will permit a useful reading to be obtained should be used. By doing so, you are obtaining the greatest possible degree of accuracy from the meter.

Another useful piece of information to be obtained from measuring the voltage across the anode resistance is the amount of anode current flowing through the circuit. For example, in Fig. 86 suppose R was 50,000 ohms. We know that current $= \frac{\text{volts}}{\text{resistance}}$, so in the present case we have current $= \frac{120}{50{,}000}$ in ampères, or $\frac{120}{50} = 2{\cdot}4$ milliampères. It is thus seen that where a resistance is joined in the anode circuit a ready means is obtained of finding the current flow without breaking the circuit and inserting a milliammeter. This applies to all valves. The reading obtained in this way is approximate only, because of the inaccuracies in resistance value and meter reading, but it is often all that is required to find out how a valve is working.

Grid Bias Resistance Breakdown

Sometimes there is a complete break in the grid-bias resistance connections or the resistance itself. This resistance is in the cathode leg of the valve. In order to check its working, we will assume that the voltmeter is joined from valve-cathode terminal to chassis, as shown in Fig. 83. Now, although there is a break in the cathode connections, there will be a voltage indicated at the meter, and we might be rather puzzled, because the voltage so shown is usually much higher than required by the valve as bias. It will be seen from Fig. 83, however, that the cathode circuit is actually completed by the meter itself, and the voltage indicated is that due to the current passing through the valve only when the voltmeter completes the circuit. The final check then is to connect a milliammeter in the anode or cathode circuit: no current flow indicates a break in the circuit.

During our voltage testing we may find that the voltage at a screen-grid condenser is very low, or even zero. There are two reasons for this. One is a break in the supply from the main H.T.+. This can be checked by taking a screen-grid current reading. Another reason is a short-circuit in the screen-grid condenser. This has the effect of allowing the current from H.T.+ to pass directly to chassis, leaving the screen-grid at chassis or zero voltage. Such a fault usually causes the screen-grid feed resistance, if one is used, to heat up excessively and become charred. When the set is in operation, this resistance will generally sizzle, revealing this fault.

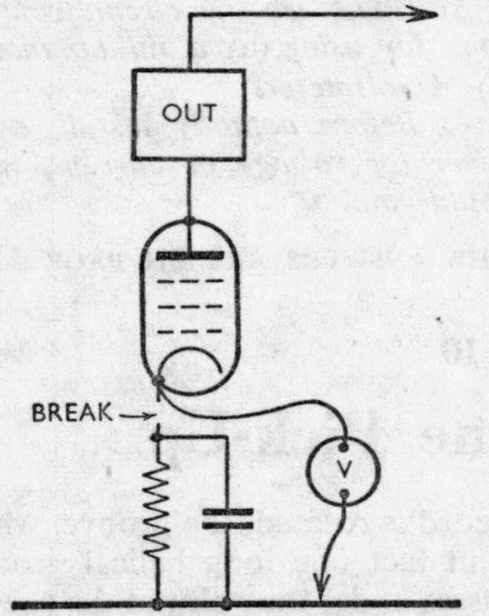

Fig. 83. *The voltmeter itself completes the cathode circuit.*

Screen-Grid Condenser Faults

Sometimes the screen-grid condenser becomes broken, or open-circuited. This often causes the valve to go into self-oscillation, with resulting squeals.

This is usually an indication that the supply voltage is low, and that some defect has occurred in the mains supply equipment. Logically, it is better to test the supply voltage at the beginning, but until we are completely familiar with the receiver it will be found easier to check anode and screen voltages than to trace out and check supply voltage and current.

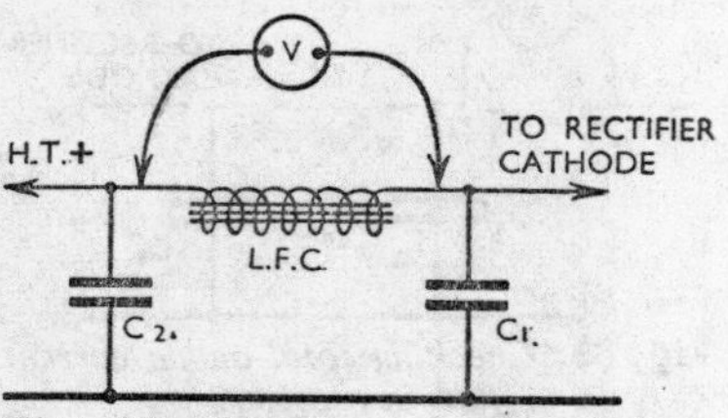

Fig. 84. *Checking drop of voltage across smoothing choke.*

In order to test the output of the mains supply equipment, we can insert a milliammeter in the main H.T. — lead and find out how much current is flowing. An easier method, however, is to test the voltage drop across the smoothing choke as shown in Fig. 84. For this test to be effective we must know the resistance of the choke, but this can be found out, before switching on the set, by means of the ohmmeter which forms part of our combined meter.

The method of finding total current flow is as follows. Suppose the resistance of the coil *L* (which is likely to be the loudspeaker field winding) is 1,200 ohms and the voltage indicated in the test across it is 62·4. We know that current = $\frac{\text{volts}}{\text{resistance}}$, so current = $\frac{62{\cdot}4}{1{,}200}$ ampères = $\frac{62{\cdot}4}{1{\cdot}2}$ = 52 milliampères.

This gives us the current flow. If desired, the total current flow can be found by inserting the milliammeter (range 0–100 mA) in the main H.T.+ line as indicated in Fig. 85.

If the voltage drop across the

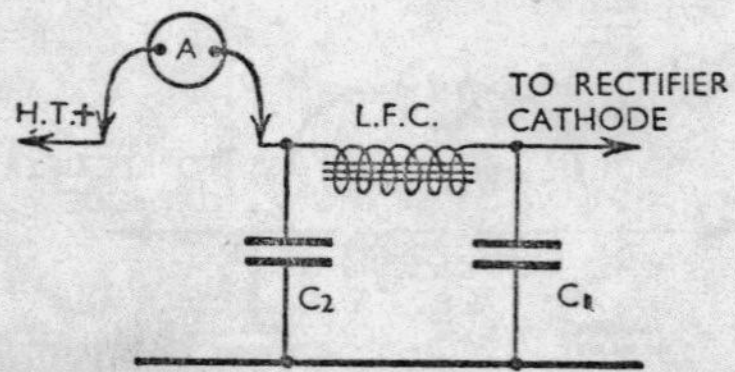

Fig. 85. *Checking total anode current flow in receiver.*

smoothing choke *L* is higher than normally, this indicates excessive current flow. There may be two reasons for this. Either there is something at the receiver which is passing too much current, or the smoothing condenser C_2 is doing so. The latter fault can be checked by inserting the milliammeter in the connections between the condenser and the choke, but leaving the H.T.+ line intact.

At the receiver we should look for a short-circuited grid-bias resistance. The most likely place to find the short-circuit is across the grid-bias resistance for the output valve, probably a shorted by-pass condenser. As this passes a much larger current than the other valves in the receiver, a short-circuit across the bias resistance will make a notable difference in total current flow and, so will greatly increase the voltage drop across the smoothing choke.

Self Testing Questions

(1) *When servicing a receiver, what would you examine first?*

(2) *If a valve heater in an A.C./D.C. set became broken, what indication would be given?*

(3) *What are the circuit connections for using* (a) *a milliammeter?* (b) *A voltmeter?*

(4) *Before actually testing a receiver for voltage or current, what would you do?*

THE ANSWERS ARE ON PAGE 312.

LESSON 10

The Gramophone Pick-Up

A GRAMOPHONE pick-up is a device which, when suitably placed over a revolving gramophone record, is capable of producing a voltage representative of the sound that originally formed the record. What actually happens is that as the record is rotated by the gramophone turn-table, the needle fitted to the pick-up is vibrated by the form of the groove in the record. It is this vibrating needle that operates a mechanism in the pick-up to produce the voltage.

Why does the needle vibrate? Everyone can see from an examination of a record that the surface over which the needle moves consists of a series of grooves. As the record is rotated, the groove, which is in fact one long helical groove, passes under the point of the needle. Now, inside the groove there is a fine wave-like track that moves from side to side of each groove. It is this wavy track that represents the sound of the record, for the shape and size of the wave track controls the sound picked up either by the pick-up or by an ordinary gramophone sound box.

For high notes, the wavy track does not take up much space inside the groove, but for low notes the wavy track takes up all the available width of groove. In fact, with very low notes special precautions have to be taken to ensure that the cutter that originally cut the groove in the master record does not jump over into the next groove and so spoil the record. The needle of our gramophone pick-up moves along the wave track known as the sound track, and as the record is rotated the needle is vibrated backwards and forwards across the groove. This mechanical vibration of the needle is changed into electrical voltage.

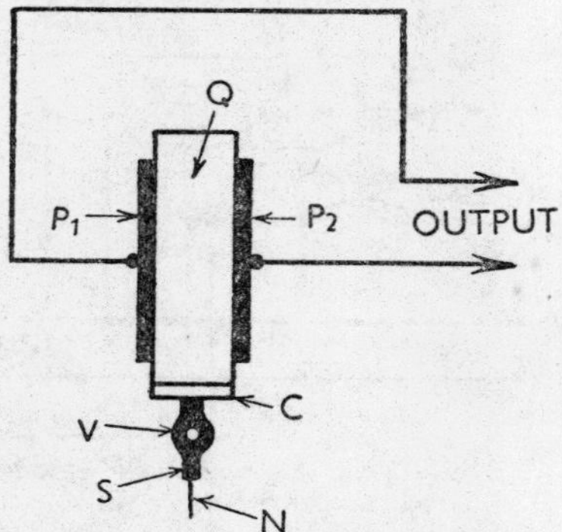

Fig. 87. *Showing principle of piezo-electric gramophone pick-up.*

Electromagnetic Pick-Up

One commonly used type of pick-up makes use of the principle of what we already know as electromagnetism. We know that if a varying magnetic field cuts a conductor, a voltage is set up in that conductor in accordance with the variations in the magnetic field.

The manner in which this principle is used in modern types of gramophone pick-up is illustrated in Fig. 86. The magnetic field that has to be varied is produced by a permanent magnet *M* which has its poles at *P*. Fitted in the poles of the magnet is a coil of wire *C*, and mounted in the centre of this coil is a soft iron armature *A* fixed to the shaft *S* holding the pick-up needle *N*. With the armature *A* in the central position, that is to say, before vibration begins, the magnetic field between the poles passes across the armature *A*.

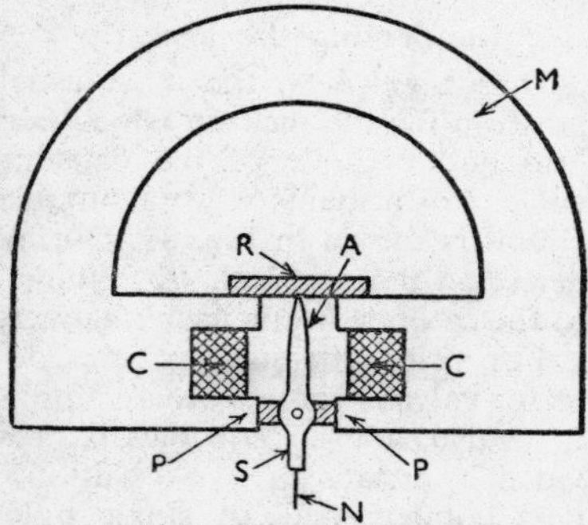

Fig. 86. *Construction of electro-magnetic gramophone pick-up.*

When the needle *N* is placed in the sound track of the gramophone record, it is vibrated in the manner described above and movement takes place along the variations of the track. As the armature moves to and fro in response to the vibrations of the needle, the normally steady magnetic field passing between the poles *P* is distorted. In other words, the magnetic field passing through the wire in the winding *C* is varied, and hence we have set up in this winding a voltage. Such a voltage corresponds to the variations in the magnetic field, and as these in turn are produced by the needle vibrations from the sound track, we can see that the voltage in the pick-up coil *C* is a representa-

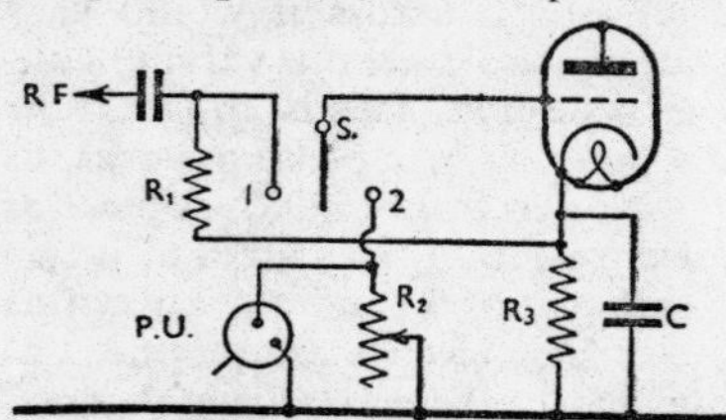

Fig. 88. *Grid detector connections for pick-up for use with a mains valve.*

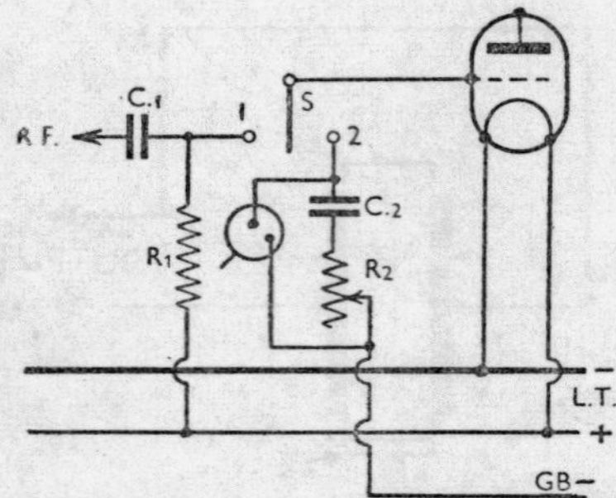

Fig. 89. *Circuit diagram giving pick-up connections for battery valve.*

tion of the sound required to be reproduced from the record. As this voltage is low frequency we apply it directly to an L.F. amplifier in the receiver, from where it is passed to the output stage and loudspeaker.

The term piezo-electric is a rather impressive name for a very interesting condition of a certain type of quartz crystal. It is found that if certain types of quartz crystal have a pair of metal plates suitably placed on them, and the mechanical pressure applied to the crystal is varied, a voltage is produced across the plates in proportion to the mechanical pressure applied (up to certain limits, of course). This is known as the piezo-electric effect.

Piezo-Electric Pick-Up

Now suppose we arranged for our gramophone pick-up needle to alter the pressure on the quartz crystal. The voltage across it would vary and we should get our varying voltage as desired. This is, in fact, how the piezo-electric pick-up works, as can be seen from Fig. 87. A piece of quartz crystal Q has fitted to it two metal plates P_1 and P_2, known as the crystal electrodes. Mounted at one end of the crystal is a clamp C holding the shaft S into which the needle is fitted, a pivot being at V.

When the needle is placed in the sound track of the gramophone record and the record rotated, the needle moves in response to the sound track along the grooves cut on the record. The movement of the needle results in a variable pressure being put upon the crystal, and this in turn causes a correspondingly variable voltage to be produced at the electrodes P_1 and P_2 of the crystal. This voltage is passed by the leads to the L.F. amplifier and so to the loudspeaker. It will be noticed that the arrangement shown in Fig. 87 is similar to a condenser. The electrodes P_1 and P_2 are the condenser plates, while the crystal is the dielectric. We shall have to remember this when arranging a tone control.

Connecting the Pick-Up

In straight sets, the most usual position for the pick-up is between grid and cathode of the detector valve. For a mains valve a suitable circuit is shown in Fig. 88. During detection the grid leak R_1 is joined to the cathode in the usual manner.

For using the pick-up, the detector valve is changed to an amplifier valve, and so grid bias is provided by means of R_3 with its bypass condenser C. A single pole, two-way switch is connected as shown, so as to join the pick-up to the grid and chassis, the latter connection bringing into circuit the bias arrangement. A volume control consisting of a potentiometer R_2 is joined across the pick-up, and this acts as tone control at the same time.

When battery valves are employed, the circuit is given in Fig. 89. Condenser C_1 and R_1 are the usual grid condenser and leak. Grid bias is obtained by the connection to $GB-$ on the battery or common bias resistance. A tone and volume control is shown at C_2 (about ·001 mfd.) and R_2.

The value of resistance used for volume control is dependent upon the type of pick-up. With electromagnetic pick-ups the value varies from 50,000 ohms to 250,000 ohms. The reader should find out from the manufacturers what value to use.

Self Testing Questions

(1) *What is the actual source of operation of gramophone pick-ups?*

(2) *How is the voltage produced in the electromagnetic pick-up?*

(3) *How is the piezo-electric pick-up operated?*

THE ANSWERS ARE ON PAGE 312.

LESSON 11

Car Radio

THE normal car radio is a four-valve superheterodyne receiver, with a radio-frequency amplifier and oscillator (mixer) valve, an intermediate frequency amplifier, a double-diode-triode as detector, A.V.C., and first stage low-frequency amplifier, and a pentode as output valve. There is also a rectifier valve.

The differences between this type of set and the normal domestic receiver lie in these directions:—

(1) The source of power.
(2) The disposition of the components.
(3) The screening of the leads.
(4) The aerial.

Source of Power

The power for a car radio receiver must come from the only electrical generator on the automobile—the dynamo. This generates 6- or 12-volt current, which is stored in the car battery. Therefore a 6- or 12-volt supply has to suffice for the high-tension and low-tension needs of the radio set.

Dealing with the low-tension side, for the filaments, valves operating from 6·3 volts—now the normal standard filament voltage—are generally used: if the car has a 12-volt battery a suitable resistance is included to absorb the excess voltage. The valves are wired in parallel, as in the ordinary mains set. In certain cases 13-volt valves (for use with 12-volt batteries) are employed.

The high-tension supplies present a different problem. There are two general ways of providing the necessary 250- to 300-volt H.T. current. One—not very widely used—is to have a small motor generator. The motor works from the 6- or 12-volt supply, and drives a dynamo which gives, say, 300 volts 100 milliamps. On the output side are smoothing chokes and condensers, as on a mains set, to eliminate ripple and reduce hum.

The more common method is to instal vibrator-type rectifiers.

Any transformer works by virtue of the *varying* electric current in its primary winding, as we have seen in the lesson on Electricity (pages 200–209). What we have to do, then, is to interrupt the D.C. supply from the battery, and apply the interrupted current to the primary of a transformer, which will step it up to the required voltage.

An ordinary electric bell is an example of an "interruptor" in an electric circuit; and the vibrator—made up in a form to "plug in" very similar to that of a valve—is really a very robust electric bell movement, made to work silently.

The output is applied to a transformer, and since the shape of the voltage wave produced by a vibrator is not as uniform as that from the mains, special care is taken with the smoothing of the output from the high-tension side; and unless the chokes and condensers on this part of the circuit are in good order, serious hum in the loudspeaker will be the result.

Components

The set itself is usually disposed on or near the car dashboard.

The loudspeaker is sometimes in the set itself, and sometimes built into the roof of the car. The power supply is often taken from the car's main fuseboard on the ignition circuit, so that when the automobile is unattended, and the ignition circuit switched off, the radio cannot be inadvertently left on, resulting in draining the battery. The demand is about 8 to 10 amps. for 6-volt circuits, and half that figure for 12-volt batteries. The dynamo output, if adjustable, should be slightly increased to deal with the extra load on the battery.

Screening

As the ignition circuit of a motorcar sets up electrical disturbance, there will be considerable danger of loud, unwanted interference noises, unless certain precautions are taken. The leads to the sparking-plugs should have "suppressors" fitted. These take the form of non-inductively-wound resistances, made up in convenient form to clip on the top of the plugs themselves.

They prevent the spark impulses from reflecting back on to the car wiring generally, and thus penetrating the radio receiver.

The dynamo, with its commutator ripple, also needs attention to prevent hum and electrical disturbances from reaching the radio set. This is done by fitting specially designed condensers between the output leads and earth—earth in this case being the chassis of the car. Similarly, the lead from the aerial, as we shall see later, needs to be screened, and so do the leads from the loudspeaker if it is separate from the radio set itself.

Aerial

The radio aerial must be situated so that it is as clear of the body as possible. The usual methods are to have an extensible and flexible rod mounted either on the rear bumper and sticking up above the total height of the car or to have an aerial of copper or bronze rod mounted on the roof of the vehicle. While the roof fitting is preferable from the radio point of view, in that there is the maximum freedom from directional effects, it has the disadvantage of needing holes drilled through the metal work of the roof in at least one, and generally two places, while provision must also be made for bringing in the screened aerial lead.

The rod-type aerial, if fixed to the bumper, can be applied easily without disfiguring or damaging the bodywork, and if it is sufficiently high and disposed as far away from the body as possible, it can be quite satisfactory.

A third method which is occasionally used is to employ a net, or even a single wire, under the running-board or under the car body.

In all cases the aerial lead must be of cable in which there is an outer "stocking" or fine mesh screen of interlaced copper wires, and underneath this a substantial insulation. The screen or outer casing must be carefully connected to earth at each end.

Self Testing Questions

(1) *Name the source of power for a car radio.*

(2) *What is a common cause of serious hum in the loudspeaker?*

(3) *What steps must be taken to eliminate interference noises?*

THE ANSWERS ARE ON PAGE 312.

Answers to Self Testing Questions

LESSON 1

(1) To change the sound which reaches it into voltages that represent the sound.

(2) A carrier wave generated at the transmitter and the low-frequency wave from the microphone representing the L.F. signal.

(3) Ether.

(4) $\text{Wave-length} = \dfrac{300{,}000{,}000}{\text{frequency}}$

$\text{Frequency} = \dfrac{300{,}000{,}000}{\text{wave-length}}.$

LESSON 2

(1) Because the wireless waves passing through it set up a voltage corresponding to the signal.

(2) Lack of height, poor insulators, break in aerial or earth-wire, dry earth, bad joints in aerial or earth, earth-wire too long.

(3) An aerial in two halves, joined at the centre to the receiver. For short-wave reception.

LESSON 3

(1) A coil that may be tuned over a given frequency band either by a movable iron core (permeability tuning) or by a variable condenser connected to it.

(2) A coil that prevents currents of undesired frequency from passing while allowing currents of other and lower frequencies to pass.

(3) For the same capacity, they are much smaller; usually have + and — leads.

(4) Body violet, green end, yellow band or dot.

(5) Mains energised type, with field winding. Permanent magnet type.

LESSON 4

(1) Heat applied to the cathode increases the speed of movement of the electrons until some shoot off. These are attracted by the anode- and screen-grid.

(2) To shield the control grid from harmful valve capacities, so that the valve will operate better as an R.F. amplifier.

(3) Because it enables a valve to provide a larger signal output than an ordinary screen-grid valve.

(4) Check its anode current at a given anode voltage and grid-bias and compare with correct value at these operating voltages.

LESSON 5

(1) A stage in which the output voltage is greater than the input voltage.

(2) No. The circuit design, especially that of the output circuit,

determines the amplification in combination with the valve.

(3) A valve *and circuit* in which the low-frequency signal is separated from the carrier wave.

(4) The frequencies of audible sound waves, *i.e.* frequencies within the range 20 to about 16,000 cycles per second.

(5) To change the low-frequency voltage provided by the receiver into a large current for operating the loudspeaker efficiently.

(6) Triodes are less sensitive than pentodes, but pentodes cause more distortion than triodes. For the size and cost of valve, pentodes provide a greater power output. Pentodes are more suitable for small receivers.

LESSON 6

(1) A receiver in which the signal-carrier frequency is changed.

(2) It is mixed in a valve with oscillations generated in the receiver itself, and the difference between the oscillator and signal-carrier frequency is selected by a tuned circuit in the output of the mixer valve.

(3) The use of an oscillator and mixer valve.

(4) Because they can handle without distortion the high signal voltage provided.

(5) An arrangement for levelling out the alterations in received signal strength due to fading.

LESSON 7

(1) Valve-heater current at low A.C. or D.C. voltage, high-tension direct voltage at 200 volts or more, grid-bias direct voltage.

(2) A.C. valves are usually wired in parallel, A.C./D.C. valves are in series.

(3) To change the A.C. into D.C. for the H.T. voltage and grid-bias.

(4) At the rectifier valve cathode.

LESSON 8

(1) Chemical action between sulphuric acid and lead plates.

(2) Positive of accumulator to positive of charging voltage, negative to negative.

(3) The normal discharge current in ampères multiplied by the number of hours it will provide that current.

(4) Positive is carbon, negative is the zinc container.

(5) 1·5 volts. 2 volts.

LESSON 9

(1) All external connections, such as aerial, earth, batteries, external loudspeaker.

(2) All valves remain cold when set is switched on, because the entire heating circuit is broken.

(3) A milliammeter is connected in series with the circuit; a voltmeter across the circuit.

(4) Trace out the circuit wiring carefully, and note the connections of the valve-holders.

LESSON 10

(1) The vibrations in the pick-up needle produced by the sound track in the gramophone record.

(2) By the variations in magnetic field caused by the armature fixed to the vibrating needle.

(3) By mechanical pressure on the side of the crystal, this being produced by vibrating needle.

LESSON 11

(1) The dynamo.

(2) Faulty chokes and condensers—especially the latter.

(3) Sparking plugs—fit suppressors; dynamo—fit condensers between output leads and earth; screen leads from aerial and from loudspeaker.

METALWORK AND SIMPLE ENGINEERING

By J. St. Denys Reed

LESSON I

The Metal-Worker's Bench and Equipment

STRENGTH, firmness and rigidity are the chief requirements for the metal-worker's bench. It must be of a suitable height for comfortable work, and be adapted to the stature of the man who is to use it. Many operations are performed standing, so that at least one bench should be proportioned for this kind of job. During the long winter evenings it may be convenient to have a small and portable bench somewhere in the house, and this can quite well be a *standing bench* of the sort now to be described. In the actual workshop—such as every metal-worker will desire—the bench may be a longer one, of a lower height, similar to a wood-worker's bench but stronger.

Making the Bench

In the following description purely wood-working methods are omitted unless they are special to the job in hand. The top of the bench should be at breast height, which means somewhere about 42 in. from floor level: this can be settled by individual needs. The top should be 2 ft. 9 in. wide, and 2 ft. 3 in. from back to front. Turned endwise, this bench will pass easily through common doors, and the proportions will permit a comfortable stance with ample elbow room. A 3-in. guard along the back, extending 5 or 6 in. along the right and left sides also, will stop tools falling off; the rest of the sides must be left clear to allow for long pieces of work to lie across the bench.

The legs are of 3 in. × 3 in. deal, made up in two pairs. Each pair is joined at the top, flush with the under-side of the bench, by a rail of 6-in. × $\frac{3}{4}$-in. board tenoned into each leg; there is a similar rail at the bottom, but its lower edge comes about $1\frac{1}{2}$ in. above the floor level. The two pairs are joined at the back by two similar rails; but at the front by one only, at the top.* This leaves the front of the frame open and gives leg-room. Moreover, the front rail should be of 1-in. × 4-in. stuff. The front and back rails are screwed on to the legs, not tenoned into them. The bench top projects over the frame $1\frac{1}{2}$ in. at the back, so as to allow the bench to stand close against a wall and clear the skirting-board almost invariably found in living-rooms. It can project 3 or 4 in. at each end, to give room for cramps to grip jobs being done. At the front a projection of 4 in. should be allowed. The reader can work out the size of the frame from these requirements.

Since the front board of the bench top is to project a good deal,

* For special arrangement of side rails to take treadle wheel, see page 315.

this board should be 9 in. wide in order to allow a firm and solid fixing on the frame despite the cantilever effect. If a bench drill is in use at the front, or some other tool is clamped down, there will be a strong thrust against the projection, and the board would be loosened unless properly fixed and supported as described. The remaining boards may be narrower. Make the entire top of sound deal not less than 1¼ in. thick: only the top surface and the edges need be planed. When cut, fitted and assembled, nail on a stout batten at each end of the under-side of the top, to fit easily inside the end rails of the frame. Finally, place the top in position and nail it firmly to the end and front rails.

Strengthening the Legs

There is one refinement that will add considerably to the life and strength of the bench—the provision of three iron tie-rods passing through the legs and nutted inside and outside the frame, one at each side and one at the back. The height should be about midway between top and bottom rails. The rods can be made of ½-in. round rod, screwed at each end for about 4½ in. with Whitworth thread to take a standard nut. The rods must be inserted, with a washer and nut on each end, when assembling each pair of legs, and when connecting the two pairs to form the complete frame.

Owing to the fact that the back-nuts come inside the frame (between the legs), the rods cannot conveniently be put in place after the legs have been put together. (This could be done by making the rods considerably longer, and cutting the thread farther along, so that the rod could be passed through one leg far enough to clear the other end, and permit the back nut to be placed on before bringing the end back through the second leg.)

Instructions for preparing the tie-rods are given in Lesson 7. If the worker should prefer to get his bench ready straight away he could get a blacksmith to make up the three rods from the information given in Fig. 1. This diagram shows the back legs with rails and back tie-rod. The tie-rods for the sides must go through a little higher or lower than that at the back, to clear the latter. When the glue-joints have hardened, carefully screw up the inside nuts first until they are just finger-tight, and then draw up the outside nuts with a spanner. The idea is to hold the frame tightly at its present spacing, as determined by the shoulders of the rails: too much tension either inside or outside will "start" the glue-joints and loosen the frame.

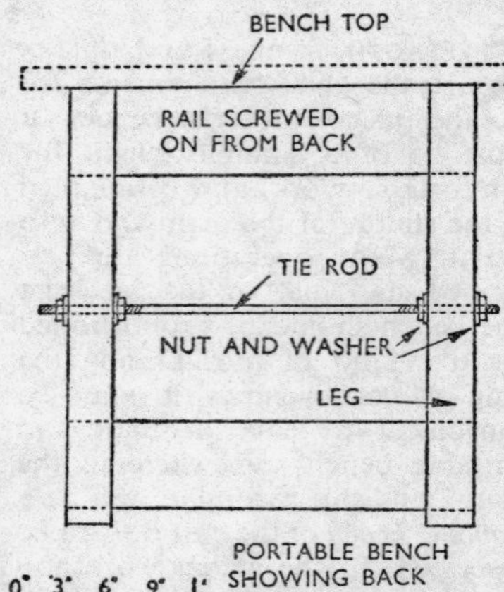

Fig. 1. *Portable bench, showing back, legs and rails, and back tie-rod.*

A polishing head is very useful, since it has a drill-chuck (capacity up to ½ in.) at one end and a taper spindle at the other on which a polishing buff can be fixed; it also has a pair of flanges between which a grinding wheel can be gripped. A fractional h.p. electric motor can be fixed under the bench to drive the head by means of a belt to the pulley, with a switch fixed conveniently to the hand.

Fitting a Treadle Wheel

Another method—and probably a better drive for the beginner—is to fit a light "foot motor" or treadle wheel either on the floor or to the frame of the bench, and bring up the belt through two holes in the bench top. It will be noted that the lower rails of the bench-frame are not close to the floor, but are located 1½ in. up, leaving room for battens to be fastened under, on which the treadle wheel could be mounted complete. If this plan is to be adopted, the lower side rails should be formed of 3-in. × 2-in. stuff instead of 6-in. × ¾-in. board, and the bottom battens bolted up to the rails. The polishing head is to be bolted down to the bench top, in proper alignment. Keep it to the left-hand side as far as possible.

The Vice

There are many good patterns of mechanic's vice on the market; one with jaws about 4 in. long, opening to 4 in., should be chosen for the large bench. It is bolted down through the bench-top, and placed so that the thrust is taken by one of the bench-legs. The vice for a portable bench can be lighter—with, say, 2½-in. jaws, opening to about 2½ in. This also should be bolted down. Portable vices, which are attached by a screw-clamp, may have their uses, but are unsatisfactory in general, since the vice, under pressure of work, tends to swivel round on the screw-clamp and become loose. "Quick-action" vices are more expensive: the movable jaw can be slid along to meet the job that is held, and the screw-grip then applied in the ordinary way. There is a similar quick-release action.

A pipe-vice is very useful for holding rods, besides all sorts of pipes and tubes within its scope. It is made with a flat base to bolt down to the bench, or with a side flange. A suitable size would be one that takes tube from ⅛ in. to 1 in. diameter. The work is held securely for screwing or cutting to length.

An Anvil is Useful

For the workshop a smith's anvil of about 20 lb. weight, mounted on a wooden block, is desirable—especially if the worker expects to do a little forging. Short of this, a bench anvil of about 6 lb. can be procured and fixed to the large bench. A much smaller anvil will do for the portable bench, where it will be needed only for light jobs. An old flat-iron can be turned into a useful anvil by letting it into a hardwood block, upside down, and screwing the block to the bench. Beware of using any part of a vice as an anvil; some bench-vices are provided with a kind of anvil, but even then it is not advisable to use the vice for anything but its proper function—the holding of work for cutting, filing or other operations that do not entail hammering.

The length of the workshop bench should be about 4 ft. 6 in., and the other proportions somewhat like those of the portable bench, but the height of the top ought not to be greater than about 2 ft. 5 in. from floor level. A centre pair of legs should be provided in addition to the end pairs, and the three should be connected by two diagonal braces rising from the lower rail of the outside leg to the top rail of the middle pair—notched over the top of the lower rail and under the lower edge of the middle rail. A low rail should be provided at the front as well as at the back. Further, nail two 6-in. × 1-in. boards to the lower rails of all three pairs of legs, on top of the rails at front and rear, clearing the diagonal braces. No ironwork is necessary with a bench constructed in this manner.

Self Testing Questions

(1) *Why is it necessary to pay special attention to security of fixing in the front board of the work-bench?*

(2) *How and where should tie-rods be fixed to the legs of a portable bench?*

(3) *Why is a fixed vice to be preferred to a portable vice?*

THE ANSWERS ARE ON PAGE 374.

LESSON 2

Properties of the Common Metals

The metals with which we are here concerned are those sometimes known as the "heavy" metals: Aluminium, Copper, Iron, Lead, Tin and Zinc. Besides these there are the "noble" or "precious" metals: Gold, Platinum and Silver. This last class received its former name in the days of the alchemists, and it is worth pointing out that their value was—and is—due to the distinctive property of these metals of not being oxidised by the atmosphere and not being attacked by most acids.

Heat Conductivity of Metals

Metals are crystalline in structure; they are lustrous in appearance. Those we are dealing with are denser than water or the non-metals; they have higher boiling and melting points than non-metals; they are good conductors of heat and of electricity.

Taking the best conductor (silver) as 100, the figures for the others are as follows:

METAL	CONDUCTIVITY VALUE	
	ELECTRICITY	HEAT
Aluminium .	57	35
Copper . .	94	92½
Gold . .	67	70
Iron . .	17	16
Lead . .	7¼	8½
Platinum .	13½	17
Tin . .	11¼	15¼
Zinc . .	25½	26¼

TABLE I

There is an important practical consideration which follows from the heat conductivity. In soldering copper a much greater quantity

PROPERTIES OF THE COMMON METALS

METAL	MELTING POINT, IN DEG. C.	COEFFICIENT OF EXPANSION (PER DEG. C.)	DENSITY, IN LB. PER CU. FT.
Aluminium . .	659	25·5	165
Copper . . .	1083	16·7	556
Gold . . .	1063	13·9	1205
Iron . . .	1530	10–11·9	440–485
Lead . . .	327	29	706
Platinum . .	1755	8·9	1344
Tin . . .	232	21·5	460
Zinc . . .	419	30	440

TABLE II

of heat is required to keep the job hot than is the case with zinc. Note that it is not a higher temperature that is needed, but more heat.

Melting Points

The melting points of the common metals are as shown in the table above, in degrees Centigrade.

The third column of the table above shows the "coefficient of linear expansion," and is a guide to the extent to which metals expand lengthwise under the effect of heat. As a practical application of this fact we may note that, in order to secure a very tight fit between metal parts, the member to be inserted into an opening is sometimes shrunk by refrigeration and then put in place while very cold. On returning to normal temperature it expands and becomes immovably fast. Sometimes one member (a bush, for example) will be refrigerated and the other member gently heated. At the other extreme is the ancient practice of the wheelwright, who, in order to get the iron tyre to pass over a wagon wheel, makes the tyre hot in a ring-shaped fire built on the ground and then hammers it down on to the wooden wheel.

Cheap types of soldering-bit consist of an iron shank screwed into a block of copper: under the influence of heat the bit generally becomes loose on the shank, and it is therefore an unreliable tool. Other patterns have the copper bit held in a Y-shaped iron yoke by rivets passing through; this also becomes loose in time. A better pattern has the bit held by bolts which can be tightened up when necessary.

Besides fusibility (ability to be melted), the other main properties of metals are tenacity, ductility and malleability. Tenacity is power to resist breakage; ductility, ability to be drawn out: malleability, the quality by which metals can be forged by the smith to desired shapes. It is generally known that copper can be drawn out into wires of almost hair-like thinness, owing to its ductility. It is also malleable, and can be wrought into intricate ornamental forms by being hammered cold. It requires "annealing" from time to time, since hammering makes it harder.

An interesting index of malleability is given by the smallest thickness of leaf to which a metal can be hammered in ordinary commercial practice. Thus gold leaf, used for gilding, can be produced as thin as $\frac{8}{1,000,000}$ cm. For other metals the figures are:

Aluminium 20; Copper 34; Platinum 25; Silver 21; all expressed in millionths of a centimetre.

Tensile Strength of Metals

We are not here considering alloys (compounds of two or more metals). The tensile strength is measured by stretching a test-piece. The figures below give the maximum stress in tons per square inch:

METAL	TENSILE STRENGTH
Aluminium . .	40
Copper, annealed .	14
Cast Iron . .	9·7
Wrought Iron .	23·4
Cast Steel . .	28
Bessemer Steel .	52
Lead . . .	1
Tin . . .	2
Zinc . . .	2·5

TABLE III

Points worth noting are the poor figure for cast iron, and the low strength of lead, tin and zinc. The striking improvement conferred by the manufacture of iron into steel is seen by comparing the figures for (1) cast iron, made by melting pig iron in the cupola; (2) wrought iron, made in the puddling furnace from pig iron; and (3) Bessemer steel, produced by treating pig iron in a "converter" and depriving the molten metal of most of its carbon by forcing an air-blast through it. These varieties of iron will be discussed in a later lesson.

When metals are alloyed the resulting product may have properties a good deal different from those of the parent metals. Strictly defined, an alloy is a compound or association of two or more metals, and by extension the term is used for compounds of metals with non-metals. Thus steel is an alloy of iron with carbon (non-metal) and various other metals, usually in small quantities. The object of such compounds is to secure certain special properties such as extreme hardness, or resistance to corrosion.

Solders

Solders consist of varying proportions of lead and tin: the object here is to make an alloy which fuses at a lower temperature than the metals it is used to join. Bearings of machinery are lined with *tin-lead alloys* having a low melting point: with the bearing brasses in position and the shaft—or a piece of shafting of similar size—in place, the molten bearing-metal is poured in and flows round it. Should extreme heat be set up by friction when the machine is in use, the bearing-metal melts before damage is done to the bearing or shaft. Other alloys are used for the purpose, and "Babbitt" metal, one of the earliest, is composed of tin, copper, antimony and sometimes lead.

Alloys Old and New

Other important alloys are the *brasses* (tin-zinc) and the *bronzes* (tin-copper); the fairly new group of aluminium bronzes contains from 1½ to 10 parts of aluminium per 100, sometimes with 2 parts of silicon, and the rest copper. An entire new series of aluminium alloys has lately been developed, stimulated by the demand for light yet strong metals for aircraft construction. In another direction the search for metallic materials which resist corrosion has given us "stainless" steels, alloyed with nickel and chromium; and copper-steels, containing a small percentage of copper, for marine work. Copper, silicon and manganese have been alloyed to yield a product of great tensile strength combined with resistance to corrosion. In short, by suitable combinations, metallurgists can turn out an alloy with almost any qualities desired in any required degree.

Characteristics of Other Alloys

Some of the brasses and bronzes are mentioned in Table IV. A few notes follow, since certain of these alloys will be met with by the metal-worker. *German silver* is hard and withstands corrosion. It is also known as "nickel silver," and is used for taps and water fittings, besides ornamental articles, jewellery and plate. Cutlery also is made from this metal. *Naval brass* is used for parts exposed to the action of sea-water; *Muntz metal* or "yellow metal," which works well when hot, is used for articles which do not require much cold work during manufacture, such as brass sheets, etc. It is also made into parts of water-pumps. *Cartridge brass* is very ductile, and hence is employed for stampings and pressings. *Admiralty gun-metal* and *phosphor-bronze* are used for bearings, and the former

NAME	COMPOSITION (%)	TENSILE STRENGTH, IN TONS PER SQ. IN.	MELTING POINT
German Silver .	Copper, 60; Zinc, 20; Nickel, 20.	18	1030° C.
Muntz Metal .	Copper, 60; Zinc, 40.	25	890° C.
Naval Brass .	Copper, 62; Tin, 1; Zinc, 37.	23	1570° F.
Brass (Cast) .	Copper, 66; Zinc, 34.	14	—
Cartridge Brass .	Copper, 70; Zinc, 30.	23	1645° F.
Admiralty Gun-metal . .	Copper, 88; Tin, 10; Zinc, 2.	14	995° C.
Monel Metal .	Copper, 29; Nickel, 67.*	38	1370° C.
Phosphor Bronze.	Copper, 95; Tin, 5; Phosphorus, minute amt.	25	1040° C.
Statuary Bronze .	Copper, 90; Tin, 2; Zinc, 5.	—	—
Stereo Metal .	Lead, 72–80; Tin, 5–10; Antimony, 15–18.	—	—
Pewter . .	Tin, 85·5–91·5; Copper, 1–2·5; Zinc, 0–3·5; Lead, 1·5–2·5.	—	400° F.
Wood's Alloy .	Lead, 30·8; Tin, 15·4; Bismuth, 38·4; Cadmium, 15·4.	—	71° C.

TABLE IV

COMPOSITION AND PROPERTIES OF COMMON ALLOYS

* Also contains carbon, iron and manganese in small amounts.

for water fittings also. Phosphor-bronze can readily be drawn into wire of great strength, and is used for electrical conductors.

Another corrosion-resisting alloy is *Monel metal*, produced direct from the ores of the component metals. It has wide uses for steam fittings, chemical plant, parts of engines and boilers, condensers, etc. *Pewter* was once extensively used for household utensils, drinking vessels, etc., and is still made into tankards. Sinks, counters and trays are lined or covered with the sheet metal, and it is made into pipes and tubes. Occasionally the worker may come across old-fashioned teapots in this metal, and in recent times there has sprung up a fashion for all sorts of fancy articles in pewter, worked or hammered—sometimes plated with silver, but often left plain. On account of its low melting point (about 400 deg. F.) it must be soldered with care, and a flux of olive oil, tallow or Gallipoli oil used.

So-called "bronze" ornaments are often made of a material such as stereo metal, coloured to resemble the real thing. Fixing screws are cast in, and can generally be mended by soldering with care. The material is brittle.

Gilding metal, composed of 90 per cent. copper and 10 per cent. zinc, is used mainly for decorative purposes in architectural and similar work.

Wood's alloy, melting at well below the boiling point of water, is something of a curiosity among alloys; one use of it was to fix a "wireless" crystal in the terminal cup of early broadcast receiving sets.

Since brasses harden under cold working, it is generally necessary to anneal or re-soften the metal between successive processes by heating it to a dull red and letting it cool slowly.

Self Testing Questions

(1) *Place the metals aluminium, iron, lead and copper in their order as regards conduction of heat—from the highest down to the lowest.*

(2) *From the data in Table II determine the weight of* $\frac{1}{3}$ *cubic foot of* (a) *aluminium;* (b) *iron; and* (c) *lead.* (*Where two values are given in the Table, take the higher.*)

(3) *Assuming that identical strips of the metals aluminium and iron—similar in width and length and thickness—are joined "sandwich fashion" by rivets and then exposed to considerable heat, what would be the result on the bi-metal strip of the unequal expansion* (*see column ii, Table II*)?

(4) *Which of the two solders here specified would have the lower melting point?*

(a) *Lead,* 50 *parts; tin,* 50 *parts.*

(b) *Lead,* 70 *parts; tin,* 30 *parts.*

(5) *How do the brasses differ from the bronzes in composition?*

(6) *What is the purpose of lining a bearing with Babbitt metal or a similar alloy of low fusion point?*

(7) *Name a metal present in naval brass but absent from cartridge brass.*

(8) *Why is Admiralty gun-metal classed as a bronze? State its main divergence from naval brass in composition.*

THE ANSWERS ARE ON PAGE 374.

LESSON 3

Iron and Steel: Varieties and Qualities

WHEN iron ores are smelted, the molten metal is run into sand moulds and forms what is known as *Pig Iron*. The carbon content of this blast-furnace product is about 2–4 per cent.

Pig iron is melted in a cupola and cast into machinery parts, structural members and a large variety of other things.

Cast Iron and Semi-Steel

Cast Iron contains carbon in two forms: (*a*) graphite or free carbon; and (*b*) cementite (iron carbide)—combined carbon. Different varieties of metal are produced by controlling the ratio of (*a*) to (*b*), for when there is more carbide and less graphite the cast iron is harder, denser, more brittle and more difficult to machine.

In "white" iron the carbon is mainly in form (*b*); in "grey" iron it is mainly graphitic. "Mottled" iron is a variety intermediate between the others; the names refer to the appearance when fractured.

By adding steel scrap to pig iron in the cupola the variety known as *Semi-Steel* is obtained. Despite its name, it is a true cast iron, and not a steel. The addition of steel scrap lowers the total carbon content and imparts greater strength. The total carbon content may be about 2·5 per cent., and of this about 1·5 per cent. would be free carbon.

Articles cast in certain special white irons can be heat-treated to make them less brittle and permit a limited amount of working. The castings are annealed for several days at a temperature of 750–950 deg. Centigrade, and, as a result, the combined carbon is changed at the surface into graphite ("blackheart" process), or reduced by oxidation ("whiteheart" process).

The product of this long annealing process is called *Malleable Cast Iron*, but from what has been said above the student will realise that the term is a misdescription, for the metal is not malleable. The process is a convenient one, however, for small and intricate articles which are required to stand more shock than is possible with ordinary cast iron, and are to permit a little manipulation. An example is the use of malleable cast iron for the "fittings"—elbows, tees, etc.—of gas-pipes: when the tapered threaded end of the pipe is screwed into the elbow the latter will yield a little instead of fracturing. Blackheart malleable is more ductile, but whiteheart is stronger.

Wrought Iron

An alternative material for pipe fittings is *Wrought Iron*, a pure form of iron with about ·25–·5 per cent. carbon content. It is made in the "puddling furnace," by hammering the plastic mass of iron, slag and oxide, while at a low temperature, and forming it into lumps. Most of the slag is expressed, but that which remains is drawn out into fibres, giving wrought iron its typical fibrous appearance when fractured. Afterwards the lumps are rolled into "puddled" bars; then these are cut, piled, and again rolled ("merchant" bars). The process may be carried to two or three further similar stages, improving the quality.

Uses of Wrought Iron

Wrought iron is thus composed of a number of layers or laminations pressed together by the rolling process. It is ductile and tough, and can be welded, forged and "wrought" in various ways. Unlike steel, it is not hardened by quenching from the hot state. It is used for a variety of ironmongers' goods; and, in thin sheets, for the manufacture of hollow-ware and enamelled ware.

So far we have seen that by reducing the amount of carbon present in the original pig iron we have obtained various products with widely differing qualities. In the cast irons alone a wide range has been developed for special purposes, by alloying them with such other metals as aluminium, nickel, chromium, silicon, etc. In the *Steels* the specialisation has gone even farther, and it would require a treatise to discuss briefly even the most important.

Steel

The carbon content of steel is lower than that of cast iron, and is in the form of combined carbon. Steel is ductile, tough and malleable; more important still for many uses, it is amenable to heat-treatment and can be hardened and tempered. By alloying with other metals special qualities can be imparted—for example, resistance to corrosion, extreme hardness, enormous strength, the capacity to retain a sharp edge. The *plain carbon steels* are as follows:

1. *Mild Steel.* Carbon content up to ·35 per cent. Used for structural work, pipes, forgings, castings. Does not harden under heat-treatment.
2. *Medium Steels.* Carbon content ·35–·55 per cent. Used for machinery, certain structural parts, etc.
3. *Tool Steels.* Carbon content ·5–1·0 per cent. Used for dies, tools such as cold chisels, etc.
4. *Blister Steel; Shear Steel; Crucible Cast Steels.* Carbon content 1·0—about 1·5 per cent. Wrought iron is heated for several days in charcoal by what is termed the cementation process, producing "blister steel"—with its surface covered with blisters—which after forging at red heat is known as "shear steel," two bars of blister steel being welded and rolled down to a single one. The bar may then be doubled and hammered or rolled to form "double shear steel." The name "spring steel" is given to blister steel reheated and again rolled. Blister steel is melted in a crucible and then cast into bars to make "crucible steel," to be manufactured into cutting tools and other small tools. Shear steel is used for tools and cutlery.

Bessemer and Open-Hearth Processes

The following is a brief description of steel manufacture. In the Bessemer process molten pig iron with a high content of phosphorus is placed in a special furnace (the converter) and subjected to an air blast, which furnishes oxygen sufficient to burn out the excess carbon and the impurities. A controlled amount of carbon is then added in a subsequent process. According to the character of the material used for lining the converter, the process is termed the "basic" (alkaline lining) or the "acid" process.

In the open-hearth process pig iron with steel scrap and iron ore is melted on a hearth—actually a shallow bath—and the impurities and carbon are oxidised out. As in the Bessemer process, the required amount of carbon is added at a later stage. Both basic and acid linings are used for the furnace, each imparting to the steel certain characteristic properties in different degree.

The Bessemer process is used for mild steel, and has today been largely superseded by open-hearth processes, which are employed for mild steel and medium steel, besides certain alloy steels.

The student will note that up to the present we have been dealing with "plain carbon steels"—*i.e.* steels without alloy. The alloy steels are discussed in Lesson 4.

Self Testing Questions

(1) *What is the main difference between* (a) *cast iron, and* (b) *steel?*

(2) *In text-books there used to be some confusion between the terms malleable iron and wrought iron. Give a short definition of wrought iron and state how it differs from malleable cast iron.*

(3) *State the uses of a steel with a carbon content of, say, ·75 per cent.*

(4) *Supposing that a wood chisel were to be made from mild steel and furnished with an edge by grinding, would such a tool be serviceable in use? Give a reason for the reply.*

THE ANSWERS ARE ON PAGE 374.

LESSON 4

The Alloy Steels: Theory of Heat-Treatment

SOME of the special steels have only an academic interest for the metal-worker, but others concern him directly. *High-speed steel* for machine tools, containing minute percentages of vanadium, silicon and manganese, with about ·7 per cent. of carbon, 4 per cent. of chromium and 14 per cent. of tungsten, enables heavier cuts to be taken without overheating, so that the tool can be operated at a temperature double that at which one made of plain carbon steel would begin to soften. A smaller proportion of tungsten in steel will give an alloy very suitable for tools such as screwing taps.

While dealing with tungsten we may mention tools tipped with tungsten carbide, which have revolutionised machining practice. This substance is not a metal, but is made of the powdered carbide incorporated with a binding medium and brazed on to the tool-shank. The tip is almost equal in hardness to a diamond, and, when needed, the edge is sharpened on a grinding wheel. A cutting speed of up to 600 or even 1,000 ft. per minute is possible with tools tipped with tungsten carbide, and many of the machines in use when such tools were first introduced were not suitable in design or construction for the heavier cuts and higher speeds possible with the new material. Thus a radical change was brought about.

Nickel Steels

Stainless Steel contains about 12–18 per cent. of chromium and ·3–·4 per cent. carbon; nickel is added also to yield a steel resistant to acids. *Nickel steels,* containing up to about 30 per cent. of nickel, have been used for boiler tubes, and a steel with about 25 per cent. is non-magnetic. With a much smaller amount of nickel (3 per cent.) a tough steel suitable for construction work and for machinery is produced.

Nickel-chrome steels are widely used for structural work, parts of machinery, etc. For parts that have to withstand great and prolonged heat a steel with up to 15 per cent. nickel and up to 20 per cent. chromium is employed.

At the other end of the scale is a steel with 3 per cent. nickel and 1 per cent. chromium, used for gear-wheels and similar parts of machines.

Pearlite

In Lesson 3 it was explained that the carbon in iron takes two forms: free carbon and combined carbon. In steels the carbon is all in the combined form. Part of the combined carbon (iron carbide, also known as cementite) is associated with the pure iron (known as ferrite) in layers, and the name given to this laminated material is pearlite. This, then, is the condition in steel before heating. When during heat-treatment a certain temperature is attained, the ferrite gradually becomes dissolved, and there remains, in what is termed a "solid solution," the substance called austenite. Another name for the latter is "hardening carbon."

During slow cooling from the "critical" temperature the changes take place in the reverse order until the austenite is again replaced by pearlite and free cementite. The rate of cooling affects the structure of the pearlite, which is coarser for slow cooling, and finer when the steel is cooled more quickly. We are not here dealing with sudden cooling by "quenching." The practical value of this reaction lies in the fact that, broadly speaking, a steel with fine-grained pearlite is stronger than one with a coarse-grained structure. Thus, in *annealing* (heating followed by slow cooling) the metal, the object is to make it more ductile and less brittle, or to free it from stresses set up by previous working. In *normalising,* the metal is cooled more rapidly in air in order to refine its granular structure.

Hardening Steel

Here only the simple theory is explained. Whenever a piece of steel is made red-hot and cooled suddenly by plunging into water it becomes hard; on the other hand, if the steel be allowed to cool slowly it becomes soft. Take the former case: when the metal is heated to some suitable temperature above the critical, the pearlite becomes changed into austenite, as we saw earlier. Upon quenching the steel in water the austenite alters into a new substance called martensite, very considerably harder than the materials from which it was formed: thus the steel has been *hardened.* But the martensite itself will change to other forms on the metal being reheated and quenched again, the eventual hardness varying with the temperature at which the cooling is suddenly terminated by quenching.

In short, by stopping the cooling process at a particular point we can attain any degree of hardness required, and thus *temper* the metal. Steel goes through a characteristic series of colour changes on cooling, and these are used as "indicators."

Self Testing Questions

(1) *A worn-out file is worth keeping for its steel, but the file is very hard, and must be softened before it can be shaped into another tool. If made red-hot and allowed to cool in the usual way, it may still be brittle. What is the proper treatment?*

(2) *Copper sheet which is normally soft becomes hard after hammering. How can this hardness be removed?*

THE ANSWERS ARE ON PAGE 374.

LESSON 5

Working, Shaping and Manipulation of Metals

METALS are cast into ingots or billets and rolled into bars, rods or sheets; tubes and pipes are formed from a strip, bent up into a tubular form and welded along the seam. Copper tubes are made from billets, which are then formed into seamless shells and further elongated in a drawing machine, somewhat in the same manner that wire is made, until the required dimension is obtained.

Pipes and Rods

Lead pipe is formed from the metal in a semi-plastic state, forced through a die so that it takes on the form of a continuous tube; the metal passes between a stationary core and the wall of the die. Pressure required is applied by hydraulic means. Large lead pipes are made from flat strips of metal bent round and joined by "lead-burning," which is a process of welding.

By a somewhat similar process to that for making lead pipes the softer metals are formed into rods and moulded sections of various shapes by "extrusion"; a hot billet is pushed through the die and issues in the required form. Copper, brass and aluminium are thus made into mouldings for shop-fittings and similar work.

Many small-sectioned rods and strips are made by drawing through dies: *e.g.* angles, round, rectangular and polygonal sections. Tubes also are "solid drawn" in much the same way. Though similar sections are made by extrusion they have not the accuracy of the drawn material. Rolling processes produce rods, strips, bars and sheets; in heavier work steel beams up to, say, 24 in. × 7½ in. and weighing 100 lb. per foot run are so made.

Corrugated "iron"—actually steel—as well as the flat steel sheet is made by rolling.

Wire is manufactured by inserting the thinned-down end of a rod through the opening of the drawing die and then drawing the metal through, thus reducing its diameter. A number of dies, progressively decreasing in diameter, may be employed in series. This was originally a hand process, like that used today by jewellers and silversmiths for occasional work. It is worth noting that all these "cold-working" operations harden the metal, which has to be annealed either during or at the end of the process, unless the quality of hardness is desired.

When copper wire is drawn down so as to reduce its sectional area by 50 per cent., its tensile strength is increased from 15 to 25 tons per square inch. Copper strip rolled to effect a reduction of 50 per cent. in sectional area undergoes a similar increase in tensile strength—from 15 to 25 tons—and its hardness is increased by more than 100 per cent.

Cutting Metal

So much, then, for the processes used in manufacturing what to the metal-worker are "raw materials" of his trade. Now let us see in turn how he works and manipulates these metals to form them into parts of machines and appliances, or utensils.

Metal rod, bar or thick sheet is *cut* with the hacksaw, using a size of tooth suitable to the kind of material and its thickness and hardness. There is another important point about choice of tooth size—the size, by the way, is denominated by the number of "points" to the inch. In cutting thin-walled tubes of a metal such as copper or brass the teeth must not be so coarse that they catch in the edge of the metal, but must be fine enough for two or more to rest on the edge during sawing.

Thin sheet—the question of hardness also comes into the matter—can be *cut* with the shears or tinman's snips. In workshops quite heavy steel plate is cut by shearing machines. Thicker material is severed or shaped with "cold" chisels, so named in distinction to the blunter chisel used by the smith on hot metal.

Forging and Filing

Wrought iron and steel can be shaped and manipulated by *forging*—usually after being heated to redness in a fire kept going by an air blast. Pieces can be united by *welding*, a method of which the ancient variety known as fire-welding is still in frequent use. Today there are also the newer welding methods in which (*a*) the intense heat of the oxy-acetylene flame, or (*b*) that of the electric arc, is employed to fuse the metal at the joint. In another electrical method, "resistance" welding, the metal in the neighbourhood of the joint is heated by the passage of a heavy electric current while the joint surfaces are pressed together by hydraulic means. In spot welding, as its name implies, the seam is united or tacked in spots along its length (see Fig. 10, Lesson 12). Fusion cutting by the oxy-acetylene blowpipe is used to sever girders and heavy plates, and also for shaping steel parts. The work is made hot by the combined flame, and then the cutting is done by directing a stream of oxygen upon the line of cut, so that the metal is burned through.

Metals are shaped by filing, a process in which a cutting rather than an abrasive action is obtained; also by *grinding*, a method in which the hard particles embedded in the binding medium of the wheel are caused to abrade or rub away the metal surface. In the comparatively modern process of *precision grinding* even such things as screwing taps can be shaped up accurately; and the process is used for a whole host of other tasks demanding absolute precision, such as the finishing of gear-wheels, etc. Taps made by cutting the thread in the softened steel may lose their shape or become deformed in the subsequent process of hardening and tempering; but those made by the grinding process are free from this risk, since the thread is ground after the blank has been hardened.

Other Modes of Treatment

Precision grinding is also used for the final finishing, to within close limits, of machinery parts, giving results not obtainable so easily by other means.

Metals can be *turned* and shaped in the *lathe*; some metals in sheet form can be "spun" in the lathe—that is, formed up to hollow shapes from a disc—an ancient process used for bowls, pots, drinking vessels and numberless ornamental articles. Holes are formed in metal by *punching* (cold, for soft or thin material; hot, for thicker metal, as in smith's work); also by *drilling*. Holes are formed in castings by means of "cores" in the mould. Cored holes are *bored out* in the lathe or on a boring machine; a boring tool, comprising a cutter fixed at the end of a boring bar, is brought into contact with the surface of the hole and a cut taken all through until the hole has the desired diameter.

External or internal screw-threads are cut in the lathe, or formed by means of screwing dies or taps.

Uniting Metals

Some methods of joining or uniting metals have been instanced above—welding in its different forms; others are *soldering*, *brazing* and *riveting*. The tinman uses various joints for thin metal sheet, turning over the edges and hooking them together for the vertical seam of a drum or a canister, for example; knocking up and paning down the edge where the bottom disc is fixed to the body. In brazing a copper vessel the abutting edges of a joint are dovetailed into one another. Soldering is often employed to seal or complete a joint made by seaming, riveting, or other means. Riveting is employed for such widely different jobs as (1) fixing the hinge-pieces to the frame and sides of tortoise-shell spectacles; and (2) connecting the beams and girders and stanchions of structural steelwork.

Bolts and Screws

Metal parts both large and small are fixed together by means of *bolts*, which may range in diameter from ·9 mm. for B.A. No. 15 to 6 in. for Whitworth Standard 6-inch, a comparison giving some idea of the versatility of this method of joining members. *Machine screws* are employed in a similar way, except that there is a plain hole in one member and a threaded hole in the other, the screw passing easily through the clearing (plain) hole and being turned into the threaded one until the members are brought tightly together. The importance of an easy clearance is often overlooked by beginners in metal-work, and some have been known to thread *both* holes, with disastrous results for the job. The outside member cannot be brought up close unless the screw passes easily through it. The principle is seen in the ordinary vice.

Securing Machine Parts

Special methods are used for securing together parts of machinery: thus, a wheel is fixed to its shaft by a shaped *key* driven endwise into a slot made partly in the wheel hub and partly in the shaft. On light machines a wheel or gear member may be fastened to the shaft by a *pin* passing down through both wheel and shaft. Another method is to pass a threaded pin or peg down through the collar of the wheel and into a tapped hole in the shaft; a variation—only suitable for light loads—is to fix the wheel by a set-screw working in a tapped hole and gripping the shaft by frictional pressure: a shallow "centre" is sometimes drilled in the shaft to receive the shallow-pointed end of the set-screw and afford a fastening.

Avoiding Shearing

Pins and screws will shear under a load which is too great; the key in its various forms is a better arrangement, and is commonly used in machinery. Sometimes the end of a shaft is squared to fit a corresponding rectangular hole in the wheel; or in an inferior method only a flat is formed on the shaft, with a hole in the wheel to suit.

As regards pulleys, we may mention the split pulley used on line shafting for convenience of attachment. It is formed in two halves, bolted together to grip the shaft between them. There is a wide variety of these securing devices, and only representative kinds have been touched on here.

Transmission Lines

It is an elementary principle of design—which should be remembered by the student in dealing with domestic machinery and appliances, and with his own tools such as drilling machines, bench-grinders, etc.—that when a "drive" has to be transmitted the gear-wheels, pulleys, etc., forming the transmission line must be firmly secured to their shafts or spindles. As an example, a set-screw may be used to fix the knob on the condenser spindle of a radio set, but a stout taper pin would be employed to attach the gear-wheel of a bench-grinder to the crank-spindle or one of the intermediate spindles.

Self Testing Questions

(1) *Wooden dowels are made by forcing a rectangular rod in succession through a number of holes in a steel die-plate until ultimately the rod becomes circular in section. Mention a metal-shaping method which resembles this method.*

(2) *Mention one effect upon copper of rolling or drawing the metal in its cold state.*

(3) *How can undue hardness in a brass or copper member be removed? (In beaten copper work the metal soon becomes hard under prolonged hammering. When brass is being spun in the lathe a similar hardening occurs.) Refer back to Lesson 4.*

(4) *How does a bolted joint differ from one made with machine screws?*

THE ANSWERS ARE ON PAGE 374.

LESSON 6

Bolts and Screws

British Association Bolts are generally used for small work, and the British Standards Institution (hereafter abbreviated B.S.I.) recommends this system for sizes up to ¼-in., beyond which the Whitworth Standard or the British Standard Fine are suggested. The included angle in British Association (B.A.) threads is 47½ deg.; for practical purposes Numbers 0 to 14 only are employed, though the series ranges further in a downward direction—to No. 25. Moreover, only the "even" numbers are worth while keeping in taps and dies, except that the full range of 0, 1, 2, 3 and 4 might be stocked where much small work is likely to be done. For such jobs as the regulating screw for a clock pendulum No. 10 or even No. 12 would be suitable.

Standard Threads and Bolts

The shape of the B.A. thread is shown in Fig. 2, with the Whitworth and other standard threads. The numbers and diameters are given in Table V. B.A. bolts are dimensioned in millimetres, the diameter of No. 0 being 6 mm. and that of No. 14 being 1 mm. At one time not so very long ago the worker was inclined to look askance at dimensions quoted in the metric system, but in fact the finer subdivisions of this system enable closer measurements to be taken with greater ease than in the British system, while the decimal notation is in itself a great advantage.

British Standard Whitworth (B.S.W.) Bolts. The sizes (¼ in. upward) recommended by the B.S.I. are those shown in Table VI, which omits certain intermediate sizes. The angle is 55 deg.

Black Bolts are made from rod as received from the rolling mills. *Bright Bolts* are turned in the process of manufacture, and are therefore more accurate. Hexagon nuts are used; as compared with square nuts, they are stronger, and are more easy to manipulate with the spanner.

British Standard Fine Bolts range from 7/32 in. diameter upward, and the thread is finer than in the B.S.W. series. For example, B.S.W. size ¼ in. has 20 threads to the inch, whereas B.S.F. size ¼ in. has 26 threads to the inch. Recommended sizes are shown in Table VI.

In column 4 of Table V the nearest drill number is given for making a hole that is to be tapped for a B.A. bolt of the size specified. Similarly, columns 4 and 5 of Table VI show the proper tap-drill sizes for B.S.W. and B.S.F. threads respectively. Note that a larger

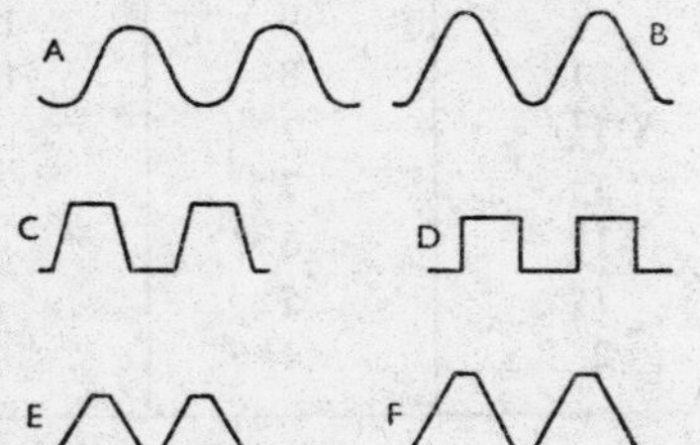

Fig. 2. A, *British Association* (47½ *deg.*). B, *British Standard Whitworth* (55 *deg.*). C, *Acme* (29 *deg.*). D, *Square*. E, *American National* (60 *deg.*). F, *International* (*Metric*) *Standard* (60 *deg.*).

NUMBER	DIAMETER, IN MM.	THREADS TO IN.	SIZE OF DRILL FOR TAPPING
0	6·0	25·4	No. 10
1	5·3	28·2	No. 16
2	4·7	31·3	No. 24
3	4·1	34·8	No. 29
4	3·6	38·5	No. 32
6	2·8	47·9	No. 43
8	2·2	59·1	No. 50
10	1·7	72·6	No. 55
12	1·3	90·7	No. 61
14	1·0	110·0	No. 69

TABLE V

NUMBERS AND DIAMETERS OF BRITISH ASSOCIATION (B.A.) STANDARD BOLTS, WITH TAPPING DRILL SIZES

DIAMETER (IN.)	THREADS TO IN.		SIZE OF TAP DRILL	
	B.S.W.	B.S.F.	B.S.W.	B.S.F.
$\frac{7}{32}$	—	28	—	No. 15
$\frac{1}{4}$	20	26	$\frac{3}{16}$ in.	$\frac{13}{64}$ in.
$\frac{5}{16}$	18	22	$\frac{1}{4}$ in.	$\frac{17}{64}$ in.
$\frac{3}{8}$	16	20	$\frac{19}{64}$ in.	$\frac{5}{16}$ in.
$\frac{7}{16}$	14	18	$\frac{11}{32}$ in.	$\frac{3}{8}$ in.
$\frac{1}{2}$	12	16	$\frac{25}{64}$ in.	$\frac{27}{64}$ in.
$\frac{9}{16}$	12	16	$\frac{29}{64}$ in.	$\frac{31}{64}$ in.
$\frac{5}{8}$	11	14	$\frac{33}{64}$ in.	$\frac{35}{64}$ in.
$\frac{3}{4}$	10	12	$\frac{41}{64}$ in.	$\frac{21}{32}$ in.
$\frac{7}{8}$	9	11	$\frac{47}{64}$ in.	$\frac{49}{64}$ in.
1	8	10	$\frac{27}{32}$ in.	$\frac{7}{8}$ in.
$1\frac{1}{8}$	7	9	$\frac{15}{16}$ in.	$\frac{63}{64}$ in.
$1\frac{1}{4}$	7	9	$1\frac{1}{16}$ in.	$1\frac{7}{64}$ in.
$1\frac{1}{2}$	6	8	$1\frac{9}{32}$ in.	$1\frac{11}{32}$ in.
$1\frac{3}{4}$	5	7	$1\frac{1}{2}$ in.	$1\frac{37}{64}$ in.
2	$4\frac{1}{2}$	7	$1\frac{23}{32}$ in.	$1\frac{53}{64}$ in.

TABLE VI

BRITISH STANDARD WHITWORTH BOLTS (B.S.W.); BRITISH STANDARD FINE BOLTS (B.S.F.): SIZES RECOMMENDED BY THE BRITISH STANDARDS INSTITUTION. CERTAIN INTERMEDIATE SIZES ARE OMITTED.

drill is required in the case of B.S.F. threads.

A washer is interposed between the nut and the face of the member being clamped. The shank of the bolt should be of a length suited to the thickness of the work, and when tightened up not less than one thread or more than three threads should project above the nut. A *lock-nut* may be used on top of the first nut in order to prevent loosening. It is chamfered on both faces, and is thinner than the ordinary nut; the latter is chamfered only on the top face.

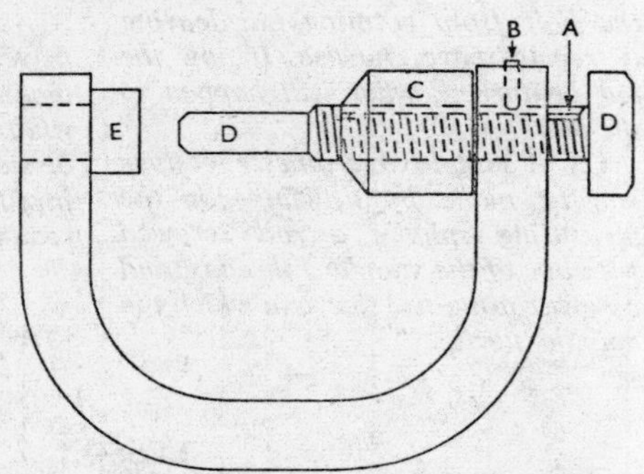

Fig. 3. *Screw in simple micrometer.* A, *shallow groove in threaded spindle,* D, *preventing rotation of* D; B, *pin engaging with groove* A; C, *internally threaded sleeve or nut;* D, *anvil or stop.*

Other Locking Devices

A *castle nut* is an alternative locking device; the top portion, standing up above the hexagon, is slotted to receive the ends of a split-pin passed through a hole in the screwed part of a bolt after the castle nut has been screwed down. A *slotted nut* is similar, and answers the same purpose; the slots are cut in the body of the nut. There are many other locking devices in use, among them being a barbed *spring washer*, which, under pressure from the nut, bites into the nut and into the face of the member clamped and holds the nut fast.

Coach bolts are black bolts having a mushroom head with a short squared portion of shank beneath. The square fits into a similarly-shaped hole in a plate—for example, in bolting down a hasp or staple to a garage door—and is thus prevented from turning. If a fitting were to be screwed to a door from the outside, the door could be forced by merely unscrewing the fitting; but if the fitting were held by a bolt passing through and nutted inside the door, it would be safe. Another use of the coach-bolt is in fastening timber to timber; the square bites into a round hole in the wood only just big enough to pass the round part of the shank.

Coach screws are large wood screws often used to fasten down machines to a wooden floor or to other supports. The screw has a squared head for turning with a spanner. A larger form is sometimes called a *lag screw.* As in the case of all wood screws, it is important to bore out a clearing hole to the depth of the unthreaded portion of the shank, with a smaller hole further in for the screwed part.

Self Testing Questions

(1) *Besides their use for fastening parts of machines and apparatus together, screwed members have other applications. In normal use the nut of a bolt is turned, while the bolt stays fast. Suppose we cut a lengthwise groove on the bolt, and insert a short pin through a hole in the bearing (see Fig.* 3), *preventing*

the bolt from rotating but leaving it free to move endwise. If now the nut be turned, what will happen to the bolt?

(2) *A simple micrometer caliper can be made by utilising for the measuring spindle a rod screwed with one of the standard threads, and by graduating the sleeve in which the spindle turns.*

Assuming that the spindle is to travel forward one-twentieth of an inch at each complete revolution, what B.S.W. or B.S.F. thread would be suitable? By graduating the sleeve in fifths it is desired to obtain a reading of one-hundredth of an inch.

THE ANSWERS ARE ON PAGE 375.

LESSON 7

Screw-Threads, Taps and Dies

THREE of the principal systems of screw-thread were dealt with in Lesson 6. Two others should be noticed here—the *American National* and the *International* (Metric) *Thread*. The included angle in both cases is 60 deg., and the thread has a flat top and bottom.

Where motion has to be transmitted by a screw, as in the lead-screw of a lathe, a *square thread* is usually employed in order to reduce friction. The *Acme thread*, which has an included angle of 29 deg., is often used for this purpose, as it is stronger than the square thread. Both forms are shown in Fig. 2, Lesson 6. A special thread of a somewhat similar shape is used for worms in worm gearing.

"Lead" and "Pitch"

When a screw is turned it advances in the nut a certain distance for each complete turn. This distance is the *lead*. The *pitch* is the distance between two successive crests of the thread. In an ordinary screw the lead is equal to the pitch, but a screw used in machinery to impart motion may have a double, triple or quadruple thread, the object being to obtain a quicker travel of the screw for a single revolution. The rule for finding the lead is to multiply the pitch by the number of "starts": thus the lead in a double-threaded screw is twice the pitch, and so on.

Measuring Threads

The diameter of a screw at its valley is called the *root diameter*; that at its crest the *pitch diameter*. The depth of a thread is measured between the valley and the crest, and therefore is one-half the difference between the root diameter and the pitch diameter. The angle of a thread is the angle included between the flanks, or sloping sides, of two adjacent crests. Most threads are right-hand ones, and the screw advances when turned "clockwise"; occasionally, in a machine or appliance, a left-hand thread is employed instead; this must be turned "counter-clockwise" to advance it.

Threads both internal and external can be cut quickly and accurately on the lathe, but there are many jobs in which this work must be done instead by means of taps and dies. Since bolts and machine screws are readily procurable in standard sizes, there is less occasion for the worker to cut external threads, except for odd jobs, but it is often necessary to tap a hole to take a bolt, stud or set-screw. (A stud is a headless bolt which is turned tightly into a hole in one member and used for the attachment of another by means of the usual nut.)

Repairing a Broken Metal Frame

As an example of the use of hand-taps let us take the job of repairing a mangle whose cast-iron frame has cracked across, as shown in Fig. 4. The mangle was not disturbed after the fracture was noticed, and the crack was closed up by making a tourniquet of rope and twisting it up by means of a short piece of broomstick. Two pieces of mild-steel plate were obtained from the blacksmith and one drilled with four holes to clear a $\frac{3}{8}$-in. B.S.F. bolt. The other plate was drilled with four corresponding holes $\frac{5}{16}$ in. in diameter, for tapping. In the web of the mangle frame four easy clearing holes were drilled to register with those in the first plate: the plate was put in position and held fast by a clamp while the mangle web was marked with a centre punch through the holes. The present job is to tap the holes in the second plate and to screw both plates in place.

Grip the plate in a vice so that the top two holes are accessible and that there is room for the tap-holder to swing. Select the proper tap and fix it firmly in the holder or wrench. Strictly speaking, a set of three taps ought to be employed —"taper," "second" and "plug" taps, but on thin stock or for shallow holes the intermediate one

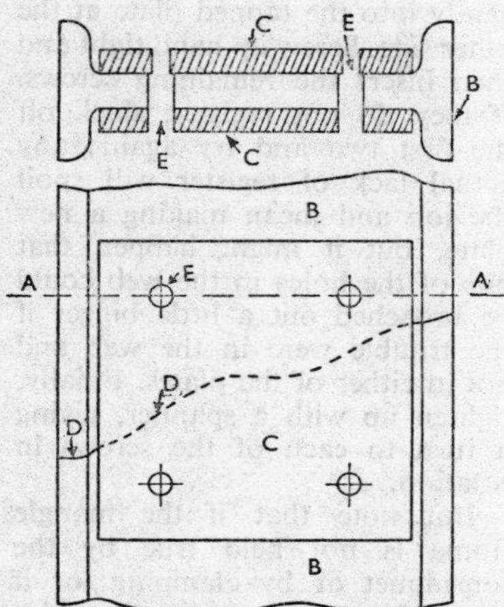

Fig. 4. A, *section line.* B, *web of mangle frame.* C, *front repair plate.* D, *line of fracture in mangle frame.* E, *holes for bolts: clearing holes in front plate; tapped holes in back plate.*

will suffice. Insert the tap into the hole, making sure it is square to the face of the work, and turn gently, with just enough pressure to make it cut. Continue for two or three strokes and bring the tap back again a half-turn; then carry on further, and so gradually complete the work. The tap will run through more easily toward the finish, and should be twisted well in to shape the thread. Then withdraw the tool. Use a little oil to lubricate the tap, and do not attempt to force the tool or to carry the job through at one stroke. Reversing the turn enables the tap to clear itself of metal cut from the hole.

Complete the task by tapping the remaining holes; try in a B.S.F. set-screw at each hole and make sure it will enter freely. Then put the two plates in position, insert a set-screw at opposite corners, pass through mangle web and turn them gently into the tapped plate at the other side. Screw up hand tight and then insert the remaining screws. If they do not register, slack off the first two and try again; any actual lack of register will spoil the job and mean making a new plate, but it might happen that one of the holes in the web could be broached out a little bigger if the trouble were in the web and not in either of the plates. Finally, tighten up with a spanner, giving a turn to each of the screws in rotation.

But note that if the mangle frame is not held true by the tourniquet or by clamping, or if the surface of the web is irregular (perhaps because of a boss or raised lettering), the application of pressure by the spanner may cause a fracture of the appliance, since the plates will not lie flat against the web.

The Tie-Rod of the Bench

The portable bench described in Lesson 1 is strengthened by three iron tie-rods which are threaded at each end to take B.S.W. ½-in. nuts. Smooth off the ends of a rod with the file and slightly reduce the diameter, if necessary, for a short distance so that the rod will enter the die. Grip the rod in a vice so that one end protrudes far enough to allow the stock to be used comfortably. (A pipe-vice, if available, is far more convenient than an ordinary vice for this job.) Better-class sets of stock and dies have the dies provided with a collet for each size; the collet is of the proper diameter for the particular thread, and acts as a guide to the rod being dealt with. For smallish work the *circular solid dies* are convenient, and can be had with means of adjustment—a screw being turned in to open a split in the die and expand the latter slightly; when the screw is turned out, the die springs together again.

Another simple stock has *divided dies*, formed of two halves which slide in the stock and are held up to their work by a feed-screw.

Using the Dies

Sometimes the entire set of three or four dies is accommodated in the stock. In use the pair of dies is opened to embrace the rod to be threaded, and then brought into contact with the surface. As the screwing proceeds, the feed-screw is tightened. Several passes of the tool are needed to produce a finished thread, whereas the solid die cuts a thread with a single pass. In a better type of stock for larger work only one pair of dies is held in the stock at a time. Both types of die have their uses, but for work above about ½ in. diameter, the sliding type is generally more suitable—though solid dies are made up to 1½ in., and even bigger.

Whichever type of die is used, see that it goes on squarely and that the stock handles are kept square with the job during the cutting of the thread. In the task with which we are concerned, the thread must be taken far enough up the rod at each end to permit the rod to pass through the wooden frame of the bench, and provision is to be made for a back-nut and washer at each end between the legs as well as outside. This means that a length of about 4½ in. must be screwed at each end. Try on the nuts and put on washers all ready for the assembly; a B.S.W. *die-nut* of the proper size could be run over the threaded rod to true up the thread, and when divided dies are used this practice would be advisable, since the screw depends for size on the diameter of the rod itself.

A brief review of other types of screwing device is here given.

Screw-plates are made by tapping holes in a steel plate which is afterwards hardened. Early types had a single hole for each size of thread, and no true cutting action was possible. In later types, two other holes were drilled to intersect the die-hole and thus give cutting edges to the die. An improved pattern has three or four such holes, and the cutting edges are then radial. This principle is used in solid dies.

As mentioned, some solid circular dies can be sprung a little by means of a radial screw. The divided dies can also be adjusted to grip the rod more or less tightly, but real adjustment is possible only in stocks which permit the die members to be fixed at a given setting independently of the rod or pipe being threaded. This device is extensively used in American die-stocks, provided usually with four cutting members set radially and giving a true and easy cut. Four adjustable guides also are incorporated in the tool. The dies can be opened, without losing the setting, so that the stock can be taken off the rod or pipe without running the tool back over the work.

Taper Threads and Screwing Machines

Taper Threads are used for pipe-work, and in order to cut them the *receding die* has been developed. In use, the cutting members are drawn back automatically as the die passes along the pipe, so that the proper increase in diameter is given, and the desired taper ($\frac{3}{4}$ in. per foot is recommended by the B.S.I.) is produced.

Screwing Machines are used for rods and pipes. The work is held in a vice forming part of the appliance, and there is often an automatic cut-off which can be set to work at a pre-arranged length. Both hand- and power-operated machines are manufactured, and the labour of hand-screwing is reduced by the use of gearing. Larger work can be done by hand in such machines than is possible with the use of a stock, where only leverage is available to multiply the effort.

Self Testing Questions

(1) *The lists of tap-drill sizes given in Tables V and VI, Lesson* 6, *are to ensure that suitable holes are drilled for the job in hand. The hole that is intended to be tapped must be somewhat smaller in diameter than a hole which would "clear" the shank of a corresponding bolt. If too much smaller, the tap might deform (spread or squeeze) the metal around the hole; on the other hand, owing to the undue force that would have to be used to turn the tap, the latter might be broken. What would be the result of drilling a hole which, although not large enough to clear the bolt-shank, was still larger than the proper tapping size?*

(2) *In the mangle repair job given as an example of the use of bolts and nuts it was suggested that two plates should be used: this was because cast iron is a brittle metal, and even the small amount of force needed in tapping might, in unskilled hands, suffice to cause a fracture of the mangle web. But supposing that this consideration was unnecessary, indicate a method in which only a single repair-plate would be needed.*

THE ANSWERS ARE ON PAGE 375.

LESSON 8

Drills and Drilling

THERE is a wide difference between the tool used for making holes in (soft) wood and that employed for drilling metal. The carpenter's "bit" has a screw-nose or gimlet point to draw the tool into the wood, and has its cutting edge at a quick angle. For hard woods, however, the more usual tool is one resembling the metal-worker's twist drill, but having a quicker angle at the cutting edges. These differences follow from the different nature of the material being worked upon. We have seen a novice bore a hole in soft aluminium with a carpenter's gimlet—surprisingly enough, with a fair amount of success—but this malpractice would be possible only in the case of a fairly soft metal.

The Twist Drill and Straight-Flute Drill

In Fig. 5 (1–4) are different types of drill for metal—the "business" ends only. The *twist drill* (Fig. 5 (1) and (1A)) shown has two spiral flutes, but for special purposes drills are made with three or four flutes. There are three cutting edges in the double-fluted twist drill, indicated by the letters *X*, *Y*, *Z* in Fig. 5 (1A). The *angle of the point* for general work is 59 deg.: strictly, the angle should vary for different metals, but this is practical only in commercial work where there is a call for specialisation. Note that the flutes of the drill are "backed off"—the diameter being reduced at *W*, *W* to provide *clearance*. Clearance is also provided at the *lips* of the drill, which are ground away behind the cutting edges to an angle varying from about 7 to 12 deg. with the point *Y*, when the latter is horizontal. The angle made by *Y* with *X* and *Z* is usually recommended to be 135 deg.

Variations of this drill are seen in Fig. 5 (3) and (4), showing *straight-flute drills* with three and two flutes respectively. The two-flute drill is sometimes preferred for softer metals and for hardwood, and is certainly better for drilling sheet metal: a drawback of the twist drill is that when used on thin stock it tends to "cork-screw" its way through the material, forcing instead of drilling the hole once the point has penetrated.

Here it can usefully be pointed out that an important function of the drill-shank, when parallel and of the same diameter as the cutting end, is to give guidance to the tool: it is obvious that on thin stock no guidance is afforded by the twist drill, whereas the straight-sided two-flute shank does give some guidance and support.

The Flat Drill

This brings us to a consideration of the *flat drill* (Fig. 5 (2)), forerunner of the twist drill and still used in (*a*) small sizes, by jewellers and for small work; and (*b*) larger sizes, in the engineer's ratchet brace for jobs where the depth of the hole is not great. There is, of course, no guidance, and these drills are not suitable for deep holes.

The shape shown in Fig. 5 (3) is used also for "percussion drills" such as are employed for jumping holes in brick or concrete, but in this case the flutes are shallower and the point is thicker. The angle of the twist in twist drills may be the same along the drill (*constant angle*); or it may increase from the shank toward the point (*increased twist*). In the latter case the decrease backward from the point is claimed to give a better get-away for the cuttings; but, on the other hand, when the point is re-sharpened, the lip clearance will vary as more of the drill is ground away. The worker can safely stick to "constant angle" drills and leave these problems to the experts.

Drills are made of (*a*) *carbon steel* or (*b*) *high-speed steel* containing tungsten. The latter can be run at greater speeds and require sharpening less often.

Parallel-shank drills fit the chuck of a wheel-brace, breast drilling machine, or bench drill-press; for heavier duty, in power drill-presses or larger types of hand-operated drilling machine, it is customary to employ drills having a *taper shank* which fits one or other of the standard taper sockets, this socket in turn fitting the taper hole in the drill spindle. Eight sizes of Morse Taper Sockets are commonly employed; these are Nos. 0, 1, 2, 3, 4, 5, 6, 7, ranging in diameter at the small end from ·252 in. to 2·750 in., to suit drills of varying dimensions.

"Morse Wire Sizes" range from No. 80 (·0135 in.) to No. 1 (·228 in.); beyond this there are the "Letter Sizes" from A (·234 in.) to Z (·413 in.). See the Tables of Tap Drill Sizes given with Lesson 6. The actual decimal equivalents for the drill sizes are given in Table VII (p. 338). Apart from this, twist drills are made to fractions of an inch from $\frac{1}{8}$ in. up to $\frac{63}{64}$ in., and thereafter up to 3 in. diameter.

For use in the engineer's ratchet brace, short drills with a squared taper shank to fit the standard socket of this kind are made in a certain range of sizes from about $\frac{1}{8}$ in. up to 2 in. diameter. Longer drills with a similar shank are made for use in the chuck of a carpenter's brace, the usual range being from $\frac{1}{16}$ in. up to 1 in. It should be stated

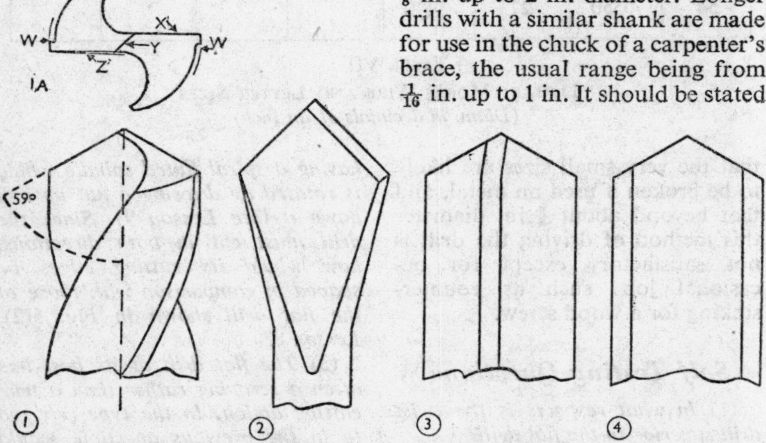

Fig. 5. *Cutting portions of various types of metalworkers' drills.* (1) *Twist drill.* (1A) W, *flutes backed off for clearance;* X, Y, Z, *the three cutting edges;* (2) *flat drill;* (3) *straight-flute drill* (3 *flutes*); (4) *straight-flute drill* (2 *flutes*).

NO.	SIZE	NO.	SIZE	NO.	SIZE	LETTER	SIZE
80	·0135	53	·0595	26	·1470	A	·2340
79	·0145	52	·0635	25	·1495	B	·2380
78	·0160	51	·0670	24	·1520	C	·2420
77	·0180	50	·0700	23	·1540	D	·2460
76	·0200	49	·0730	22	·1570	E	·2500
75	·0210	48	·0760	21	·1590	F	·2570
74	·0225	47	·0785	20	·1610	G	·2610
73	·0240	46	·0810	19	·1660	H	·2660
72	·0250	45	·0820	18	·1695	I	·2720
71	·0260	44	·0860	17	·1730	J	·2770
70	·0280	43	·0890	16	·1770	K	·2810
69	·0292	42	·0935	15	·1800	L	·2900
68	·0310	41	·0960	14	·1820	M	·2950
67	·0320	40	·0980	13	·1850	N	·3020
66	·0330	39	·0995	12	·1890	O	·3160
65	·0350	38	·1015	11	·1910	P	·3230
64	·0360	37	·1040	10	·1935	Q	·3320
63	·0370	36	·1065	9	·1960	R	·3390
62	·0380	35	·1100	8	·1990	S	·3480
61	·0390	34	·1110	7	·2010	T	·3580
60	·0400	33	·1130	6	·2040	U	·3680
59	·0410	32	·1160	5	·2055	V	·3770
58	·0420	31	·1200	4	·2090	W	·3860
57	·0430	30	·1285	3	·2130	X	·3970
56	·0465	29	·1360	2	·2210	Y	·4040
55	·0520	28	·1405	1	·2280	Z	·4130
54	·0550	27	·1440				

TABLE VII
DRILLS: MORSE WIRE AND LETTER SIZES
(*Diam. in decimals of an Inch*)

that the very small sizes are likely to be broken if used on metal, and that beyond about ⅝ in. diameter this method of driving the drill is not satisfactory except for occasional jobs such as countersinking for a wood screw.

Self Testing Questions

(1) *In what respects is the twist drill superior to the flat drill?*

(2) *Flat drills used by the metalworker for small work are often driven by an "Archimedean" stock having a spiral fluted spindle which is rotated by drawing a nut up and down it (see Lesson 9). Since the drill must cut in both directions, how would its cutting edges be shaped in comparison with those of the flat drill shown in Fig.* 5(2), *Lesson 8?*

(3) *The flat drill at its best has often a scraping rather than a true cutting action. In the type referred to in the previous question, would the action be better or worse?*

THE ANSWERS ARE ON PAGE 375.

LESSON 9

Drilling Machines and Methods

THE *Hand Drill* or *Wheel Brace* is used for drills up to about ¼ in. diameter. See that the chuck is well made and that the spindle has no undue slackness in its sleeve. The tool must be kept upright during work, and should be tested with a try-square.

The *Breast Drill* works on the same principle as the above, but has a thrust-plate in place of the top handle. In use, the plate is rested against the body of the worker and pressure applied to hold the tool up to the job. Capacity: drills up to ½ in. Some of the more expensive drills have two speeds and ratchet action. When purchasing, choose a pattern with an idler gear as well as the live gear working on the main wheel, as this equalises the bearing and gives longer life.

Drilling Machines

Bench drilling machines range from (*a*) an arrangement in which an ordinary hand drill or a wheel brace can be fastened, to (*b*) a massive machine bolted down to the bench or, alternatively, to a plate fixed to the wall over the bench. Intermediate types, capacity up to ½-in. drills, are made to clamp or to bolt to the bench. Clamp-fixed machines are seldom satisfactory, since they often twist under the leverage of the crank during use. Cheaper kinds of bench drill may have a chuck capacity that appears large, but may be insufficiently strong in construction for work with drills of the maximum size.

The *Ratchet Brace* is used with a drilling stand or pillar which holds it up to the member being drilled. Feed is by means of a nut turned by a tommy bar or a spanner to increase the effective length of the tool between the centres in which the brace works.

Older patterns take drills with square-taper shanks, but some are made with a chuck for cylindrical drills.

The *Archimedean Drill* is made in two forms: (*a*) with a simple threaded spindle and a threaded nut or sleeve which propels the spindle on both the down-stroke and the up-stroke, so that the drill bit reverses direction at each change of stroke; (*b*) with the spindle threaded so as to give motion in a clockwise direction no matter whether the driving sleeve moves upward or downward. Drills for type (*a*) must be ground so that they cut in both directions (actually the action is more of a scraping one than a true cut). Drills for (*b*) are the normal ones. The stock is usually furnished with a chuck to take parallel shanks.

Marking the Work

The work should be carefully marked out with a scriber, giving intersections where the holes are to come. (See Fig. 4, Lesson 7, showing the method of repairing a mangle: note the lines that indicate the positions for holes.) With a centre-punch and a medium-sized hammer, form an indentation exactly on the crossing of the lines; hold the punch upright and see that it does not shift or chatter.

(For large holes it is customary also to scribe a circle about the centre, marking just outside the diameter of the hole to be made, as a guide.) If a bench drill be used —provided it works truly and the job is securely clamped to the machine table—such precautions are not needed, and the operation can proceed as soon as the centres are punched.

Lubrication

The drill should be lubricated with oil occasionally as the work proceeds. Feed and speed are governed by the nature of the material and the size of the drill. Do not force a drill, and if undue pressure seems required, make sure that the tool is not blunt. When getting nearly through the metal, ease off the pressure and proceed cautiously, or the drill may break; this is specially necessary on small work.

Using the Hand Drill

When using a hand drill it is much more difficult to ensure accuracy, but the work should be held firmly in a vice or clamped to a piece of board fastened temporarily on the bench-top, and every care taken to hold the tool square and vertical. It may be better to take a pilot hole through first, using a drill considerably smaller than the final size of the hole, and then to go through again with the proper size. But if the finishing drill is not very much larger than the pilot drill, the bigger one may bind or chatter, and fail to cut properly. For this reason it is better on small work to use a broach or reamer to enlarge a hole already drilled, and not to attempt to drill it out again. The broach has a square-taper shank and is held in a broach-holder; the reamer has a squared top like that of a screwing tap, and is turned with a tap-wrench or tap-holder. Broaches are slow-tapered, and the hole must be opened out alternately from both sides. Reamers are made both taper and parallel, the latter being used for final sizing of a hole.

Drilling Jigs

A drill-grinding jig for clamping to a bench grinder or a grindstone will enable twist drills to be sharpened to the proper angle and to be properly backed off. There are several types. Without such a guide it is not possible to re-sharpen the drills. Some bench-grinders have a drill-sharpening rest incorporated with the usual tool rest, and this device is useful for small drills. Flat drills can be sharpened up with an oilstone, or by careful manipulation on a bench-grinder; in the latter case be careful not to overheat the tool and so draw the temper.

Self Testing Questions

(1) *The location of the drill-point on the tool is determined by the angle and length of the two sides, and if either of these differ the point will be out of centre. What would be the effect on a hole if such an eccentric drill were used?*

(2) *When drilling is continued after the drill-point has become blunted, the tool tends to burnish the metal in contact with the point. How does this affect the operation?*

(3) *Mention any disadvantage of the Archimedean drill-stock as compared with a wheel brace of the same capacity.*

THE ANSWERS ARE ON PAGE 375.

LESSON 10

Rivets and Riveting

RIVETING is a convenient method of joining sheet-metal parts, and has also many other applications—for example, joining metal parts to others of such non-metallic materials as bone, ivory, bakelite, etc. In constructional steelwork, steel rivets are used for most of the joints between beams, plates, stanchions, etc., others being made by means of bolts.

The principle of a riveted joint is to form holes in both members and then to insert through both a headed rivet; the protruding end is then hammered down to increase its diameter and to fasten the members together. In steelwork, the rivets are heated in a forge and driven while hot: the subsequent shrinkage as the rivet cools to normal temperature draws the members together.

In all forms of riveted joint it is essential to give adequate backing or support to the headed end, while the other end is being closed down. If fragile materials are being united, the parts must be protected from impact, so that the blow is transferred to the rivet and not to the surrounding material. Often in thick enough material the holes are countersunk: the rivet-head is countersunk to correspond, and the other end of the rivet is closed down into the countersink on that side of the joint.

Some of the standard shapes of rivet are shown in Fig. 6: in order these are *Pan Head, Snap Head, Flat Countersunk, Pan Head with tapered neck, Snap Head with tapered neck, Rounded Head Countersunk*, and *Flat Head*. Fig. 6 (8) shows a *split* or "*bifurcated*" *rivet*—

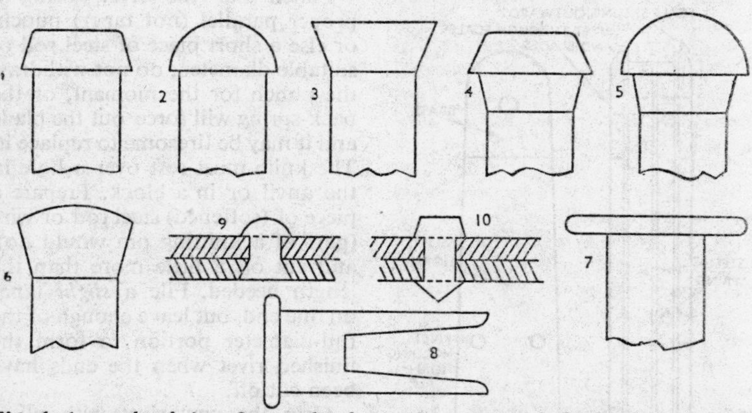

Fig. 6. 1, *pan-head rivet;* 2, *snap-head rivet;* 3, *countersunk flat-head;* 4, *pan-head with tapered neck;* 5, *snap-head with tapered neck;* 6, *countersunk round head;* 7, *flat-head rivet, shape as used by tinmen, etc.;* 8, *split or "bifurcated" rivet;* 9, *joint by means of snap-head rivet closed into countersunk hole on the under-side;* 10, *joint with pan-head rivet finished to a conical point on the under-side.*

the latter is a trade name for a particular make—useful for leather or fabric, or for odd jobs in sheet metal; when closed with the proper tools, the ends of the split portion are turned over and bite into the material being jointed.

Fig. 6 (9, 10) shows respectively a snap-head rivet closed down into a countersunk hole, and a pan-head rivet finished with a conical point on the under-side of the joint. In order to form the conical point, the worker uses a tool somewhat like a punch, having a recess of the proper shape; the tool is held on the end of the rivet and struck with the hammer. Tinman's rivet sets are made with two holes formed on the same tool—one for snap heads and the other for "set-up" finish. Boilermaker's punches are, of course, heavier, made to be held with an iron "rod" by an assistant.

After holes have been punched and drilled in the two members of the joint, and the rivets inserted, the plates are brought together and the rivet driven up by use of a hollow set—a tool having a square face at the lower end, drilled out in the centre to clear the upstanding shank of the rivet. This is employed in conjunction with a flat bar (or a "stake"), in the top face of which there is a recess to take the head of the rivet and afford a firm support to the plates. When the set is struck smartly with a hammer, the plates are driven together and the rivet brought up ready for the next operation—closing down and shaping by means of the hammer and cupped set, as described above. Three riveting jobs of different kinds will now be described.

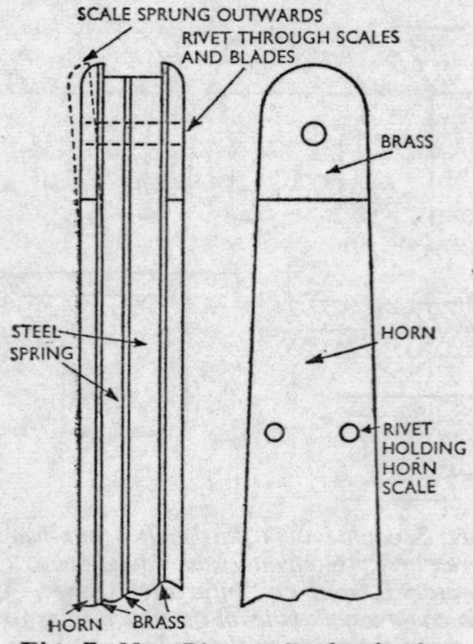

Fig. 7. *New Rivet to Pocket-knife.*

Riveting Pocket-Knife

1. The job is a two-bladed knife, with both blades at the same end; the rivet here has drawn partly through, allowing the scales to spring open. The scales are of horn, except at the top, where there is an end of brass about $\frac{5}{8}$ in. long. (See Fig. 7.)

Punch out the rivet, using a proper parallel (not taper) punch, or else a short piece of steel rod of suitable diameter; do not withdraw the punch for the moment, or the back-spring will force out the blade and it may be tiresome to replace it. The knife must rest over a hole in the anvil or in a block. Prepare a piece of (softened) steel rod or wire (part of a knitting pin would do), and cut off a little more than the length needed. File a *slight* taper on one end, but leave enough of the full-diameter portion to form the finished rivet when the ends have been cut off.

Grip the new rivet with pliers and insert from the side opposite to that in which the punch is inserted. Push in the rivet (the taper end entering first) and allow the punch to come out, making sure not to lose the register of the holes in scales and blades. A tap with a hammer will probably be needed. Now rest the knife over the hole in the anvil, with the tapered end of the rivet projecting down into this hole. Drive the rivet home by taps with a light hammer; cut off surplus portions, leaving enough, however, to form a good clench. Now, resting the knife on a solid part of the anvil, close down the rivet with light and well-directed blows from a small engineer-pattern hammer, the aim being to spread the metal. Finish off with a smooth file.

2. A shovel (see Fig. 8) has worn thin at the front, and as the rest is in excellent condition, it is decided to put on a new "foot" of sheet steel. Cut off the bad portion at right angles and knock down flat. Use a pair of snips or a cold chisel to sever the metal, according to its thickness. Cut off a strip of new metal and bend it up to the proper shape; cut off the corners at the front. The new piece rests *on top* of the old, which it overlaps for a distance of about 1½ in.

Mending a Shovel

Having tried on the new piece, take it off and proceed to punch the holes in side and bottom; the rivets should not come all in a straight line, but should be staggered as shown in Fig. 8. Rest the metal on a piece of deal stood up endwise, so that the punch goes through into end grain. Rest the new piece of metal on the old, in proper position, and, using the punched holes as a guide, make the holes now in the shovel itself: if more convenient, the position of the holes can first be marked with a centre punch, and the members separated before punching.

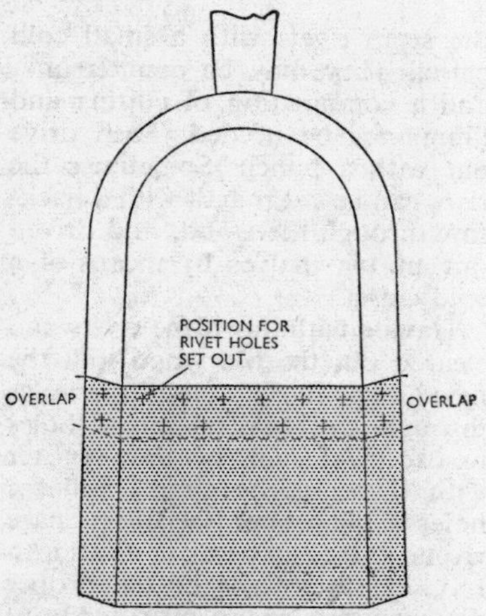

Fig. 8. *New Foot riveted to Coal Shovel.*

As a first essay in riveting, the worker may prefer to use copper rather than iron rivets, though they will not wear so well. Put the parts together and drive a rivet through from the top, somewhere near the middle of the width of the shovel. Close this rivet, and then carry on with the rest, working alternately first to one and then to the other side of the centre rivet first put in. (Should the new metal tend to cockle, only one hole at a time could be punched in the shovel itself, and rivet inserted, before proceeding with further holes; this would ensure that the holes in the shovel coincided with those in the new metal.)

Close down all rivets tightly, and trim off the edges of the sheet metal with the snips, if necessary. A final cleaning up with a file may be needed.

Riveting Handle to Spade

3. The old wooden handle of a garden spade having broken at one of the strap rivets, a new one has been procured. First cut off the ends of

the strap rivets with a small cold chisel. They may be countersunk, and a combination of cutting and filing may be needed. Then drive out with a punch. Sometimes the rivet can be cut in half with a hacksaw through the wood, and driven out in two halves by means of a cold chisel.

Having withdrawn the rivets and cleared out the old wood, put the new handle in place and bore holes through the handle—small holes first to make sure that they register with those in the straps. Enlarge holes to the proper size and prepare rivets: these can be made from iron rod, or stout nails of the proper diameter can be cut off roughly to length and inserted through straps and handle. Drive a rivet home and cut off finally to suitable length.

Lay the spade on an anvil—this is a two-handed job—and close down the rivet with smart blows. Proceed with the rest of the rivets. The top ends of the strap may be inclined to spring outward, and if so this can be stopped by putting a ¼-in. bolt through temporarily and nutting this to clamp the straps tightly to the handle. Withdraw the bolt when the other rivets have been fixed, and put in the top one; if the straps still spring out, grip them with a cramp while the rivet is being put in and clinched. The rivets must fit tightly in the holes in straps and handle: if slack in the holes, they may bend under hammering.

Self Testing Questions

(1) *How may a soft metal surface be protected from injury during the closing down of a rivet tail?*

(2) *What is the proper type of rivet shape for use in joining thin sheet metal?*

(3) *Proper length of rivet is important for a riveted job; if too short, the rivets will not spread enough. What is the consequence of using rivets that are too long?*

THE ANSWERS ARE ON PAGE 375.

LESSON 11

Files and Their Uses

Files are abrasive tools, having teeth formed in the surface by chisel-cuts in the softened metal, which is afterwards hardened and tempered. A carbon steel of special quality is employed, and the Sheffield files have long been noted for their excellence. Swiss files also have a name for their good quality; in Britain they are used generally by the jewellery and clock trades, in small sizes. Swiss files, of extreme hardness, are used, too, for fine finishing work in instrument-making and similar jobs; the metal-worker will find them invaluable for occasional jobs where a final touch is needed (for example, to rub up the cutting edges of small drill-points, or in making small tools of this kind). Normally all shaping is done on softened metal, but sometimes this is impossible or inconvenient, and then the Swiss file of suitable shape (there is a wide range of patterns) can be employed.

A *single-cut* file has a single series of chisel cuts across its face, as shown in Fig. 9 (1). The *double-cut* tool has a second series of cuts which cross the first at an angle (see Fig. 9 (2)). The effect of the double cutting is to break up the continuous ridges left by the first cut into rows of

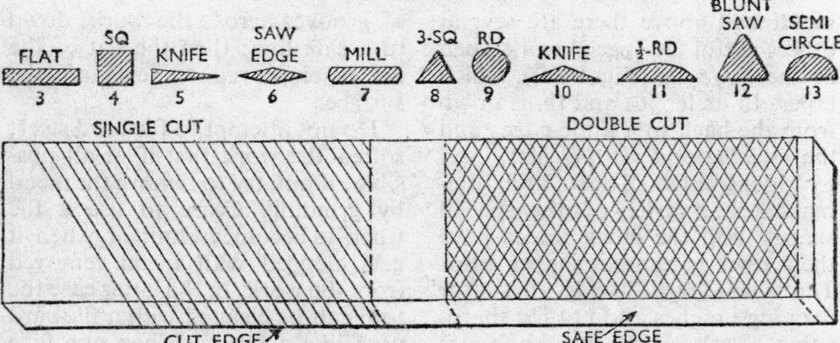

Fig. 9. *Files.* 1, *single cut;* 2, *double cut;* 3, *flat;* 4, *square;* 5, *knife;* 6, *saw edge;* 7, *mill;* 8, 3-*square;* 9, *round;* 10, *knife;* 11, *half-round;* 12, *blunt saw;* 13, *semi-circle. Terms applied to file surfaces and edges are illustrated below.*

points, so that the file cuts faster and, of course, less smoothly than the single-cut file, assuming the same degree of coarseness in both tools. The single-cut is used on softer metals (where the double-cut would be more inclined to clog), and also on hard metals in the finer degrees for finishing work. Double-cut files are employed for roughing out work, and in the finer cuts for general fitting and finishing.

Hand Files

The engineer's general utility tool is the so-called *hand file*, which is flat and parallel, and usually has one "safe" edge (with no teeth cut in it). The safe edge enables work to be done on a vertical shoulder, for instance, without marring the horizontal surface at right angles to the shoulder. The ordinary *flat file* (Fig. 9 (3)) tapers slowly from about one-third of its length toward the point; it is cut on both flats and both edges. Another generally useful shape for the metal-worker is the so-called *half-round file* (Fig. 9 (11)); actually its section shows a flat on one side and an arc of a circle on the other. *Square* (Fig. 9 (4) and *round* (Fig. 9 (9) files, parallel in their length, are useful for cleaning up holes, forming slots or notches, and generally finishing rectangular or curved apertures. Do not use *square-tapered* or *round-tapered* files for such jobs if the edge of the hole is to be left square. Tapered files can be properly employed for enlarging or roughing out holes or slots, and for cleaning up curved work. The *three-square file* (Fig. 9 (8)), triangular in section and parallel throughout its length, must also be distinguished in its form and uses from the *tapered saw-files* and the *blunt saw-file*—Fig. 9 (12)—(the latter is parallel and not tapered).

Some Special Files

The three-square, like the other parallel files described, is intended for producing or finishing apertures of the shape conforming with its section. Saw-sharpening files are extremely useful for odd metal-work jobs, but after they have been used to sharpen saws are only fit for cleaning off solder, etc. One other shape which comes in the general category is the *millsaw-file* (Fig. 9 (7)); it is flat and parallel with rounded edges. In fine tooth it is used for finishing work, shaping up tools, etc.

Besides the more common shapes

mentioned above there are several others useful for special work, such as the *knife-file* (Fig. 9 (5)), which tapers in its length and thins down from the back to a knife-edge; and the *warding* and *slotting* files, used by locksmiths. Tool- and die-makers use a variety of other special shapes, and the clock trades have their own particular shapes also. The "*saw-edge file*"—Fig. 9 (6)—(for forming notches and not for sharpening saws) is like two knife-files placed back to back. Sometimes the sloping facets are cut, and sometimes only the two edges. Another similar pattern has the section of a squat triangle (Fig. 9 (10)), so that it furnishes one flat face and two knife edges.

The *milling file* ("dreadnought") has coarse teeth cut in a convex arc pointing forward; it is used for roughing out work.

Files are made in the following degrees of coarseness; *dead-smooth*; *smooth*; *second-cut*; *bastard*; *middle*; *rough*. These apply in the main to both single-cut and double-cut types, though not all may be regular stock. Smooth and bastard will see the worker through most jobs, if he has also one or two milling files.

How to Use the File

In using the file, steady pressure, combined with a forward motion, must be applied; the file must be kept level on the work. Pressure must cease during the return stroke, when, of course, the tool does not cut. Except on the largest sizes the file should be put in a handle, and is better for this aid and protection in all cases. Sometimes it is better to cross the work at an angle than to push straight forward. When some mass of metal is to be removed from a surface it is better to use the edge of the file first and to form a number of grooves across the work, down to a safe line; then the flat of the file is employed to level off the surface.

Do not attempt to file hard steel; soften the work first if at all possible; if not, try to remove the metal by grinding. Cease to use a file when it becomes blunt or when it gets clogged with metal removed from the work. In the latter case the tool can be cleaned with a file-card used like a brush. When one face of a flat file becomes dull, mark that face at the butt with chalk and thereafter use the opposite face; when both sides are dull, reserve the tool for cleaning off solder, or for use on soft metal. Probably the edges are still usable in any case. There is no convenient means of re-sharpening a spent file, though sand-blasting is employed to some extent for this purpose; the tools should be treated carefully and protected when not in actual use.

Self Testing Questions

(1) *State the proper files to be used in cleaning up and levelling off a brass block which has been severed with the hacksaw.*

(2) *What file could be used to cut the screw-driver slot in a grub-screw?*

(3) *Warding files are made to the customary thickness of the "steps" in door-keys, so that they produce slots to fit the wards of the lock. How would the worker go about the task of cutting a new key from a blank of the proper gauge and shape but somewhat larger than the key needed?*

(4) *An iron rod of $\frac{3}{8}$-in. diameter section has to be severed, and no hacksaw or cold chisel is available. What sort of file would be used for the job?*

THE ANSWERS ARE ON PAGE 375.

LESSON 12

Soft Soldering

SOLDERING is the uniting of two metal parts by means of a film or layer of another metal which melts at a lower temperature than the metal to be united. Sometimes soldering is used merely to seal an opening (as the vent-hole in a can of preserved food), or to seal a seam which has been welded. Fig. 10 shows a lapped joint in the metal plating of a motor-car body; after being spot-welded for strength, the seam is filled with solder to seal it.

Kinds of Solder

Soft soldering implies the use of "soft" solders, with a comparatively low melting point. See Table VIII, from the British Standard Specification No. 219—1932, giving the proportions and use of different solders for various purposes. Soft solder is an alloy of tin and lead: the more tin in the alloy, the lower the melting point. Thus *Plumber's Solder* (for wiped joints to lead pipes) liquefies at 496 deg. Fahrenheit; its composition is roughly tin 30 per cent., lead 70 per cent. *Tinman's solder*, with a composition of about tin 50%, lead 50 per cent., liquefies at 414 deg. Fahrenheit. Pure tin is sometimes used, or an alloy of tin, 95 per cent. with 5 per cent. antimony, for conditions where great heat has to be withstood: here, however, we encounter a contrast, for the liquefying temperature of pure tin is 450 deg. Fahrenheit. This points to the circumstance, explained in Lesson 2, that an alloy may behave very differently from the individual metals of which it is composed. Here again it should be noted that the tensile strength of tin is about ·94 tons per sq. in. and that of lead about ·89 tons, while the figures for the 50/50 tinman's solder are 2·75 tons, and for the 70/30 plumber's solder 2·66 tons per sq. in. The tin 95 per cent., antimony 5 per cent. alloy mentioned above has a tensile strength of 2·81 tons per sq. in.

The essentials for successful soldering are as follows. The work must be chemically clean; it must be freed from metallic oxide, which always forms on metal when exposed to the atmosphere; the surface, once cleansed, must be protected by a *flux* while soldering is being done; surfaces other than tinplate must be "tinned"—that is, pre-coated with a film of solder; the surfaces to be joined must be heated to a temperature sufficient to cause the solder to flow freely over them; solder must be applied and heat maintained until it runs between or into the joint; the job must be held rigid in the proper position until the solder has cooled and set.

Fluxes

"*Killed spirits*" is one of the commonest and most useful fluxes, but has the drawback (*e.g.* for electrical work) that, owing to its acid and corrosive nature, it may eat away the material of the joint or that near it, unless all traces are carefully removed after the solder-

Fig. 10. *Sealing a lapped end spot-welded seam by means of solder.*

	GRADE AND USES	COMPOSITION (PER CENT.)
A.	Work requiring low melting points. Steel tube joints.	Tin, 64–66; Antimony, 1; rest, lead.
B.	Tinsmiths' and coppersmiths' fine work. Hand soldering.	Tin, 49–51; Antimony, 2·50–3·00; rest, lead.
C.	General work. Hand soldering.	Tin, 39–41; Antimony, 2·0–2·40; rest, lead.
D.	Plumbers' wiped joints to lead pipes.	Tin, 29–31, Antimony, 1·0–1·70; rest, lead.
E.	Special electrical purposes.	Tin, 94·5–95·5; Antimony, ·50; rest, lead.
F.	Machine soldering. General electrical purposes. Zinc and galvanised iron-work.	Tin, 49–51; Antimony, ·50; rest, lead.
G.	Dipping baths. Zinc and galvanised iron-work. Tinned electrical joints.	Tin, 41–43; Antimony, ·40; rest, lead.
H.	Lead-cable wiped joints.	Tin, 34–36; Antimony, ·30; rest, lead.
J.	Dipping baths.	Tin, 29–31; Antimony, ·30; rest, lead.
K.	Special machine soldering.	Tin, 59–61; Antimony, ·50; rest, lead.

TABLE VIII

BRITISH STANDARD SOFT SOLDERS

Extracted from British Standard Specification No. 219—1932.

ing job is done. Such thorough cleansing may be possible on tinman's work, but is obviously not practicable where joints of electrical wiring, connections to instruments, etc., are soldered: in the latter cases a *non-acid flux* must be employed. The commonest flux of this nature for general work is *powdered resin*, but resin is only efficacious on "tinned" surfaces, or on tinplate. (Here we must point out that "tinned" in soldering or plumber's work means coated with a film of solder.) Other non-acid fluxes are *Gallipoli oil*, *tallow*, *olive oil*. Tallow is much used in plumber's work for joints of lead to lead, lead to brass or lead to gun-metal—in each case when plumber's solder is to be used and a wiped joint obtained. Any of the three may be used for soldering block tin or pewter with the copper-bit.

Resin may be made into a solution with methylated spirits or paraffin and applied with a stick or a brush. Various non-acid fluxes are on the market, several in paste form. The writer prefers a liquid flux, of whatever character; and in all cases where a non-acid flux is not demanded "killed spirits" will be found a reliable stand-by.

To prepare killed spirits, procure from the oilman's some strong spirits of salts (hydrochloric acid). This is a corrosive poison and will burn the flesh. Keep it in a proper ribbed and coloured POISON bottle (glass stoppered, if possible). For the prepared flux obtain a wide-mouthed glass bottle with a glass stopper. Pour in some of the spirits of salts, to about an inch up the jar. Cut up some scraps of sheet zinc and drop them in the jar; leave the top open, as a gas is given off. Put the jar out of doors while the zinc is dissolving. Continue to drop in scraps of zinc until no further effervescence takes place and some of the metal is still not dissolved. The acid must be neutralised, or it will corrode the metal in any case. As the remaining zinc dissolves (it may do so later) add a little more zinc. A wooden spill is used to apply the flux—*not* a metal rod or wire. Into another small jar pour a little neat (unkilled) spirit, for use when the ordinary flux does not work well—for example, on galvanised iron, stainless steel, etc.

The Copper-Bit

The copper-bit, used for most kinds of soldering, is made in various shapes, some of the most useful being shown in Fig. 11. A small bit is of little use, as there is not enough metal to retain the heat long enough for most jobs. The pointed bit (Fig. 11, *centre*), even of fair size, can be used for quite small work after a little practice. Hatchet bits (Fig. 11, *below*) are useful for seams, and the fact that the copper portion is at right angles to the shank is an advantage for such work. Two bits should be kept going together if a longish job is in hand—one being heated while the other is in use.

Self-heated bits are a convenience where a quantity of work has to be done. Either the gas-heated (Fig. 11) or the electric tool will then prove a great asset. An electric bit also is indispensable for fine work on wiring, where the heat must be kept away from all but the part to be soldered: a small and fine-pointed bit can then be used to reach nooks and corners that would be inaccessible to a large tool of the ordinary sort, whose hot shank might do damage. (As pointed out earlier, a small ordinary bit would be difficult to keep hot long enough for the work to be done.)

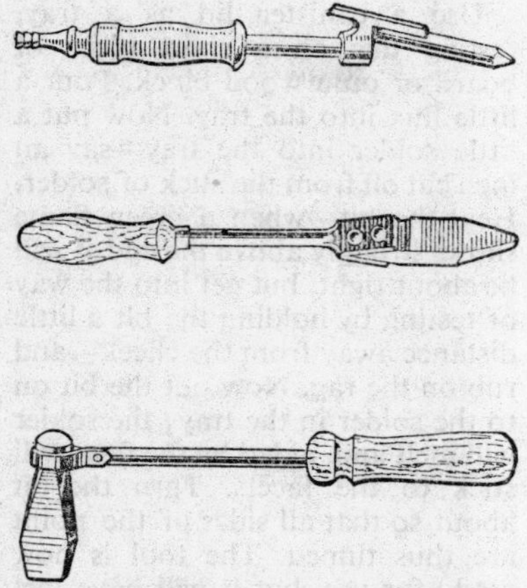

Fig. 11. (Above) *Gas-heated soldering bolt for light work;* (middle) *straight (square) copper soldering bit;* (below) *hatchet bit, at right angles to shank.*

Cleaning the Bit

Whatever the type of tool, it will become foul and dirty in use unless it is prevented from over-heating—this is just as likely with a self-heated bit as with the other kind—and unless it is wiped on a rag frequently. A block of sal ammoniac should be kept handy to rub over the facets of the bit each time it is removed from the fire or from the gas flame; a self-heated bit should also be cleaned with the block occasionally. After the block has been used, rub the bit on the rag again. If the bit becomes very dirty or gets overheated and the tinned surface burnt off, clean up the facets with a coarse file while hot, rub on the sal-ammoniac block, and tin the surface again.

Use a canister lid as a tray, resting this on a short piece of board or on a wood block. Pour a little flux into the tray. Now put a little solder into the tray—say an inch cut off from the stick of solder. Heat the bit—when a green flame shows strongly above the end it will be about right, but get into the way of testing by holding the bit a little distance away from the cheek—and rub on the rag. Now put the bit on to the solder in the tray; the solder will melt and, aided by the flux, will stick to the facets. Turn the bit about so that all sides of the point are thus tinned. The tool is now ready for use, but it will have lost heat and must be returned to the flame for a short while to warm up.

Self-heated bits are tinned in the same way, though when purchased the tool will probably be ready tinned.

Mending a Kettle

A typical domestic job will explain the method of soldering as commonly practised. Owing to a flaw in the plating, a minute rust spot has formed in the bottom of a tinplate kettle, and after a time has eaten a hole through the steel underlying the tin. Now a hole about $\frac{1}{8}$ in. across has appeared and the utensil leaks badly. Empty the kettle and swab it out until dry; both inside and out, scrape around the hole with a file end or an old knife to remove the rust. Finish with a rub of an emery cloth. Cut a tinplate octagon and bend the sides downward slightly so that the patch will come close to the kettle-bottom at the edges. Stand the kettle upside down and fix it with wooden blocks on either side so that it will stand firmly.

Apply flux to the hole and around it; turn the patch upside down and apply flux to the surface. Have a pair of pliers handy, also an old file. Heat the soldering bit, dip the end into the tray, and thus pick up on it some molten solder; rub the end of the bit over the surface around the hole in the bottom of the kettle, so that a film of solder is applied to the job. Put the bit back over the flame for a moment and put the patch in place on the kettle.

Applying the Solder

Take up the bit again, collect more solder from the tray, and apply bit to an edge of the patch. (With the file in the left hand, press with the end on the centre of the patch to hold it in place.) Run the bit around the patch, so that the solder flows. The solder film previously applied underneath will melt and run also. Apply gentle pressure with the file-end as the solder melts, and continue the pressure until the job has cooled and become firm. If necessary, re-heat the bit and finish the work at a second stage.

Any troubles will be traceable to the work not being clean, or to the copper-bit having become cool, or to faulty fluxing. Absolute cleanliness is essential to success. Do not forget that one function of the copper-bit is to warm the surfaces being jointed. On brass or copper work the heat will run away quickly, and a hotter bit can be employed with safety. Do not attempt to work with a corroded bit: clean it and re-tin the facets.

Treatment of Zinc

Wash away the flux from the repaired surface, using a little soda. All cooking utensils should be boiled out thoroughly after repair, with a little soda in the water, and should be given several rinses. On zinc-work especially, be careful to remove all flux from the soldered parts. Neat spirits or partly killed spirit is used on zinc, according to results, and is, of course, corrosive.

Self Testing Questions

(1) *In soldering, the solder penetrates to some extent the metal being jointed and alloys itself with it. But almost invariably the metal oxidises under heat and becomes coated with a film of oxide which is resistant to the desired action. How can this be overcome in soldering operation?*

(2) *Certain fluxes "bite" into the metal of the joint and clean it chemically, as well as assisting the flow of the solder by a mechanical action and protecting the surface from the oxygen of the air. Give the names of* (a) *a flux which thus cleans the surface; and* (b) *one which merely fluxes and protects the surface.*

(3) *Why is resin used as a flux on tinned surfaces?*

THE ANSWERS ARE ON PAGE 375.

LESSON 13

Brazing of Metals

BRAZING is similar in principle to soldering, and differs only in the composition of the "solder" employed and in the higher temperature at which the operation is carried out. The brazing solder or "spelter" is usually a brass, but may be an alloy of silver termed a *silver solder*, having a lower melting point than a brass. Since the articles usually united by brazing are copper and brass, which are ready conductors of heat, not only a higher temperature but a greater amount of heat is needed, and this is supplied (1) by a gas blowpipe with forced air blast; (2) by a paraffin or petrol brazing-lamp; or (3) by an oxy-acetylene or air-acetylene blowpipe.

The *brazing-lamp* is a fair-sized blow-lamp. The paraffin lamp (petrol lamps are not recommended) is shown in Fig. 12. The lamp is primed by lighting methylated spirit in a cup (*B*) around the vertical pipe from which the nozzle branches off, the air inlet (*C*) being closed. This creates a pressure inside the reservoir and warms the feed-pipe to the jet (*E*), vaporising some of the paraffin. The spirit-cup is of such a size that when the spirit has been almost consumed the lamp is ready to be started up; the air-pump (*D*) may be given a few strokes, and the lamp should then light up at the nozzle with a flame that soon becomes a blue atmospheric one. Continue pumping cautiously until a steady and powerful flame is established, with the familiar "roaring" sound. It should now burn with little attention as long as the fuel lasts.

Caution: If pumping is begun too soon, liquid oil and not vapour will

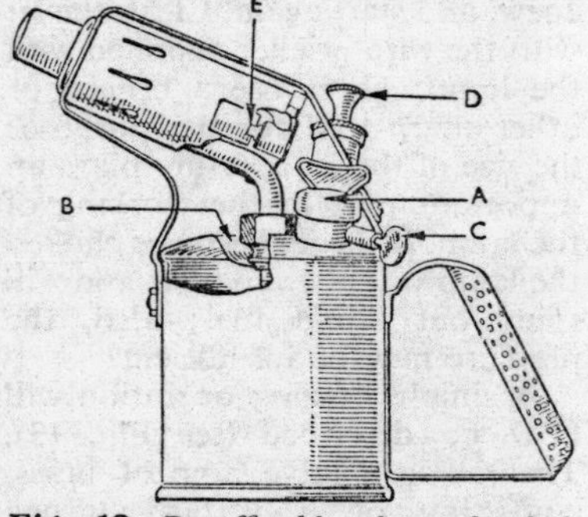

Fig. 12. *Paraffin blow-lamp for light brazing work.* A, *filler cap;* B, *priming cup for methylated spirit;* C, *air inlet screw;* D, *air pump;* E, *jet nipple.*

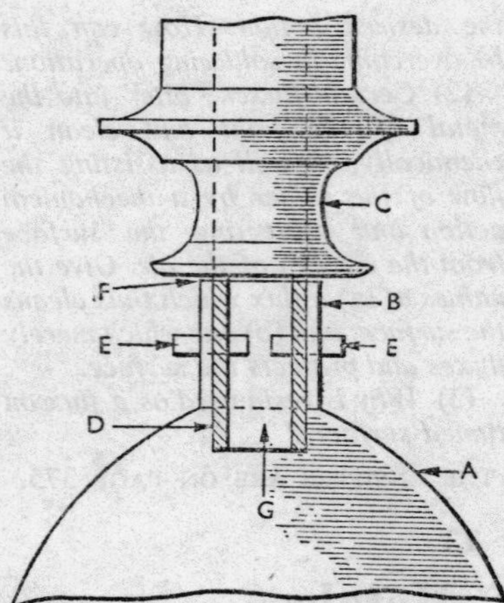

Fig. 13. *Table lamp: brazed joint of pillar to base shown in part section.* A, *bell of base;* B, *socket on base;* C, *pillar;* D, *spigot on pillar, which fits into socket* B*;* E, *brass pins to hold parts in position (cut away later);* F, *joint-line where shoulder of stem meets socket;* G, *hole for flexible wires to lamp holder.*

issue from the jet, spurting a long flame; moreover, some oil may flow down into the cup, where it will burn furiously. In such a case, *open the air inlet* and the pressure will cease; the flame will go out. Let the lamp cool, fill the spirit cup anew, and start again. Clean the jet with the wire pricker supplied with the lamp; never use a broach or other sharp tool for the purpose: the size of the jet aperture plays an important part in the working of the lamp. If the jet becomes choked the lamp will not vaporise, and will spurt out liquid fuel; also, the pressure may be insufficient.

A simple brazing operation will now be described (see Fig. 13). The job is a table-lamp of brass, consisting of a vertical turned member, or pillar (*C*), which fits into a socket in the spun member (*A*) that forms the base of the lamp. The joint of the vertical pipe to the boss is to be brazed with spelter. Fit the parts together tightly, and drill two holes for brass pins (*E*) which go through the neck of the socket into and through the vertical pipe, holding the parts in position during the brazing operation.

After the members to be jointed have been thoroughly cleaned and the vertical one pinned to the base, turn the job upside down and rest the top end (now, of course, at the bottom) in a hole in a metal block, or wedge it between two pieces of brick in the abutting edges of which a notch has been chiselled out. The work should rest on a stout piece of sheet iron and have another piece behind standing up vertically, to concentrate the heat of the lamp. (A proper *brazing-tray*, complete with shield, can easily be made from the design given in Fig. 14. Cut where indicated, bend on the dotted lines, and rivet corners. The shield fits in two slots formed in the back side of the tray.) The heat in the present case is to be applied at the top of the job, but often, in brazing, the joint will come lower, and in such cases it is customary to surround the job (and back it up) with small coke. The coke is placed around and at the back of the article being brazed, and retains the heat from the lamp.

The flux is powdered borax made into a paste with water. The paste, in an almost liquid consistency, is applied to the joint after gently warming the parts: make sure that the flux gets down between the end of the stem (*D*, Fig. 13) and the wall of the socket (*B*). Since the lamp-stand is in the inverted position, there should be no difficulty about this. Also apply flux to the shoulder of the stem at *F* (Fig. 13), where it fits against the socket below.

Now take the lamp and direct the

flame below the joint (*F*), keeping the flame steadily pointing in the proper direction; the lamp can meanwhile be supported on bricks. Move the flame up occasionally so that it warms the bell of the base just above the joint, or else the heat will travel up and be lost. Carry on in this manner until the borax begins to fuse and run; at this stage dip a steel wire into the flux, and then into a canister lid in which some powdered brazing spelter (resembling brass filings) has been placed ready. The wire will collect some spelter, which is now to be conveyed to the joint (*E*), inside the upturned bell of the base. If the joint is hot enough, the spelter will fuse and run down the stem and fill the space between the stem and the socket. Leave undisturbed to cool, after removing the lamp. Do not cool suddenly by plunging in water, or the stresses set up may crack the joint.

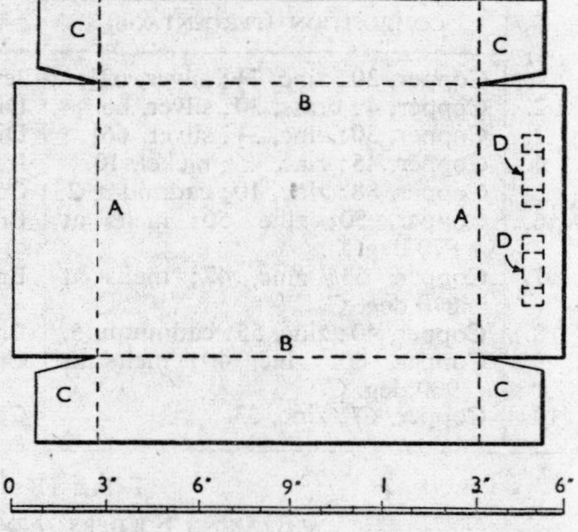

Fig. 14. *Brazing tray in sheet iron. Making up: Bend on dotted lines first* A *and then* B. *Lugs* C *come outside upstands* A *and are bent around* A *when rest of tray has been formed up. Put* 3 *rivets in each lug* C, *through upstands* A. D *are straps for tongues* F *of screen* E.

Requisites for successful brazing are as follows. Clean the joint surfaces with emery cloth and by filing or scraping; remove any emery dust from the parts. Make the members a tight fit, and pin them to hold them rigidly in the proper location: if anything slips or gets out of place while under heat, nothing can be done to remedy the mishap until the work has cooled, and by then it may have become brazed in a wrong position. Support the work adequately for the same reason. Provide plenty of insulating and/or heat-retaining material, and *apply enough heat, for a sufficient time.*

The beginner will probably find it easier to use silver solder than one of the spelters. It is much more expensive, but is economical (of material) in use. It is sold in thin sheet, from which a narrow ribbon should be cut off with the snips. After warming and fluxing the joint, little pieces of solder are placed around and the lamp directed on the job. Sometimes it may be more convenient to cut off a ribbon of solder and bend it around the part to be brazed. A neat joint can be made with greater ease than with spelter—at least by the beginner. The jeweller supports his work on a charcoal block during soldering, and for fine work may use a mouth blowpipe to direct a gas flame on the work.

The governing consideration in

	COMPOSITION (PERCENTAGE)	USES
1.	Copper, 30; zinc, 7½; silver, 62½.	Jewellers' work.
2.	Copper, 4; brass, 30; silver, 66.	Ditto.
3.	Copper, 30; zinc, 3½; silver, 66½.	Ditto.
4.	Copper, 45; zinc, 45; nickel, 10.	Iron, steel.
5.	Copper, 88; zinc, 10; cadmium, 2.	Copper, brass, gun-metal, bronze.
6.	Copper, 50; zinc, 50; melts at 870 deg. C.	Brass.
7.	Copper, 53; zinc, 47; melts at 870 deg. C.	Brass.
8.	Copper, 40; zinc, 55; cadmium, 5.	Brass (tubes, thin sheets).
9.	Copper, 60; zinc, 40; melts at 900 deg. C.	Copper, brass, gun-metal.
10.	Copper, 67; zinc, 33.	Copper, brass, gun-metal.

TABLE IX

BRAZING SOLDERS AND SPELTERS

Notes.—In *silver solders* the temperature of melting is lowered when the percentage of silver is increased as compared with that of copper. On account of their expense they are used on small work generally, but have come into vogue for jointing copper and brass pipes and fittings. In *spelters* the fusing temperature becomes lower with an increase of zinc over copper in the composition, but 50 per cent. zinc is the practical limit.

No. 6 (50/50) is a spelter of general utility with which "general brass" can safely be brazed. For copper-work, spelters of a harder nature—melting at a higher temperature—can be employed. Besides their availability for extremely hard joints on iron or steel, spelters containing copper, zinc, nickel (*e.g.* No. 4) are useful when the brassy colour of yellow spelters is not desired. The *flux* for all the varieties given above is borax.

the choice of solder or spelter is the melting point as compared with that of the metal forming the job. Silver solder is thus convenient for soldering brass fittings to a model steam boiler, or similar jobs where the brass must not be raised to too high a temperature. There is, of course, a safety margin of some 20 deg. C. when the proper spelter is used, but it is only too easy to overheat the work, and the flame of a brazing lamp tends to get hotter as it works up after the start. Model engineering firms supply a special low-melting-point solder particularly intended for use on fittings to boilers, etc.

Self Testing Questions

(1) *A safety-valve bush is to be hard-soldered into a hole made in a copper model boiler, and silver solder is to be used. Describe briefly how the work should be set up for soldering.*

(2) *From the information given in Table IX state which of spelters Nos. 9 and 10 melts at the lower temperature.*

(3) *How should the worker deal with a brazing-lamp which suddenly changes its roar to an intermittent popping note and then throws out a long, luminous jet of flaming oil?*

(4) *When the lamp flame begins to die down and there would still appear to be plenty of fuel in the reservoir, what is the proper remedy to be applied?*

THE ANSWERS ARE ON PAGE 376.

LESSON 14

The Lathe and its Tools

THE basic principle of the lathe is that the work to be "turned" or otherwise shaped is caused to rotate against a fixed (though adjustable) cutting tool. Lathes were used for wood-turning long before they came to be employed for metal, and primitive "pole" lathes are still to be seen in much the same state of development as hundreds of years ago—for turning spindles, parts of chairs, table legs, etc. Earliest forms were operated by a cord wound around the spindle to be shaped, which was supported between centres, and given downward motion by a pedal below: the top end of the cord was fixed to a springy wooden rod some feet above the lathe. When pressure on the pedal was relaxed, the cord was pulled upward by the spring above. Thus the work had a reciprocating motion, changing direction according as the pedal or the spring was imparting motion.

Watchmaker's Lathes

Reciprocating motion, with all its obvious drawbacks, was employed in the little turning machine known as the watchmaker's "turns" —still used to some extent; this is in effect a small lathe, but motion is given by the string of a bow which passes round a pulley on the work —the latter being held between centres.

In the metal-turning lathe of today, of course, the motion is continuously toward the worker; in hand-turning, almost obsolete, the tool is supported on a rest and fed in toward the work as needed. But little work of any consequence can be done on metal without the use of a *slide-rest*, in the tool-post of which the various tools are clamped one by one as required. (On larger lathes there is a *turret* in which several tools can be fixed ready for use, the turret being loosened in its fixing and rotated to bring into position the next tool required. (A simplified type can be fitted to smaller lathes also.) The slide-rest is attached to a *carriage* or *saddle*, which is driven lengthwise by the *lead-screw*, and so brings the tool along toward the left-hand end of the lathe. The lead-screw is rotated by gears which link it up with a gear-wheel on the outer end of the spindle of the *headstock*. According to the particular *change-wheels* brought into use, so the speed of rotation of the lead-screw as compared with that of the headstock spindle is regulated; thus the slide-rest can be made to travel along faster or slower in proportion to the speed of rotation of the work fastened to the *face-plate* or held in the *chuck* attached to the headstock. This regulation of travel is used mainly in screw-cutting.

The Slide-Rest

The compound slide-rest has two *slides*: the lower one (*cross-slide*) can travel across the lathe-bed, at right angles to the face-plate; a wheel and screw enable it to be advanced or drawn back. On top of this slide is the *top slide*, which moves along parallel to the lathe-bed and, like the lower slide, is driven by a wheel and screw. In the

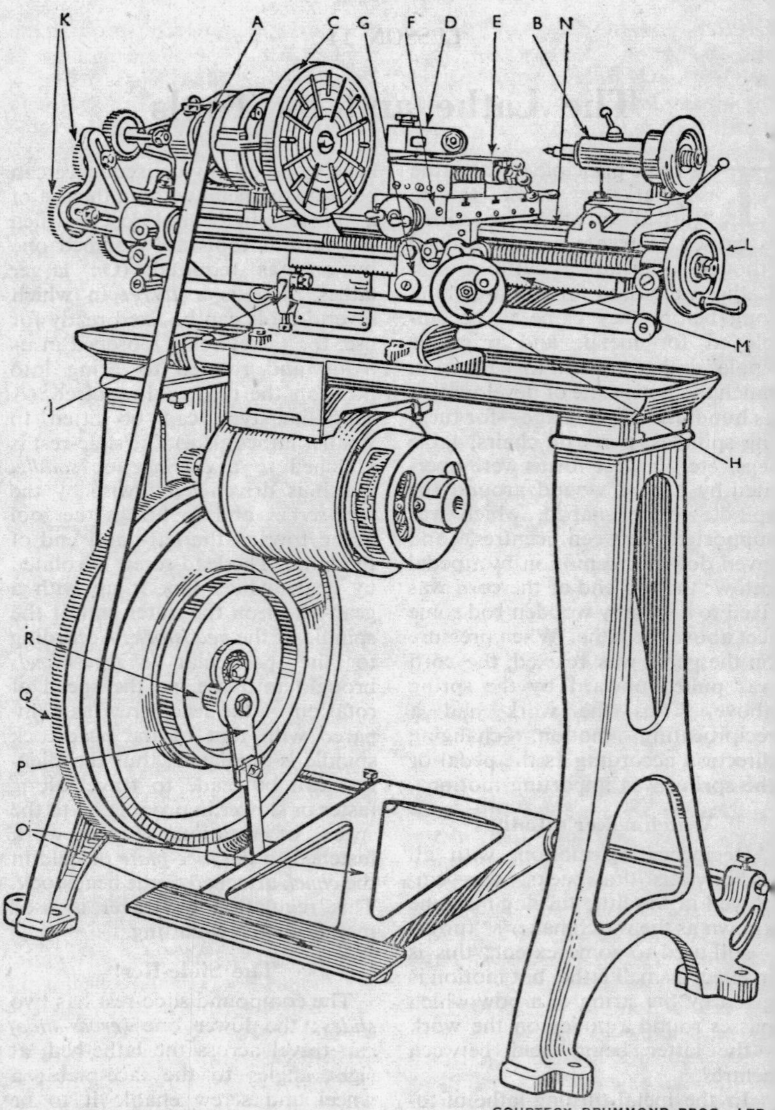

Fig. 15. *Motor-driven Drummond 3½ in. lathe.* A, *cone pulley on headstock;* B, *tail-stock;* C, *face-plate;* D, *tool-post;* E, *top slide;* F, *cross slide;* G, *carriage;* H, *hand-wheel for carriage;* J, *cut-out for lead-screw;* K, *change gears;* L, *hand-wheel for lead-screw;* M, *rack for carriage;* N, *lathe bed;* O, *treadle;* P, *pitman;* Q, *flywheel;* R, *crank. The action of the lead-screw can be reversed at will.*

Drummond lathe shown in Figs. 15 and 16 the top slide can be placed n one of several tee-slots formed in the upper surface of the cross-slide, which surface forms a boring-table. In other lathes the same adjustability is obtained by connecting the two slides by means of a dovetail in the top of the cross-slide, so that the latter can be moved bodily across the lathe-bed and locked at any desired setting.

The Top Slide

The top slide (to which the *toolholder* is attached) is arranged to swivel through a semi-circle, so as to alter the angle at which the tool s presented to the work. The base or top of the swivelling member is graduated so that a given setting can be noted and repeated when required. The slide-rest is clearly shown in Figs. 16 and 17 (the latter illustrating the process of boring work held in a chuck).

The lead-screw can be disengaged from the gears and manipulated by the hand-wheel (seen at the right-hand end in Fig. 15). There is also provided an automatic throw-out, brought into action by a stop which can be set to disengage the lead-screw at any required point in the longitudinal travel of the carriage. Apart from the action of the lead-screw, the carriage can be moved along to right or left by turning a hand-wheel which operates a pinion working in a rack (seen in Fig. 15). Reverse action can be imparted to the lead-screw at will.

The headstock is fixed to the bed of the machine. On its spindle is fastened the *cone-pulley* for the belt from the fly-wheel or countershaft. A gear-wheel is keyed to the spindle at the left, and the cone-pulley can be disengaged at will from this geared spindle, so that the spindle is then driven indirectly through the *back-gears*. (The transmission is then (*a*) by a gear-wheel fastened to the cone-pulley and turning freely on the headstock spindle; this engages with (*b*) a gear keyed to the back-gear layshaft, on the left-hand end of which is (*c*) a larger gear-wheel which engages with the gear keyed to the spindle. Back-gear drive gives a lower speed but increased power, whereas direct drive, with its greater speed, is used for lighter work.

On the headstock spindle outside the back bearing is attached the gear, which, by means of a train of *change-wheels*, drives the lead-screw when the lathe is used for screw-cutting. The ratio of the change-wheels is then arranged (by interposing suitable gears between the spindle gear and the gear on the end of the lead-screw) so that the lead-screw turns at such a speed that the carriage is moved along—taking with it the cutting-tool—a certain distance for each revolution of the headstock spindle. Thus the pitch of the screw-thread is regulated. The reader may with advantage turn back to Lesson 7 to refresh his memory about pitch and lead of screws.

The Face-Plate

The nose of the headstock spindle is threaded to take the *face-plate*, which may be (1) a small one having a radial slot and a catch-pin for driving work between centres; or (2) a larger plate (see Fig. 15), with a number of slots, to which the work to be turned is affixed by means of bolts and clamps. There is a hole through the length of the spindle—sometimes the latter is called the mandrel—and in the tapered nose a *centre* is fixed, pro-

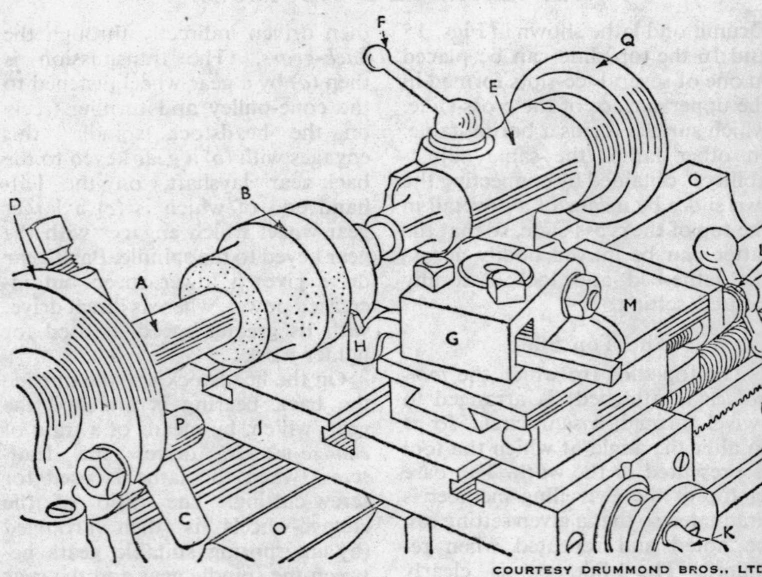

Fig. 16. *Work being turned on Drummond* $3\frac{1}{2}$ *in. centre lathe.* A, *arbor on whic work* (B) *is mounted between centres to be turned on top diameter after being borea* C, *carrier clamped to* A *and driven by stud* (P) *in face-plate* D; E, *tailstock, wit spindle lock* (F) *and hand-wheel* (Q); G, *tool holder with cranked tool* (H); J, M *compound slide-rest;* K, L, *screws for slides;* N, *lead-screw;* O, *lathe bed.*

truding though the central hole in the face-plate.

Clamped to the lathe-bed at the right-hand end is the tailstock; it can be slid along the bed guides to a suitable distance from the head-stock centre, according to the length of the work that is to be turned. It is locked to the lathe bed by turning a lever (see Fig. 16). The tailstock spindle is advanced or drawn back by turning a hand-wheel at its end. The nose of the spindle is bored out taper to take a centre like that of the headstock spindle. In order to adapt it for taper-turning, the tailstock can be "set over" from the central axis of the lathe. A drill chuck with standard taper shank may be placed in the tailstock spindle, and brought up to work (*a*) revolving with the face-plate, or (*b*) gripped in a chuck mounted on the headstock spindl nose. This is a method of drillin the centring holes in a cylindrica piece of work, ready for drivin between centres.

The lathe chuck is of two mai types: *concentric* or "universal," for holding round work; an *independent*, for gripping work o rectangular shape. In the firs named, the three jaws close in o open out in unison when a key i turned; the four jaws of the othe type are independently adjustable and can be set at varying distance from the centre. A cylindrical piec can be automatically centred in a concentric chuck, by turning th key until the rod is firmly grippe by the three jaws. In addition to th two types described there is an other, which combines both con

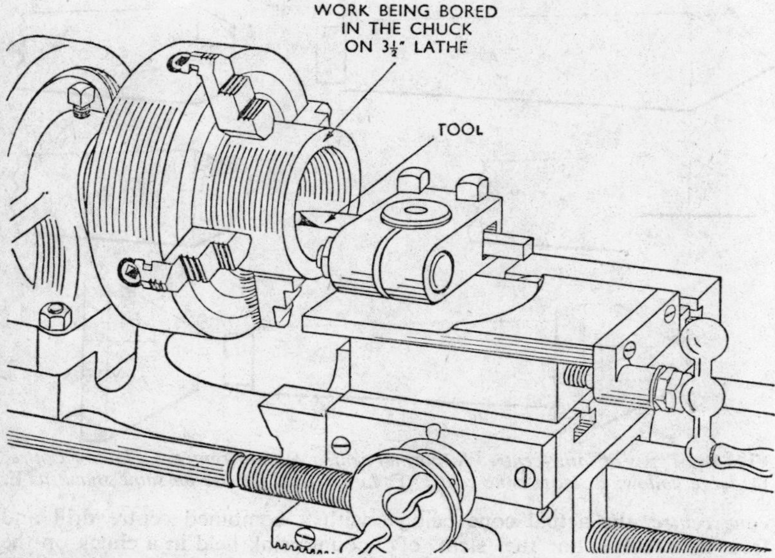

Fig. 17. *Work set up for boring on Drummond 3½ in. centre lathe. Note 4-jaw chuck.*

centric and independent systems, of which either can be used at will. (A four-jaw chuck is seen in use in Fig. 17.)

The small lathe (up to about 3½-in. centre) may be driven by a *foot-motor* built in with the lathe-bench. Power-drive by an electric motor whose gear engages with the cogged edge of the foot-motor fly-wheel is shown in Fig. 15. Where line-shafting is to be utilised an overhead countershaft will be needed, with a belt coming down to the cone-pulley of the lathe. When a machine of this sort is arranged as a bench-lathe the motor may be located at the rear at bench level, and the drive be taken by way of a short belt from a countershaft parallel with the headstock spindle. In such cases the brackets for motor and countershaft are built in as part of the lathe itself.

The longitudinal movement of the carriage by means of the lead-screw has been described; automatic power-feed may be applied to ordinary turning as well as to screw-cutting. A separate feed-shaft is often fitted in larger lathes, geared to the spindle and giving a power drive to the carriage. Automatic lateral feed is provided on many lathes, in which the cross-slide with the tool can then be moved across the lathe bed by power.

Various types of lathe-centre are illustrated in Fig. 18. Besides the ordinary centres, of the shape shown by *A*, there are special types: the *half-centre* (*B*) which is cut away to allow the tool to come up close to the centre for facing; the *hollow* (*C*), for work with a pointed end; the *female centre* (*D*) having a larger cup to take a rod with a rounded end. All these are fast in the spindle nose, rotating with the spindle. The pattern shown in *E* and *F* is a

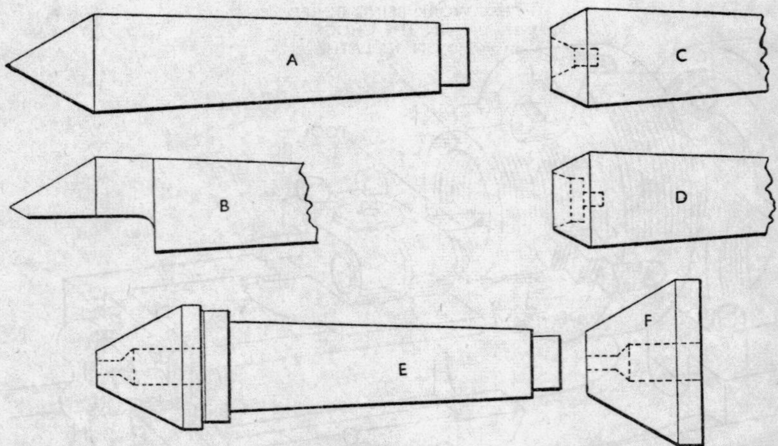

Fig. 18. *Types of lathe-centre.* A, *normal centre;* B, *half-centre;* C, *hollow centre;* D, *large hollow;* E, *loose cone centre;* F, *larger cone for use on same shank as* E.

cone centre, the actual cone being free to revolve on the stem of the taper shank, the latter being fixed by friction in the spindle nose. Several cones of varying diameters are interchangeable with the same shank, and the purpose of this type is to centre hollow pieces, or other work having a central bore. In order to obviate friction still further, the cone in another type is furnished with ball bearings to take the thrust.

The standard angle of the centre point is 60 deg., and, of course, a suitable countersink must be formed in the end of the rod or bar which is to be turned. Generally this is done

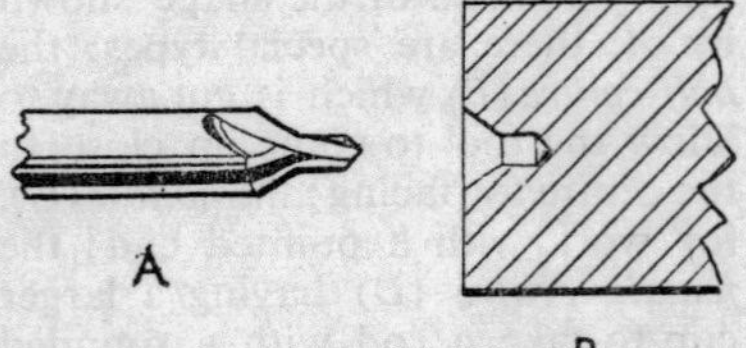

Fig. 19. *Combined centre drill and countersink; section at right shows the sinking which is produced by the tool.*

with a combined centre drill and countersink held in a chuck on the spindle nose or in the tailstock. A centre pop is first made with a centre punch after the exact centre of the rod-end has been marked. The *combined centre drill* (Fig. 19) forms a small clearance hole at the bottom of the countersink, so that the end of the lathe centre does not touch the bottom and makes contact only with the sides of the countersink.

When work is mounted between centres, it must be driven by a carrier or dog (shown at *C*, Fig. 16) clamped to it and connected to the face-plate stud or catch-pin *P* by the tail; or the tail of the carrier is bent (Fig. 20) so as to engage in a slot in the face-plate (Fig. 21).

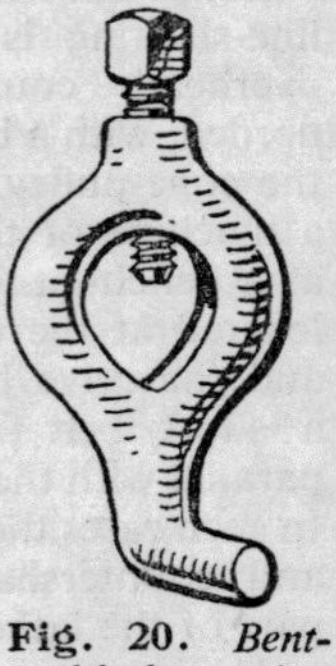

Fig. 20. *Bent-tail lathe carrier.*

When a long

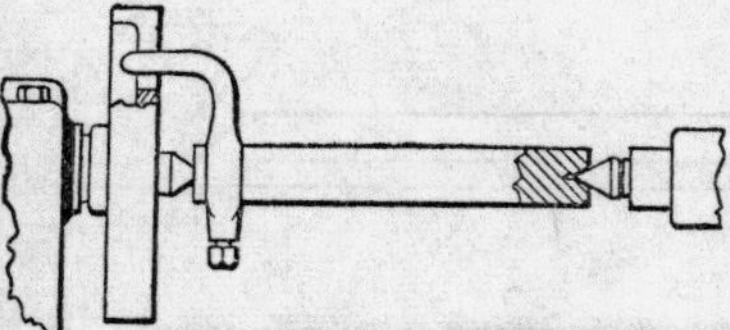

Fig. 21. *Cylindrical work on centres, driven by carrier whose bent tail engages in slot in face-plate.*

shaft is to be dealt with it will need some support besides that given at the ends, and a *rest* or *steady* (Figs. 22 and 23) is used for this purpose. The fixed or centre rest (Fig. 22) is fastened to the lathe-bed and is thus stationary; the *follower* or *travelling rest* is attached to the carriage and moves along with the work.

A selection of the commoner lathe tools is illustrated in Fig. 24 (*A–O*). These figures, with certain others, are reproduced by courtesy of the South Bend Lathe Works, of Indiana, U.S.A. The firm produces a well-known American range of lathes which embody certain applications and principles of design not yet common to smaller lathes, though standard practice with the larger and more complex machines employed in commercial manufacture. The South Bend lathe is much used in educational workshops and technical schools in the U.S.A., and can be obtained in Britain. The model with 9-in. "swing"—equivalent to 4-in. "centre" in British nomenclature—would be an excellent one for the home worker.

The lathe-tool may be compared to a chisel in its action, but, of course, the tool is stationary and the work rotates to bring fresh surfaces of metal under its point. Like the chisel, and for a similar reason, the edge is relieved or given clearance so that the chip comes away freely; again like the chisel, the angle of the cutting edge and that at which the tool is applied to the work are extremely important. Unlike the chisel, however, the lathe-tool derives its energy not from blows applied to its end, but from the steady pressure exerted by the lathe mechanism through the

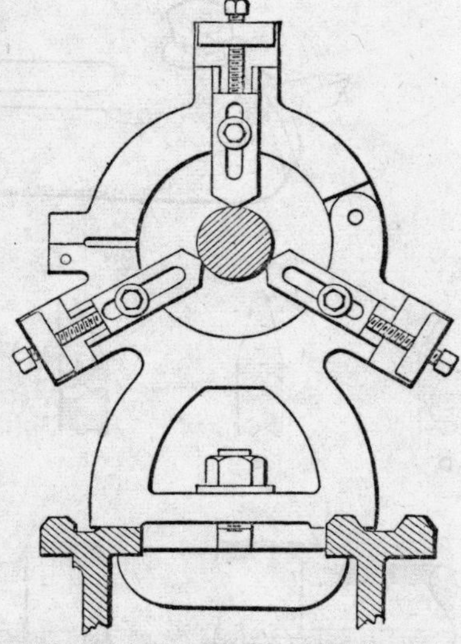

Fig. 22. *The centre rest on the lathe.*

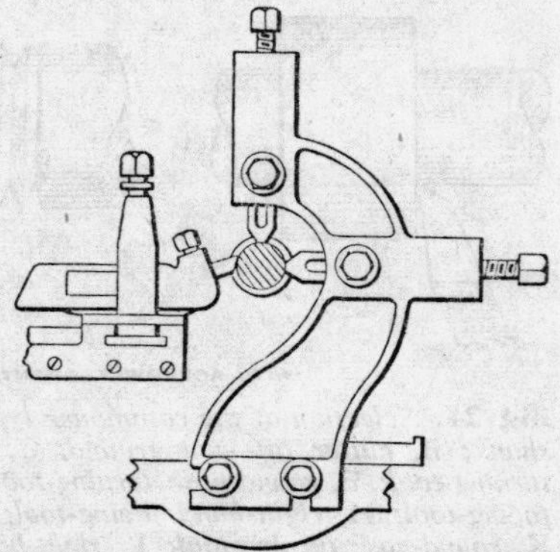

Fig. 23. *The follower rest on carriage.*

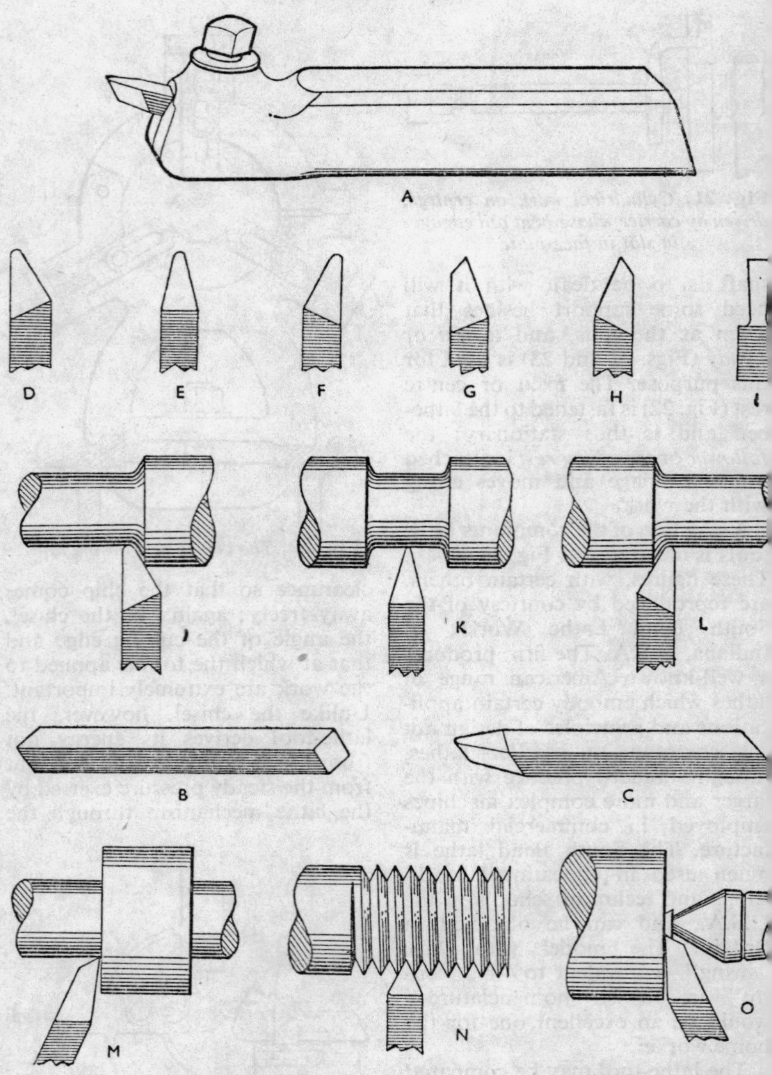

WITH ACKNOWLEDGMENT TO SOUTH BEND LATHE WORKS, INDIANA, U.S.A.

Fig. 24. *Selection of the commoner types of tools.* A, *lathe tool holder—straight shank;* B, *cutter bit—not ground;* C, *cutter bit—ground to form;* D, *left-hand turning-tool;* E, *round-nose turning-tool;* F, *right-hand turning-tool;* G, *left-hand facing-tool;* H, *right-hand facing-tool;* I, *cut-off tool;* J, *left-hand turning-tool;* K, *round-nose turning-tool;* L, *right-hand turning-tool;* M, *left-hand facing-tool;* N, *threading tool;* O, *right-hand facing-tool.*

revolving headstock. Though the tool was said to be stationary, this is only true in a relative sense, for the traversing motion of the carriage brings the tool along toward the headstock, to remove fresh metal; and by means of the cross-slide the tool can be fed farther in toward the centre of the work, as a fresh pass is made. Then, too, the depth of cut is governed by the amount by which the tool is advanced by the cross-slide; a light or a heavier cut can be made at will.

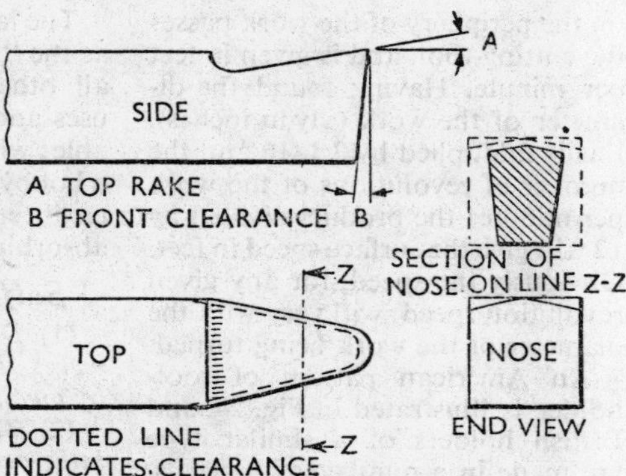

Fig. 25. *Details of round-nose lathe tool.*

Let us examine the round-nose tool shown in Fig. 25: from the nose view and the sectional drawing (on the line *ZZ*) it will be seen that the tool point is ground away from the centre line on its top surface toward either side to give *side-rake*, and can be used for both left-hand or right-hand. Compare its shape with tools shown in Fig. 24, *F* and *D*, intended for right-hand or left-hand turning respectively, where the surface is ground away back from the right or left edge, as the case may be. Now examine the side view, Fig. 25; the front of the tool is ground back at an angle to give *front clearance* (*B*), and the top is sloped back to give *top-rake* (*A*). The angle formed by the top and front is the *lip angle*, and depends on the amount of top-rake and front clearance. Clearance is needed also at the sides of the nose, and this is shown by (*a*) the sectional view on line *ZZ*; and by (*b*) the broken line in the top view (Fig. 25). In the case of a tool ground for right-hand turning the *side clearance* would be given on only one side, of course; and in a left-hand tool would come on the opposite side.

Side clearance prevents the tool-body below the cutting edge from rubbing against the side of the work; front clearance acts in a similar way at the front. The top- and side-rake endow the cutting edge with a shearing action, a principle which is universal in tool design. (Compare the scraping action of a flat drill for use in a reciprocating drill-stock with the true cutting action of a drill-point backed off for use in a brace having continuous one-way rotation, as explained in Lesson 8.) The shape of the cutting edge is the product of both rake and clearance angles, and if the tool is fed in above or below the line of the lathe-centres the angle is altered in relation to the work.

Whereas the clearance angle may be the same for a number of different materials, the rake will vary from nil to an angle of some 20 deg. or so for hard metals, and to a considerably greater angle for softer materials. The question is affected by the speed of cutting and the rate of feed. Speed here means surface speed, or the rate at which a point on the periphery of the work passes the cutting-tool, and is given in feet per minute. Having found the diameter of the work (say in inches), this is multiplied by 3·1416 and the number of revolutions of the work per minute; the product divided by 12 will give the surface speed in feet. Obviously the speed, for any given revolution speed, will vary with the diameter of the work being turned.

An American pattern of tool-holder is illustrated in Fig. 24, and British holders of a similar type are made in a number of patterns. Owing to the now common use of comparatively expensive alloy steels for lathe-tools, and the employment of such other materials as "stellite" (a cast metal composed of chromium, cobalt and other metals), it is an advantage to form the only actual cutting-tool of these and to use a tool-holder in which interchangeable cutter-bits can be secured for use. It will be noted that the bit is itself held at an angle which provides top-rake, so that only the clearance angle has to be ground; further, the tools can be sharpened without grinding the top surface.

The lathe has well been described as the "master" tool, by whose use all other machines are made. Its uses and applications are innumerable; whether turning is taken up as a hobby or as an introduction to an engineering career, it will prove of absorbing interest.

Self Testing Questions

(1) *Describe the different movements that can be given to the tool by means of the compound slide-rest.*

(2) *The standard countersink for lathe-centres has sides sloping at an angle of* 60 *deg., and at the bottom the hole continues with a short straight portion of small diameter. What is the purpose of the straight portion?*

(3) *Sometimes the lathe-tool is fed in from the rear of the work; assuming the normal direction of rotation, toward the front of the lathe, what must be the position of the tool?*

(4) *A cutting speed of* 70 *ft. per minute is recommended for cast iron; what should be the spindle speed for turning a piece of work whose diameter was* 5 *in.?*

THE ANSWERS ARE ON PAGE 376.

LESSON 15

Sheet Metal-Work: Simple Examples of Pattern-Making

SINCE this subject is sometimes found difficult to understand, we will begin with a simple practical illustration. Procure a piece of cardboard tube about a foot long—the sort that is used for sending things through the post. Lay this in a carpenter's mitre-box and saw it across at an angle of 45 deg., at a point about half-way in its length. Now bring the two cut ends together so that they join up in a right angle. (This is a practical method of making an elbow in metal tubing of zinc, copper or brass, when the joint can be soldered or brazed.)

Take one portion of the tube and slit it vertically along the shortest side; then carefully flatten the tube so that it will open out. Note the shape at the end where the 45-deg.

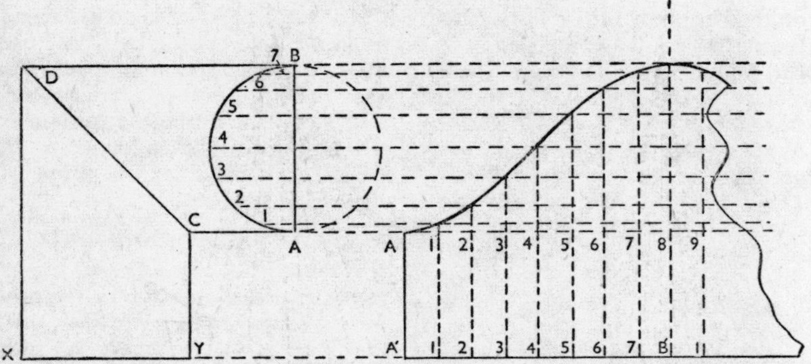

Fig. 26. *Right-angled pipe elbow. An example of a shape derived from the geometrical cylinder. The portion* XDCY *is a frustum of a cylinder.*

cut was made: compare with the outline given in Fig. 26, which shows the development for forming a right-angled pipe elbow in sheet metal. Instead of an oblique straight line, like that formed in a flat piece of material by a saw-cut at 45 deg., we have a compound curve.

The outline for the *pipe elbow* is derived from the geometrical cylinder, and the portion of the vertical pipe shown in Fig. 26 and bounded by *X, D, C, Y* is a "frustum" of a cylinder. The line *DC* denotes the place where the vertical and horizontal parts of the elbow are joined; it also denotes a plane inclined to the base of the cylinder. Reverting to our cardboard tube, note that, at the end opposite to the mitre cut, the flattened tube shows a straight line. When a cylinder is cut by a plane parallel with the base, the section produced is a circle; when, on the contrary, the cylinder is cut by a plane oblique to the base, the

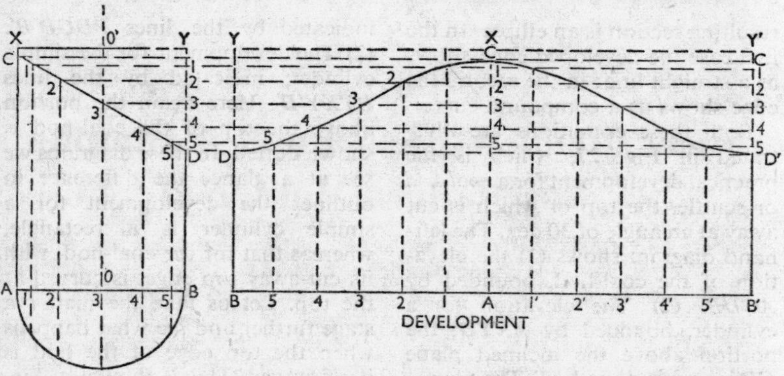

Fig. 27. *Pattern derived from cylinder cut by an oblique plane: elevation and half plan.* A, B, X, Y = *cylinder;* A, B, C, D = *frustum of cylinder cut by line inclined to the base: taken as pattern for coal-hod. Development shown on right.*

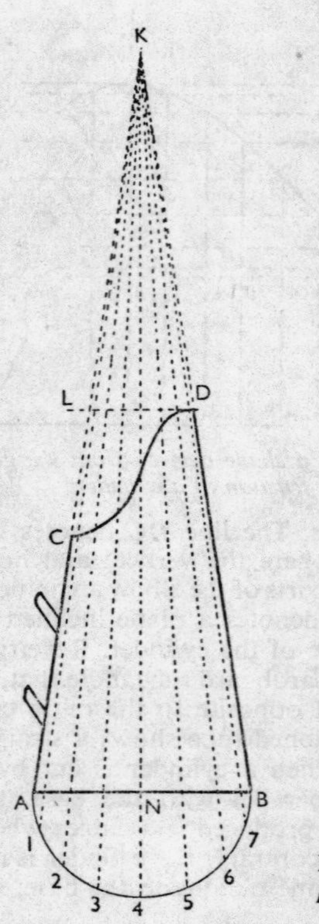

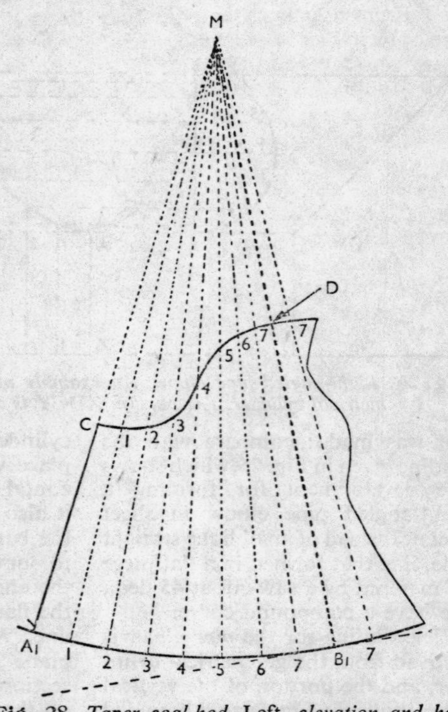

Fig. 28. *Taper coal-hod.* Left, *elevation and half plan;* right, *half pattern. Shape is based on a cone.*

resulting section is an ellipse. In the first case the developed edge shows as a straight line; in the second the edge shows as a compound curve.

Both these conditions are illustrated in Fig. 27, which is the practical development for a *coal-hod* or scuttle, the top of which is cut away at an angle of 30 deg. The left-hand diagram shows (1) the elevation of the coal-hod, bounded by *ACDB.* (2) The elevation for a cylinder, bounded by *AXYB*; the portion above the inclined plane *CD* is shown dotted. (3) The plan—only half indicated—shown by the semi-circle below the base-line *AB.* The right-hand diagram shows (1) the development for the coal-hod, indicated by the lines *BDCD'B'.* (2) The development for the simple cylinder, indicated by the lines *BYXY'B'.* Here again the portion above the top of the coal-hod is shown dotted. In these diagrams we see at a glance the difference in outline: the development for a simple cylinder is a rectangle, whereas that for the coal-hod, with its cut-away top edge, is curved at the top. Let us take the matter a stage further and see what happens when the top edge of the hod is itself curved. This is shown by Fig. 28, to which we will return later. At present, all to be noted is that the curved top edge of the taper hod, indicated by the line *CD* in the left-hand diagram, is represented in the development by the curved line *CD* of the right-hand diagram.

We will take Fig. 27 as an example of how the development is obtained. First draw the elevation of the coal-hod—composed of the base *AB*; the verticals *AC* and *BD*; and the oblique line *CD*. The length of these lines is determined by the proportions desired for the utensil. Next describe the semi-circle, to radius *AO*, setting the point of the compass on *O*. Divide the semi-circle into a number of equal divisions—we have used six. Note that it is the arc and not the base-line which is thus divided: on the base-line the spaces will be unequal. Now run up verticals from the stepped-off points of the semi-circle, taking them up to cut the oblique line *CD* at the top of the hod.

Set out a base-line for the development, a prolongation of the line *AOB* on the elevation. With dividers set to the exact distance between any two points on the curved outline of the semi-circle—say *A*-1—step off the points on the base-line: *B*,5,4,3,2,1; *A*,1,2,3,4,5, *B'*. Next, draw the *horizontal* lines from points where the verticals in the elevation cut the oblique line *CD*, as in the left-hand diagram. These lines mark the heights to which verticals on the development are to be carried. Thus line 5 gives the points where lines *B*5 and *B'*5' terminate, and so on. From the base-line *BAB'*, at the points previously stepped off, erect *verticals* to cut the respective horizontals: 5 to 5, 4 to 4, and so on.

All that remains to do now is to join the points *DCD'* by a curved line touching the points of intersection of the verticals and horizontals, at *D*,5,4,3,2,1, and *C*, etc. The portion *D* to *C* gives a half-pattern, which with a symmetrical object is usually sufficient for working purposes. The profile is merely repeated from *C* to *D'*.

In the development obtained as above no allowance is made for a lap at the point where *DB* meets *D'B'* when the hod is formed up; neither is there any allowance for a portion to be turned over the wire which reinforces the top edge (*DCD'*) of the hod, or the bottom edge of the coal-hod.

The bottom (*BA B*) is a disc,

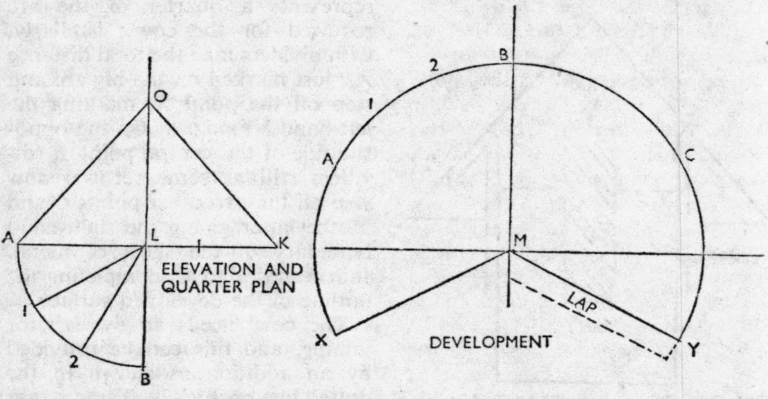

Fig. 29. *Cowl for stove pipe in sheet iron. The dotted line shows overlap for joining.*

larger in diameter than the cylinder by an amount sufficient to provide a turnover at the edge all round.

The *taper coal-hod* shown in Fig. 28 is an example of a shape based on the cone. The elevation is in the form of a triangle (*ABK*) and the half-plan is a semi-circle. Owing to the conical shape of the utensil the base-line of the developed shape is not a straight line (as in shapes derived from the cylinder) but a curve, as shown by the right-hand diagram of Fig. 28.

Other examples of conical shapes are seen in funnels and in the cowl placed as a down-draught baffle on top of stove or ventilator pipes. The latter shape is usually more obtuse, based on a shallower cone, whereas the funnel, in order to promote a ready flow of its contents, is sharper in shape. Since both forms provide the base for a number of useful articles we will take an example of each.

The piece of material from which the cowl is formed is a circle from which a sector has been cut. Here we are ignoring the question of lap at the joint. The cowl is intended to fit a 3-in. pipe, and with its overhang will be 6 in. in diameter, finished size. Draw an elevation as Fig. 29, which is in effect a triangle with a base 6 in. long and a height determined by the "slant-height" of the cone which we select as a standard. In this case a slant-height of three-quarters the diameter of the base is adopted.

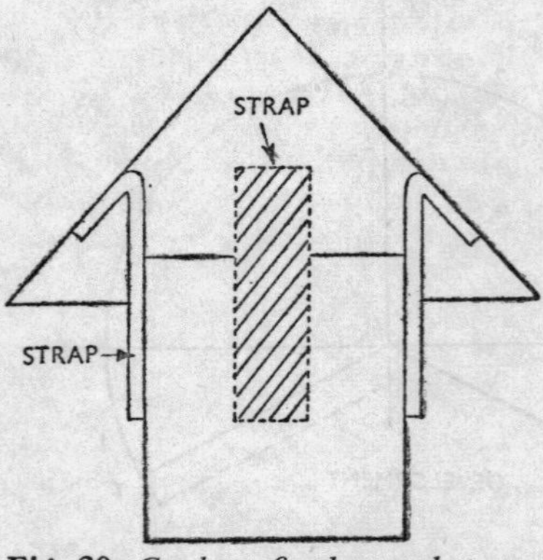

Fig. 30. *Cowl top fixed to socket over pipe by three iron straps. Part section.*

On a base-line *ALK*, with *L* as centre, describe the quarter-circle *AB*, with *AL* as radius. Next, setting dividers to three-fourths the diameter of cone-base (that is $\frac{3}{4}$ length of *AK*), prick off the point (*O*) on the vertical to mark the apex of the triangle. Join *O* to *A* and *O* to *K* to give the complete elevation of the cowl. Divide the quarter-circle *AB* into a number of equal parts: three have been taken in the example.

Now for the development itself: set compasses to the radius *AO* and describe about the centre *M* an arc which will be great enough to give the required area; something more than two-thirds of a circle will do in the present case. From the central vertical *MB*, step off along the arc three divisions equal to the distance *A*1 on the quarter-circle in the left-hand diagram. This represents a quarter of the arc required for the cowl; similarly, with dividers take the total distance *AB* just marked on the big arc and step off the point *X*, marking the left-hand boundary. On the opposite side of the central point *B* (dividers still at same setting) now step off the two other points *C* and *Y*, the latter giving the right-hand boundary of the sheet of metal. Join *X* and *Y* to *M*, completing the outline of the developed surface.

The cowl needs an overlap for joining, and this can be provided by an addition as shown in the dotted line on Fig. 29. Three straps connect the cowl top to the short

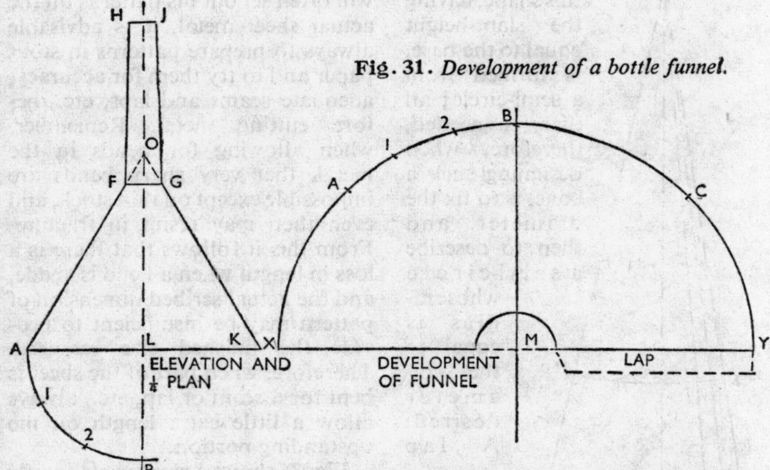

Fig. 31. *Development of a bottle funnel.*

socket which fits over the stove pipe. The arrangement is shown in Fig. 30.

Bottle Funnel

The common bottle funnel is usually based on a sharper form of cone, of which an example is given in Fig. 31. For ease of comparison the same length of base is taken as for the cowl shown in Figs. 29 and 30. Note that the slant-height (*AO*) in the present case is equal to the diameter of the funnel—in other words, is equal to the base length of the cone (*AK* in Fig. 31). Set out the base of the cone; with the dividers set to this length, rest one leg on *A* and step off the height on the centre vertical line at *O*: join *A* to *O* and *K* to *O* to give the outline of the elevation. Draw short horizontal lines to mark the base and top of spout in the elevation; prick off with the dividers a point at each side of centre line at base and top to give diameter *FG* and *HJ* respectively; then join *F* to *H* and *G* to *J* to complete the outline of the spout.

Prolong base-line of the cone *AL* rightward to give the base for the development, *XMY*. Fix a centre point, *M*, and erect a vertical here. Set the compasses to the radius *AO* on the elevation and, with *M* on the development as centre, describe the arc *XABCY*. (Actually the developed shape is a semicircle, but we will prove it to explain the process of determining the shape of any similar cone.) Carry the arc somewhat further than the base-line at each end.

On the quadrant *AB* below the elevation, prick off three equal divisions: take the setting for one division (say, *B*-2) and step it off three times along the arc of development, beginning from the centre point *B* on that arc. Now open out the dividers to the complete distance, *A*,1,2,*B* (on the development) and prick off *C* and *Y* on the right-hand half of the arc; similarly, rest the dividers on *A* and prick off the point *X* on the left-hand side of the arc. Join *X* to *M* and *Y* to *M* to obtain the boundaries of the developed surface.

Note.—It is clear that a cone of

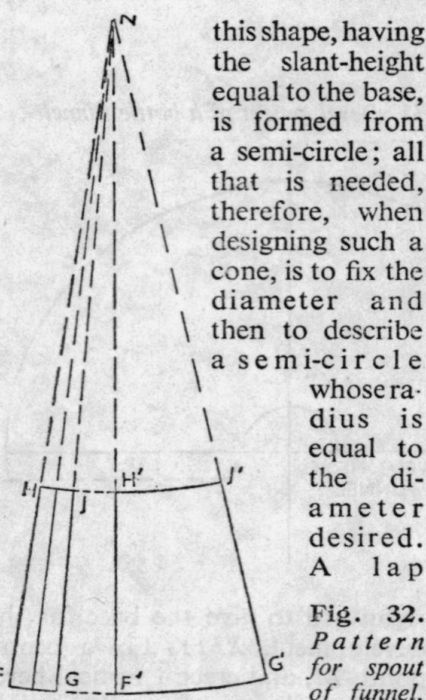

Fig. 32. *Pattern for spout of funnel.*

this shape, having the slant-height equal to the base, is formed from a semi-circle; all that is needed, therefore, when designing such a cone, is to fix the diameter and then to describe a semi-circle whose radius is equal to the diameter desired. A lap must be allowed for, as indicated by the dotted outline in Fig. 31.

A hole for the spout is allowed in the base of the semi-circle, the diameter of the spout giving the radius for the hole. Owing to the slowness of the taper, a long radius is needed to describe the arcs for development (see Fig. 32). Make a separate drawing of the spout, as Fig. 32, allowing ample height above the top for the converging lines that determine the radius. Prolong the lines *FH* and *GJ* until they meet in *N*. Having thus obtained the radius of that particular taper, describe the arcs *F′H′* and *G′J′*, giving top and bottom outlines of the spout. For the width, take about 3½ times the diameter *FG* (Fig. 31, elevation) at the bottom of the spout, and prick off along the arc *F′G′* in Fig. 32. Connect *F′* and *G′* to the point *N*, thus completing the profile of the spout.

Although the experienced worker will often set out his patterns on the actual sheet metal, it is advisable always to prepare patterns in stout paper and to try them for accuracy, adequate seams and laps, etc., before cutting metal. Remember, when allowing for bends in the metal, that very sharp bends are impossible except on thin stock, and even then may result in fracture. From this it follows that there is a loss in length when a bend is made, and the actual scribed dimension of pattern may be insufficient to provide the finished size required. Therefore, when part of the sheet is bent for a seam or lap, etc., always allow a little extra length on the upstanding portion.

Fig. 26 shows a *right-angled elbow* such as might occur in a stove-pipe or ventilation pipe. The line *DC* is the mitre joint. A small-diameter tube could be cut to a 45-deg. mitre in a mitre-box, as described earlier; the two parts could be soldered or brazed on the line *DC*. In a similar manner, a pipe not required to stand heat could be soldered after forming up from the sheet; but in other cases a properly formed seam would be necessary,

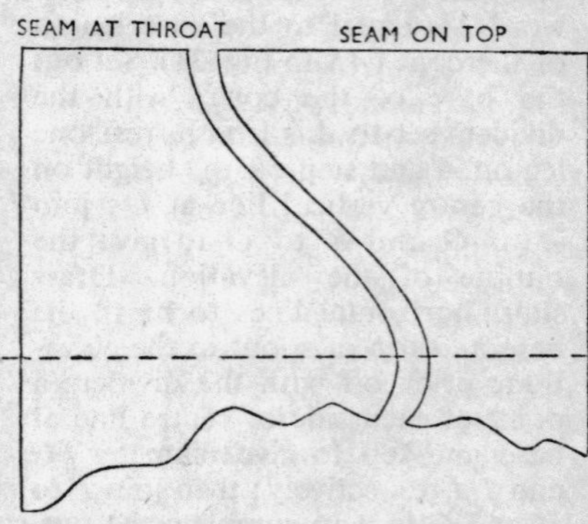

Fig. 33. *Right-angled pipe elbow. Diagram showing how both pieces can be cut from the same sheet of metal.*

and extra material would have to be provided at the joint, over and above the developed surface shown in Fig. 26.

Draw an elevation of the elbow, and then describe the semi-circle on the line *AB*, to represent the half-plan. Divide the arc into eight equal parts; carry along the horizontals as shown. Obtain the divisions along the base-line of the development, as explained in earlier examples, giving points *B*,5,4,3,2,1,*A*, and run up verticals to intersect the horizontals. With a curved line connect the points: *A*,1,2,3,4,5,6,7, 8. This gives a half-pattern of the complete development, and is sufficient for working purposes when the pattern is bilaterally symmetrical (*i.e.*, has both sides alike), as in the present case.

Fig. 33 shows how both parts of the pipe elbow may be cut without waste from the same piece of sheet. Note that the seam in the upper member would come on top of the pipe in this case, and not on the throat of the elbow as in the lower member.

It is worth while noting the similarity of the pattern in Fig. 26 to that in Fig. 27: supposing that an elbow with a 30-deg. joint were needed, the pattern given by Fig. 27 would be suitable. If other angles be needed, all that has to be done is to draw the elevation and indicate the desired angle; the pattern for development can be constructed in a precisely similar manner by first describing a half-plan and then obtaining the intersecting verticals. Horizontals are drawn and the divisions stepped off along the base-line as before.

A different method of obtaining the development is used in Fig. 28 (*taper coal-hod*). The elevation and half-plan are drawn as before. The proportions and actual dimensions of the coal-hod are settled first: width at top (*LD*) and bottom (*AB*) are set off on horizontals which cross the centre vertical *NK*. Next, lay a straight-edge on *A* and *L* and run a line upward until it intersects the centre vertical; in the same manner connect *B* and *D* and continue upward to the point of intersection. The latter gives *K*, the centre for obtaining the desired radius.

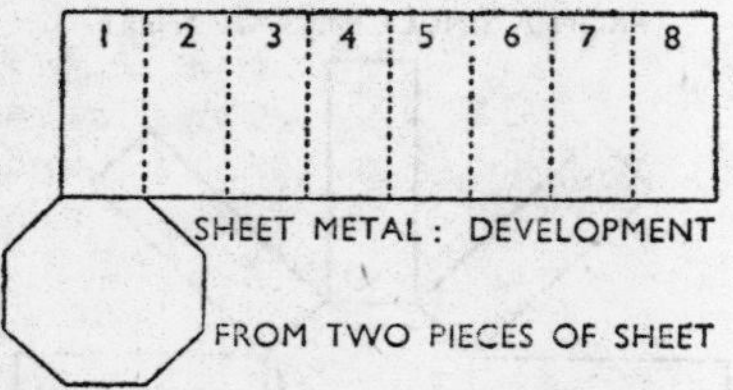

Fig. 34. *Pattern for octagonal flower or fern pot. Compare Fig.* 35.

Now for the development: on a base-line which is a prolongation of *AB*, mark off a centre-point and erect the vertical B_1M; from *M*, with compasses set to radius *KB*, describe an arc A_1B_1, etc., as in Fig. 28. Beginning at the central point B_1 of the arc, step off the points 7,6,5,4,3,2,1,A_1. This gives a half-pattern; the construction of the remaining half is optional. Connect these points with the top centre *M*. With one leg of the dividers on *B* in the base-line *ANB* of the elevation, and the other leg on *D*, obtain the length *BD* for transference to the centre vertical of the development (B_1D). Next obtain the length of 7 and transfer in the same way.

Continue until all the divisions have been marked in this way, finishing with *AC*, which gives the left-hand boundary of the half-pattern (A_1C). All that now remains to be done is to join up the points

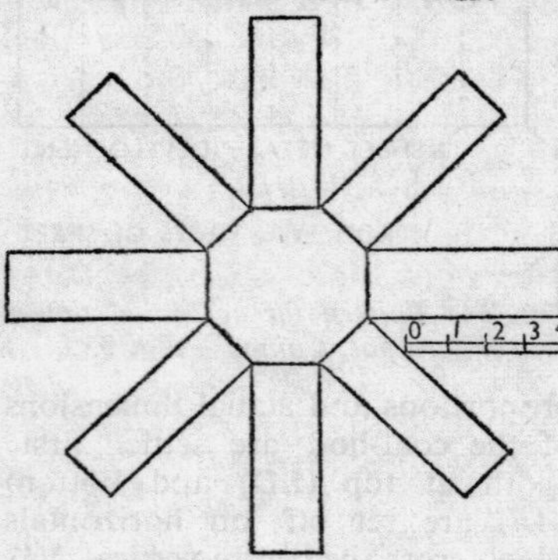

Fig. 35. *Octagonal fern pot developed from one piece of sheet metal.*

with a curve passing through all of them, as in Fig. 28.

As an example of simple development of rectangular or polygonal patterns we may take the little fern-pot shown in Figs. 34 and 35. Fig. 34 shows how the dimensions and shape for the sides are obtained from the octagonal plan. The dotted verticals show the bends. Note what was said earlier about allowing for loss of material at bends. Unless a butt-joint is to be used, there must be an allowance at one margin for lap. Also, unless the side is to be merely butted to the bottom octagon, upstanding lugs will have to be provided on the octagon at each of the facets. In the latter case the lugs would come inside the casing and be inset or bent inward a little.

Another method is shown in Fig. 35. Here the entire article is formed up from a single piece of metal sheet. The idea is to solder (butt-joints) the side-seams; the top edge is turned over a wire first bent to correct octagonal shape and proper size. This method calls for careful cutting and fitting, and is given as exercise in practical work. An example in simple rectangular work is given by the brazing tray illustrated in Lesson 13.

Manipulation of Sheet Metal

Sheet metal, after being marked with chalk and a straight-edge, can be cut with a pair of tinman's snips. Bent snips will be needed for small curved work. Begin the cut and carry on with as few "bites" as possible, since each fresh start will probably leave a small, sharp sliver of metal outstanding—marring the work and endangering the operator's fingers. Wear an old pair of stout gloves for all such jobs. The edges can be cleaned up with a coarse flat file, working along and not across the edge. Careful preliminary marking and accurate cutting should not leave much to be cleaned up.

Sheet iron and tinplate are most difficult to cut, especially in stout gauges. Zinc cuts easily, and soft copper also. Hard copper needs more care. Bending at right angles or similar large angles will be helped by preparing a few *edge-turners* out of clean deal batten (oak would be better): pieces 6 in., 9 in., 15 in., and about 2 ft. long, about 2 in. × 1 in. in section should be cut. The next job is to make a saw-cut about $\frac{3}{4}$ in. to 1 in. deep in one edge. In use, the grooved edge is slipped on to the edge of the sheet to be turned up, and while the rest of the sheet is firmly clamped the wooden turner is bent upward or downward, taking the metal with it.

This device serves for bends close to the margin of the sheet. When the upstand has to be formed farther away—as in the case of the brazing tray illustrated in Lesson 13—another means must be employed.

Obtain two longer pieces of batten, which need not be grooved. Lay them on the bench and let them come to the end of the bench at each side, so that, after the metal sheet has been sandwiched between them at the chalk line, both they and the sheet can be clamped firmly to the bench top. The part of the sheet to be bent up should project over the front edge of the bench, with the edge of the clamp just flush (or a little way in) from the bench front. Now grip the free edge of the metal with one of the grooved strips of batten mentioned above; holding a clean and square piece of 2 in. × 2 in. against the front edge of the clamp, against and beneath the sheet, bend up with the turner, pressing in firmly meanwhile with the 2 in. × 2 in. block. This will start the bend, which can be completed by gentle blows of a mallet against the front of the 2 in. × 2 in. block, still held squarely on the sheet.

Take the sheet out of the clamp and true up the upstand by mallet blows while the bend rests on the angle of the wooden block, the latter resting on the bench. Another way to finish a bend—useful where several of the same dimension are to be made—is to cut a block 2 in. × 2 in. the proper length to fit nicely inside the work (the brazing tray, for instance) at one end, and another block for the longer side. Place the blocks (one at a time) inside after two opposite upstands have been bent up—that is, between these upstands crosswise—and hammer up the sides of the tray at each end; it is presumed that the two long sides have first been bent up, and that a short block (same length as the short side) is being used to square up the extreme end-parts of these upstands, which are hammered from the outside against the *ends* of the block.

Take out the block and start to bend up one *short* side: place the block inside the tray at one end, across the tray as before, and hammer the short upstand against its *side*, while the block is held down firmly. Repeat for the opposite short end. Next place a long block inside the tray (same length as the long upstands first bent up) and true up the end parts of the *short* upstands. After this, use the long block to true up the sides of the *long* upstands by tapping with a mallet lengthwise against the block.

Self Testing Questions

(1) *What section is produced when a cylinder is cut by a plane parallel with the base?*

(2) *What shape is produced by the development of a cylinder?*

(3) *How does an increase in the height of a cone affect the shape produced by development of its surface? Explain by comparison of Figs.* 29 *and* 31.

(4) *A cone similar in angle to Fig.* 29 *is to be constructed with a diameter of* 16 *centimetres. What should be its slant-height?*

(5) *A funnel, having the same angle as that shown in Fig.* 31, *is required to have a slant-height of* 25 *centimetres. What should be the length of the base-line in the elevation?*

(6) *If no extra material for lap were allowed in the development given by Fig.* 29, *what would be the effect upon the shape of taking the lap from the edge* MY *or the edge* XM?

(7) *In Figs.* 26 *and* 28 *a half-pattern only is provided; how can the complete pattern of the development be obtained from these?*

(8) *In the pipe elbow illustrated in Fig.* 26 *the joint or seam is intended*

to come at the line AA′, *on the throat of the elbow. Suppose the seam were desired instead on the line* BB′: *how would this be effected in laying out the shape for the surface?*

THE ANSWERS ARE ON PAGE 376.

Answers to Self Testing Questions

LESSON 1

(1) Because when a drill or bench-tool is clamped on it, the thrust would loosen the board unless it were strongly secured.

(2) They should be fixed one at each side and one at the back, with washers and nuts, about midway between top and bottom rails.

(3) Because portable vices tend, under pressure of work, to swivel round on the screw-clamp and become loose.

LESSON 2

(1) Copper, Aluminium, Iron, Lead.

(2) Aluminium, 495 lb.; Iron, 1455 lb.; Lead, 2118 lb.

(3) The aluminium would lengthen more than twice as much as the iron, and the bi-metal strip therefore would bend.

(4) The lead, 50-tin 50-solder has the lower melting point.

(5) Brasses contain copper and zinc; bronzes contain copper and tin.

(6) The object is that in case of overheating of the bearing the lining metal would soften and prevent damage to the shaft and brasses.

(7) Tin (1 per cent., in naval brass).

(8) Admiralty gun-metal contains 10 per cent. of tin and only 2 per cent. of zinc; naval brass contains only 1 per cent. of tin, so that in effect it is a copper–zinc alloy.

LESSON 3

(1) The main difference lies in the percentage of carbon: it is lower in steel and is in the form of combined carbon.

(2) Wrought iron is a pure form of iron made in the puddling furnace; it contains up to ·5 per cent. of carbon and can be forged. Malleable cast iron is not really "malleable," but by a process of heat-treatment (long annealing) the hard carbon for some little distance from the surface is altered into graphite or reduced by oxidation, and therefore parts cast in this metal will stand a certain amount of working.

(3) It can be used for tools such as cold chisels.

(4) A tool made from mild steel would not hold its edge, since this metal cannot be hardened by heat-treatment.

LESSON 4

(1) The file should be heated and allowed to cool very slowly —for example, by leaving it in the hot ashes beneath a grate for some hours.

(2) Sheet copper can be annealed again by heating the metal.

LESSON 5

(1) In wire-drawing the rod is drawn through holes (progressively diminishing in diameter) to reduce its thickness to that desired.

(2) The cold-working of brass or copper hardens the metal.

(3) Hard brass and copper can be softened by heating them, which relieves strain set up in the metal by hammering or spinning, for example.

(4) In a bolted joint the holes are clearing holes; in a joint made with machine screws the screws go into threaded holes in one member and pass through clearing holes in the other.

LESSON 6

(1) The bolt will be drawn along or moved backward, provided the nut, though it can turn freely, is not permitted to move lengthwise.

(2) Either of the following would give an advance of one-twentieth of an inch per complete revolution: B.S.W. $\frac{1}{4}$-in. or B.S.F. $\frac{3}{8}$-in.

LESSON 7

(1) If too large a hole were drilled, enough material would not be left to provide proper full-size threads, and the screw at the best would be slack.

(2) The mangle might be mended by making a repair plate with clearing holes (like the front plate in the two-plate method), and tapping holes to correspond in the mangle web.

LESSON 8

(1) Apart from the more scientifically designed cutting edges of the twist-drill, the parallel shank provides guidance in the hole, and the spiral flutes bring the cuttings away upward.

(2) The cutting edges of the drill mentioned must be ground flat, at right angles to the lip-faces, so that there is no cutting angle.

(3) The drill would have no front rake, since the cutting angle would be zero, and could function only as a "scraper."

LESSON 9

(1) The hole made would be greater in diameter than the drill, for it would be twice the width of the longest cutting edge.

(2) The metal becomes hardened and the drill ceases to cut it.

(3) The Archimedean drillstock is difficult to keep upright (*a*) because of its height above the work, and (*b*) because the action of raising and lowering the threaded sleeve tends to cause the spindle to wobble.

LESSON 10

(1) A washer or "clinch" is put over the rivet-tail and the rivet is closed down on top.

(2) A flat-head rivet.

(3) If the rivet-shank is too long it will not receive support at its end and will probably bend instead of closing down nicely.

LESSON 11

(1) Flat files, bastard or second cut and smooth.

(2) Saw-edge file (best), or a small size saw-sharpening file.

(3) Mark off the blank to the proper height and length; cut away outside waste metal with a fine hacksaw; put blank and pattern side by side (warded ends together) in a vice and file out the wards with a warding file; test callipers, bevel off outside front edges; test length and bore of "pipe," or length of stub, and try in lock; ease off notches with file until easy action is obtained.

(4) Make a notch on either side with a saw-sharpening file and snap off.

LESSON 12

(1) By the proper use of a flux, which cleans the surface, keeps

the air away, and helps the solder to flow where it is needed.

(2) Killed spirits cleans the metal; resin fluxes and protects the surface.

(3) Tin is resistant to atmospheric corrosion and hence presents a clean and relatively oxide-free surface, so that a non-corrosive flux may be used; a corrosive flux might eat through the tin plating of the iron or steel, and in any case the cut edges are vulnerable.

LESSON 13

(1) The boiler is set up horizontally in the tray on two pieces of brick, with the bush upward; borax paste is applied inside the hole in the boiler and around the top surface, and also to the bush-socket; a narrow strip of silver solder is cut and bent around the bush, the latter being in its proper position.

(2) No. 9 melts at the lower temperature.

(3) Open the air inlet and point the nozzle where the flame can do no harm; let the lamp cool, and then prick out the burner nipple; re-fill the spirit cup and re-light.

(4) Give a few strokes to the pump; if the lamp still fails to work properly, or flame spurts out, open the air inlet and proceed as in previous answer; the jet may have become blocked.

LESSON 14

(1) A longitudinal movement, by the carriage hand-wheel; a movement across the lathe-bed, by the cross-slide, to feed the tool into the work; a movement parallel to the line of centres, by the top slide (which can also be swivelled within 180 deg.).

(2) The small hole extending inward from the end of the countersunk end lessens friction; only the sloping sides of centre and countersunk hole should make contact.

(3) The tool must be inverted so that the cutting edge is at the bottom.

(4) The answer is given by the following:

(*A*) Cutting speed (ft. per min.) 70×12 (to reduce to inches).

(*B*) Diameter of work (inches).

(*C*) 3·1416.

(method of working $\frac{A}{BXC}$

$$= \frac{840}{3{\cdot}1416 \times 5} = 53{\cdot}5 \text{ r.p.m.}$$

LESSON 15

(1) The section produced is elliptical.

(2) The shape produced is a rectangle.

(3) An increase in height for a given base diameter reduces the radius of the circle from which the development is constructed.

(4) The slant-height should be 12 centimetres.

(5) The length of the base is 25 centimetres, equal to the slant-height.

(6) Taking lap from the edges would sharpen the cone.

(7) The pattern can be completed by repeating on the right of the central line the profile obtained at the left.

(8) By beginning the development on the line *BB′* and continuing to the corresponding line, thus completing the development.

MOTOR ENGINEERING

Edited by Harold Jelley

Editor of *Motor-Car Maintenance, Overhaul and Repair*

LESSON 1

The Motor-Car and Motor-Cycle Simply Explained

PETROL engines are divided into two main types, (1) four-stroke, (2) two-stroke, and these work on somewhat different principles. The two-stroke engine is economical and simple, but its use is confined mainly to motor-cycles. The four-stroke engine is the type generally favoured, and the student can best begin by studying the single-cylinder four-stroke engine. The characteristics of twin-cylinder motor-cycle and multi-cylinder car engines can then be readily appreciated.

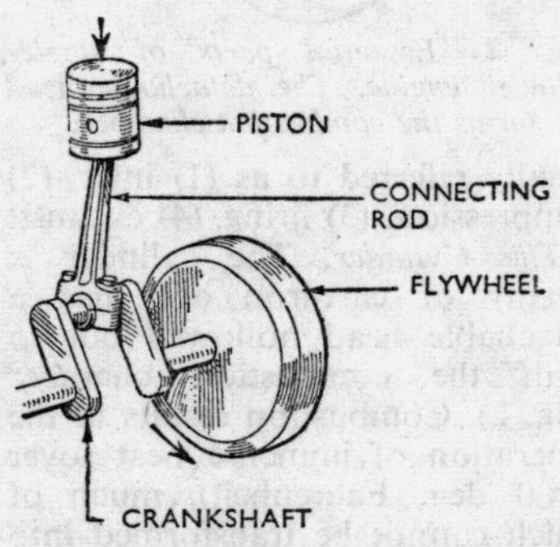

Fig. 1. *Converting up-and-down into rotary motion: the crankshaft rotates because of downward thrust on the piston.*

The Four-Stroke Engine

Fig. 1 shows how downward thrust on a piston attached by a connecting-rod to a crankshaft causes the latter to rotate. The provision of a flywheel enables the crankshaft to go on rotating for a while even if the piston thrust ceases. Thus the piston automatically rises again after completing a downward movement. Complete up or down movements are known as piston strokes. The downward thrust on the piston is obtained by the combustion of the gases, or mixture, in a combustion chamber, which is a confined space between the top or crown of the piston and the closed end of a close-fitting cylinder in which the piston slides. In order to obtain rapid and complete combustion, the mixture has to be compressed before ignition.

A German named Otto designed and made the first practicable four-stroke engine in which *one* power-stroke of the piston occurs every four strokes, and this principle remains unaltered today. On a four-stroke engine the mixture is sucked in (downward piston stroke); compressed (upward piston stroke); ignited (downward piston stroke); then expelled (upward piston stroke). It should be noted that this sequence on a single-cylinder engine involves only one firing stroke for every *two* revolutions of the crankshaft; hence the importance of the flywheel. The four strokes are

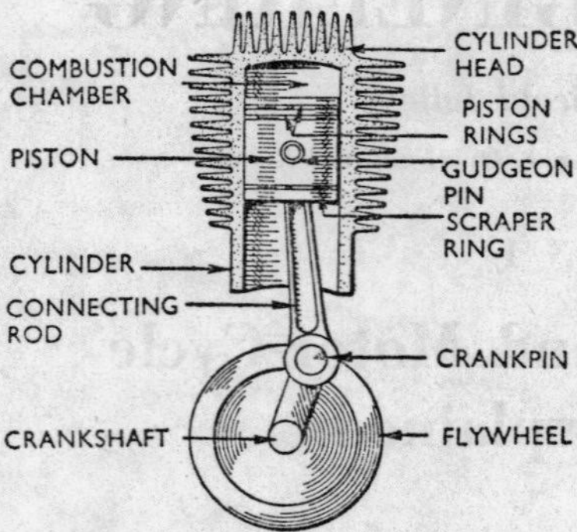

Fig. 2. *Essential parts of single-cylinder engine. The detachable head forms the combustion chamber.*

usually referred to as (1) inlet, (2) compression, (3) firing, (4) exhaust.

The Cylinder. The cylinder is usually of cast-iron and has a detachable head hollowed out to form the combustion chamber (Fig. 2). Combustion results in the generation of immense heat (over 2,000 deg. Fahrenheit), much of which cannot be transformed into useful energy. This surplus heat is dissipated on most motor-cycle engines by means of radiating fins cast around the cylinder head and upper part of the cylinder in the manner shown in Fig. 2. With multi-cylinder car engines it is usual to employ a water-cooling system (see page 395), where the cylinders are surrounded by water-jackets. The cylinder and jackets are all cast in one block.

The Piston is often made of a light alloy and is secured to the connecting-rod by means of a gudgeon-pin, a large-diameter pin passing through the eye of the connecting-rod. To reduce friction and to ensure absolute gas-tightness between the piston and the cylinder in which it slides, two or three springy steel piston rings are provided near the top of the piston. They fit closely in grooves and press outward against the inside of the cylinder. A scraper ring is generally provided near the base of the piston. Its knife-like lower edge scrapes surplus oil from the cylinder.

The Crankshaft. The crankshaft is of robust design, as it has to take terrific piston thrusts and rotary impulses. On single- and twin-cylinder motor-cycle engines it is usually built up of two heavy-rimmed flywheels and a detachable crank-pin. In this case the big-end of the connecting-rod is not split, but has a roller bearing fitted. On multi-cylinder car engines, however, the crankshaft is in one piece, and split plain bearings are used (except on some twin-cylinder engines) for the big-ends.

The Valves. The combustion chamber on four-stroke engines has two mechanically-operated valves known as the inlet valve and the exhaust valve. When both valves are closed, the combustion space is a sealed gas-tight chamber. When the inlet valve is open, the combustion chamber is in direct communication with the carburettor which supplies the gas mixture. When the exhaust valve is open, the combustion chamber is in communication with the outside atmosphere *via* a silencer. Most valves are of the poppet type (Fig. 3), mushroom-shaped steel members with long stems. The heads have bevelled

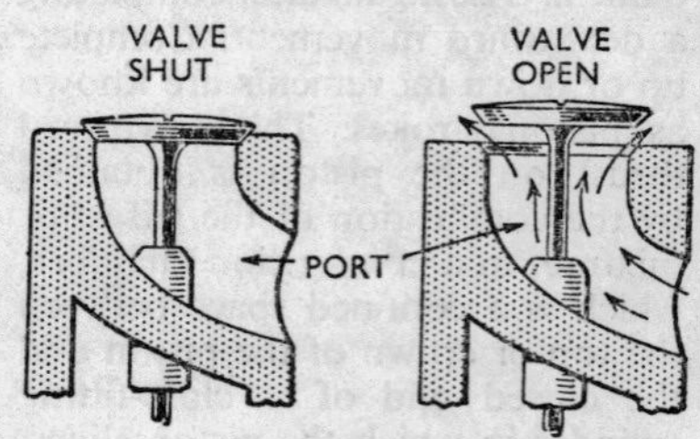

Fig. 3. *Mushroom-shaped poppet-type valve, shown* (left) *shut, and* (right) *open.*

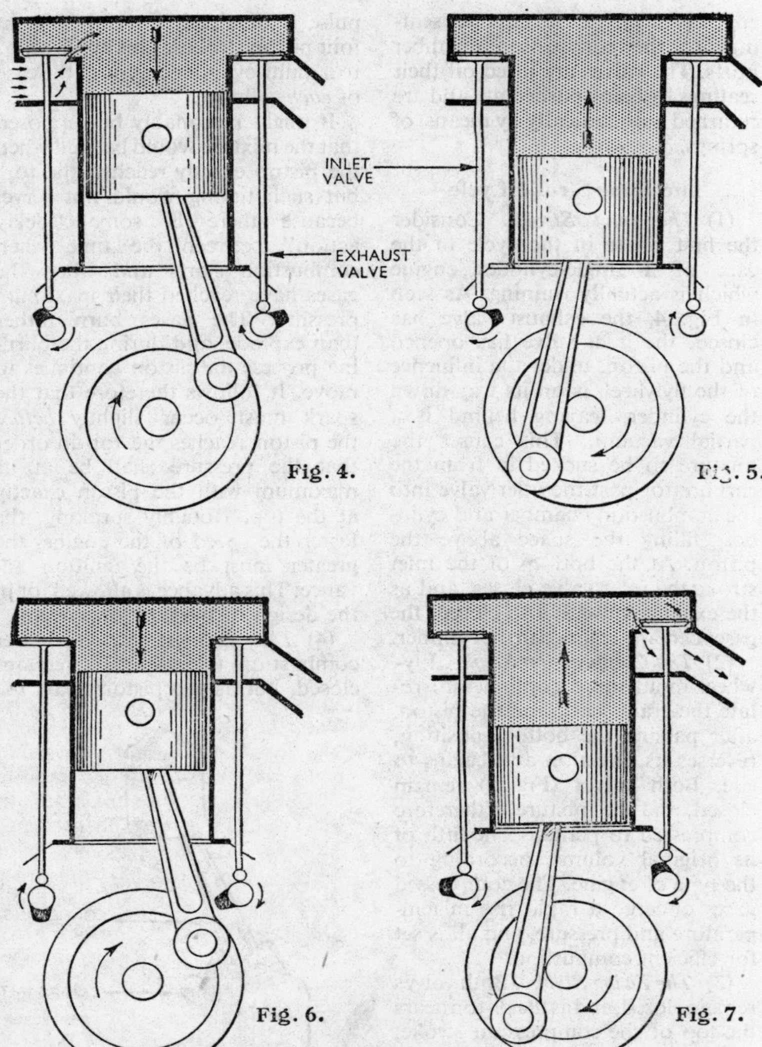

Figs. 4–7. *The four-stroke cycle.* Above, left, *the inlet stroke; the exhaust valve is closed, the inlet valve open, and the piston falling.* Right, *the compression stroke; both valves are closed, and the piston is beginning to rise.* Bottom, left, *the firing stroke; both valves are still closed, and the piston is again falling.* Right, *the exhaust stroke; the exhaust valve (at right of diagram) is open, and the piston rising.*

edges which seat on circular seatings in the combustion chamber ports. The valves are lifted off their seatings by being pushed up, and are returned automatically by means of springs.

The Four-Stroke Cycle

(1) *The Inlet Stroke.* Consider the first phase in the cycle in the case of a single-cylinder engine which is actually running. As seen in Fig. 4, the exhaust valve has closed, the inlet valve has opened and the piston, under the influence of the flywheel, is on its way down the cylinder, leaving behind it a partial vacuum. This causes the mixture to be sucked in from the carburettor past the inlet valve into the combustion chamber and cylinder, filling the space above the piston. At the bottom of the inlet stroke the inlet valve closes, and as the exhaust valve is also closed, the gases become trapped in the cylinder.

(2) *The Compression Stroke.* Flywheel momentum continues to rotate the crankshaft, and the piston, after passing the bottom position, reverses its direction and begins to rise. Both valves (Fig. 5) remain closed, and the mixture is therefore compressed to perhaps one-fifth of its original volume, according to the type of engine. The compressed gases undergo a rapid rise in temperature and pressure, and all is set for efficient combustion.

(3) *The Firing Stroke.* Both valves remain closed, and as the piston nears the top of the compression stroke, the mixture is ignited by the flash of an electric spark across the points of a sparking plug (see page 390). Rapid combustion ensues (Fig. 6), and the piston, after reversing its direction on passing the top position, is driven down the cylinder with great force. Thus a power impulse is obtained, the only one in four piston strokes. This applies also to a multi-cylinder engine in the case of *each* cylinder.

It might reasonably be supposed that the mixture would be fired when the piston exactly reached the top, but such timing would not serve, because there is some "delay action" between the time when combustion starts and when the gases have reached their maximum pressure. The gases burn rather than explode, and during the burning process the piston continues to move. It follows therefore that the spark must occur slightly *before* the piston reaches the top in order that the pressure shall be at its maximum with the piston exactly at the top. Roughly speaking, the faster the speed of the engine, the greater must be the ignition advance. This advance is allowed for in the design of the ignition system.

(4) *The Exhaust Stroke.* After combustion, the inlet valve remains closed, but as the piston nears the

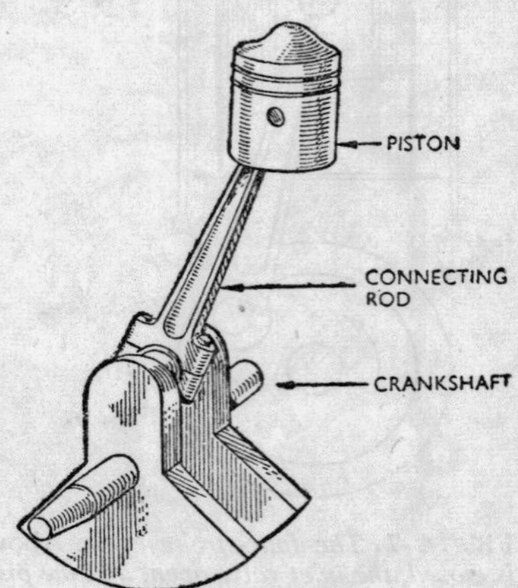

Fig. 8. *These are the three main working parts found in the two-stroke engine. The piston rings are pegged to prevent the ends fouling the ports.*

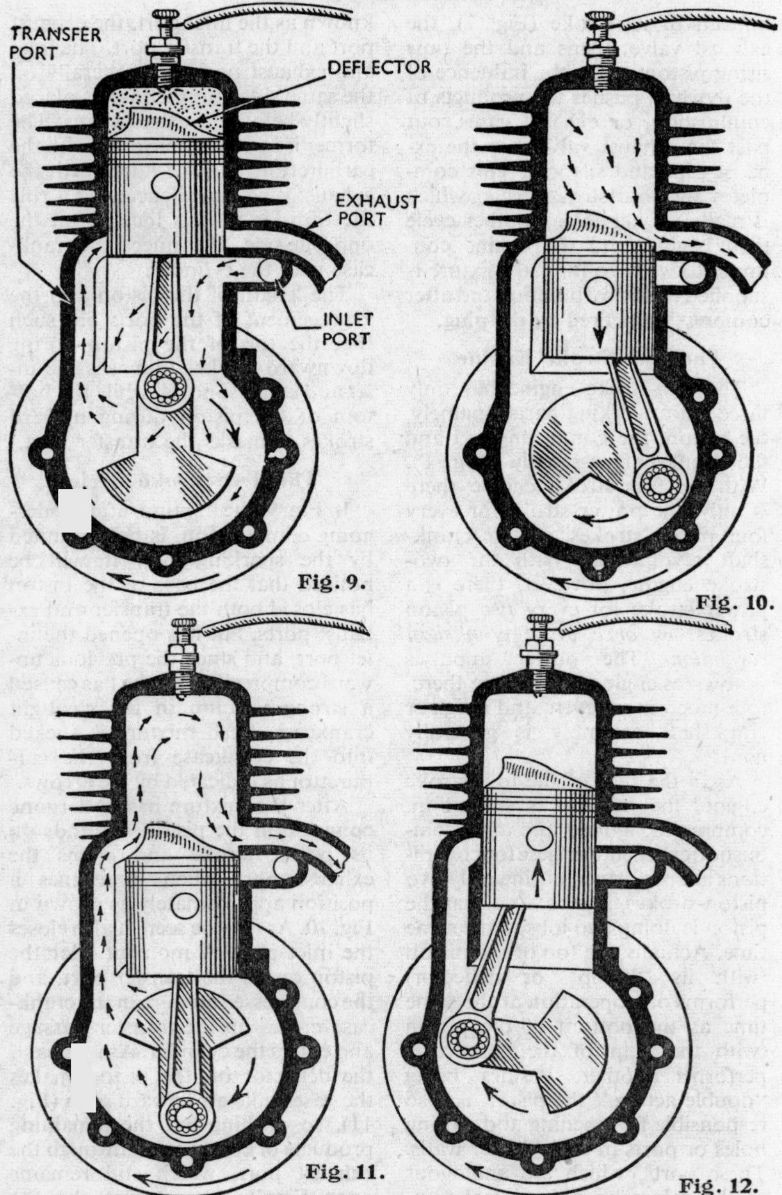

Fig. 9.

Fig. 10.

Fig. 11.

Fig. 12.

Figs. 9–12. *Phases of the two-stroke cycle. Compare Figs.* 4–7 *on page* 379.

bottom of its stroke (Fig. 7), the exhaust valve opens and the now rising piston under the influence of the flywheel pushes the products of combustion, or exhaust gases, out past the exhaust valve into the exhaust pipe and silencer. This completes the four-stroke cycle, which is really very simple. Another cycle then begins, and the engine continues to work so long as mixture is supplied by the carburettor and after compression is fired by the plug.

The Two-Stroke Engine

The two-stroke engine has only three main working parts—namely, the piston, the connecting-rod and the crankshaft assembly (Fig. 8). With the four-stroke engine there is only one power stroke for every four piston strokes, or two crankshaft revolutions. With the two-stroke engine, however, there is a power stroke for every *two* piston strokes, *or once every crankshaft revolution.* The power impulses (known as engine torque) are therefore much more even, and a lighter crankshaft assembly is generally used.

As in the case of the four-stroke engine, the mixture is sucked in, compressed, ignited and after combustion expelled. As these four operations are performed during only two piston-strokes, it is obvious that the piston is doing two jobs at the same time. Actually the top of the piston (with its "hump" or deflector) performs one operation at the same time as the bottom of the piston (with the help of the crankcase) performs another. Besides being "double acting," the piston is also responsible for opening and closing holes or ports in the cylinder walls. These ports, which are analogous to the valves on a four-stroke engine, are three in number, and are known as the inlet port, the exhaust port and the transfer port. The inlet and exhaust ports are generally on the same side, but the inlet is placed slightly below the exhaust port. The former is in communication with the carburettor, and the latter with the exhaust pipe and silencer. As a rule the transfer port is located on the opposite side. It connects the crankcase with the cylinder.

The length of the piston and the arrangement of the ports are such that the top of the piston during downward strokes unmasks the inlet and exhaust ports, while the bottom of the piston during upward strokes unmasks the transfer port.

The Two-Stroke Cycle

In Fig. 9, the mixture, after undergoing compression, is being ignited by the sparking-plug. It will be noticed that the base of the piston has closed both the transfer and exhaust ports, but has opened the inlet port, and since the previous upward compression stroke has caused a strong vacuum in the gas-tight crankcase, fresh mixture is sucked into the crankcase from the carburettor as indicated by the arrows.

After the mixture has undergone combustion the piston descends on its power stroke and opens the exhaust port when it reaches a position approximately as shown in Fig. 10. As may be seen, it also closes the inlet port. A moment later the piston opens the transfer port, and the compressed mixture in the crankcase passes up the transfer passage and enters the cylinder. As it does so the deflector on the piston makes the gases take an upward path (Fig. 11), so pushing out the remaining products of combustion through the exhaust port, which still remains open. Finally the piston reaches the bottom of its stroke and begins to rise again, closing all three ports when in the position shown in Fig. 12, and compressing the mixture ready for ignition. A fresh charge of mixture enters the crankcase, and so the cycle continues.

On some modern two-stroke engines the piston has no deflector, a tangential arrangement of twin transfer ports causing the ingoing gases to collide and take an inverted upward curve which does away with the necessity for a deflector.

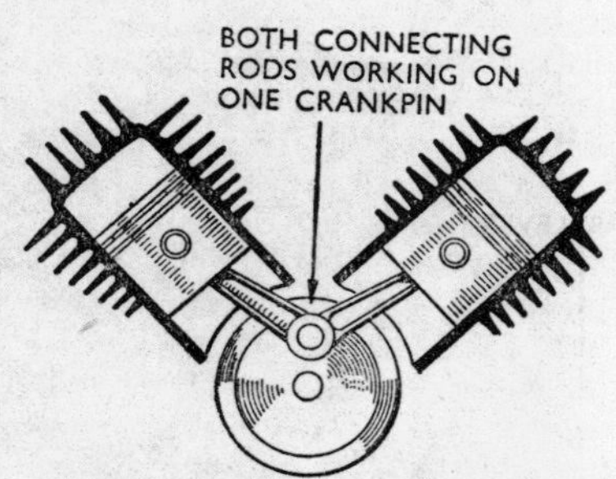

Fig. 13. *In the twin-cylinder engine, as in a motor-cycle, both connecting-rods work on the same crank-pin.*

Multi-Cylinder Engines

As has already been stated at the beginning of this lesson, the single-cylinder engine of comparatively low horse-power is used on motor-cycles only. All cars have multi-cylinder engines.

Twin-Cylinder Engines. Quite a large number of motor-cycles, especially those used for passenger carrying, have twin-cylinder engines with the cylinders arranged usually in the form of a "V." This type of engine is also much used on three-wheelers and on a few light cars. In a few instances the cylinders are horizontally opposed, a type having excellent balance. The method of working is basically the same.

The twin-cylinder engine may be likened to two single-cylinder units, both connecting-rods working on the same crank-pin side by side or with one big-end forked over the other. It is obvious (see Fig. 13) that while one piston is travelling downward the other is moving in the reverse direction. Assuming the piston in No. 1 cylinder begins with an inlet (downward) stroke, No. 2 piston must be doing either a compression or an exhaust stroke (both upward strokes). Now the most even firing order or torque is required, and the only combination which provides this is tabulated above. Two power impulses are obtained for every two crankshaft revolutions,

REVOLUTIONS	NO. 1 CYLINDER	NO. 2 CYLINDER
1st ½ Rev. . . .	Inlet	Compression
2nd ½ Rev. . . .	Compression	*Firing* (power)
3rd ½ Rev. . . .	*Firing* (power)	Exhaust
4th ½ Rev. . . .	Exhaust	Inlet

PISTON STROKES ON TWIN-CYLINDER ENGINE

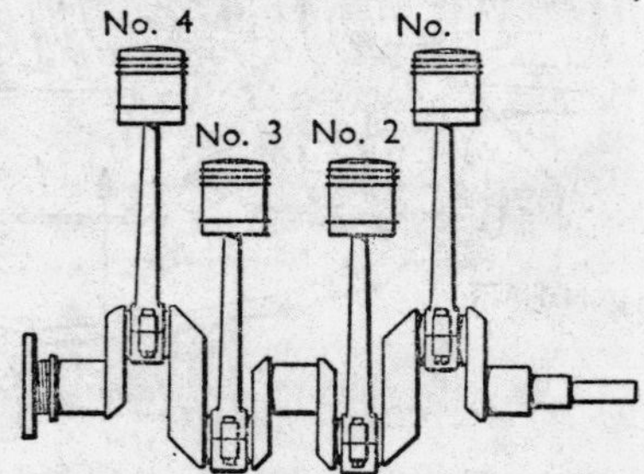

Fig. 14. *In the four-cylinder-in-line engine, the crankshaft arrangement is as shown above, with split big-ends.*

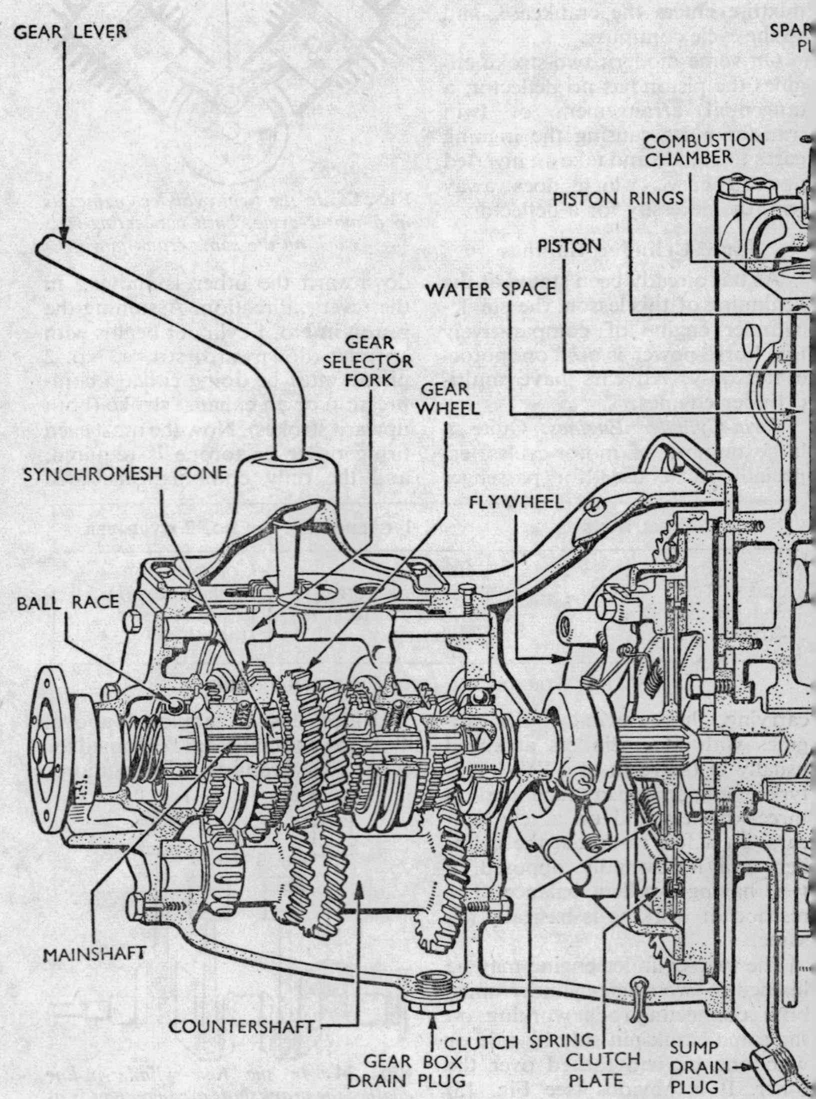

Fig. 15. *Cut-away view of an Austin Eight four-cylinder engine and ge*

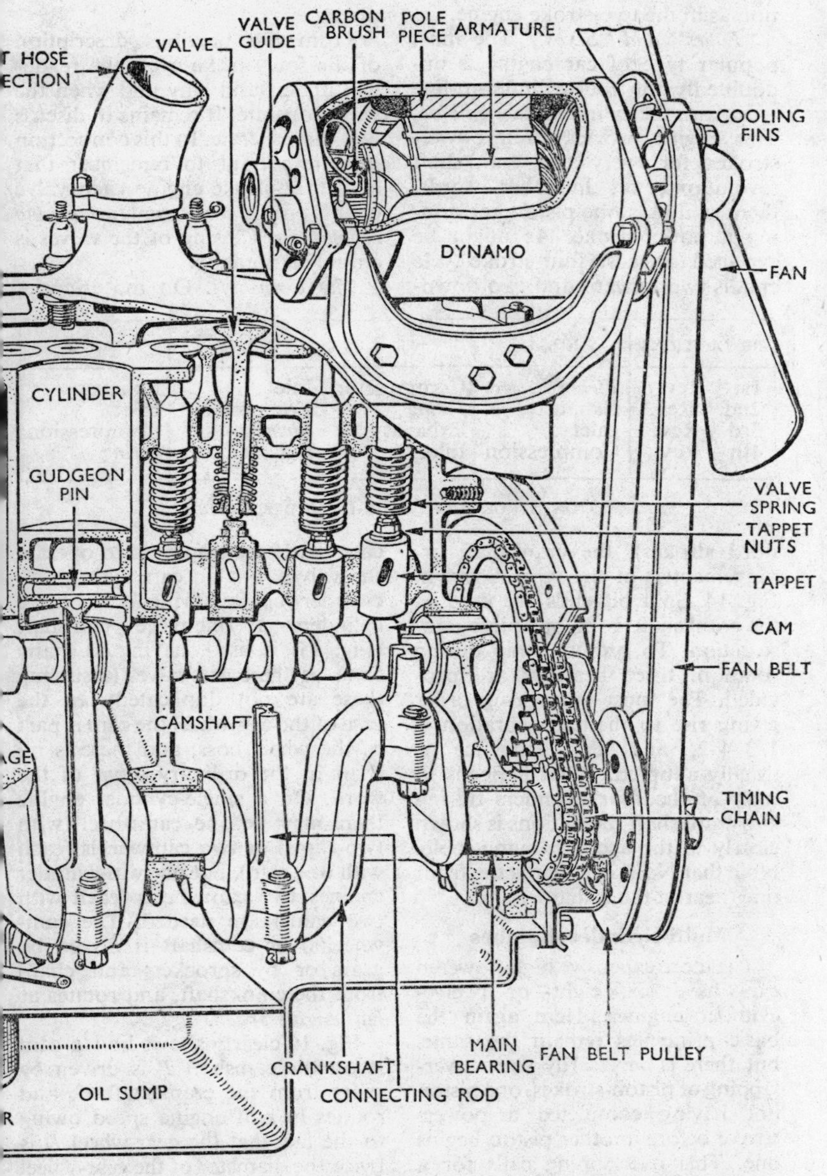

vorking of the various parts indicated is fully explained in the text.

i.e., one impulse for every revolution as in the two-stroke engine.

"Fours" and "Sixes." The most popular type of car engine is undoubtedly the four-cylinder-in-line type, with the cylinders cast *en bloc*. This engine provides four power-strokes for every two crankshaft revolutions, or, in other words, there is always one piston performing a power-stroke. As might be expected (since the four-stroke cycle entails two upward and two downward strokes), the crankshaft arrangement is of the type shown in Fig. 14. Split big-ends are used as the crankshaft is of one-piece construction. To prevent whip during rotation, three bearings are provided. The most even firing order giving rise to the least vibration is 1–3–4–2, and this sequence is usually adopted. What happens in each of the four cylinders during two crankshaft revolutions is shown clearly in the accompanying table. Note that No. 1 cylinder is the front one (nearest the radiator).

REVOLUTIONS	NO. 1	NO. 3	NO. 4	NO. 2
1st ½ Rev.	*Firing*	Compression	Inlet	Exhaust
2nd ½ Rev.	Exhaust	*Firing*	Compression	Inlet
3rd ½ Rev.	Inlet	Exhaust	*Firing*	Compression
4th ½ Rev.	Compression	Inlet	Exhaust	*Firing*

PISTON STROKES ON FOUR-CYLINDER ENGINE

Multi-Cylinder Engines

The more expensive high-powered cars have six, eight- or twelve-cylinder engines. Here again the basic principles remain the same, but there is necessarily some overlapping of piston-strokes, one piston not having completed a power-stroke before another piston begins one. This overlapping calls for a rather complicated crankshaft with the cranks not all in the same plane.

From the previous description of the four-stroke cycle the reader will understand why and when the valves operate. It remains to discuss *how* they operate. In this connection it is important to remember that on a four-stroke engine each valve opens only *once every two engine revolutions*. Closing of the valves is entirely automatic.

The Camshaft. On motor-cycles camwheels are employed to operate the valves, but on cars with multi-cylinder engines having four or more cylinders a one-piece camshaft (Fig. 15) is used, having as many cams as there are valves (assuming these are not duplicated). In the case of the camwheel the cam is part of the wheel boss, and there is no shaft in the ordinary sense of the word. On a single-cylinder engine there may be one camwheel (with two cams) or two camwheels (each with one cam), but on twin-cylinder engines two camwheels (each with two cams) are needed. The camwheel(s) or camshaft is driven by gears or by sprockets and chain from the crankshaft, and rotates at *half engine speed.*

Fig. 16 clearly shows how a cam *A* on the camshaft *B* is driven by gears from the crankshaft *C*, and rotates at half engine speed owing to the fact that the gear-wheel *D* is twice the diameter of the gear-wheel *E* and has twice as many teeth.

Imagine the gears in motion. Once every two crankshaft revolutions the nose of the cam rises to the extreme upper position (shown dotted) and lifts the tappet *F* up to its full extent. The tappet pushes the inlet or exhaust valve (not shown) from its seating in the cylinder or cylinder head.

Further rotation of the engine causes the cam nose to move away from the tappet until the latter (Fig. 16) is resting on the circular part of the cam (a rocker is sometimes interposed) and the valve is completely closed with its bevelled and ground-in face resting on the bevelled seating in the cylinder. A strong valve-spring sees to it that the valve closes as the nose of the cam recedes, and it keeps the valve firmly closed. A valve-guide is responsible for keeping the valve steady during its movement.

To allow for expansion of the tappet and valve it is necessary on most engines for a clearance to exist between the tappet-head and valve-stem when the engine is cold. On side-valve engines (where the valve stems point downward) each tappet usually has a screwed adjustable head and locknut, but on a few engines automatic

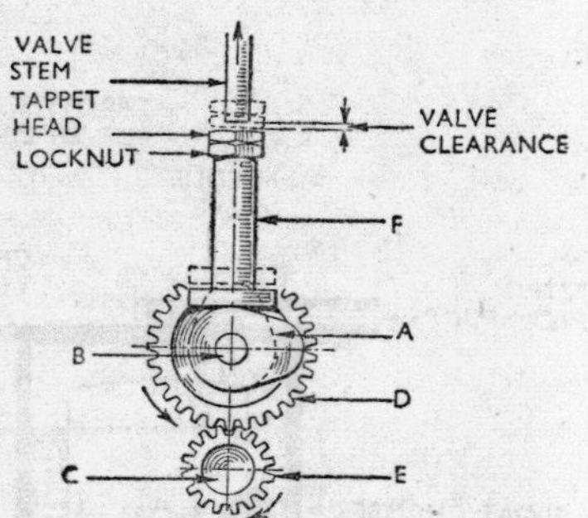

Fig. 16. *Camshaft operation.* A, *cam;* B, *camshaft;* C, *crankshaft;* D, E, *large and small gear-wheels;* F, *tappet.*

compensation for expansion is provided. On overhead-valve engines (where the valve stems point upward) an overhead rocker or push-rod adjustment is provided and smaller valve clearances are needed than for side-valve (S.V.) engines.

Overhead Valves. A large number of modern engines are of the overhead-valve (O.H.V.) type. With this type the valves are located over the piston, with the valve-stems pointing upward, not downward. Four typical valve arrangements are shown diagrammatically in Fig. 17. At *A* is an arrangement used widely (with push-rods and rockers) for

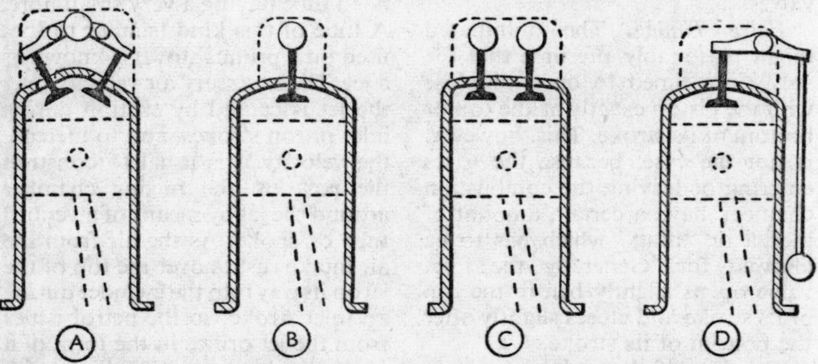

Fig. 17. *Arrangements of overhead-valve engines.* A, *type in common use for motor cycles;* B, *single overhead camshaft;* C, *overhead twin camshaft;* D, *push-rod and rocker with camshaft arranged low down as on a side-valve engine.*

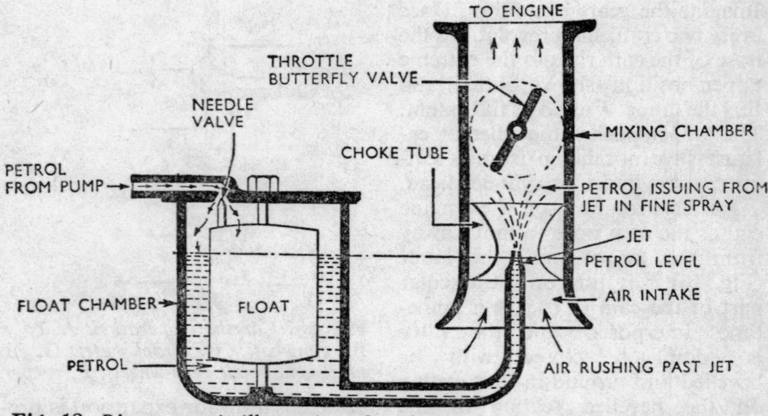

Fig. 18. *Diagrammatic illustration of working principle of a simple carburettor.*

motor-cycles, at *B* a single overhead camshaft arrangement, at *C* an overhead twin-camshaft system, and at *D* a push-rod and rocker type with the camshaft arranged low down as on a S.V. engine. On motor-cycle O.H.V. engines the push-rod arrangement is very popular, but on car engines it is usual to adopt an overhead camshaft. Whatever the method adopted, the general principles are unaffected. Where twin overhead camshafts are fitted, one camshaft operates the inlet valves, while the other operates the exhaust valves.

Valve Timing. The uninitiated might reasonably presume that the valves are timed to open or close with the piston exactly at the top or bottom of its stroke. This, however, is not the case, because the gases entering or leaving the combustion chamber have a certain amount of inertia or "drag" which has to be allowed for. Generally the inlet valve opens slightly before the top of its stroke and closes slightly after the bottom of its stroke.

The duty of *the carburettor* is to provide correct carburation, or, in other words, to supply the engine at all times with a correctly proportioned mixture of petrol vapour and air (in proportions of about 1 to 14).

The Carburettor

We shall consider the principle on which an elementary form of carburettor works. Such a carburettor is shown diagrammatically in Fig. 18.

The Jets. It has been found that the best method of converting liquid petrol into finely divided particles of fuel is to pass a high-velocity air current over the orifice of a petrol-filled tube having a very small bore. A tube of this kind (similar to that used on a primus stove) is known as a jet. The necessary air velocity over the jet is caused by suction during inlet piston strokes, and to increase the velocity it is usual to constrict the part of the mixing chamber around the jet by means of a venturi tube or choke. As the air from the air intake rushes over the top of the jet on its way into the cylinder during an inlet stroke, so the petrol issues from the jet orifice in the form of a finely divided spray and mixes with the air. The atomised fuel and air together form the mixture, which is ignited in the combustion chamber, as already explained on page 377.

In practice there are generally one or more main jets and also a pilot jet for slow-running. This has a small auxiliary air intake of its own (usually adjustable). The pilot jet cuts out automatically as soon as the engine speeds up and the air velocity over the main jet increases. Where a single main jet is employed, this is generally of the variable type, the size of the opening being controlled by means of a sliding tapered needle

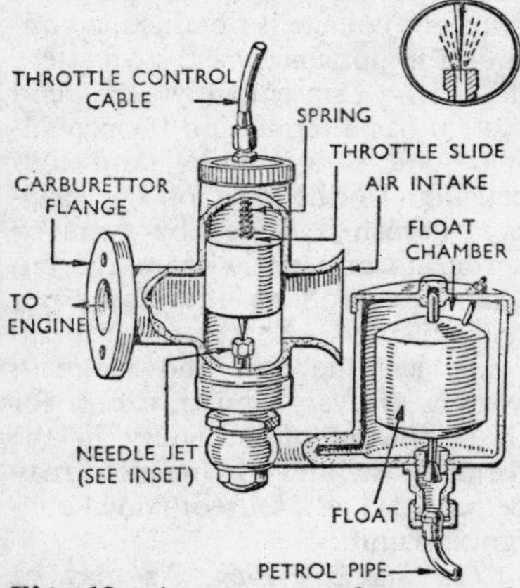

Fig. 19. *Arrangement of motor-cycle carburettor, in which the upper part of the needle is attached to the throttle.*

according to the requirements of the engine. On motor-cycle carburettors the upper part of the needle is attached to the throttle slide (Fig. 19), but on cars (with no throttle slide) the needle is fixed to a piston which slides in a closed cylinder above the jet (Fig. 20). The space above the piston communicates with the inlet pipe, and therefore as the engine suction increases, so the piston is drawn up, together with the needle, thus allowing more petrol to issue from the jet. Some carburettors have quite a

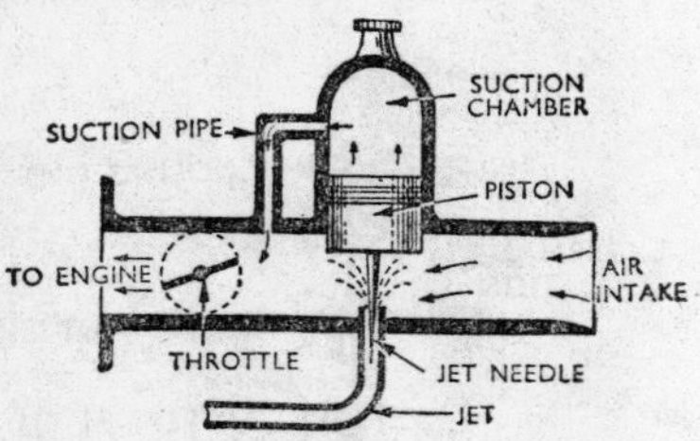

Fig. 20. *In carburettors of cars the needle is fixed to a piston sliding in a closed cylinder placed above the jet.*

number of main jets, so arranged as to give a correct mixture at all engine speeds.

The Throttle. On cars the throttle consists of a butterfly valve (similar to a gas-tap valve) in the inlet pipe, but on motor-cycles it comprises a slide in the mixing chamber. On the car type the butterfly is moved by means of rod-and-crank mechanism terminating at the accelerator (Figs. 21 and 21A). As the accelerator is depressed, so the butterfly disc is moved to the horizontal position, where the maximum amount of gas can pass. On the motor-cycle type the throttle slide (and tapered jet needle, where fitted) is connected by a Bowden cable to the handlebar twist-grip or lever. The main point to note is that opening the throttle increases the suction over the main jet(s), resulting in a greater volume of mixture being drawn into the cylinder or cylinders.

The Air Control. On motor-cycle carburettors there is usually a

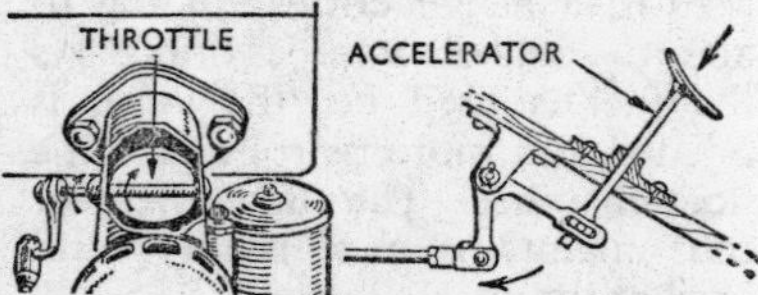

Figs. 21 and 21A. *The throttle on cars is a butterfly valve in the inlet pipe (Fig.* 21) *moved by a rod and crank ending at the accelerator pedal* (*Fig.* 21A).

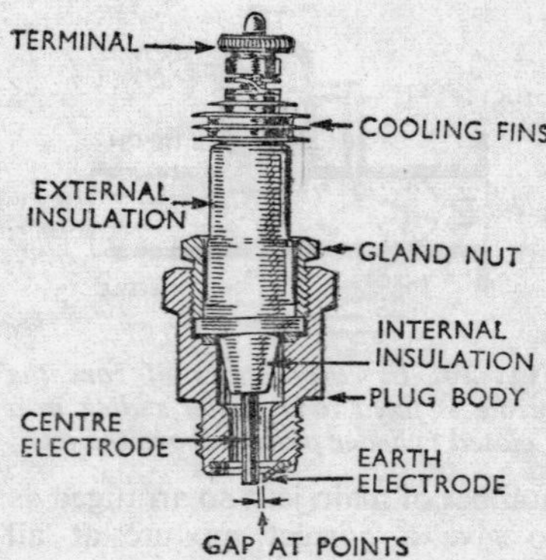

Fig. 22. *Sparking plug and its terminal, shown partly in section.*

second slide inside which the throttle slide operates. When this second slide is lowered completely it entirely obstructs the air intake, and is thus used for starting purposes where engine suction is small and maximum suction is required over the pilot jet. It is thus really a strangler, and, except for starting, the air control is kept wide open (lifted). On cars a strangler device is also fitted. This takes the form of a butterfly valve in the induction pipe, and is used solely for starting.

The Float-Chamber. At the side of the main body of the carburettor is the float-chamber, which, as its name implies, has a float (made of brass) to which a needle valve is fitted. This needle presses on a seat in the float-chamber and cuts off the petrol supply when the petrol level rises to a height corresponding to about $\frac{1}{16}$ in. below the jet orifice. As the fuel is used up, the valve is opened and more petrol enters the float-chamber. The float-chamber thus maintains a constant petrol level at the jet.

At one time the feed to the float-chamber was by gravity, but this has been superseded by the pressure system, which allows of the main storage tank being located in a safe position and independent of the height of the float-chamber. An electric or a mechanical pump is utilised, into details of which it is not necessary to enter here.

The Ignition System

With the coil ignition system (used on almost all cars and many motor-cycles) the dynamo supplies current to the battery, which is used for both lighting and ignition. It thus follows that a current of almost constant voltage is obtained, a condition impossible where no battery is used. Consequently the coil system has a reputation for providing good slow running and easy starting. In the case of the magneto (which is driven by gears or sprockets and chain from the engine), the voltage increases with engine speed. As regards general principles, the coil and magneto systems are very similar, except for the inclusion of a battery in the former case, and the magneto may be regarded as a self-contained coil-ignition unit.

The Sparking-Plug. As may be seen in Fig. 22, which shows a typical sparking-plug partly sectioned, this comprises an internal insulator held in a metal body screwed into the cylinder head. Passing right through the centre of the insulation is a long metal rod known as the centre electrode. This electrode is not electrically in contact with any part of the plug body, and at the upper portion is protected by external insulation. At the extreme top of the centre electrode is the plug terminal to which the high-tension lead conveying the high voltage current is attached. Close to the bottom, and projecting from the body of the plug, is a small

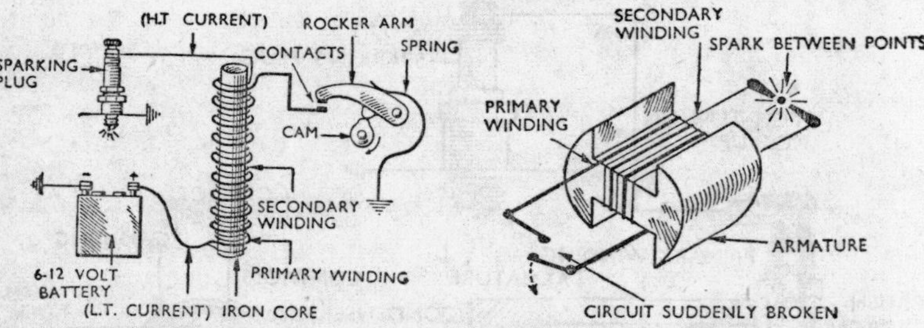

Figs. 23 and 24. Left, *the principle of coil, and,* right, *of magneto, ignition.*

"earthed" electrode (sometimes there are three). Now, when a high voltage current reaches the centre electrode, it immediately flashes across to the earth electrode, provided the gap between the two electrodes is not excessive.

The Primary and Secondary Windings, together with the device known as the contact-breaker, or make-and-break, are responsible for transforming a comparatively low voltage current (6–12 volts) into an extremely high voltage one (700–1,000 volts). Everyone is familiar with the medical or shocking coil which enables a small 3½-volt battery to make one literally jump, and with the ignition system a similar principle is employed to convert a low-voltage current into a high-voltage one which will jump across the gap at the plug points.

Fig. 23 illustrates in a simple manner the essence of coil ignition. Wound around an iron core (insulated) are two windings, the primary and secondary. The primary winding is of fairly thick wire, and has about 100 turns. It is wound over the secondary winding, which is of very fine wire and has several *thousand* turns. The two windings and the core constitute the ignition coil, which is a separate unit. One end of the primary is connected to the battery and the other end to the contact-breaker, which has a cam and rocker arm enabling the primary circuit to be broken by the opening and closing of contacts. One end of the secondary is joined to the primary, and the other end leads to the sparking-plug. Now, if current is permitted to pass through the primary from the battery and the contacts are suddenly opened by the cam (as shown), the primary circuit is suddenly interrupted, and this causes a high-voltage electric current to be induced momentarily in the secondary winding, with the result that the high-tension current takes the path of least resistance and a spark takes place at the plug.

Much the same effect occurs in the case of magneto ignition, the principle of which is also shown simply in Fig. 24. Here the primary and secondary windings are wound on a bobbin-shaped iron core, and the whole constitutes the armature.

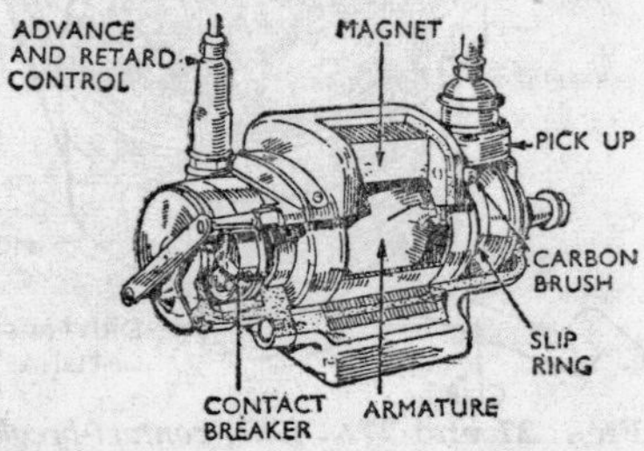

Fig. 25. *Cut-away view showing the parts of a typical magneto.*

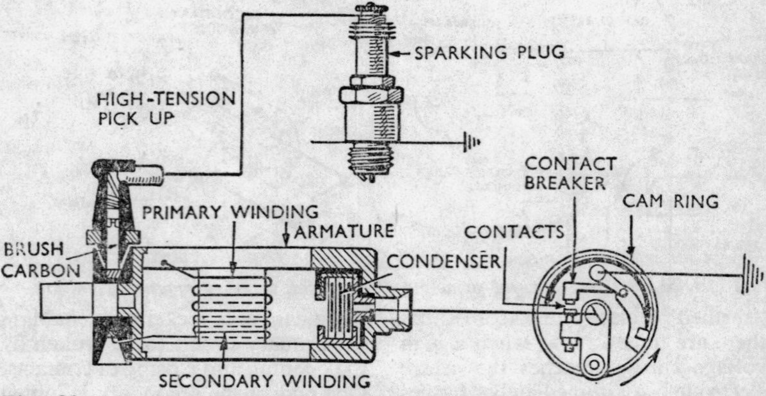

Fig. 26. *Magneto ignition circuit for single-cylinder engine, showing essential components. The working principle is shown in Fig.* 24.

This armature rotates between the iron pole pieces of a permanent steel magnet. Rotation generates a low-voltage electric current in the primary winding. With the assistance of the contact-breaker the primary circuit is broken and a high-tension (or voltage) current is then induced in the secondary winding and the necessary spark is obtained at the plug.

The Contact-Breaker. The contact-breaker, whose function is to interrupt the primary circuit when a spark is required at the plug, varies somewhat in design, but always runs at half engine speed (or rather part of it does) for reasons which will be understood from the description of the four-stroke cycle. Contact-breakers are broadly speaking of two types: one where the cam rotates and the rest of the mechanism is stationary; the other where the cam is stationary and the other parts rotate. The latter type is used

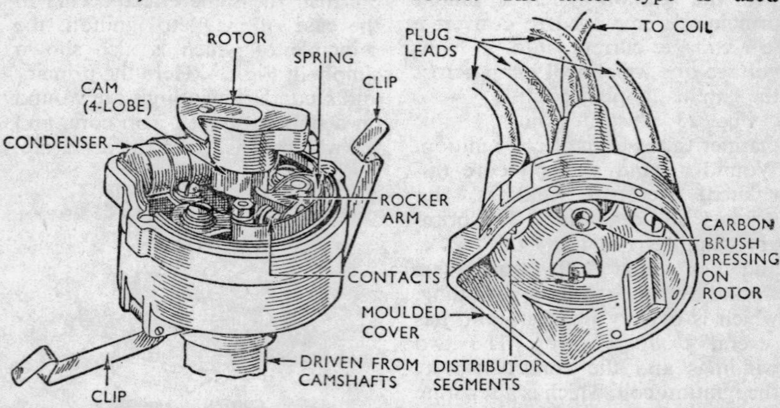

Figs. 27 and 27A. Left, *contact-breaker, showing the rotor fixed to the spindle which forms the distributor;* right, *distributor cover, the four equally-spaced segments connected to the wires leading to the appropriate sparking-plugs.*

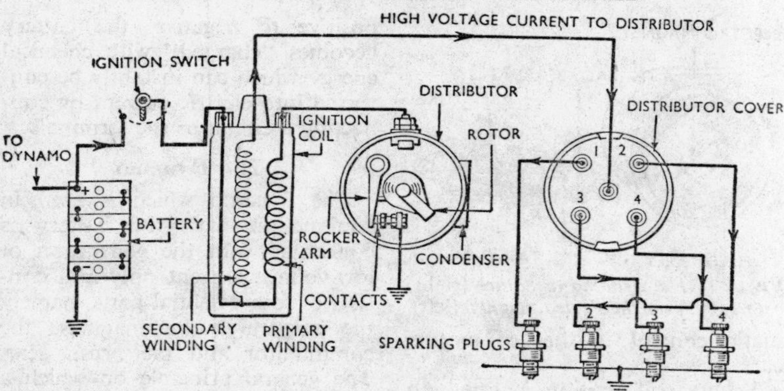

Fig. 28. *Diagram showing the coil-ignition equipment for a four-cylinder engine.*

mainly on magnetos. Multi-cylinder engines almost invariably have rotating cam contact-breakers with the drive taken from the camshaft.

A typical car-type contact-breaker mechanism is shown in Fig. 27. As may be seen, there is a movable rocker arm with one contact. This contact is pressed firmly against a second *fixed* contact by means of a spring, but when the nose of the cam pushes against the rocker arm it causes the first contact to move apart from the fixed contact, thus breaking the primary circuit (see page 391). The contact-breaker shown is for a four-cylinder engine, and therefore the cam has four lobes, one for each cylinder. The cam spindle is, of course, driven from the camshaft by gears at half engine speed. The general principle of all contact-breakers is the same. Connected with the contact-breaker is the condenser, which prevents arcing across the contact points while they are open.

The Distributor. On page 386 the importance of the correct firing order has been discussed, and it follows that the high-voltage current from the coil or magneto must be led to the correct plugs at the right time. For instance, on a four-cylinder engine the usual firing order is 1, 3, 4, 2. Hence as the four "breaks" take place at the contact-breaker the current must be conveyed to the cylinders in this order. This is simply carried out by means of the distributor, which consists of the rotor (Fig. 27) fixed to the contact-breaker spindle, and the distributor cover (Fig. 27A) containing the four equally spaced segments connected to the wires leading to the appropriate sparking-plugs. The high-voltage current reaches the rotor, and as the rotor rotates and passes each segment in turn, the current jumps across to the segment and reaches the sparking-plug. The arm of the rotor is so located on the spindle that whenever its outer tip is in line with a segment, a "break" takes place at the contact-breaker.

Ignition and Speed

It has been stated (page 380) that increase in engine speed requires the ignition to be advanced. This is arranged for by making the contact-breaker movable relative to the cam. Manual control is provided in the case of motor-cycles and auto-

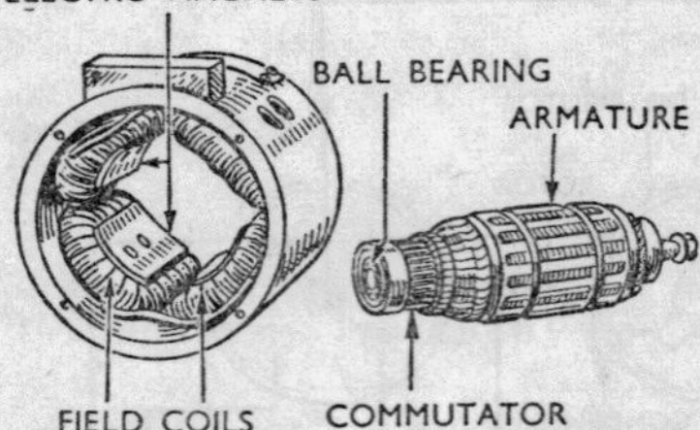

Fig. 29. *The dynamo armature* (right) *rotates between the electro-magnets* (left).

matic control in that of motor-cars.

Where coil ignition is fitted an ignition switch is provided. Referring to Fig. 28, which shows the general lay-out of coil ignition equipment for a four-cylinder engine, imagine what would happen if no switch was fitted and the contacts were closed. Clearly the low-voltage current from the battery could flow through the primary winding and the contacts to earth, a state of affairs which would soon result in a ruined battery. An ignition switch *must* be fitted between the battery and the primary winding of the coil. The coil windings, by the way, are shown side by side for clarity, whereas they are actually wound one above the other as indicated in Fig. 23.

The Battery

Most batteries are of the lead-acid type, the cells containing groups of lead frames pasted over with lead oxide. These frames are the plates, one group of which are positive and the other negative. The positive plates of one cell are connected to the negative plates of the adjacent one.

A diluted sulphuric acid solution, known as the electrolyte, is poured into the cells until the plates are just submerged. If an electric current from the dynamo is now passed through the acid and plates from positive to negative, the battery becomes "charged" with chemical energy which can instantly be converted into electric current by connecting a circuit to the terminals.

The Dynamo

The dynamo which is used in conjunction with the battery is concerned with the generation of low-voltage current only and consists of four essential parts, namely the armature, the magnets, the commutator and the brush gear. The general principle on which a dynamo operates is very similar to that of the low-tension side of a magneto, already dealt with. There are, however, some important differences. On a magneto armature there is only one primary winding, whereas on a dynamo armature there are many windings, each of which as it rotates in the magnetic field of the magnets produces a current which is passed on to the commutator and collected by the brush gear. Again, whereas on a magneto a *permanent* horseshoe magnet is employed, in the case of the dynamo electro-magnets are used. The dynamo provides the necessary magnetism by means of coils of wire surrounding the poles. These field coils magnetise the magnets when current is passed through them by dynamo rotation.

The dynamo armature (see Fig. 29) rotates between the electro-magnets, which are usually four in number and retain some

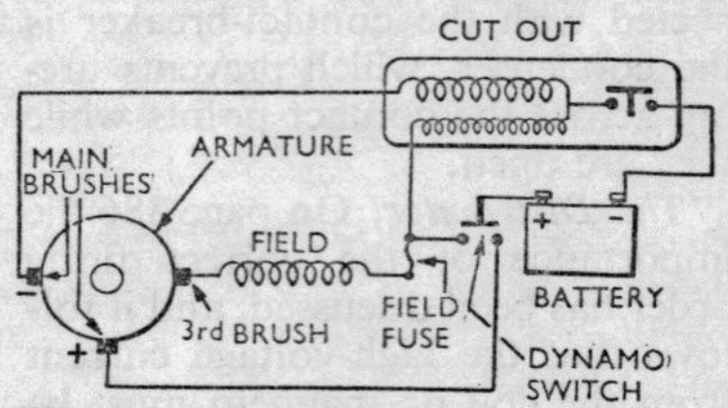

Fig. 30. *Dynamo wiring circuit for a "third brush" system.*

magnetism which builds up with increase of armature speed. The commutator to which the windings are connected is built up of a number of copper segments separated from each other by mica insulation. Two carbon brushes (one positive, one negative) pressing on the commutator segments collect the current and pass it on to the battery *via* an ammeter (which shows the amount of current passing) and a cut-out which prevents the battery discharging back to the dynamo. A third brush energises the fields of the electro-magnets and is so arranged that by a rather complicated electrical action the output of the dynamo is prevented from increasing beyond a certain point, however fast the dynamo may be running.

A recent improvement used on many cars and motor-cycles is the battery-controlled charging system. Here the dynamo output is varied automatically according to the state of charge of the battery.

Cooling System

On motor-cycle and three-wheeler engines, air-cooling is generally used, the cylinders being cooled by fins arranged so that air passes over them. Practically all car engines, however, are water-cooled by means of a thermo-syphon or assisted thermo-syphon system.

The Thermo-Syphon System. This is based on the fact that hot water is lighter than cold water, and therefore rises. A typical thermo-syphon cooling system is shown in Fig. 31, and it will be noticed that it consists of the water-jackets surrounding the cylinders and a radiator with header tank (a mere reservoir). The radiator is responsible for cooling the water, and comprises a number of tubes through which water circulates and between which air passes, or, alternatively, a number of tubes through which air passes and between which water circulates. The cooling air passes through the radiator when the car is in motion, and when the car is stationary is sucked through by means of a fan placed between the engine and radiator. The top and bottom of the radiator are connected to the top and bottom of the water-jackets respectively.

As the engine becomes hot the water in the jackets rises and passes up to the radiator; there it is cooled and descends to the bottom and returns to the base of the jackets. Thus circulation of water is continuous and automatic and the water surrounding the cylinders conveys the heat away from the engine.

Assisted Thermo-Syphon Systems. On high-powered cars it is common practice to supplement the thermo-syphon system by an impeller-type pump (Fig. 32). The impeller is generally housed high up in the water space at the front of the

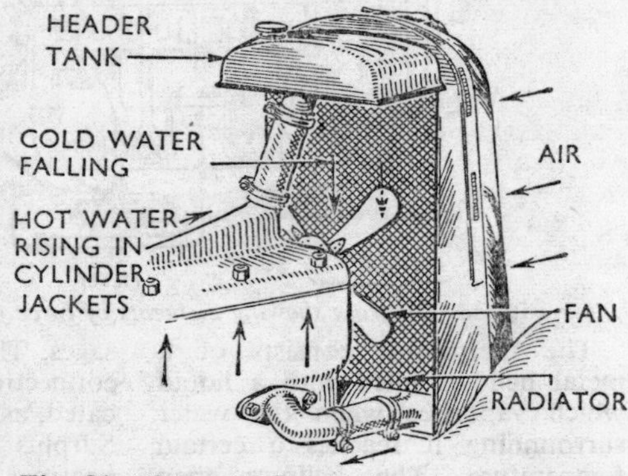

Fig. 31. *Thermo-syphon cooling system, consisting of the cylinder-jackets and radiator with header-tank.*

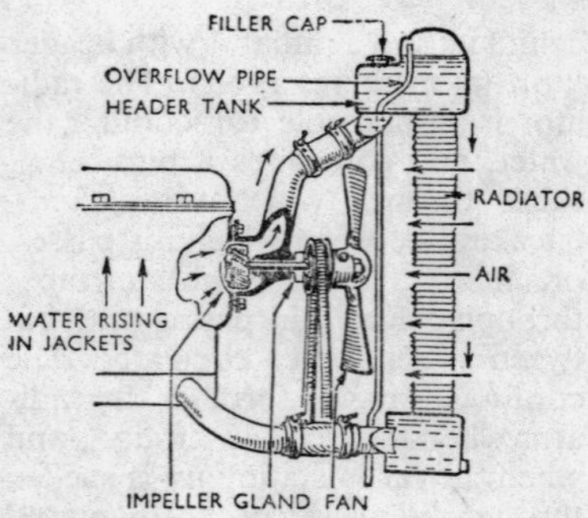

Fig. 32. *Impeller-type pump supplementing thermo-syphon system.*

cylinder block, and comprises a series of curved blades driven from the camshaft extension or from the crankshaft. With this system the water circulation is accelerated, and some considerable circulation occurs even when starting up from cold.

Thermostat Control of Temperature. On a large number of cars automatic temperature control is fitted. This takes a number of forms, all operated by a thermostat device. to operate a valve or move a shutter. On some cars the thermostat automatically closes and opens radiator shutters. Similarly on other cars the thermostat prevents water reaching the radiator, by obstructing the inlet pipe to the radiator or by-passing the supply, until the engine is properly warmed up.

The function of the lubrication system is to provide a film of lubricating oil between all moving parts, especially those that move very fast and are subject to the heat of combustion (*e.g.*, the piston).

The Full Force Feed System. On a car engine the oil supply is carried underneath the engine in an oil reservoir called the sump, which is cooled by the car's motion through the air. Fig. 33 is a diagram of a typical full force feed lubrication system.

Referring to Fig. 33, the oil-pump feeds oil drawn from the sump past a filter to the main crankshaft bearings through drilled oil pas-

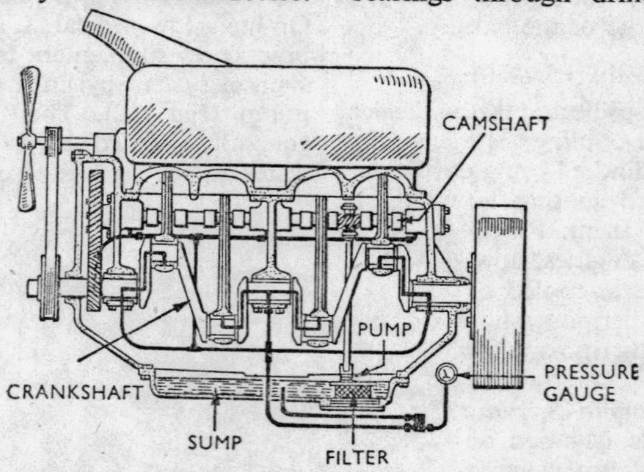

Fig. 33. *Diagram showing elements of force feed lubrication system.*

The thermostat consists of a metal bellows filled with a liquid which vaporises when the water surrounding it reaches a certain temperature. The bellows then expands, and this expansion is used sages. The big-end bearings of the connecting-rods are similarly lubricated, as are the camshaft bearings. Surplus oil flung from the big-end bearings lubricates the cylinder walls and the small-end connecting-rod

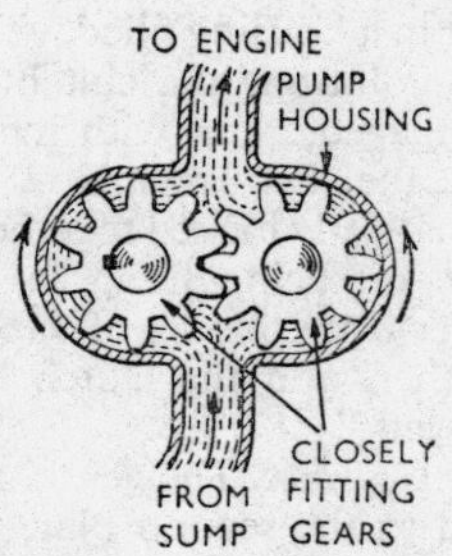

Fig. 34. *Showing arrangement of typical gear-type oil pump.*

bearings, and then drains back to the engine-sump. On certain engines there is a small oil-jet formed by a hole drilled on the upper side of the big-end bearings; this causes a jet of oil to be squirted up into the cylinders. Incorporated in the full-pressure system is generally a spring-loaded valve which acts as a safety-valve, permitting oil to drain back to the sump if the oil pressure becomes excessive. An adjustment is sometimes provided, and often there is a pressure-gauge on the dashboard to warn the driver if the pressure falls to a dangerous extent.

With regard to the valve-gear, oil mist is sufficient for lubrication on side-valve engines, but in the case of overhead-valve power units, oil is forced up a pipe to the camshaft bearings and overhead rockers. On some side-valve engines the camshaft is also pressure-lubricated. A modification of the full-pressure system is the dry-sump system used on some cars and most motor-cycles. Here the sump is kept dry, the oil being housed outside the crankcase. This system is similar to that described, except that a duplex pump is used, all surplus oil being picked up by the scavenger pump and returned to the external oil reservoir.

On motor-cycle engines it is common to have a pressure-feed to the cylinder walls as well as to the big-end, the crankshaft bearings and the overhead valve-gear.

The Oil-Pump. Oil-pumps are of two main types: the gear type and the plunger type. The former is used on a great many cars, and the latter type is to be found on many motor-cycle engines. Fig. 34 shows the arrangement of a typical gear-pump. Where a dry sump system is used, the pump is duplicated, one pump being required for oil delivery from the reservoir, and the other for scavenging the sump and returning oil to the reservoir. Referring to Fig. 34, two small gears with coarse teeth mesh together in a close-fitting case. The engine drives one gear, and as the two gears rotate, oil is carried round between the gear-teeth and forced out through a pipe on the delivery side of the pump.

The plunger-type pump has an action similar to that of a garden syringe, the plunger drawing in oil through a one-way valve during one stroke and forcing it out past a second valve during the return stroke. The pump is usually driven from the crankshaft on motor-cycles and from the camshaft on cars. Oil before being drawn up by the pump is purified by a detachable filter made of fine gauze or else of a special fabric.

The Transmission

In the case of a motor-cycle the power is transmitted by chain and sprockets from the crankshaft to the clutch, through the clutch to the gearbox and from the gearbox to the rear wheel by chain and sprockets. In the case of a car (and also a few motor-cycles) the drive is taken direct from the flywheel to the clutch, through the gearbox, along the propeller shaft, and finally to the rear axle, to which the road

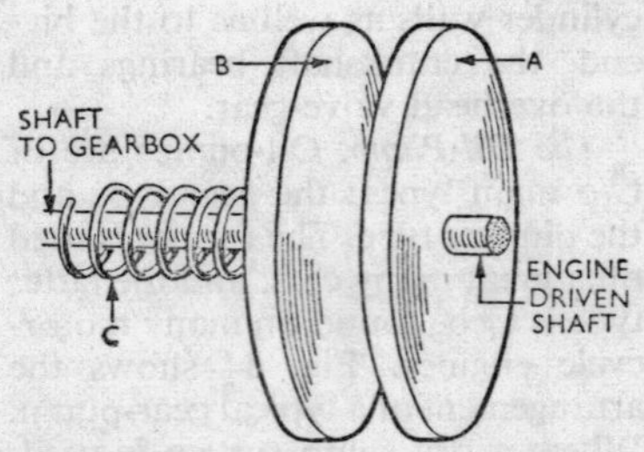

Fig. 35. *Clutch.* A, *circular plate driven by engine;* B, *second plate connected to gearbox;* C, *spring.*

wheels are fitted. The gearbox and clutch are generally built as a unit, and on cars the flywheel itself forms part of the clutch.

The Clutch. The clutch enables the engine to be disconnected from the gearbox when desired (*i.e.*, when stopping) and assists smooth gear-changing. Basically it consists of a circular plate (*A*, Fig. 35) driven by the engine (it constitutes the flywheel on cars) and a second plate (*B*, Fig. 35) connected to the gearbox. A strong spring *C* keeps the two plates normally pressed tightly together, and as there is friction-material inserted between the plates, rotation of the first plate turns the second plate and transmits the drive from the engine to the gearbox. In actual practice a number of plates and springs are provided, and a clever lever and fork mechanism enables the pressure of the springs to be gradually released on depressing a clutch-pedal or raising a clutch-lever in the case of cars and motor-cycles respectively. This disengages the engine from the gearbox, and the clutch is said to be "disengaged" or "out."

Many modern cars dispense with a friction type clutch and have a fluid flywheel instead. Here the two plates *A*, *B* (Fig. 35) are replaced by vaned members rotating close together in a housing filled with oil. At low revolutions the clutch remains "disengaged," but with increase of speed the two members become automatically locked together owing to the oil being flung in a spiral manner from one set of vanes on to the other, and the clutch becomes "engaged."

The Gearbox. The gearbox is connected to the second plate (*B*, Fig. 35) of the clutch, and one set of gears is mounted on the same shaft as *B*. Another set of gears is mounted below or beside the first set, and the gears are so arranged that the drive is taken from the first shaft (mainshaft) to the second shaft (layshaft). According to the number of gears engaged and the difference in the number of teeth, a difference in the speed of the mainshaft and layshaft is obtained. Fig. 35A shows how a mainshaft may rotate three times as fast as a layshaft by the meshing of two gears, the layshaft gear having three times as many teeth as the mainshaft gear. Now, as the mainshaft is connected to the engine (through the clutch) and the layshaft is connected to the rear wheel(s) through the propeller shaft and rear axle, or chain as the case may be, it follows that the engine rotates much faster than the wheel(s). This gives a low gear suitable for hill-climbing. Other gear engagements can be made, giving a variety of gear ratios. Actually the gears are not moved into engagement, but are in constant mesh, the same effect being obtained by means of positive dog or friction type clutches which enable various gears to be connected to or disconnected from their shafts. In practice a somewhat complicated train of gears is used, and on cars a reverse gear is provided. On both cars and motor-cycles the gear changes are effected by a hand-operated change-speed lever, though some motor-cycles have foot control.

The Propeller Shaft

The drive is taken from the gear-box (layshaft) to the rear axle through a tubular propeller shaft. Now, the rear axle moves up and down under the influence of the suspension springs, and therefore flexible couplings are required at both ends. Metal universal joints are generally used. Each universal comprises two yokes joined by a cross-piece, enabling one yoke to pivot vertically and the other horizontally.

The Rear Axle. The propeller shaft drives the rear axle through a large crown wheel and a small bevel pinion. A number of small bevel pinions are also included, and they are ingeniously arranged about the crown wheel so as to give a differential action to the road wheels (the axle is in two parts), necessitated by the difference in speed of the two wheels when rounding a bend.

Steering-Gear. The steering-wheel is attached to a steering-column at the lower end of which is a miniature gearbox designed to obtain a small wheel movement from a fairly large turn of the wheel. The connection between the steering gearbox and the wheels is by rod-and-lever mechanism. Cranks on the front-axle pivots are connected together, so that the steering movement is taken to one stub-axle crank only. The other wheel is thus moved automatically.

Brakes. Internal-expanding type brakes, operated by a foot pedal, are used for cars and motor-cycles. With this type friction-lined shoes on an anchor plate secured to the frame or rear-axle casing are expanded against the inside of a drum fitted to the wheel. Operation is by

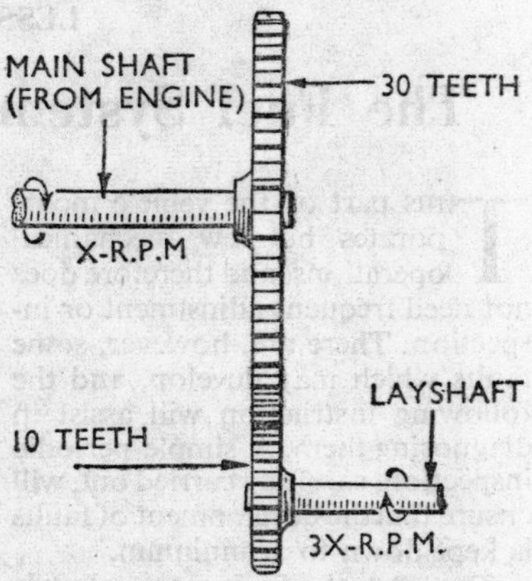

Fig. 35A. *Principle of gearbox. Meshing gears enable mainshaft to rotate three times as fast as layshaft.*

rod-and-cable mechanism or by hydraulic action, depressing a foot pedal causing a small piston to move in a cylinder and force oil through pipes to the four brakes, each of which also has a small piston and cylinder. Generally the four brakes are inter-connected, and often the shoes are of the self-energising type, the shoes tending to be dragged round the drum and automatically expanded by a slight movement of the driver on the foot pedal.

Self Testing Questions

(1) *On a single-cylinder four-stroke engine how many firing strokes are there every two engine revolutions?*

(2) *On a single-cylinder two-stroke engine how many firing strokes are there every two engine revolutions?*

(3) *What is the object of the contact-breaker?*

(4) *What is the choke tube on a carburettor for?*

THE ANSWERS ARE ON PAGE 443.

LESSON 2

The Fuel System and Carburettor

THIS part of the vehicle incorporates but few mechanical operations, and therefore does not need frequent adjustment or inspection. There are, however, some faults which may develop, and the following instruction will assist in diagnosing them. A simple periodic inspection, carefully carried out, will ensure that the development of faults is kept down to a minimum.

The Petrol Tank. An electric petrol gauge is the usual fitment for indicating the quantity of petrol in the tank, and, as this is wired through the ignition switch, it will register only when the ignition is switched on. Gauge faults are rare, and are only likely to affect the cable which carries the current from the switch to the terminal on the tank. The method of checking for a fault in this circuit, if the gauge fails to register, will be found in Lesson 3, under Cable Faults.

Flushing the Tank

There are several ways in which dirt may accumulate in the tank, and this, if allowed to continue, will result in constant pipe-line, filter and carburettor-jet obstructions. Should any of these faults develop, the tank must be flushed out. The following is the procedure. Place a clean container, of sufficient capacity to hold the petrol, under the tank drain-plug (which will be found at the lowest level), unscrew the plug and, while the petrol is draining, rock the vehicle from side to side to disturb the sediment. When the tank is drained, replace the plug, strain about a gallon of petrol through a fine wire mesh, pour this into the tank and repeat the operation of draining. All the petrol may be replaced if passed through a fine gauze.

Pipe Line. The only pipe in the system which is likely to give trouble is that which runs from the tank to the fuel pump, and, if the tank is neglected, this is likely to collect solid matter and dirt to the extent of becoming obstructed. If petrol does not flow freely as a result of the pump operation, this pipe, amongst other things, must be suspected, and should be disconnected from its union on the fuel-pump and blown through with a tyre-pump. The difficulty of making a good joint between the pump connection and the pipe will be overcome if a rubber washer be inserted between the pipe and the pump connection. There is also a possibility that this pipe may develop a kink owing to accident; an examination will reveal this cause of obstruction.

Fuel Pumps

The gravity feed from the tank to the float-chamber is now obsolete except on motor-cycles, where the construction of the vehicle lends itself to this simple method.

The car differs in its requirements in the fact that the float-chamber is at a higher level than the petrol-tank, and a low-pressure pump, either mechanically or electrically operated, is the popular fitment in use on the modern car.

There is always a possibility of the float-chamber needle not completely shutting off when the vehicle is not running, and on all gravity-feed systems a cock at the tank outlet should be turned off to prevent petrol leakage. The pump type does not incorporate a shut-off cock, as petrol cannot flow when the engine is switched off.

The Mechanical Pump. Fig. 36 shows an example of the most popular pump of this type; it is mounted on the engine, and operated by a cam, rocker arm and diaphragm. The pump should be examined for leaks and deposits at intervals of 3,000 to 5,000 miles (more frequently if jet blockage is experienced). The procedure is as follows:

Clean the exterior of the pump in position; remove filter bowl-screw (1); lift off filter-bowl (2); bowl-washer (3); and gauze-filter (4). Next unscrew sediment plug (5), and flush out the chamber beneath the gauze with clean petrol. Clean all these parts removed—the gauze with a small brush—examine the washers under the bowl and fixing-screw, renew if damaged, and replace all parts. When assembling the bowl, press and rotate it on its washer while finally tightening—this will assist in making an air-tight joint.

The engine should now be started up, and the pump examined for leaks. Some of these pumps are provided with a hand priming-lever (6), and this should be operated to fill the chamber before attempting to start the engine. Leakage may possibly occur at cover-joint (7), in which case the screws on its upper face should be tightened alternately from side to side. Union nuts should also be checked and tightened if leaking. If there is a leak from vent-hole after the cover-screws have been tightened, a fractured diaphragm is indicated, and the pump should be removed complete and sent to the service station for replacement.

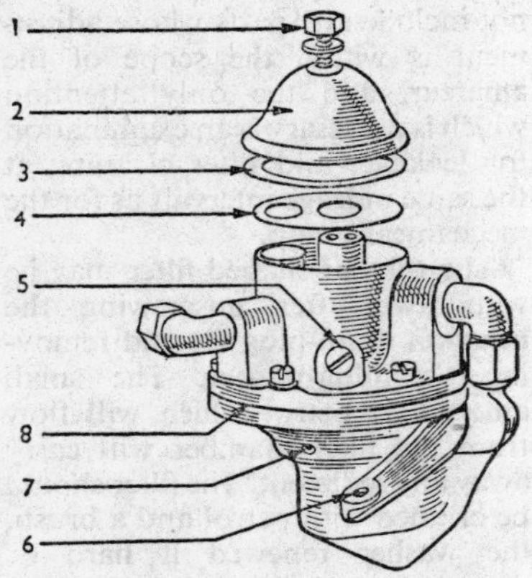

Fig. 36. *Diagram of mechanical fuel-pump of the most popular type.*

The Electrical Pump. This type of fuel-pump (Fig. 37) will generally be bolted to the front of the dashboard. Attached to its terminal is a cable which carries the current from the car battery, and as this flows *via* the ignition switch, the pump is inoperative until the ignition is switched on.

The principle of operation incorporates a fabric diaphragm, which is given its movement by an electro-magnet. This movement is carried through on a brass rod to operate a contact-breaker. The operation does

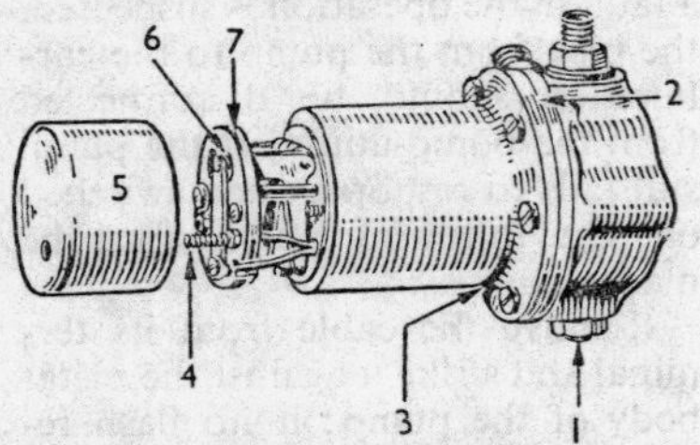

Fig. 37. *S.V. electrical type of fuel pump. For references see text.*

not include any parts whose adjustment is within the scope of the amateur, and the only attention which is necessary is an examination for leakage, and filter cleaning at the same mileage intervals as for the mechanical pump.

The tubular-shaped filter may be withdrawn after unscrewing the hexagon drain-plug (1) and removing the plug-washer. The small amount of petrol which will flow from the filter-chamber will carry away any sediment. The filter should be cleaned with petrol and a brush, the washer renewed if hard or damaged, and the parts then reassembled.

Inspecting for Leaks

Inspection for leaks should be made while the pump is in operation, and, as in the case of the mechanical pump, at cover-joint (2). In the event of a leak occurring at the vent-hole (3) in base of diaphragm chamber, the pump must be removed for service replacement.

Fuel-Pump Faults. There are a number of faults which are common to both types of pumps, but those which are peculiar to the electric model are dealt with first.

It must be understood that when the carburettor float-bowl is filled, or the supply line blocked, the pump will not respond with its usual clicking noise when switched on. If a fault in the operation is suspected, the pipe from the pump to the carburettor should be disconnected from the pump-union. If the pump still fails to respond when switched on, the following check must be made.

Remove the cable from its terminal and strike it against the metal body of the pump: if no flash results, strike it against the metal of the engine; if, again, no flash occurs, the cable is at fault (see Cable Faults in Lesson 3).

If a flash does result when striking against the engine, but not against the pump-body, the pump is badly earthed (see Lesson 3).

If a flash occurs when striking against the pump, next strike across the terminal (4), and if no flash results, the contact-breaker mechanism is at fault. This will be exposed if cover (5) is removed.

Examine contact points for moisture or dirt, and dress if necessary, but notes on contact-breakers in the electrical ignition section should first be consulted. If the pump still proves faulty, the wire connections to the bakelite block (7) should be examined for fracture or bad contact.

The most troublesome fault likely to develop is an air leak between the petrol-tank and the diaphragm chamber. The indication will be a reduced or total cessation of delivery. After uncoupling the pipe from the delivery side of pump to ensure that the trouble is not due to blockage on this side, an inspection should be made on the following lines.

Tracking an Air-Leak

Disconnect the pipe from the suction side of the pump, and substitute a short length of pipe to reach a container of petrol 20 in. or so below the pump level. If the pump now functions in its delivery, the trouble is located to the suction side, and is either blockage or air leak. An inspection of the pipe and its connections is the only method of tracing a leak, unless the pipe is removed and tested under pressure.

Should the pump fail to deliver when the short pipe is attached, the filter-bowl should be suspected for leaks at both the bowl and the fixing screw washers; and the cover-joint for loose screws.

Float-Chamber

Before dealing with the complete carburettor, the float-chamber (Fig. 38), which is common to all types fitted on both cars and motor-cycles, will be considered separately.

A gauze filter will usually be found at the position (1) where the petrol pipe connects to the carburettor, and this should be cleaned every 3,000 to 4,000 miles, or more frequently if petrol flow is suspected. If the pipe connection is of the banjo variety, the two fibre washers which form the petrol-tight joint must be renewed if brittle or damaged.

The shut-off needle valve (2), positioned at either the top or bottom of the chamber, is unlikely to give trouble unless a small piece of grit becomes embedded between the valve and its seating, when flooding will occur. To remove the grit, the needle should be held in a pair of pliers, lightly pressed on to its seating, and rotated. To gain access to the valve, the chamber cover must be removed, or on some carburettors the chamber detached from its cover after withdrawing two or three screws.

Removing the Float

If the float (3) is to be removed from the bowl, it must be handled carefully, as denting or puncture is likely to result from rough treatment.

Should there be any sediment in the bottom of the bowl, it should be removed, and care must be taken that it does not deposit in the passages leading to the jets. Some chambers are provided with a sediment drain-plug for the purpose of cleaning the bowl.

There are two types of carburettors in common use on the modern car; both are automatic in their control of the mixture ratio throughout the full range of engine speed. One of these is known as the static type and the other as the constant-vacuum type.

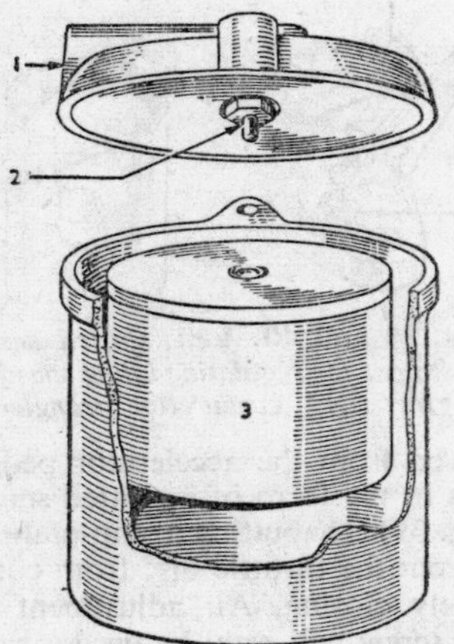

Fig. 38. *Float-chamber of the carburettor:* (1) *filter;* (2) *needle valve;* (3) *float.*

Provided that the carburettor is subjected to a thorough cleaning of the float-bowl, jets and passages when the engine is being decarbonised, and an occasional inspection for leaks, it is unlikely to require any attention, excepting for a slight adjustment of the slow-running control to suit summer and winter conditions.

There are, however, possibilities of carburettor troubles on the road, and a knowledge of the position and function of the various parts will enable the motorist to arrive at the cause, and effect a cure. For more detailed instruction the reader is advised to consult the maker's instruction book.

An adjustment is provided to regulate the speed at which the engine idles when the foot is re-

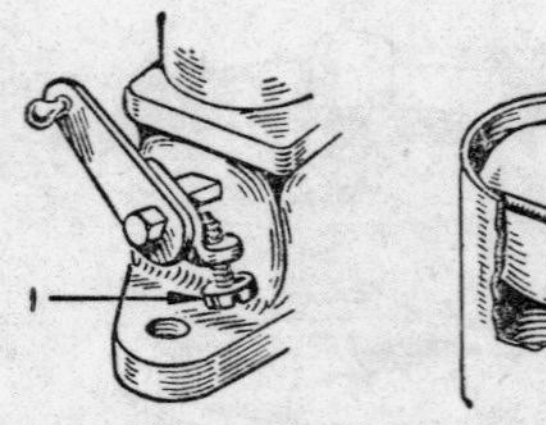

Figs. 39 and 40. Left, *slotted screw adjustment for regulating idling speed of engine;* right, *carburettor strangler.*

moved from the accelerator pedal. It is in the form of a slotted screw (Fig. 39) (1) abutting a stop-plate to prevent the throttle disc from completely closing. An adjustment of this screw will only be necessary if the idling speed is too fast or if the engine stalls frequently when the accelerator pedal comes to rest.

Static Carburettor

Starting Device.—If difficulty in starting is experienced, the cause may be that the strangler (see Fig. 40) disc does not completely close. The air-cleaner, or cowl, should be removed, the movement examined, and the pull-rod adjusted. Another trouble is likely to occur, and will cause a heavy petrol consumption, if the strangler fails to move completely out of operation. This fault may be due to maladjustment of the pull-rod, and this should be examined also for sticky movement, which may be caused by excessive tightening of the air-cleaner clamping screw, thus distorting the spindle bearing.

The latest type of starting device in use on cars is one which delivers a metered quantity of petrol and air through a port situated on the engine side of the throttle. An instance of the type is shown in Fig. 41. A lever (1) controls the device in and out of operation, and is in turn operated from the driving position by a cased wire. Like the strangler control, the wire is liable to stretch, and should be checked in case of a suspected fault for full movement between its two stops. An occasional drop of oil applied at both ends of the wire casing will assist in retaining a free movement. (2) indicates the position of the air-jet, and (3) the petrol-jet.

Slow Running

A separate device for controlling the mixture for slow running is always incorporated in this type of carburettor, and the motorist will be well advised to become familiar with its parts and operation, as it not only plays an important part in starting, accelerating and in petrol economy, but is also the only phase of the carburettor which needs periodic adjustment.

Pilot Jet

A petrol-jet, called the pilot, is usually screwed into the top of

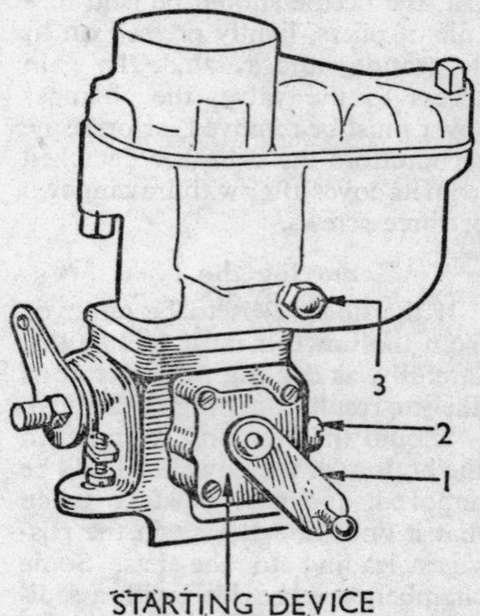

Fig. 41. *Starting device, controlled by lever* (1), *operated by cased wire from driving position;* (2) *air-jet;* (3) *petrol jet.*

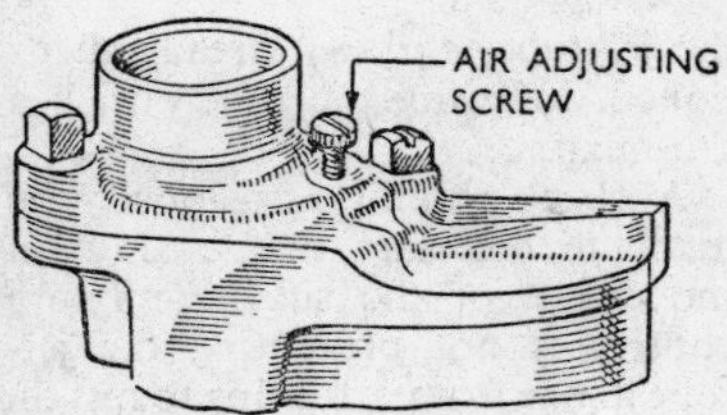

Fig.42. *Headed screw for air adjustment.*

the float-chamber beneath a duct which terminates at the edge of the throttle disc. Also entering this passage is a vent to the atmosphere, and the quantity of air drawn through it is controlled by the position of a headed screw shown in Fig. 42, usually referred to as the air-adjusting screw. In its commonest form, clockwise rotation will enrich the mixture, and counter-clockwise weaken.

The pilot-jet has a very small bore, and is consequently liable to blockage should any foreign matter get past the filters. As an assistance to diagnosing faults, it should be noted that the average slow-running device is responsible for supplying the mixture over approximately the first $\frac{3}{16}$ of the throttle's movement.

The petrol for main or power running is metered through jets. In some cases a single jet covers the whole range from the slow-running,

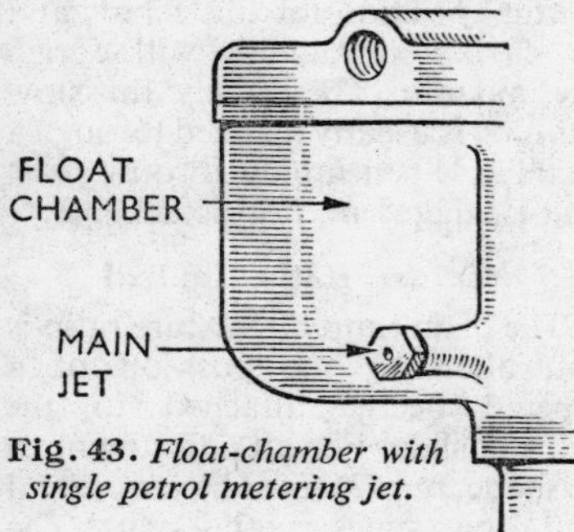

Fig. 43. *Float-chamber with single petrol metering jet.*

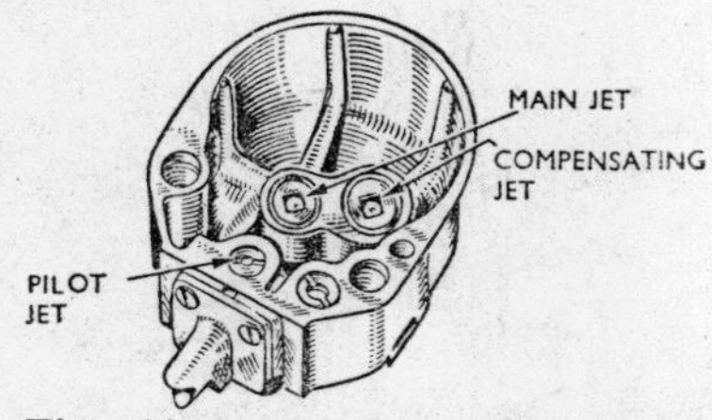

Fig. 44. *Arrangement of main and compensating petrol jets.*

while other models have two jets for the same purpose, known as the main and compensating jets. Figs. 43 and 44 illustrate the two types.

For the purpose of their removal, some jets are provided with a screw-driver slot; while others have two flats for the use of a special key. Yet another type has a sunk square for the engagement of a key which is formed at the end of the float-bowl fixing screw.

When replacing jets after cleaning, be sure that their fibre-washers are in good condition, and that the jets are securely tightened.

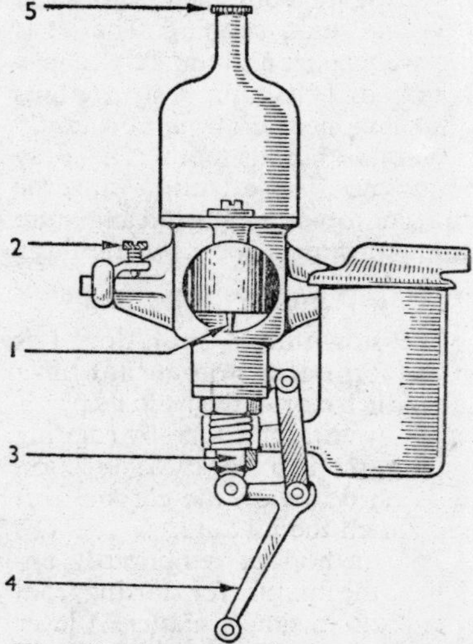

Fig. 45. *Diagram of constant-vacuum carburettor with single metering jet.*

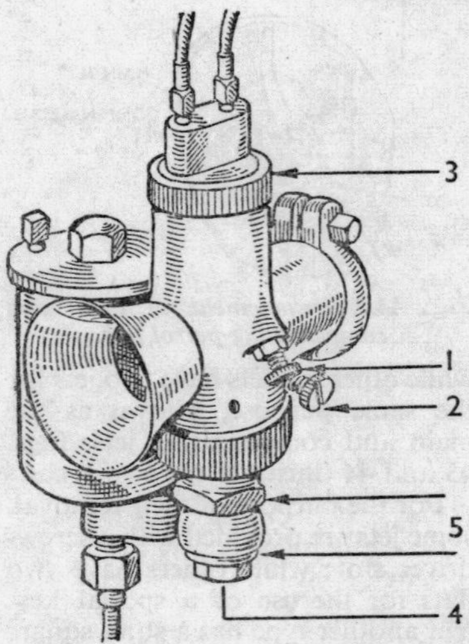

Fig. 46. *Motor-cycle carburettor:* (1) *throttle stop-screw;* (2) *normal position;* (3), (4) *nuts;* (5) *fibre washer.*

The Constant Vacuum Carburettor is a less complicated type (Fig. 45) from the motorist's point of view, as one petrol metering jet serves for the combined purpose of slow and main running. The jet is relatively large, and unlikely to give trouble by becoming obstructed, as a tapered needle (1) is constantly moving within its bore. The only points needing attention are the throttle stop-screw (2) and a mixture ratio adjustment for slow running.

Slow-Running Adjustment

The slow-running adjustment is in the form of a stop-nut (3) for a tube which carries the jet in its upper end. Lowering this tube by rotating the stop-nut in a clockwise direction (looking down on the carburettor) will enrich the mixture.

The method of temporarily enriching the mixture for starting from cold is also a simple matter. A lever (4), controlled from the driving position, is attached to the lower end of the jet tube, and, as already mentioned, lowering the tube enriches the mixture.

A check should occasionally be made to ascertain that a sluggish movement of the starting-mixture control is not preventing the jet-tube flange from returning to rest on the stop-nut when the control is moved out of operation.

One more point in the maintenance is that of lubricating the guide spindle, at intervals of about 1,000 miles, by applying two or three drops of thin oil through the hole in cap (5).

Motor-Cycle Carburettors

The most popular design of carburettor used on the motor-cycle differs from the car type in that it does not completely automatically control the mixture ratio. The rider will already have mastered the control of the throttle and air-slides, the latter for mixture regulation.

A throttle stop-screw (1) to control the slow-running speed when the lever is in a closed position is usually to be found at an angle beneath the slide as shown in Fig. 46. Mixture ratio adjustments are provided for both slow and main running, the former taking the form of an air-adjusting screw, which controls the ratio up to approximately $\frac{1}{8}$ throttle. (2) shows the normal position for this screw, and its clockwise rotation will enrich the mixture. The supply for slow running is usually metered through a small hole beneath the throttle slide, and is, therefore, not detachable.

Mixture Ratio Control

The main running mixture ratio is controlled by the position of a tapered needle attached to the throttle slide. For an adjustment to be made, nut (3) must be unscrewed and the slides withdrawn. The apered needle is positioned at its ıpper end by a spring clip engaging n one of three, or sometimes four, grooves. Positioning the needle by ısing the lowest groove supplies the ichest mixture. This adjustment will ıffect the ratio from about $\frac{1}{8}$ to $\frac{3}{4}$ hrottle.

From $\frac{3}{4}$ to full throttle, the metering of the petrol is taken over by a et through which the needle passes, ınd in the unlikely event of this jet ıaving to be changed, it can be unscrewed from its position after removing nut (4) and detaching the loat-chamber.

When re-assembling the float-chamber, be careful to note that the panjo faces are free from burrs and dirt, and that both fibre-washers (5) ıre in good condition, otherwise a petrol leak will occur.

Non-Needle Carburettor

Fig. 47 shows the details of a design of wholly automatic single-slide non-needle carburettor which is a more common fitment on small motor-cycle engines, particularly on two-strokes. On this type of engine, fine tuning is not so necessary, and the carburettor incorporates no adjustments. Two jets are employed, (1) for metering the slow-running petrol, and (2) for the main running.

In the event of blockage or the need for changing, both jets can be unscrewed from their positions after the removal of plug (3). Although the amateur is well advised not to interfere with the carburettor setting, it may be of interest to note that the mixture ratio can be varied over approximately $\frac{1}{4}$ to $\frac{5}{8}$ throttle by changing the throttle slide for one which is a different shape at its base.

Assuming that the carburettor has been correctly adjusted and properly

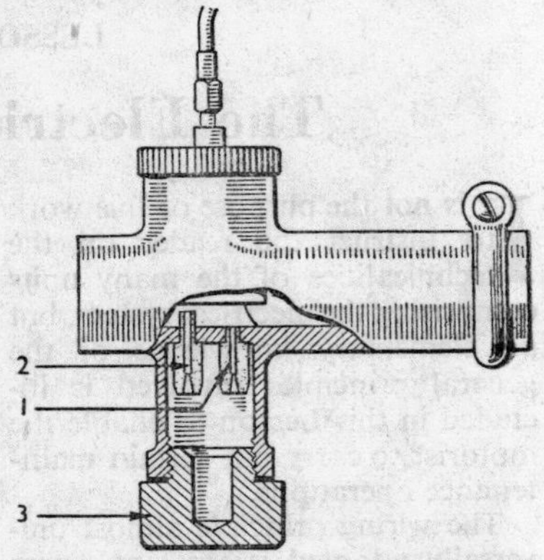

Fig. 47. *Automatic single-slide non-needle carburettor, as used for small motor-cycles.* (1), (2) *jets;* (3) *plug.*

assembled in the first instance, faults are unlikely to develop beyond an occasionally blocked jet. If this trouble becomes at all frequent, the petrol-supply system, including all filters, should be overhauled.

Carburettor Faults

A blocked slow-running jet will result in the engine stalling when the throttle is closed, and starting will be very difficult unless the starting device is brought into operation, even when the engine is hot.

An obstructed main jet will usually be indicated by a violent back-firing through the carburettor, and in the exhaust system when the throttle is opened.

Self Testing Questions

(1) *What steps would you take to deal with the cause of frequent jet blockage?*

(2) *What fault would you suspect if banging occurs in the silencer when the throttle is opened from the slow-running position?*

THE ANSWERS ARE ON PAGE 443.

LESSON 3

The Electrical System

It is not the purpose of this work to instruct the reader on the technicalities of the many units comprising the electrical system, but an elementary knowledge of the general principles involved is included in this Lesson to enable the motorist to carry out certain maintenance operations.

The wiring principle almost universally adopted is the single-wire earth return. Earth is the metal framework of the vehicle, and earth return means that the current flow is from the battery through the circuit to earth, and back to the battery *via* a heavy cable; or, *vice versa*, from the battery to earth, through the circuit, and back to the battery. Fig. 48 is a simple circuit incorporating a lamp, and illustrates the principle of all vehicle circuits.

An electrical unit is usually earthed by making use of its metal casing, and attaching it to a metal part of the vehicle, which in turn is bolted to the frame. It is therefore important for each unit to make a clean connection at its bolting face. Note that loose fixings or rust between the surfaces will cause a faulty earth return, which is equivalent to a break in the circuit. In cases where it is not convenient to fix the unit to metal, an earthing wire, or braided copper strip, is used to earth the casing.

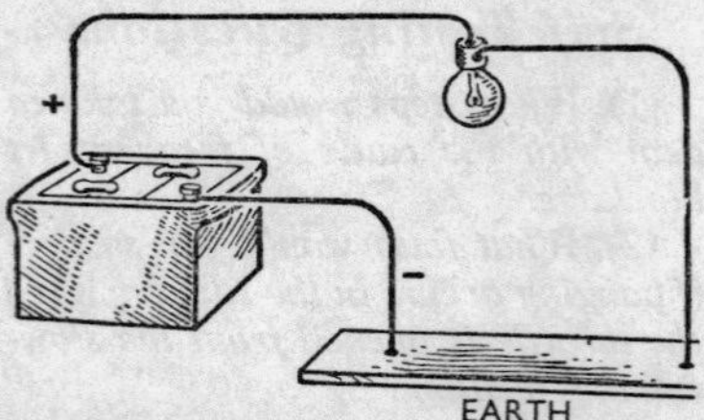

Fig. 48. *Principle of simple vehicle lighting circuit, incorporating lamp.*

The Battery

This may be termed the nerve-centre of the system, as all the circuits are dependent upon its condition for their proper functioning. The battery is either 6 or 12 volts and has two terminals, one a *Positive*, marked + (the larger of the two), and the other a *Negative*, marked −. To these are affixed heavy cables, one running to the frame and the other to a point from which all the circuits emerge.

The useful life of the battery will be greatly prolonged if it is used and maintained carefully. Be sure that it is held firmly in position—all possibility of sliding must be checked, or damage to the case will result. If it is held in position by two long bolts, be careful not to over-tighten, or a strain will be set up on the lugs and eventually fracture the case. The screwed end of these bolts and the nuts should be covered with petroleum jelly to retard corrosion.

The screwed plugs in the top of each cell should be removed every two or three weeks (the shorter period in warm weather) to enable the acid level to be checked. If the battery incorporates external level indicators, the removal of the plugs is unnecessary.

Correct acid level is approximately ¼ in. above the top edge of the plates. Do not use a naked light to check this level, as there is some danger of fire. Should the acid level be low it must be "topped-up" with distilled water; on no account must any other liquid be used for this purpose. Keep the top of the battery dry, and do not allow dirt to accumulate on its surface. Occasionally check the terminal connector bolts for tightness, and keep the connectors covered with vaseline.

Sparking plugs are common to both types of ignition (Magneto and Coil), and these will need some attention to maintain them in good condition.

Provided that the engine fires evenly during all running after warming up, and that starting is not difficult, the plugs should not be disturbed except during decarbonising, or at intervals of 2,000 to 3,000 miles, when the gap will need adjusting; cleaning will be necessary also, if the engine uses too much oil. If the plugs are of the non-detachable type shown in Fig. 49, and are carboned inside the body, they should be taken to a garage for blast-cleaning. The detachable type (Fig. 50) may be dismantled and cleaned by scraping the metal parts with a knife and washing in petrol. The centre-piece of the plug must not be scraped with a knife; clean it with a petrol-soaked rag.

Magneto Ignition. The principle of magneto ignition comprises an electric generator which is a self-contained unit, and is quite separate from the rest of the electrical system. It is driven from a convenient position on the engine and, when coupled, is timed for the spark to take place in the correct relation to piston movement. It should, therefore, not be removed unless the rules of timing have been mastered.

Fig. 51 shows a typical four-cylinder magneto, and the only regular maintenance concerns its lubrication. A spring-cap (1) covers a receptacle into which four or five drops of oil should be applied every

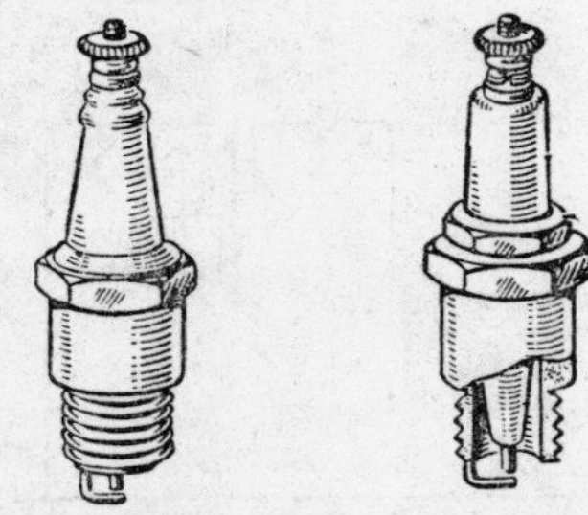

Figs. 49 and 50. *Sparking plugs:* left, *non-detachable;* right, *detachable.*

3,000 miles. If there is no obvious oil-cap on the magneto, it can be assumed that the bearings are loaded with grease when assembled, and no further lubrication is necessary.

The distributor cover (2) can be easily removed, and will reveal the rotor (3) carrying a spring-loaded carbon brush which makes contact with brass segments on the surface of the rotor path (4) in the distributor. In the event of misfiring or difficult starting, the trouble can sometimes be traced to this part of the magneto, in which case the distributor path and the end of the carbon brush should be cleaned with a petrol-damped cloth and finished with a clean dry cloth.

The contact-breaker mechanism (5) should be examined during the decarbonising operation and the points cleaned and the gap adjusted if necessary. If the maker's gauge is

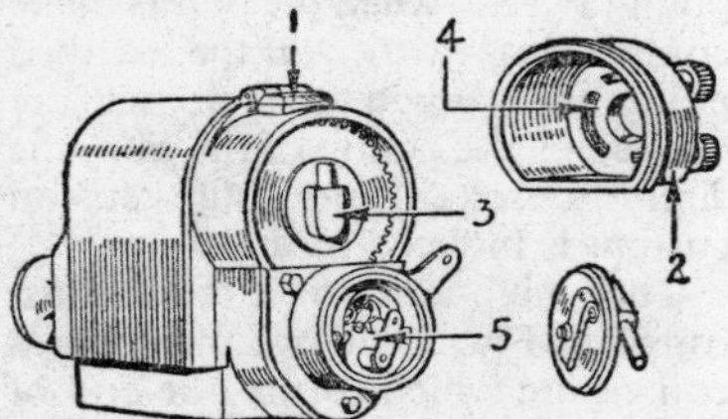

Fig. 51. *Four-cylinder magneto.* (1) *spring cap;* (2) *distributor cover;* (3) *rotor;* (4) *brass segments contacted by carbon brush;* (5) *contact-breaker.*

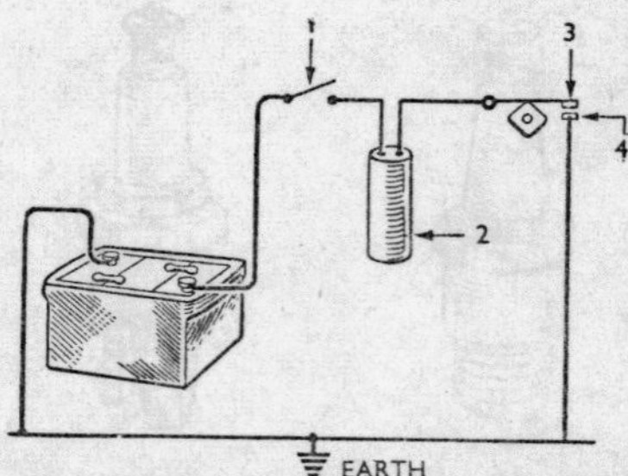

Fig. 52. *Low-tension circuit for coil ignition. For references see text.*

not available the points should be adjusted to take a ·015-in. feeler. Some more detailed notes on contact-breaker points will be found in the Coil Ignition section. The cam-ring should be wiped clean and very lightly smeared with oil, and the spring-loaded rocker checked for free movement. The switch-wire attached to the contact-breaker cover should be checked for good connection.

Coil Ignition. Unlike the magneto, which generates its own electricity, the coil system takes its electrical supply from the battery. Two complete circuits are involved, the low-tension and the high-tension. Fig. 52 is a diagram of the low-tension circuit, showing the flow from the battery through the ignition switch (1) to the coil (2), through the coil to the insulated contact-breaker point (3), and, when the points make contact, to earth *via* the earthed point (4). When the points are opened by the action of the cam, the circuit is broken, and a high-tension current is induced in the coil.

The high-tension circuit illustrated in Fig. 53 shows the earthed coil casing which forms one end of the circuit, the other side passing out from the coil through the heavily insulated centre cable (1) to the distributor (2), where it makes contact with the rotor (3), which is carried on the cam spindle. From the rotor centre, the current passes along a metal plate and jumps a gap to the brass segments (4), to which the sparking-plug cables are attached. From the plug cable (or lead) the insulated metal centre carries it to the sparking point, from which it jumps to the earth point. This, of course, is earthed through the cylinders.

An oil-cup or a greaser will be found under the contact-breaker housing, and a few drops of oil or a half turn of the grease-cap should be given every 1,000 miles. Unless the ignition develops symptoms of trouble there is no further maintenance necessary, provided the following overhaul is carried out during decarbonising or at intervals of 4,000 or 5,000 miles.

Give a sharp gentle pull to all the cables where attached to terminals; this will reveal such faults as broken cable strands and badly soldered connectors. Check all terminal nuts for tightness, and wipe all insulated parts free of dust, as this is likely to absorb moisture and cause a leakage or shorting of the current.

The contact-breaker unit (Fig. 54) should next receive attention. Remove the distributor cover and examine for surface cracks which

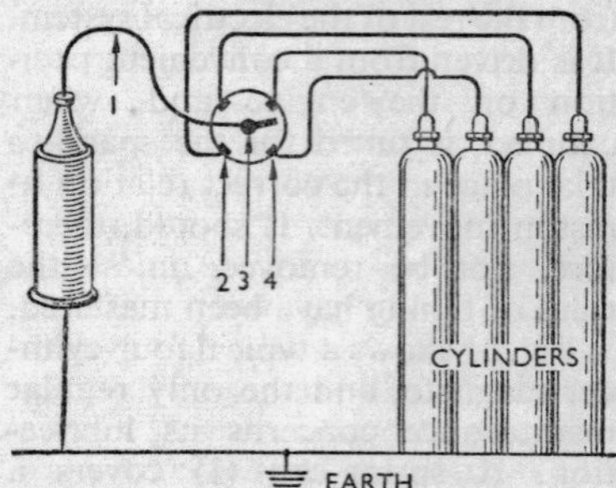

Fig. 53. *High-tension circuit for coil ignition. Compare Fig. 52, above.*

may cause current leakage in damp weather. Lift off rotor and apply four to five drops of oil around the head of the screw beneath.

The contact-breaker points should now be cleaned. The best tool in the hands of the amateur for this job is a thin carborundum card, which can be purchased from a garage. This should be inserted between the closed points and gently rubbed backward and forward until a clean surface is obtained on both points.

The points should now be checked for correct gap, and this must be measured when the points are fully open. If the maker's gauge is not available for this purpose, a ·010 to ·012-in. feeler blade may be used. Should an adjustment be necessary, it will be found that one of the points is adjustable, either by slackening the locking device (a nut or a clamping screw) or by slightly loosening two screws which secure a plate carrying the earth point, and sliding the plate to obtain the correct gap. Take care to lock the parts securely after the adjustment is made.

Finally, clean the unit with compressed air (the tyre pump will do), carefully wipe all dust from the contact points, smear a little oil or vaseline on the cam, and replace all parts.

Ignition Faults. Misfiring is the most likely fault, and this may be due to a faulty plug. To locate this the engine should be run at a fast idling speed and the plugs shorted to earth one at a time by resting a wooden-handled screw-driver on the cylinders and holding it lightly against the plug terminal. This action prevents the current passing to the plug points, and the alteration of engine note, or speed, either when the plug is cut out or in, will indicate whether it is at fault. The faulty plug should

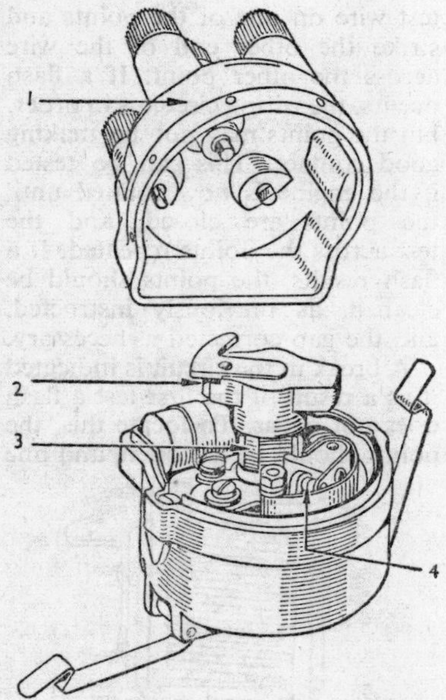

Fig. 54. *Contact-breaker unit.*

be removed, cleaned and correctly gapped, replaced and tested again.

A fault in the low-tension circuit will probably cause starting trouble, and should be diagnosed as follows.

First test for a spark at the high tension by detaching one of the leads from the sparking plug and, holding its metal end about $\frac{1}{8}$ in. from the metal body of the plug, rotate the engine. If a spark jumps this gap, it indicates that both high- and low-tension circuits are in order; if no spark occurs, the low-tension circuit should be tested.

A length of insulated wire, between 2 ft. and 3 ft. long, should be bared for about $\frac{1}{2}$ in. at each end, and the strands tightly twisted (this is for general test purposes).

Remove the distributor cover and rotate the engine until the contact-breaker points are open, and switch on the engine. Place one end of the test wire on one of the points and strike the other end of the wire across the other point. If a flash occurs, the wiring circuit is in order, but the points may not be making good contact. This can be tested if the engine is now rotated until the points are closed, and the test across the points repeated. If a flash results, the points should be cleaned, as previously instructed, and the gap corrected as necessary.

A break in the circuit is indicated if as a result of the first test a flash does not occur. To locate this, the points should be left open, and one

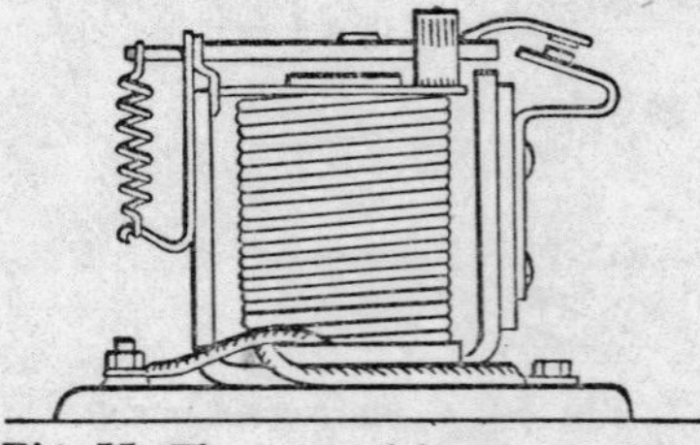

Fig. 55. *The cut-out* (above) *is included in the dynamo circuit.*

end of the test wire pressed on each terminal in turn through the circuit, starting at the one nearest the switch, and the other end of the wire struck across a metal part of the engine. A flash indicates that the current is flowing, and when no flash occurs, the fault obviously lies between the terminal which flashed to earth, and that which failed to do so.

The Dynamo

This unit is usually driven by a belt from the engine, and is for the purpose of generating electricity for the various circuits when the engine is running, and also for keeping the battery up to full charge.

Most dynamo spindles are packed with grease when assembled and require no further lubrication, but on some a small oiler will be found, usually at the drive end, which should receive one or two drops of oil every 1,000 miles.

Incorporated in the dynamo circuit is the *Ammeter*, a red warning light, and the *Cut-Out*. The purpose of the cut-out (Fig. 55) is to prevent the battery discharging through the dynamo when the engine is switched off. The warning light and the ammeter are the "tell-tales" of the system, if their indications are understood.

When the ignition is switched on, the red warning light should glow, and this should continue until the engine reaches a certain fast idling speed, when it should fade out. This indicates that the dynamo is charging. When the ignition is switched off the warning light should go out. This indicates that the battery is not discharging through the dynamo. If the warning light does not operate as explained, the cut-out cover should be removed and the contact points cleaned with a carborundum card, afterwards wiping away all dust particles.

The ammeter indicates the quantity of charge and discharge: for instance, when the ignition is switched on it should show a discharge of 2 to 3 amps., and when the engine speeds up and the warning light ceases to glow, the pointer should move to the charge side, the charge rate gradually increasing up to a certain maximum as the engine speed increases. It should then remain steady until another of the circuits is switched on, when the needle will fall back proportionally to the quantity of current being used.

If, when a circuit is switched on, the ammeter pointer flicks right across to full discharge, a short is occurring in that circuit; this means that the current is running to earth. Such a fault needs immediate attention, for if left switched on, the battery will rapidly discharge. Should the pointer flicker violently when the car is being driven at a steady speed, the dynamo brushes should be examined for stickiness. If not perfectly free to slide in their holders they should be withdrawn and the brushes and holders cleaned with a cloth slightly damped with petrol; afterwards, the whole chamber beneath the metal band should be blown out with the tyre-pump.

A fuse is included in the dynamo circuit to serve as a safety outlet if a fault develops which may cause lamps, etc., to burn out. This fuse (see Fig. 57) is sometimes mounted on the dynamo, but there is an alternative position on the dash. Should the fuse blow, the ammeter will not show a charge; also the warning light will not fade out. A new fuse is quite easy to fit, but be sure that the amperage, which is clearly marked, is the same as the one removed. If the replacement fuse blows again after a short interval, there is probably a fault in the system, and skilled assistance should be sought.

Lighting. Lighting circuits are fairly simple to follow, and in case of fault each lamp-cable can usually be traced to the junction box. Trouble is unlikely to develop between the junction box and the switch, and fortunately so, as the large number of wires between these two points is in a loom, and the wires can only be traced by the colour.

The means of dipping the near-side head lamp and switching off the off-side is electrically operated on most of the modern cars. The mechanism for this operation is mounted on the back of the near-side lamp reflector and, excepting for a fuse replacement, any fault which may develop in its operation is best left to an electrician.

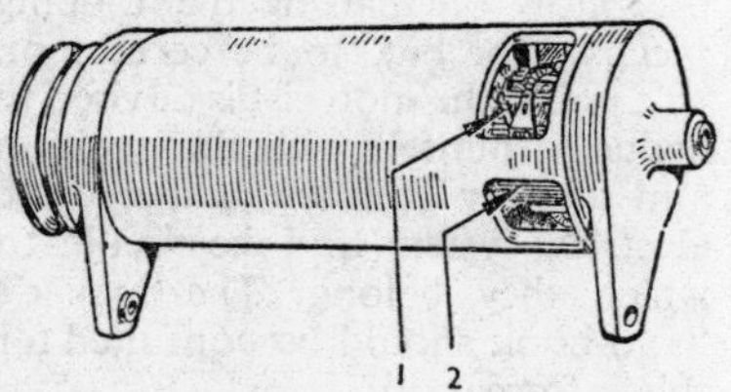

Fig. 56. *Dynamo, showing carbon brush* (1) *and commutator* (2).

The fuse in this circuit will be found on the back of the reflector, and, to gain access to this, the lamp-rim must first be removed by slacking off the slotted screw at the bottom, swinging it downward and then pulling the bottom of the rim forward and upward. Behind the rim is a cork washer for the purpose of excluding the dust, and this must be carefully lifted off. At the top of the reflector flange is a small screw which must be removed to allow a slight rotation to free the reflector from its grooves. This is best carried out by placing both hands against the rim, as care must be taken not to mark the reflecting surface, which must only be cleaned with a moist chamois leather, or polished with a soft cloth. Very little maintenance is called for on the lighting system, amounting only to a very occasional pull on the cables where they are attached to the lamps to check for broken strands and weak connections.

Lighting Faults

There is not, as a general rule, a fuse in the lighting system, with the

Fig. 57. *The dynamo circuit includes a fuse* (*above*), *to serve as a safety outlet.*

exception of that in the dipping mechanism, but, to be certain on this point, the motorist is advised to acquaint himself with the position and number of fuses in the whole electrical system, and the circuits to which they belong. The maker's hand-book should be consulted for this information.

The faults likely to be encountered are broken lamp filaments, broken cable strands and bad earth contacts. Any of these faults will put the lamp out of action, and the quickest way to diagnose in the first instance is to fit a replacement lamp.

The following test must be carried out to locate a broken wire or faulty earth. The length of test wire previously mentioned will be needed: hold one of its ends on the lamp contact point at the base of the socket, and strike the other end across a metal earth. If a flash occurs, next strike against the lamp, and if no flash results, the earthing of the lamp is at fault. The remedy is to remove the lamp from its fixing and remove any rust with an old file.

A broken cable or faulty cable connection is indicated if, when the test is made with the wire, a flash does not occur when the wire is struck across earth. In this case, the cable should be detached from the lamp and the bared end struck across earth. If a flash occurs, the connection is at fault, but if there is no flash, the cable is faulty. Trace the cable back to the junction box and hold the end of the test wire on the junction terminal and strike to earth. A flash indicates that the circuit is in order up to the terminal and that the cable is fractured. The break may be an obvious one and the broken ends may be bared, twisted together and bound with insulating tape. This, however, should only be considered a temporary job, until a new length of wire can be obtained.

Electric Starter

Although built on similar lines to those of the dynamo, the starter motor differs in that it is driven by current and does not generate. The unit is earthed by its casing, and the battery current flows direct *via* the starter switch. The starter is very robust in construction, and is unlikely to require any attention.

Self Testing Question

(1) *How would you proceed to diagnose a starting fault—carburettor in order?*

THE ANSWER IS ON PAGE 443.

LESSON 4

Engine Maintenance

OPINION varies as to the point at which, in terms of mileage, decarbonising the engine should be carried out. With modern high-compression high-"revving" engines, it can be taken to be necessary when a mileage of between 6,000 and 10,000 has been covered. On the other hand, it may not become a necessity until a far greater mileage than 10,000 has been attained. Should the engine have been allowed to run unnecessarily hot, owing to neglect on the driver's part to see that the water system is kept up to capacity, possibly running with a slipping clutch, binding brakes, insufficient clearance of valve tappets, the valves will be affected. This results in loss of compression, rough running and lack of power, and will naturally decide the decarbonising operation irrespective of mileage. The compression can be roughly tested by slowly cranking over the engine by hand with the starting handle and comparing the difference in reaction between the cylinders. They should all take about the same amount of effort to overcome each compression. Usually one or more cylinders will show very noticeably a total lack of reaction, with definite loss of compression. Bear in mind that with a four-cylinder engine two compressions during each turn of the handle should be felt, and three for each turn with a six-cylinder. On the other hand, until the carbon deposit reaches the stage sufficient to cause "pinking" or "detonation," and falling off of power combined with roughness becomes apparent, decarbonising may be postponed for mileages much in excess of 10,000.

Tools Required

Before commencing work it is essential that the following items and tools, apart from the regular car kit, should be available:

1. A strong socket spanner capable of slackening and tightening correctly the cylinder-head nuts or set-screws.
2. The correct valve-lifter; this is very often supplied in the car kit. If not, obtain one from the makers; they know better than anybody the best design of tool for their car.
3. An old blunt wood chisel or similar instrument for scraping off the carbon without unduly scratching or damaging aluminium heads or pistons.
4. Two head-lifters, very often supplied in the tool kit.
5. The proper tappet spanners for setting and locking the tappet adjusters.
6. A set of "feelers" having blades of the required thickness for checking your tappet clearances.
7. A new cylinder-head gasket for your particular model.
8. A set of manifold joints.
9. A valve-cover joint.
10. A small quantity of valve grinding paste.
11. A light coil spring to raise the valve off its seat while grinding in.
12. A large screw-driver, or, if your valves are without the slot in the head, a suction grinding tool.
13. A small quantity of clean rag and paraffin.

The following instructions are compiled to cover the process of decarbonising in a general sense. The sequence of operations will follow on more or less the same lines for most engines, and the particular points to be observed will be stressed. On the other hand, it is naturally an impossibility to cover individually even a small percentage of the makes on the market. The reader will have to consult his instruction book for any particular item peculiar to his car, and other items referred to which do not apply can obviously be ignored.

Aluminium Cylinder Heads

Where aluminium cylinder heads are fitted it is not advisable to release the tension of the cylinder-head nuts and begin to remove the cylinder head if the engine is at all hot. If carried out while hot, the risk of distortion of the metal owing to uneven cooling is great. Therefore, defer beginning work until the engine is quite cold.

First, begin operations by draining the water system. The drain-plug or tap will usually be found in the bottom tank of the radiator, or at the lowest point in the system, such as the water pump or bottom connection. If treated with anti-freeze solution it is worth preserving the contents for further use, in which case drain into a suitable container. Should the bonnet or bonnet sides restrict access to the engine, it is better to remove them. Next, if you are proud of your paint-work, cover your front wings with an old rug or similar protective material as a precaution against damage and scratching during work on the engine. Before proceeding with any further work, disconnect the battery as a safeguard against shorts or the inadvertent use of the starter motor during the ensuing operations. Detach the leads from the sparking plugs; it is a good plan to number them by file marks on the terminals or leads, so as to facilitate their correct replacement to their respective cylinders. Next remove the sparking plugs as a precaution against damage; a tap with a tool usually results in a cracked insulator.

If the dynamo is carried on a bracket secured to the cylinder head, disconnect the wires attached to it, taking note of their respective connections so that you can replace them correctly. A small label attached to each wire referring to its connection may be used. Any other auxiliary fittings, such as the carburettor air-cleaner or controls, which are secured to the cylinder head, will also have to be removed.

As is often the case with side-valve engines, the distributor drive passes through the cylinder head and will have to be withdrawn before the head can be removed. Do not loosen the clamp-bolt on the bracket, but remove the set-screw holding bracket to head. This will ensure replacement with correct timing position, as the drive itself is usually in the form of an off-set dog which can only re-engage in one position. Disconnect the low-tension wire from coil to distributor, and distributor complete with leads can be removed. Next disconnect the top water hose; always disconnect at hose in preference to unbolting a flange fitting, as these are at times difficult to re-assemble without leaks.

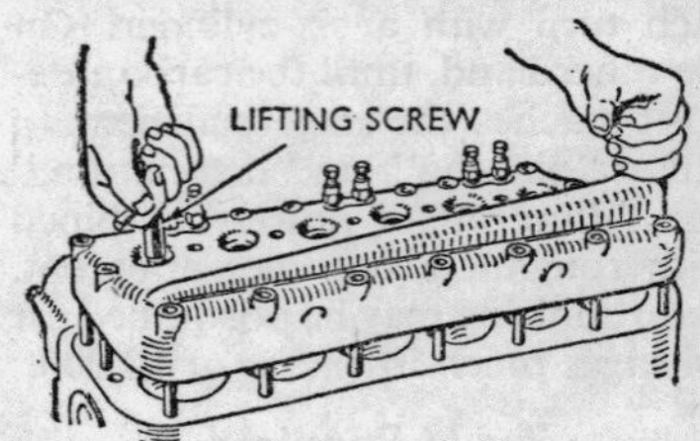

Fig. 59. *Lifting the cylinder-head by means of the lifters provided.*

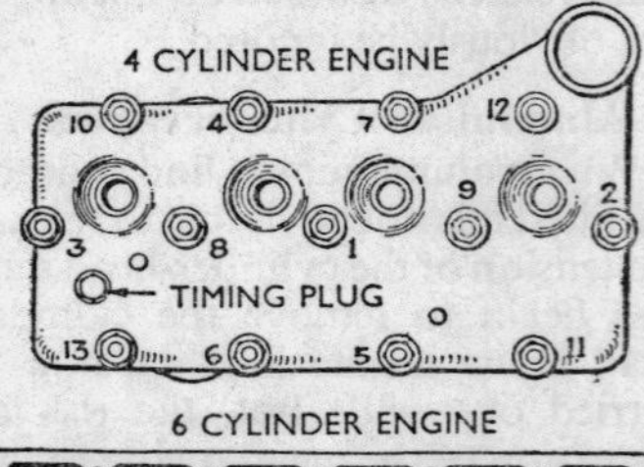

6 CYLINDER ENGINE

Fig. 58. *The numbers show the sequence which should be followed when slackening or tightening the cylinder head-nuts.*

The cylinder-head nuts must next be removed, and the method of doing this is important. Each nut should be given only a partial turn in the first instance, beginning systematically from the centre and working outward in the sequence as depicted in Fig. 58. Then return to the first nut and repeat the same process several times until all nuts are quite slack. The reason for this gradual process is to avoid uneven stress on the head, which would in all probability lead to distortion. This is particularly the case when dealing with an aluminium cylinder head. After all cylinder-head nuts or set-screws are removed, the head itself should be lifted off, using the head-lifters screwed into the plug holes; see Fig. 59. If any difficulty is experienced owing to the use of jointing on the gasket, or corrosion around the studs, the joint may be broken and the head first loosened by jarring it at several places, using a piece of wood grain endwise as a drift to take the blow of the hammer. Never resort to the expedient of driving a chisel or screw-driver between the faces of the cylinder block and head, as this inevitably damages the machined faces, apart from ruining the gasket.

In the case of an overhead-valve engine, where the valves are operated by push-rods and the rocker gear is positioned on the cylinder head, very often some of the studs are utilised for the dual purpose of clamping the rocker standards in position and holding down the head (see Fig. 67). It is therefore essential that such nuts be removed prior to trying to force the head off. At times the whole of the rocker assembly will have to be removed be-

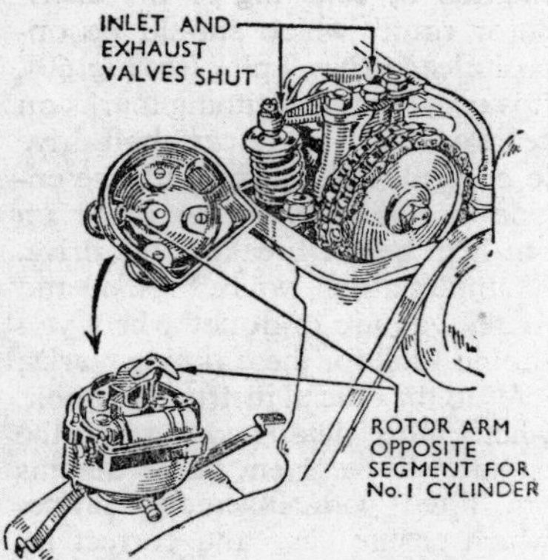

Fig. 60. *Singer camshaft drive for O.H.V. engines. The rotor should be opposite lead to No. 1 plug.*

fore the head can be lifted. Disconnect any oil-pipes attached to either rocker gear or cylinder before attempting removal of the head.

Where the design employs an overhead camshaft for valve operation, the removal of the cylinder head is more complicated. The drive to the camshaft, be it chain or gears, has to be disturbed before the head can be removed. This necessitates the correct re-timing of the camshaft when re-assembling. Before disrupting the camshaft drive, turn the engine until No. 1 piston is at the top of its stroke with both inlet and exhaust valves closed. This is the firing position of the cylinder, and can be

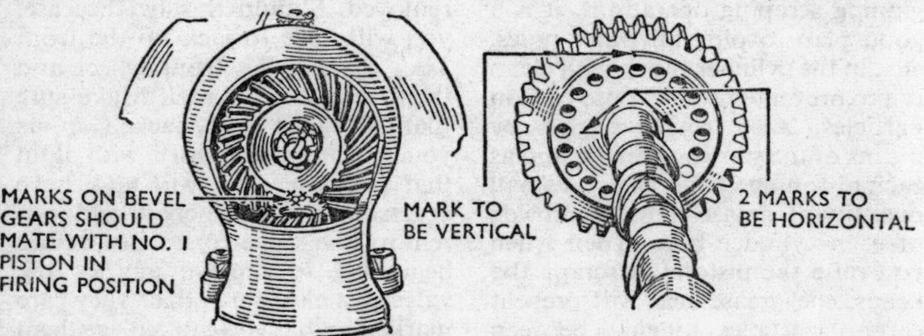

Fig. 61. *Morris overhead camshaft drive. Note the positions for the timing marks.*

checked by referring to the distributor rotor, which should be opposite lead to No. 1 plug (see Fig. 60). It is usual for such timing marks on gears on chain of the camshaft drive to coincide for mating with the engine in this position, so check up on them before breaking the drive. Examples are shown in Figs. 60 and 61. If you are in doubt where you should look for these timing marks, refer to the official instruction book, where fuller details concerning the engine will be given. Some designs are fitted with ingenious devices which ensure easy and correct replacement of the camshaft, eliminating the necessity for the more involved procedure outlined above.

Having removed the head, the cylinder-head gasket can be lifted off. Slide the blade of a table-knife between gasket and cylinder block and ease up from the face of the block. You may find some difficulty owing to the gasket being a tight fit on one or more studs; ease it over these and endeavour to keep it parallel with the face of the cylinder, not tipped up at either end. The next procedure is to clean away as much of the carbon deposit as possible before removing the valves. This will reduce the possibility of damage to the valve-seats, as compared with first removing the valves, and then removing the carbon. Before beginning scraping operations, it is a good plan to plug all water holes, etc., in the cylinder block with clean rag to prevent entry of loose carbon particles. Also rotate engine by means of the starting handle, and as each piston descends, smear a small quantity of grease round the inside of each cylinder bore. Then when you raise the pistons to scrape the heads, the grease seal will prevent carbon particles lodging between the top piston-ring land and the cylinder wall. Never, however, remove such carbon as may be deposited around the inside of the cylinders at the top. Never, moreover, use emery or other abrasive material to polish the pistons; rub hard with a rag dipped in paraffin to remove finally such small particles of carbon as may be left after scraping. When the piston heads are clean, turn the engine, and as each piston descends wipe away the grease and accumulation of carbon.

Removing the Valves. Although not always a necessity, it will certainly facilitate the removal of the valves on a side-valve engine if the inlet and exhaust manifolds are removed. This will entail disconnecting petrol pipes and controls to the carburettor and such flange bolts or nuts as attach manifold to exhaust pipe, and manifold to cylinder. Or, in the case of an overhead-valve engine, the manifolds will be attached to the head, and it will be better to remove them before lifting the head. In most cases it will be possible to remove manifolds complete with carburettor.

Removing Side Valance

With some of the latest car designs, where the engine position is such that it is a most difficult job to gain access to the valves, provision is made so that a side valance can be removed. Should this be the case, you will have to jack up the front axle, remove the front wheel and then remove the panel. Make sure that the car is safely jacked up, as you will have to work with it in that position. You will now have access to the valve-chest and can remove the valve-cover. But before beginning to remove any of the valves, make sure that they are marked so that you can replace them in their original positions. The

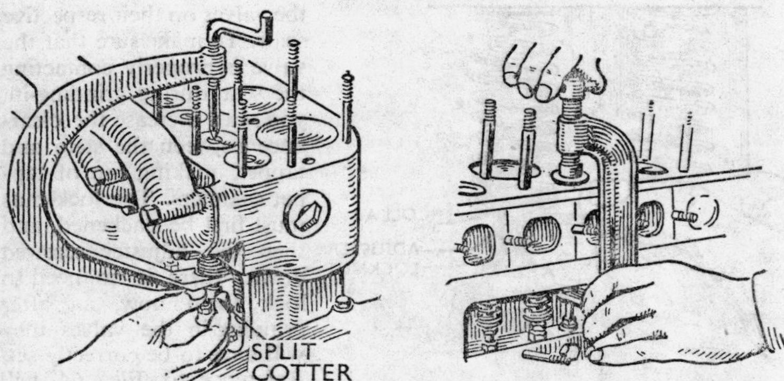

Fig. 62. *Two types of valve lifters. Begin operations with a centre valve.*

makers usually stamp them in sequence, No. 1 being that nearest the radiator. If not marked, you can use a centre punch to dot them, the number of dots denoting the valve position, as they should always be replaced in the guides and seats they have been operating in.

As a precaution against dropping cotters, etc., into the crankcase, it is advisable to plug any oil-vents or apertures in the valve-chest with clean rag before beginning to remove the valves. Now take the valve-lifter and choose a valve in the centre of the engine to begin operations on, as these are usually more accessible, while the other valves are in position, than those in the corner of the valve-chest. Insert the open end of the lifter under the valve-collar (see Fig. 62) and position the screwed or adjustable part over the valve-head. Compress the valve-spring by operating the lifter, and the valve-collars can then be removed. Fig. 63 shows the standard type of valve with split cotters, and will make clear the operation for their removal. There are, however, many other different types of cotter in use, but, whatever the type, the valve-collar invariably keeps them in position, the collar itself being positioned by the valve-spring. When you have removed all the valves complete with springs and collars, you can clean the valve-ports of all carbon. Take care not to damage the valve-seats, for if the carbon is hard you may have to chip some of it away. Finally, blow all carbon particles from ports and cylinders, using your car tyre-pump.

Next scrape all carbon off the valves; chipping may have to be resorted to again, but take care of the valve-faces. When free of carbon, wash valves, springs, col-

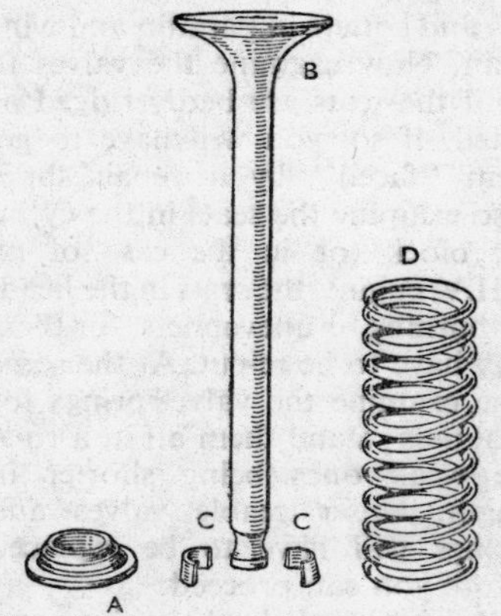

Fig. 63. *Valve components.* A, *collar;* B, *valve;* C, *cotters;* D, *spring.*

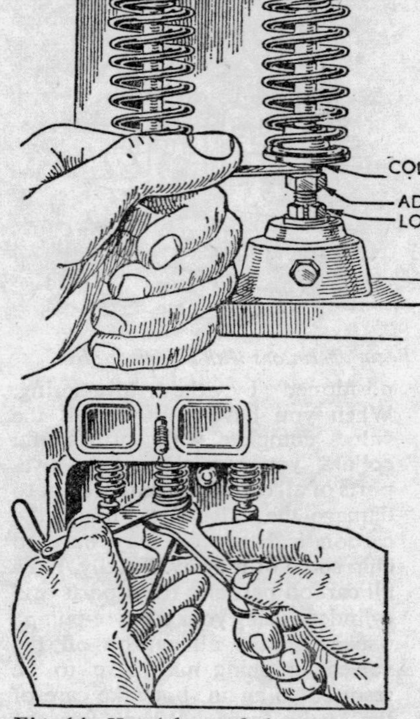

Fig. 64. *How* (above) *feeler gauge, and* (below) *tappet spanner, are used.*

the valves on their respective seats. To make sure that the valve is properly contacting the seat during grinding-in, you must increase the clearance between the stem and tappet, making use of tappet spanners. The lock-nuts must first be slackened, and then the adjuster screwed down; there is no need to lock them now, as after grinding-in the valves they will have to be correctly set. Reference to Fig. 64 will make this operation quite clear. Smear a small quantity of the grinding paste on the face of the valve, then slip the light spring on the stem before inserting valve into guide, and using the large screw-driver or the suction tool, press valve on to its seat and impart a reciprocating motion to it (see Fig. 65). Every now and again allow the spring to raise the valve off the seat and give the valve about a half turn before depressing on seat and again reciprocating it. Repeat until a clearly defined matt-surfaced ring shows round the valve-face.

The following simple check will give you an idea when the valve-face and seat are gas-tight and need no further grinding. Wipe off all grinding paste from valve and seating, make a series of pencil lines across

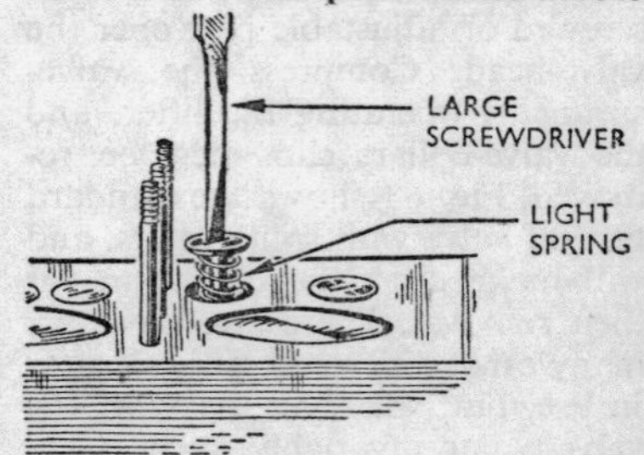

Fig. 65. *Method of grinding-in the valves.*

lars and cotters in paraffin and wipe clean. Now examine the valves to see if the seats are badly ridged or pitted. If so, you will have to get them "faced" by a repair shop. Also examine the seats in the cylinder block (or in the case of an O.H.V. engine, the seats in the head) for burning or unevenness, for these may have to be re-cut. At the same time examine the valve-springs for weakness; stand them all in a row, the weak ones being shorter in length. Unserviceable valves and springs will have to be replaced before you can proceed.

Having settled the valve and spring question, begin to grind the valve-face, insert valve into guide, and using slight pressure with screwdriver or suction tool give the valve several reciprocations of not more than a quarter of a turn. This means that the valve must not make a full turn, otherwise the test is futile. On removing the valve and examining the face, all the pencil lines should be cut through at the matt ring. If not, repeat the grinding-in process.

After all valves are seating correctly, they should be washed in paraffin and wiped clean. Remove all traces of grinding paste from valve-seats and ports; an old toothbrush can be utilised to advantage. The valves can then be replaced in the opposite sequence of operations to removal. First springs and collars are positioned, then the valve inserted through the guide. Next compress spring and collar with valve-lifter, until cotters can be inserted, and then let down spring and collar, making sure that the cotters are not pushed out of position or jammed by the descending collar, and removing the lifter. Now re-set the tappet adjusters to give correct clearance, and to ensure that the cam is in the correct position while this is being done, refer to the tables at bottom of page.

The valves, springs, etc., having been replaced, and tappets correctly set and securely locked with the locknuts, replace the valve cover-plate with the new joint.

The cylinder head should next be scraped of all carbon, washed throughly in paraffin and dried. If using the new cylinder-head gasket, make sure it is the correct one by checking up all water passages, etc., with those on the cylinder block. Smear both faces of the gasket with ordinary household soap and fit over studs on to cylinder face, making absolutely certain it is the right way round. Some care will have to be taken not to burr up the gasket

Four-Cylinder Engines.

Adjust No.	1	tappet with No.	8	valve	fully	open.
,,	3	,, ,,	6	,,	,,	,,
,,	5	,, ,,	4	,,	,,	,,
,,	2	,, ,,	7	,,	,,	,,
,,	8	,, ,,	1	,,	,,	,,
,,	6	,, ,,	3	,,	,,	,,
,,	4	,, ,,	5	,,	,,	,,
,,	7	,, ,,	2	,,	,,	,,

Six-Cylinder Engines.

Set No.	1	tappet with No.	12	valve	fully	open.
,,	6	,, ,,	7	,,	,,	,,
,,	9	,, ,,	4	,,	,,	,,
,,	11	,, ,,	2	,,	,,	,,
,,	5	,, ,,	8	,,	,,	,,
,,	3	,, ,,	10	,,	,,	,,
,,	12	,, ,,	1	,,	,,	,,
,,	7	,, ,,	6	,,	,,	,,
,,	4	,, ,,	9	,,	,,	,,
,,	2	,, ,,	11	,,	,,	,,
,,	8	,, ,,	5	,,	,,	,,
,,	10	,, ,,	3	,,	,,	,,

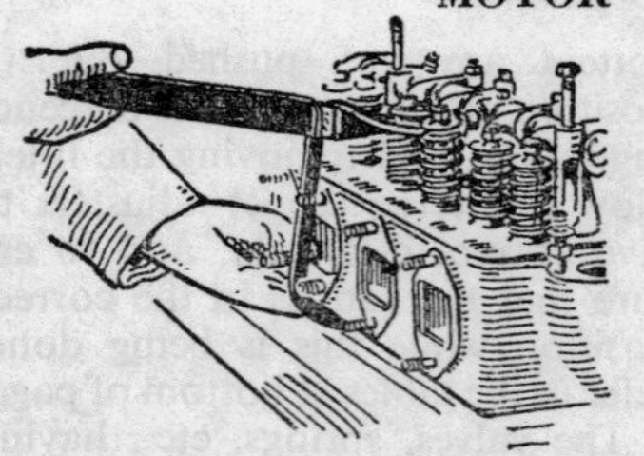

Fig. 66. *Showing the way in which a lifter is used for dismantling the valves on an overhead-valve engine.*

around the studs; endeavour to keep gasket level with face of head, and ease down over the studs where necessary with a small box spanner or piece of tube. Finally replace the cylinder head, taking care to tighten all nuts gradually in the sequence already explained for removal as shown in Fig. 58. All other remaining parts can be replaced in the reverse order to that in which they were removed. On completion, the engine should be run until normally warm; first turning off the drain-cock and refilling the water system, after which the cylinder-head nuts may be finally tightened down.

When working on an overhead-valve engine remove most of the carbon from the head before dismantling the valves. Should it be necessary to remove the valve push-rods, slide them through numbered holes in a piece of thick paper to facilitate their correct replacement, which is advisable. The rocker gear may or may not have been dismantled, and the removal of valves will be along the same lines as already described (Fig. 66). Valve grinding and checking are also carried out on the same lines, but after having re-assembled and replaced the cylinder head, roughly set valve-clearances and run the engine until normally warm. Then, after having finally tightened down the head nuts, re-check and set the tappet or rather push-rod clearances (Fig. 67). With the overhead-valve camshaft engine, after decarbonising and grinding-in the valves, retime the camshaft on replacing head. As already pointed out, there are many different ways of eliminating error in this respect; for full details regarding a par-

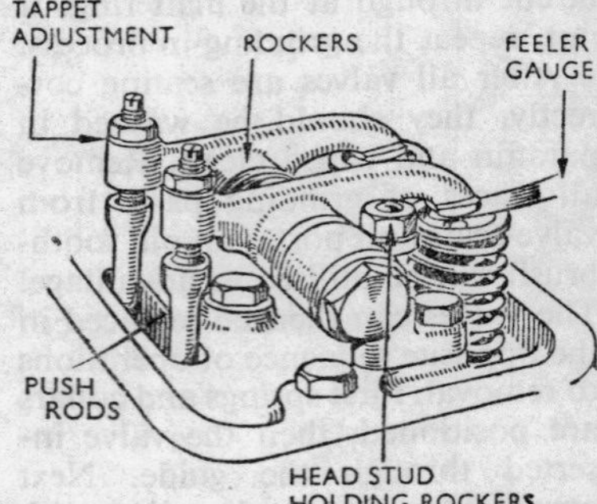

Fig. 67. *Arrangement of tappets and push-rods on an overhead-valve engine. The push-rods are seen to the left.*

ticular engine, consult the official instruction book.

After the engine has been decarbonised and re-assembled, it is a golden opportunity to clean the carburettor and its filters (Lesson 3), clean and re-set the sparking plugs (see Lesson 2), dress and set distributor contact points (see Lesson 3).

Self Testing Questions

(1) *After decarbonising an engine, having replaced the cylinder head, etc., filled up with water, and started up, what would you finally make sure of before driving off?*

(2) *Do you consider that the valve-clearances should be checked again after a small mileage has been covered since decarbonising?*

(3) *When setting valve-clearances is it necessary to follow a sequence, or is it sufficient to make sure that the valve you are operating on is closed?*

THE ANSWERS ARE ON PAGE 444.

LESSON 5

Engine Lubrication and Cooling

On the use of the correct grade of engine oil depends the operation of the lubrication system as a whole. Before attempting to trace troubles such as abnormally high pressure, leakage and similar faults, for instance, it is essential to make sure that the sump is filled with the correct grade of oil.

It may be well to stress here that in cold weather a change from a summer to a winter grade of oil is recommended in the majority of cases. Not only will a summer grade seriously increase the load on the starter motor during the winter months, but oil thrown up from the big ends will be considerably delayed, with consequent increase in cylinder wear.

Additionally, a large percentage of modern engines have an oil-feed hole drilled in the upper half of the connecting rod big-end bearing; this registers with the supply groove in the crankshaft journal when the piston is approaching the top of its stroke, so that a jet of oil is flung on to the cylinder walls. Full benefit will not be obtained from this jet if too heavy a lubricant is used.

It should also be remembered that although a very high pressure may be registered by the oil-gauge when starting from cold with too heavy a grade of oil in the sump, the oil pressure received by the bearings may amount to only 2–3 lb. per sq. in., owing to the difficulty in forcing heavy lubricant through small oil passages. Bearing failure may occur under these conditions.

The use of some form of upper-cylinder lubricant is an advantage

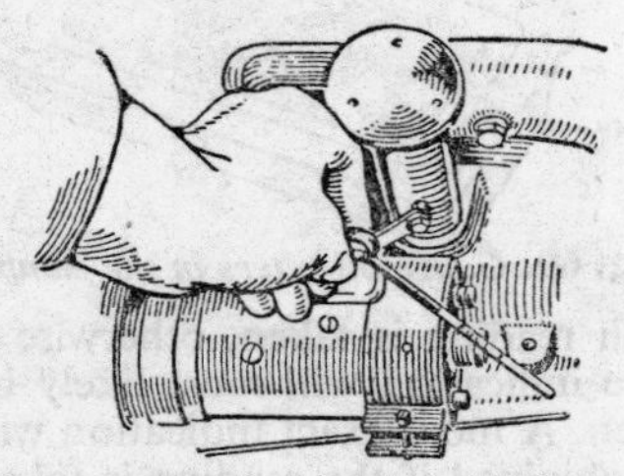

Fig. 68. *Checking sump oil level with dip-stick. Take readings with engine cold.*

not only during the running-in period, but during the whole life of the car. Upper cylinder lubricants *do* reduce cylinder wear and improve performance and petrol consumption by the formation, in the case of graphited types, of a protective surface on the cylinder bores; the valve-stems are also lubricated to some extent.

Sump Level

It is advisable to check the oil level in the sump at frequent intervals. The age of the car and the amount it is used will, of course, be the deciding factors as to how often this is necessary. For instance, an un-rebored engine which has covered something like 25,000 miles would require more frequent inspection than one that had covered only 10,000 miles. Similarly a car covering only a small mileage would obviously not require such frequent inspection as one covering a big mileage.

Broadly speaking, the readings given on a dip-stick (Fig. 68) are reliable. It is, of course, necessary to take the reading on level ground, and the dip-stick should be wiped before

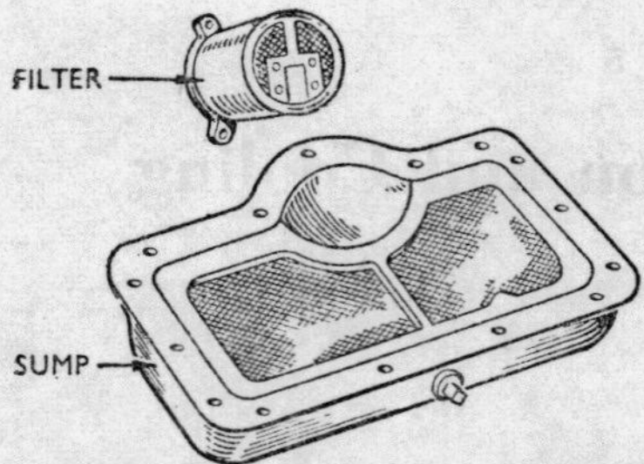

Fig. 69. *Gauze oil-filters in the sump.*

each reading is taken, otherwise a false indication will most likely be given. A more exact indication will be obtained if the reading is taken when the engine is quite cold.

One important fact to remember is that long life of an engine depends to a very great extent on frequent oil changing, and the use of one of the well-known brands is strongly recommended. Most motor manufacturers recommend changing the oil every 1,000 miles, but, if the engine of your motor-car or motor-cycle is worn to such an extent that a rebore is necessary, inferior oil may be used, but the cheapest method is to have the engine rebored.

Draining the Sump

The first thing to do is to unscrew the drain-plug which is situated underneath the engine; but before attempting this, place a suitable receptacle below to catch the waste oil. (As warm oil runs more freely, it is advisable to carry this out when the engine is at least warm.) When drainage has been completed, replace the drain-plug and insert a light "flushing oil," which can be obtained from any garage. Now start the engine and allow it to run slowly for a few minutes to circulate the flushing oil thoroughly. Allow the flushing oil to escape by removing the drain-plug. (Do not use petrol or paraffin to flush out the engine, as a certain amount will remain and the fresh oil will be diluted.) When all the flushing oil has escaped, the plug should be replaced and the necessary amount of fresh oil inserted through the filler cap.

After some 10,000 miles have been covered it is advisable to clean the oil-filter. In some cases the filter takes the form of a gauze tray covering the complete sump, as shown in Fig. 69, and in order to clean this type of filter the sump must be removed (see Fig. 70). (The oil in the sump must be drained off before this can be carried out.) The filter is cleaned by swilling in either paraffin or petrol and by the use of a stiff brush. A cloth should not be

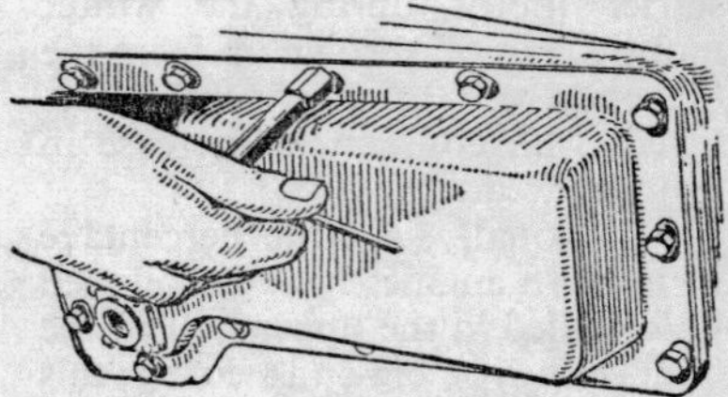

Fig. 70. *Showing method of unscrewing cover set-screws to remove sump.*

used, as pieces of fluff may adhere to the gauze and possibly cause a stoppage. The tray itself may be cleaned with a petrol-soaked rag, but here again make sure that the rag is not fluffy.

A common type of gauze filter is that surrounding the oil-pump intake (see Fig. 71). This may take the form of a long, cylindrical filter lying in the sump, and it can usually be withdrawn by draining off the oil and removing a plug on the outside of the pump. Alternatively, the filter may surround the pump itself, or be arranged beneath it. In this case withdrawal of the filter is often possible on unscrewing a ring of nuts or set-screws securing the filter cover-plate to the under-side of the sump. When the gauze filter is carried in an external housing connected to the sump by a suction pipe, it can be withdrawn and cleaned by unscrewing the cover of the housing. After cleaning and replacing the filter, the casing must be filled with suitable engine oil to prime the system, as otherwise no oil pressure will be registered on restarting the engine.

The majority of modern cars are fitted with an external filter, sometimes in addition to a gauze filter in the sump. The A.C. oil filter is a widely used type (see Fig. 72), and when the filter element becomes choked the complete unit must be disconnected from the inlet and outlet pipes and replaced by a fresh one.

Tecalemit filters are also widely used; this filter has a star type of felt element which should be cleaned in petrol at intervals of, say, 2,000 miles. The filtering element will require renewing after each 10,000 miles.

Motor-Cycle Engine Lubrication

There are three types of system employed on motor-cycles: (1) the dry sump, (2) the wet sump, (3) the petroil system. The last-mentioned system is employed on two-stroke engines. Some Villiers engines, however, employ a pressure-feed system.

The most important points in regard to maintenance are as follows:

Maintain the correct oil level,
Check oil circulation or pressure frequently,
Keep the filters clean,
Keep all pipe unions air-tight.

Oil Level. It is very important with dry-sump lubrication to keep the tank or sump reservoir at the correct level. This level should never be permitted to fall below the half-full mark, otherwise serious damage may result. On those machines fitted with a separate oil tank, keep the oil level about 1 in. below the return-pipe orifice. In the case of machines with an oil-sump reservoir, remove the dip-stick about every 250 miles and add fresh oil to the full mark, but not above it.

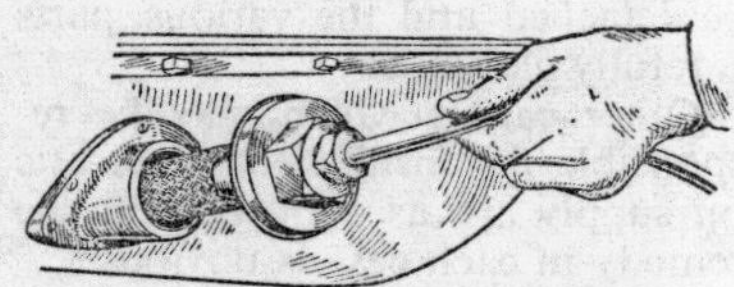

Fig. 71. *Withdrawing oil filter of the cylindrical type from sump.*

Oil Circulation. Where an oil-pressure gauge is fitted the reading given on the dial will be proof whether the system is functioning correctly. On some engines the correct average pressure is between 8 lb. and 15 lb. per sq. in., although on some of the bigger engines the pressure is as high as 40 lb. per sq. in. A high reading will be given when starting from cold, and this is quite normal. Should the oil pressure suddenly fluctuate, however, examine the level in the tank or reservoir immediately and top up if necessary. Should the oil level be correct, the trouble cannot be due to shortage of oil, and the valve of the pressure regulator (where fitted) should

Fig. 72. *A.C. oil filter; a widely used type of external filter.*

be detached and the various parts carefully cleaned.

Other causes which may be responsible for insufficient or erratic oil supply are as follows, and the remedy in each case is obvious:

Dirty filters.

Loose delivery-pipe connections.

Choked or fractured oil pipes.

Defect in the oil pump itself.

Bad joint between the pump housing and timing case.

Where only an oil "tell-tale" is fitted, on starting the engine, and occasionally while riding, glance at the "tell-tale" to see whether the small plunger or indicator rod is protruded. If it remains down there is no appreciable pressure below it, and the oil is not circulating correctly. In this case one of the faults mentioned above may be the cause of the trouble.

Should there be any reason to doubt the accuracy of the "tell-tale," remove the tank filler cap with the engine running and note whether oil is being steadily ejected from the orifice of the oil return pipe. Immediately on starting, the engine is high and sometimes erratic, but afterwards it should settle down to a steady succession of drops or bubbles. An unduly "frothy" return is suggestive of air leaks.

On certain engines with a duplex external mechanical pump it is possible to observe the oil delivery through a sight-feed glass.

Cleaning Filters. This should be carried out about every 2,000 miles, and draining the oil is best done when the engine is warm. First place a receptacle of adequate size below the drain-plug, and then remove the plug. When draining is completed clean out the oil reservoir with paraffin or petrol. Some machines employ a fabric filter in the separate oil-tank and also a gauze filter in the sump. The filter should be cleaned with petrol and a stiff brush.

Wet Sump

With this system it is not so important how much oil is in the tank provided the filter above the pipe union is correct. If this is not the case there is a possibility of air as well as oil being fed to the pump.

A gauze filter is usually fitted in the tank just above the oil-pipe union, to which it is sometimes attached, and it should be cleaned with petrol about every 5,000 miles. The sump can be drained by removing the drain-plug, and this should be carried out about every 3,000 miles.

The following are some of the maintenance points to be checked:

Keep the oil level above the tank filter.

Adjust the pump regulator correctly.

Verify oil circulation.

Clean tank-filter occasionally.

Drain and flush out crankcase periodically.

Keep the delivery-pipe unions and sight-feed air-tight.

Two-Stroke Lubrication

The Petroil System. Most small-capacity two-stroke engines employ petroil lubrication, and the usual practice is to mix approximately half a pint of oil with each gallon of petrol. It is advisable during the running-in period, however, to use slightly more oil—say three-quarters of a pint of oil with each gallon of spirit. To ensure a good mixture pour in the petrol first and then add the oil; replace the filler-cap and rock the machine sideways to facilitate mixture.

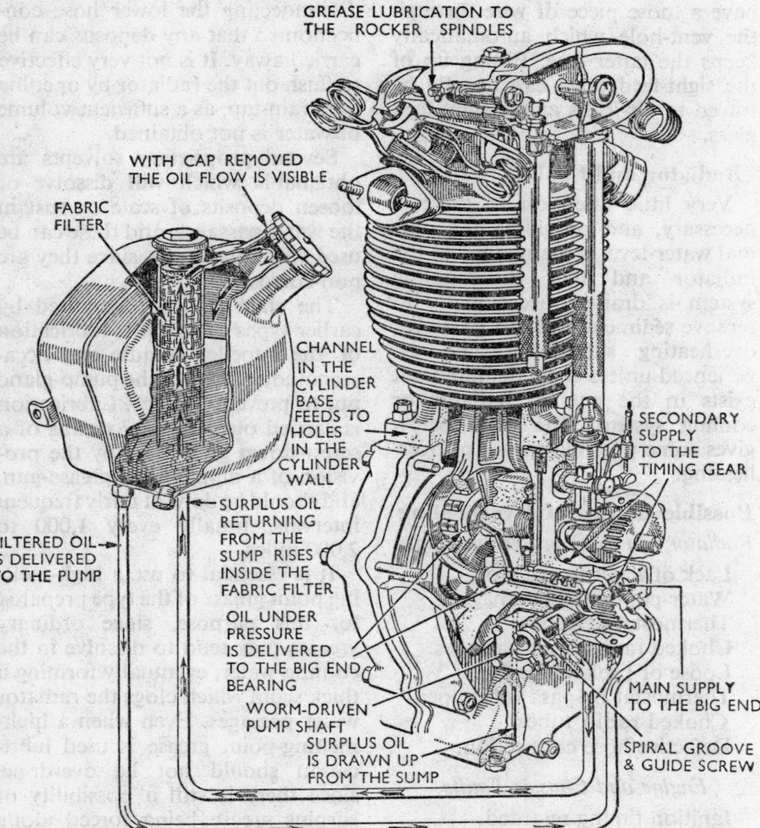

Fig. 73. *Details and arrangement of dry sump (Matchless) lubrication system.*

Villiers Pressure System. The larger Villiers engines incorporate a special pressure-feed system, and to ensure the system working properly the following points should be noted:

See that the air-pipe unions are air-tight.

Keep the sight-feed vent-hole clear.

Keep the oil-tank filler cap air-tight.

Keep the sight-feed glass air-tight.

Keep the sight-feed regulator correctly adjusted.

The oil supply should be reduced slightly after the engine is run-in, and this is effected by screwing in the regulator until a faint blue haze of smoke issues from the exhaust pipe. Special care should be taken to screw down the filler cap firmly after replenishment, and if the leather washer is worn it should be renewed. The sight-feed vent-hole may be cleaned with a single strand of Bowden wire, but recent models have a loose piece of wire through the vent-hole which automatically keeps the latter free. Filling up of the sight-feed bowl can usually be traced to air-leaks at the sight-feed glass.

Radiator and Cooling Systems

Very little attention to these is necessary, and providing the normal water-level is maintained in the radiator and that the cooling system is drained occasionally to remove sediment and rust particles, overheating should not be experienced unless some definite fault exists in the engine, radiator or cooling system. The table below gives some possible causes of overheating.

Possible Causes of Overheating

Radiator and Cooling System Faults.

Lack of water in radiator.
Water-pump drive damaged.
Thermostat defective.
Choked radiator air passages.
Loose or broken fan-felt.
Thermostat by-pass valve open.
Choked radio tubes.
Defective hose connection.

Engine and Chassis Faults.

Ignition timing retarded.
Excessive low-gear driving.
Oil-filter choked.
Pre-ignition.
Engine short of oil.
Clutch slipping.
Silencer choked.
Brakes binding.
Carburettor choke not released.

Washing Out the Cooling System

When overheating is due to choked water passages, circulation can often be restored to normal simply by flushing out the cooling system, allowing a rapid flow of water through the filler cap, and disconnecting the lower hose connection so that any deposits can be carried away. It is not very effective to flush out the radiator by opening the drain-tap, as a sufficient volume of water is not obtained.

Several proprietary solvents are obtainable which will dissolve or loosen deposits of scale or rust in the water passages, and these can be used with advantage, since they are non-corrosive.

The chief attention required by earlier types of pump is lubrication of the impeller spindle and occasional adjustment of the pump-gland nut to prevent leakage. Lubrication is carried out either by means of a screw-down greaser or by the provision of a nipple for a grease-gun, and should be done at fairly frequent intervals, usually every 1,000 to 2,000 miles.

It is essential to use a high-melting point grease of the type prepared for this purpose, since ordinary greases may tend to dissolve in the cooling water, eventually forming a thick scum which clogs the radiator water passages. Even when a high-melting-point grease is used lubrication should not be overdone, since there is still a possibility of surplus grease being forced along the impeller spindle into the pump casing. When persistent leakage of grease into the cooling system is experienced, the trouble can usually be traced to excessive wear of the impeller shaft.

Self Testing Questions

(1) *What would you do if the oil-gauge gave no reading?*

(2) *What is the most important maintenance job?*

(3) *What are some of the more common causes of overheating?*

THE ANSWERS ARE ON PAGE 444.

LESSON 6

The Transmission

THE Transmission consists of several sub-assemblies, the *Clutch, Gearbox, Propeller Shaft* (or chain in the case of a motor-cycle) and *Rear Axle* (or rear hub in the case of motor-cycle) and is placed in that sequence in relation to the engine.

The Clutch

The connection or disconnection of the driving power results in gradual wear of the parts which comprise it taking place, and adjustment is always provided to ensure its functioning properly throughout its serviceable life. The need for resorting to this adjustment becomes apparent when the clutch fails to break the drive even when the pedal is depressed to the fullest extent. This is referred to as a "spinning clutch," and makes gear-changing difficult and noisy. Alternatively, the clutch may fail to transmit the drive: this is usually due to the pedal fouling the floor-boards when at its highest position, relieving the driving faces of the clutch of sufficient friction pressure. Both these conditions can be rectified by pedal adjustment. The usual types of adjustment permit the pedal to be set in relation to the amount of withdrawal required, and may be a clamping bolt as depicted in Fig. 74 (*A*), a quadrant Fig. 74 (*B*), adjusting screw Fig. 74 (*C*) and Fig. 78, or screwed rod Fig. 74 (*D*)—attaching the pedal to the withdrawal mechanism. The pedal should be set so that when it comes back to the highest position or back-stop there should be approximately 1 in. of free movement on commencing to depress it, and that the clutch should be fully out or disconnected before the pedal pad fouls the floor-boards or back-stop. Fig. 75 will make these positions fully clear, but reference to the official instruction handbook will give fuller details concerning the particular clutch under review. Little mechanical knowledge or ability is necessary to carry out this pedal adjustment, but naturally if, after setting the pedal correctly, the clutch still fails to function properly, expert advice should be sought. Renewal of the withdrawing mechanism or relining of the friction faces may be necessary. On the other hand, where more complicated adjustments are provided, such as the insertion of shims, or screwed pins, on the clutch fingers, it is advisable to get the local service station to do the work.

Clutch Faults

Should the clutch develop "fierce" or "juddering" action, it may possibly be due to excessive movement of the engine and clutch-unit on their rubber mountings. It is generally the practice to fit tension links in the form of rods or cables, which anchor the unit against movement relative to the clutch-pedal. Inspect these links and, if slack, adjust them; they should be in slight tension with the engine at rest. Fig. 76 shows a typical example of these links. As the clutch is in continual action, unless the lubrication of the withdrawal mechanism is automatic,

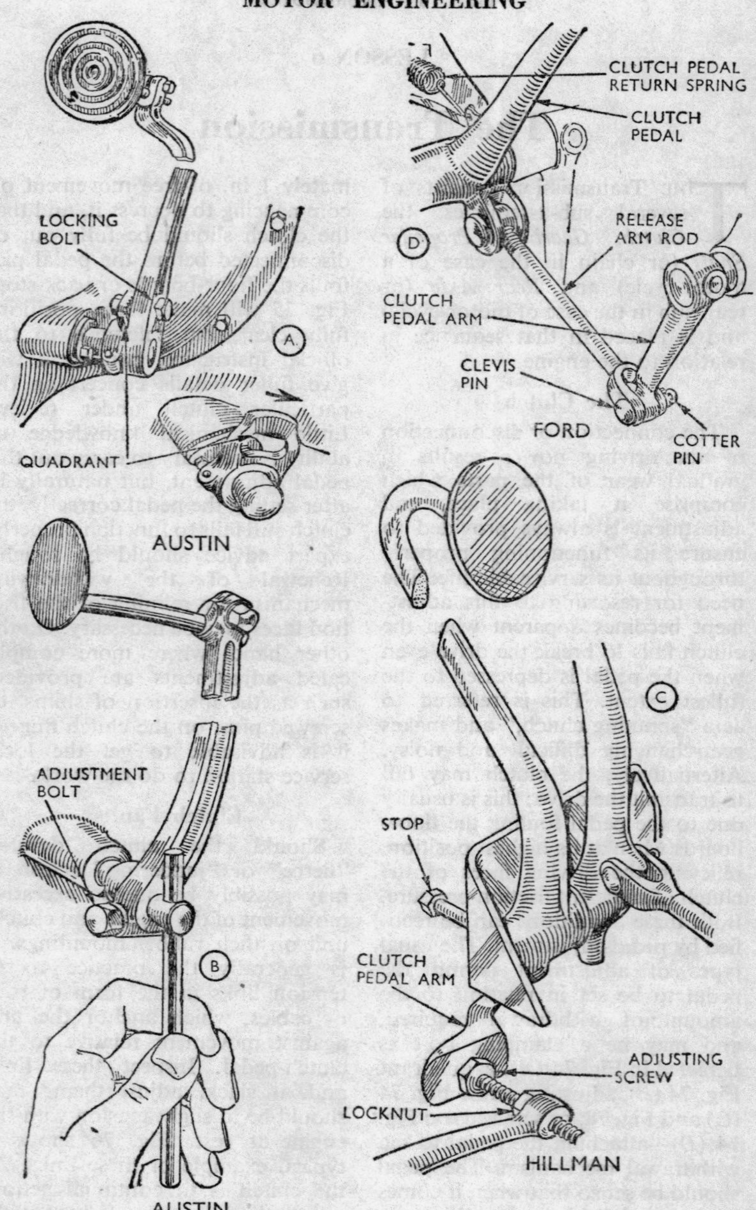

Fig. 74. *Four types of clutch adjustment: A, clamping bolt; B, quadrant; C, adjusting screw; D, screwed rod, attaching the pedal to the withdrawal mechanism.*

such greasers as are provided must be regularly attended to. The official instruction book will tell you where these are and when they need attention. Many manufacturers make use of a graphite thrust ring, and when this is fitted no lubrication is necessary.

If the car is fitted with a centrifugal clutch, compensation for wear in service is usually automatically carried out and therefore needs no attention. Slight lubrication of the working pins and levers with an oil-can is to be recommended, but use care not to get oil on the friction linings.

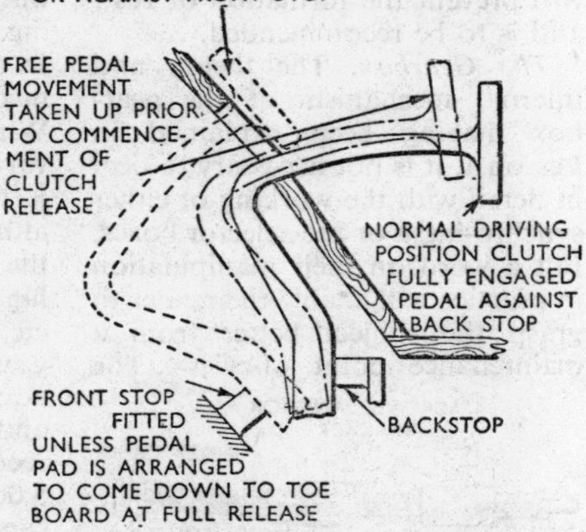

CLUTCH FULLY RELEASED
PEDAL DOWN TO TOE BOARD
OR AGAINST FRONT STOP
FREE PEDAL
MOVEMENT
TAKEN UP PRIOR
TO COMMENCE-
MENT OF
CLUTCH
RELEASE
NORMAL DRIVING
POSITION CLUTCH
FULLY ENGAGED
PEDAL AGAINST
BACK STOP
FRONT STOP
FITTED
UNLESS PEDAL
PAD IS ARRANGED
TO COME DOWN TO TOE
BOARD AT FULL RELEASE
BACKSTOP

Fig. 75. *Clutch pedal adjustment. Diagram showing successive positions of pedal.*

Should a fluid flywheel be fitted in place of the more orthodox form of clutch, apart from occasionally checking the oil level, nothing else is required. The engine should be cranked by hand until one of the filler plugs situated on the face of the flywheel is positioned at 12 o'clock. Remove the plug with the special key provided in the tool kit, and fill flywheel container with oil (usually the same as that used in the engine) up to the level of the filler plug, or in certain cases, if a dipstick is provided, up to the mark thereon. Should more than just topping up be required, it means that considerable leakage is taking place past the seals provided to prevent this. These glands can usually be tightened by using the special spanners in the tool kit, but should this fail to cure the trouble, new ones will have to be fitted. Such work is beyond the ability of the average motorist and must be carried out by a service station. Never continue using the car with insufficient oil in the flywheel.

Motor-cycle clutches are invariably operated by flexible cables from hand levers on the handlebars. Adjustment is carried out in the manner usually provided with this type of control, *i.e.* screwed-end sockets with lock-nuts, enabling the outer conduit to be lengthened or shortened (see Fig. 77).

On some designs, however, an adjustment pin is provided on the clutch actuating lever; always leave a little free movement so as not to relieve spring pressure. Should clutch slip be experienced, the spring tension can invariably be increased by tightening up the tension ad-

SCREWED END OF
ROD WITH ADJUSTING
NUTS
TENSION
ROD
SECURED TO
FRONT CROSS
MEMBER
BRACKET BOLTED
TO ENGINE

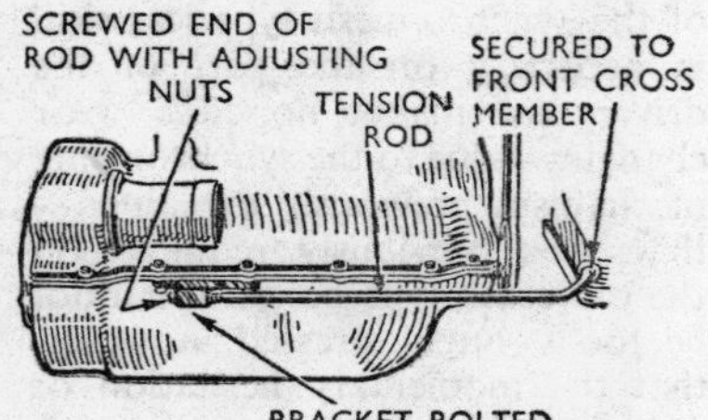

Fig. 76. *Typical example of tension links; they may be rods or cables.*

justing screws. Occasional lubrication of the inner control cable will prevent the formation of rust, and is to be recommended.

The Gearbox. The theory and internal mechanism of the gearbox having been explained in Lesson 1, it is not necessary to deal in detail with the working of either synchro-mesh or pre-selector boxes. But a word on their manipulation in practice will enable the reader to grasp the subject better from a maintenance point of view. The

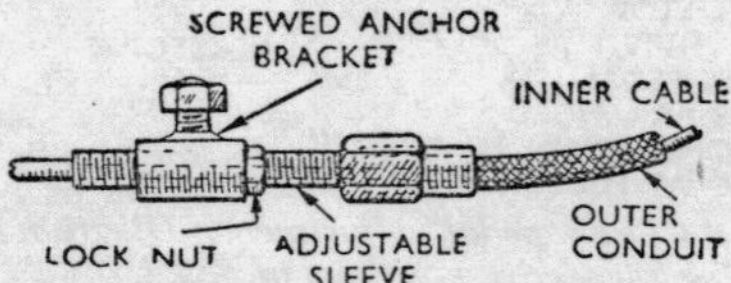

Fig. 77. *Sockets with lock-nuts provide adjustment on cable controls.*

car engine depends on the speed in revolutions per minute at which it revolves—the higher the revs. the greater the power. Hence, on the level a high gear with resulting low engine revolutions is used. On hills, however, more power is required from the engine, so a low gear and resulting high engine revolutions are necessary. It is to meet these varying conditions, and, of course, the initial work of getting the car into motion from rest, that the driver has constantly to de-clutch and change gear. With gearboxes of the synchro-mesh type less skill is necessary on the part of the driver to make noiseless gear changing—due to the synchronising mechanism previously explained—than was previously required on the old crash-type boxes. It cannot be too strongly stressed, however, that the momentary hesitation or pause just past neutral when passing the gear lever from one gear to another—as advocated in most instruction books—should be rigidly carried out. Neglect to do this will give you noisy gear changing, and if persisted in will result in damage to the intricate synchronising mechanism inside the box. When operating, the faces of the various gears and parts are subjected to very heavy work, and although the material from which the modern car is made is of very high quality, metallic rubbings, etc., inevitably accumulate in the gearbox casing. It is therefore advocated that the box be drained and re-filled with lubricant, as recommended by the makers, every 5,000 miles, or, in the case of a new car, after the first 1,000 miles and then every consecutive 5,000 miles. Always check the level of the lubricant every 1,000 miles and top up if necessary. The filler plug can usually be taken as the correct level, if as that depicted in Fig. 78 (*A*), it being impossible to overfill. Alternatively a dip-stick is provided with *FULL* and *LOW* readings clearly marked on it (Fig. 78 (*B*)). In other cases one plug is used to fill the box while another acts as a level plug. It is not usual to provide any sort of adjustment on the orthodox gearbox. Jumping out of gear, lack of synchro-meshing and undue noise indicate repairs beyond the scope of the average motorist and mean a visit to the service station.

Adjusting Selector Springs

In some cases, however, the tendency to jump out of gear can be improved by increasing the tension of the selector springs, but this is not always possible, owing to design. Fig. 79 shows a typical example where this adjustment can be carried out.

Should the car be fitted with a

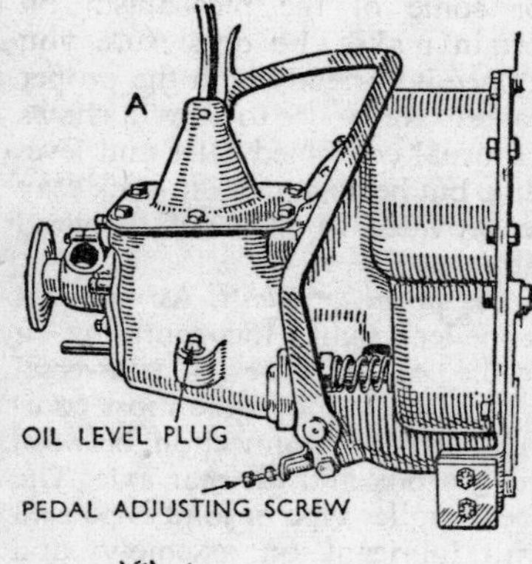

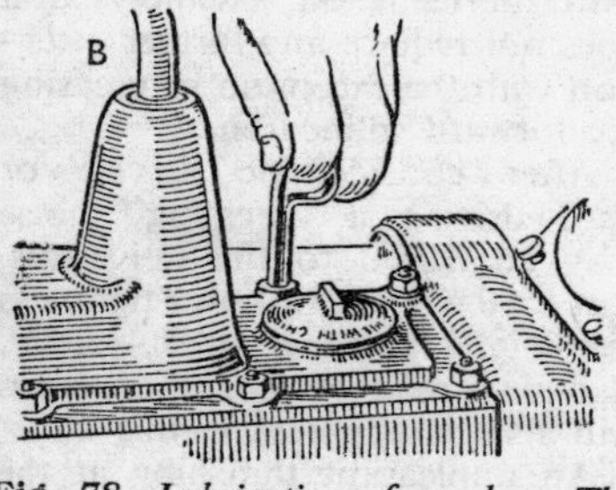

Fig. 78. *Lubrication of gearbox. The combined filler and level plug at* A *prevents overfilling.* B *shows use of dip-stick marked for "Full" and "Low".*

pre-selector type of box, more careful attention to the makers' instructions will be necessary than is called for with an orthodox box. As in the case of the clutch, the continual frictional operation of the gears results in wear taking place, but the designer has provided for the necessary adjustment to be carried out automatically. It is a good plan, however, to assist this automatic adjustment regularly, say every 1,000 miles, by "pumping the pedal." This should be carried out in the garage *without engine running*; sit in the driving-seat, set the selector lever primarily in reverse and fully depress and release left foot-pedal several consecutive times—repeat operation in all gears. Also make sure that when the pedal is released it does not foul the floor-boards, or slipping of the gears will result. The rod connecting the pedal to the lever on the box is provided with adjustment for this purpose. Make such adjustment if necessary so that the pedal has approximately 1 in. clearance from the foot-boards. Should difficulty in the selection of gears be experienced, check over the connections from selection lever on the steering column to the lever on the gearbox. One rod of the linkage will be provided with adjustment; disconnect this rod. Set the selector lever on the column in one of the extreme positions, *e.g.* reverse or top. Set the lever on the box to the corresponding extreme position. Now offer up the rod, making such adjustment as may be necessary so that it can be connected without moving selector lever or lever on box. Then check all other gear selections. Fig. 80 should make these operations clear. Very often worn connections and pins are responsible for lost motion and resulting faulty gearbox cam-

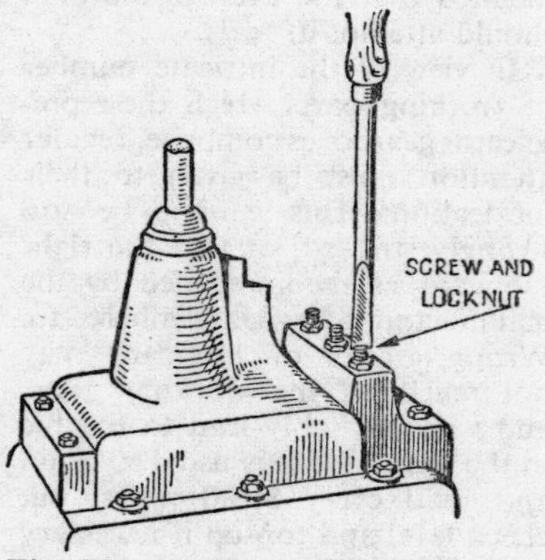

Fig. 79. *Avoiding gear jumping by increasing tension of selector springs.*

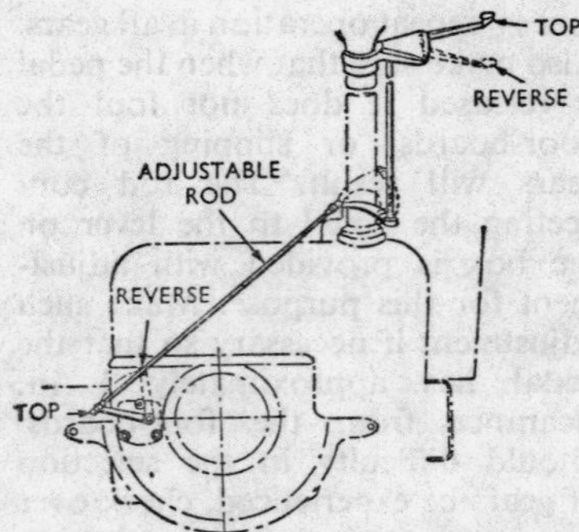

Fig. 80. *An adjustable rod is included in the connections from selection lever on steering column to gearbox lever.*

shaft lever positioning. No adjustments will rectify this, and the faulty parts will have to be renewed.

If slipping or fierceness of operation develops, and is not rectified by "pumping the pedal" or adjustment of the pedal as outlined, more intricate adjustments necessitating removing the floor-boards and gearbox cover and operating on the toggle mechanism therein will be imperative. As this is a somewhat involved procedure, a thorough knowledge of the working of the box being essential, it is not recommended that the average motorist should attempt it.

In view of the intricate number of working parts which these preselector gearboxes comprise, regular attention must be given to their lubrication. This cannot be too strongly stressed, or that the right lubricant as recommended by the manufacturers be rigidly adhered to. Wrong grades of lubricant may not reach all the working parts, and will inevitably lead to trouble in the long run. It is usual to drain and refill every 3,000 miles, but check level and top up if necessary every 1,000 miles.

As the drain-plug acts as a stop for some of the mechanism on certain makes, be quite sure you replace it correctly with the proper washer. Reference to Fig. 78 shows the usual combined filler and level plug, but here again a dip-stick may be provided in place of the level plug.

The Propeller Shaft. An exposed propeller shaft incorporating a needle roller type of universal joint at each end is the most common form of connection between the gearbox and the rear axle. The needle roller type of joint is packed with lubricant on assembly, and does not require any further attention with the exception of greasing the forward splined end.

After considerable service or hard driving a "joggling" noise may be traced to the universals. Inspect the flange bolts for tightness (see Fig. 81) and, if slack, rectify. Excessive wear of pins and bushes will also be apparent in this way.

An unpleasant thrashing at the higher road speeds usually indicates a bent propeller shaft, and is a job for the service station.

The Rear Axle. Apart from supporting the car on its casing and adjacent springs, the rear axle performs the function of dividing

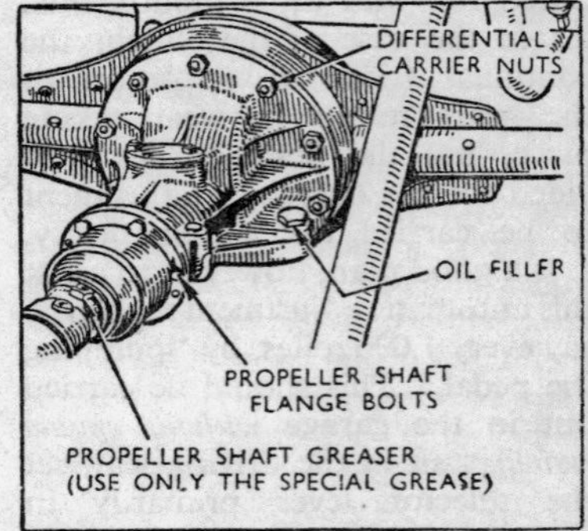

Fig. 81. *Propeller shaft. Flange bolts must be rectified if not tight.*

the drive to each rear wheel, and allows a differentiation in revolutions between each wheel. All these functions have been fully dealt with in Lesson 5, and provided the reader realises that the mechanism inside the axle casing is in continual use, he will be fully alive to the importance of maintaining the lubrication of the gears and bearings. As in the case of the gearbox, the level of the lubricant should be checked and topped up if necessary every 1,000 miles. Where a greaser is fitted for lubricating the rear wheel bearing, this should receive attention at the same time. Drain axle casing and refill with lubricant as recommended by the makers every 5,000 miles. Remember, it is easier to drain the oil when warm, as when the car comes in off a run. Should a drain-plug not be provided—and some makers do not fit them—it will be necessary to remove the axle cover-plate. Do not overfill (the combined filler and level plug as shown in Fig. 78 will prevent this), as there may be a tendency for the lubricant to exude down the axle-tubes into the brakes. Should you persistently experience this, it will probably be due to faulty oil-seals which are fitted expressly to prevent this leakage. To renew these oil-seals, it is necessary to remove the road-wheel, brake-drum and hub of the offending side. Jack up the car and support it safely, preferably with stands under the axle casing, and remove the road-wheel. In most designs the brake-drum can then be dismantled by removing two or three screws (Fig. 82) which attach it to the hub flange. The axle shaft can next be withdrawn. Before drawing the hub, the nut *B* which holds it in position on the axle-tube must first be removed. In other designs the hub is fitted to a taper on the axle-shaft, and a special hub extractor, often included in the tool kit, will be required to draw it off the shaft. The hand-brake must be off before you can remove the brake-drums. The oil-seal, which is invariably fitted in the hub *C*, must be removed and the new one fitted. Replace hub, shaft, drum, etc., in the reverse sequence to removal, making sure all parts are tight home and locked or split-pinned as originally fitted up.

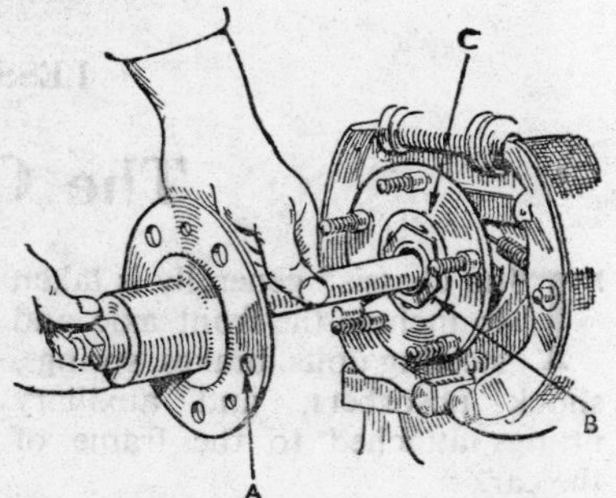

Fig. 82. *Rear axle.* A, *screw holes in brake drum;* B, *hub nut;* C, *hub.*

Self Testing Questions

(1) *If the clutch has a tendency to slip, would you continue to drive with it, or what would you do?*

(2) *What would you consult your instruction book for in regard to maintenance of the clutch?*

(3) *If on starting the car from rest, you fully depress the clutch pedal, but cannot engage first gear without noise, would you blame the gearbox or the clutch?*

(4) *Should you experience difficulty in gear selection with a pre-selector box, what would you do?*

(5) *What is the most important point for the owner to remember with regard to the rear axle?*

THE ANSWERS ARE ON PAGE 444.

LESSON 7

The Chassis

THE chassis* generally is taken to include the front axle and steering units, brakes, springs, shock absorbers, and auxiliary fittings attached to the frame of the car.

Apart from certain adjustments which vary according to the different units, regular lubrication is vital, and is less costly than repairs. It is as well to mention here that although one familiarly refers to the "grease gun," it should more correctly be termed the "oil gun," for the thicker grades of oil are invariably used for lubricating those parts of the modern car where the gun is resorted to. This is especially the case where grouped lubricators are provided to facilitate servicing, using lengths of small-bore tubing; grease is inclined to clog the conduit. Clean all lubricators before using the gun, and afterwards wipe off excess lubricant to prevent the collection of dirt. Where central shot lubrication systems are installed, use only the lubricant recommended by the makers.

The Front Axle

Apart from lubrication, regular inspection and adjustments due to derangements resulting from road shock are necessary from time to time to maintain efficiency.

The more orthodox front axle consists of an I-section beam, with swivel axles pivoted one at each end. The car is supported on springs located on the axle-beam, and the hubs, brakes and wheels are carried on the swivel. The steering box is connected to the swivel axles by rods and joints.

Pivot-Pins and Hubs

The pivot pins should be lubricated every 500 miles, and it is better to jack up the axle to relieve the weight on the pivot pin thrust-washers, and so facilitate entry of the lubricant there. The joints of the rods connecting swivels to the steering box should be lubricated at the same time. Every 5,000 miles pack the front hubs with grease if required. Do not overdo this, or there is a possibility of grease exuding on to the brake linings. At the same time check the wheel bearings by grasping the tyre, one hand on either side, and endeavour to move wheel endwise. If play is excessive and the car is fitted with roller bearings of the adjustable type, remove hub-caps, draw split pin from swivel axle nut, tighten nut up reasonably and slack back ¼ turn so that wheel spins freely, and then re-pin nut. If not fitted with adjustable bearings and play is excessive, new bearings will have to be fitted. Do not be misled in this connection by wear on the swivel pins and their bushes. This is apparent when the wheel can be rocked vertically, and if excessive means a repair-shop job.

Curbing the front wheels—that is, hitting the curb stone a glancing

* The word *chassis* is taken from the French and means frame, but through incorrect common usage it has come to mean all fittings attached to the frame of the car.

blow with the wheel—invariably upsets the track of the front wheels. As this is very often done quite unconsciously, the track of the front wheels should be occasionally checked. On the standard axle the wheels should toe-in about ⅛ in.

One should check tyre pressures weekly, as they have a very definite influence on the steering. Also, occasionally check the nuts of the bolts securing the springs to the front axle and tighten up if necessary. An item that should be inspected in connection with axles using transverse springs is the anchorage of the axle tie-rod. Excessive play at this point allows the axle to move fore and aft, affecting steering and braking. With the developments of independent suspension each individual design has its own characteristics, these being too numerous to cover generally. The reader should, however, rigidly adhere to such instructions as are given in the instruction book. For instance, regular attention to fluid level, and topping up if required, is necessary with those designs employing hydraulic actions.

The Steering

Most modern cars fit one of the proprietary makes of steering-box assembly using the "worm and nut" or "cam and follower" designs, examples of which are shown in Fig. 83. Lubricant is introduced into the box through the plug situated at the top of the casing. The box must be kept filled, but should only need attention every 2,000 miles, and it is as well, at the same time, to make sure the bolts securing the box are tight. The joints of the steering rods connecting box to front axle swivels should be lubricated every 500 miles. If not of the self-adjusting type, these joints should be checked occasionally; about the 5,000-mile mark, for undue play. If excessive, it should be rectified; this can usually be carried out by removing the split pin which secures the screwed end in place, and, using a large screw-driver, screwing in the end piece as far as it will go. Then slack back slightly to avoid binding and re-split pin. There are four joints, one at each end of the drag-link, and one at each end of the track-rod. Finally check the front wheels for track as outlined in the paragraphs on the Front Axle.

"Cam-and-Follower" Design

With the "cam-and-follower" design provision is usually made to eliminate the development of excessive play, due to wear. Up-and-down motion of the steering wheel under load indicates wear on the cam bearings, and can be rectified by the removal of one or more of the shims situated at *A*, Fig. 83. On some models, additional adjustment is given so that wear developing between cam and follower can be eliminated. Where this is so, the shims will be found at point *B*, Fig. 83, between the cover of the box and the follower. Care must be taken not to remove too many shims when carrying out either of the above adjustments, otherwise stiff steering will result.

"Worm-and-Nut" Design

In the "worm-and-nut" type the wearing contacts are spread over such a large surface that only one adjustment is provided. This adjustment is for up-and-down play of the column, and is carried out by slackening lock-nut *C*, Fig. 83, tightening race-nut *D* until all play is removed, and relocking lock-nut.

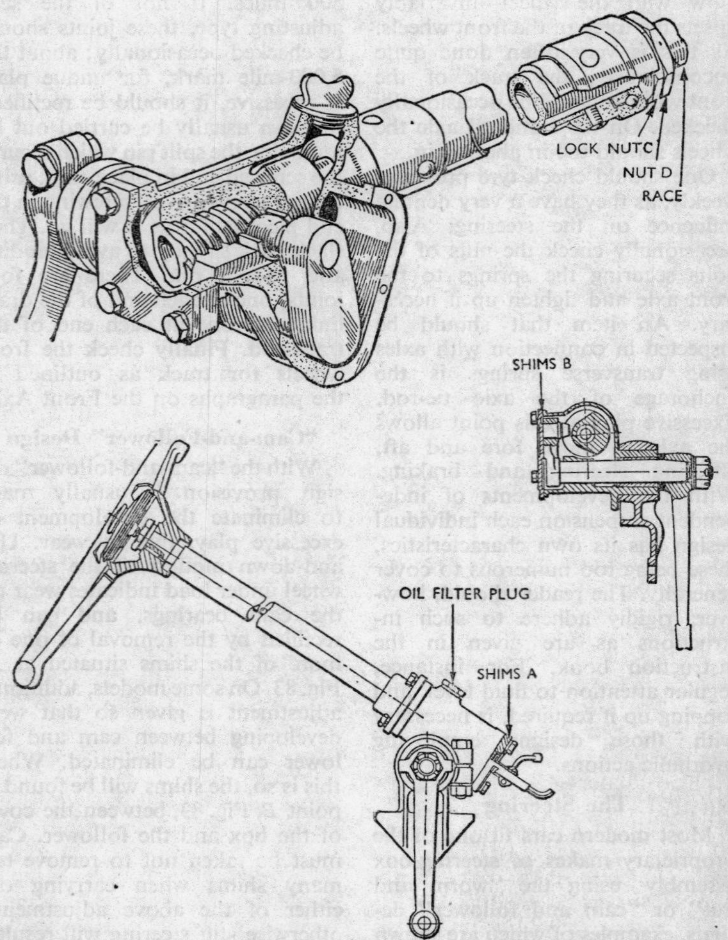

Fig. 83. *Types of steering-box assembly in ordinary use.* Above (*Burman*), *worm-and-nut steering.* Below (*Bishop*), *cam-and-follower steering.*

Wear of other bearings and bushes, if sufficient to affect the steering, will mean the reconditioning of the unit, and should be entrusted to competent repairers.

Whereas in the past each maker had his own design of brakes, peculiar to all models of his manufacture, the tendency today is to fit one of the two or three speciality designs. These systems are very complicated for the amateur to understand thoroughly, but the adjustments provided to keep the brakes efficient are reasonably simple and within the scope of any driver, who should take good care to see they are carried out.

First, such lubrication as is called for must be regularly attended to. If cables and conduits are employed for the operation of the brakes, lubricators will be provided where the inner cables work inside the outer conduits. Bearings on the chassis frame which carry cross-shafts are also invariably fitted with lubricators. Guide pulleys and links must be kept free from seizure and will need attention. Where levers and cranks fulcrum, the pivot pins will be provided with lubricators and will also need attention. In fact, all moving parts in the operating mechanism should be regularly lubricated. Where lubricators are not provided, a few drops of oil from the oil-can will keep operation smooth. All the specific points needing attention will be given in detail in the instruction book.

It is now the practice for the adjustment necessary as wear takes place on the linings to be carried out actually at the brakes themselves. It should not be necessary to make any adjustments to the operating linkage or cables, and the driver is strongly advised to leave them alone.

Jacking Up

Where adjusters are provided on the brake back-plates, that is where you must operate. It is usually necessary to jack the car up to carry out brake adjustment, although some designs are such that it is possible to do so without jacking. However, when jacking up a car in connection with brake adjustments, do not make the mistake of supporting it under the chassis, and so allowing the axles to "hang on the springs." If you do, when the car is again on its wheels the relation of the axles to the operating linkage is entirely different. The place to support the car is under the axles; this point is mentioned as there is a tendency today to supply jacking apparatus which is attached to bumpers or running-boards.

Back-Plate Adjusters

Now inspect the brake back-plates for the adjusters. These may be in the form of a squared shaft, as depicted at *A* in Fig. 84, a flexible shaft *B*, hexagon nuts as at *A*, or just slots in the back-plate for the introduction of a screw-driver, *C*. Making sure the hand-brake is off, make use of these adjusters on the back-plate, opening out the brake-shoes until they bind in the drum, making it very difficult to turn the wheel. The adjuster should then be slackened back just sufficiently to give running clearance, allowing the wheel to spin freely. These operations should be carried out at each wheel in turn. As a final precaution get an assistant to depress the foot-brake pedal sufficiently just to bind the brakes. Then go round all wheels checking the effort necessary to turn them; they should all take about the same. If any one wheel needs more effort to turn than another, slacken the adjuster slightly. This is not necessary where the system is what is referred to as fully compensated, as the designer has arranged for all the brakes to operate equally even if slight errors in shoe adjustments are made.

The car can now be jacked down and is ready for the road, but it is advisable not to take the functioning of the brakes for granted. Just take a preliminary run and apply them lightly at first to see if there is any tendency to "pull"

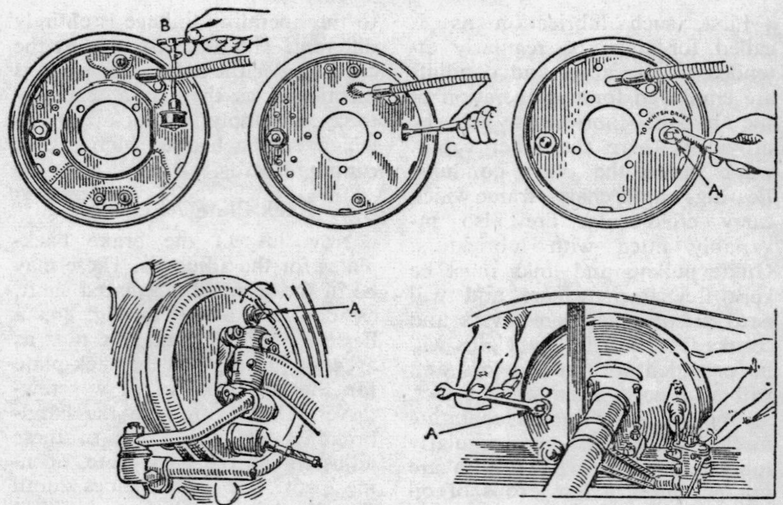

Fig. 84. *Various types of brake back-plate adjuster.* A, A, *squared shaft with hexagon nuts;* B, B, *flexible shaft;* C, *slots for screw-driver.*

right or left. If so, this must be rectified right away. If they function correctly at the lower speeds, test them at gradually increasing speeds, until finally it is possible to apply them suddenly, as would be necessary in an emergency, without the car deviating from the straight.

Should the brakes be hydraulically operated there are quite a number of items requiring attention. Apart from a spot of oil applied to the pedal connections, no lubrication is required; but regularly inspect and top up the reservoir. Use only genuine fluid as recommended. This is impervious to temperature changes and does not have an injurious effect on the composition cups and flexible connections in the system.

Should the reservoir need more than an occasional "topping up," it indicates a leak in the system, and this should be immediately traced and rectified, otherwise there is a likelihood of total failure of the brakes owing to lack of fluid. Any leakage in the metal conduit or flexible connections will be visible if inspected while someone applies the brakes hard. Fluid leaking from the wheel cylinders can as a rule be discerned seeping from the brake-drum. Another cause of leakage can very often be traced to the brake-stop light-switch attached to the master cylinder and operated hydraulically. This type of switch is now, however, seldom fitted. It is essential to maintain about 1 in. of free movement at the brake-pedal itself. It should, of course, never need altering, but if for some inadvertent reason this clearance has disappeared, the master cylinder will possibly be deprived of correct replenishing from the reservoir. Adjustment is provided on the connection between pedal and master cylinder if required. Should the reaction to the application of the brake-pedal develop into a "spongy feeling," it may indicate that the system needs "bleeding." Bleeding is the operation performed to expel air from the conduit, and will be necessary if at any time the reservoir has been allowed to empty, or if any part of the conduit has been disconnected.

"Bleeding" Valve

At the topmost point of each wheel cylinder, and projecting through the back-plate, is a "bleeding" valve. In the car kit will be found a short length of flexible rubber tubing, suitable for connecting to the "bleeding" valve. Obtain a glass jar and pour a small quantity of fluid from a spare tin into the bottom of the jar, so that after connecting the rubber tubing to the "bleeding" valve to be worked on, the other end of the tube can be immersed in the fluid. Also make sure the reservoir is full.

With suitable spanner or key from the tool kit loosen off bleeding valve, and while keeping rubber tube immersed in the fluid in the jar, get an assistant to depress the pedal several times. The pedal should be positively depressed and allowed to come back without assistance; pause a while to allow the master cylinder to refill before again depressing. This "pumping the pedal" must be continued until all air in the conduit feeding that brake is expelled. The air while being expelled will rise through the fluid in the glass jar in the form of bubbles; when bubbles no longer appear, close the bleeder valve while the assistant holds the pedal in the depressed position. This operation must be carried out at each wheel, but the master cylinder should be replenished after bleeding each brake as a precaution against its emptying. When all brakes are bled there should be a much more positive feel about the pedal when depressed. Reference to Fig. 85 will illustrate the above operations.

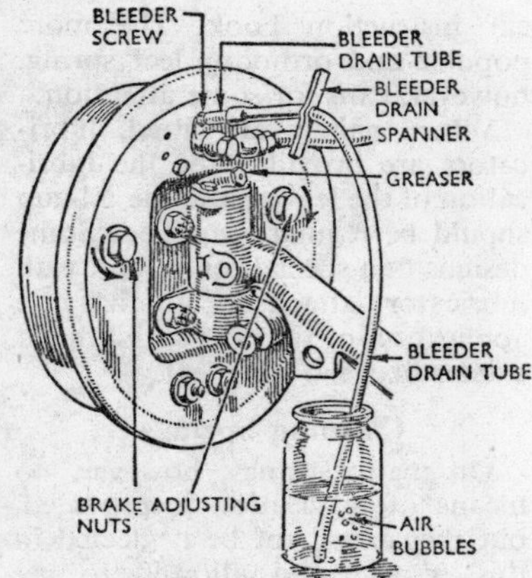

Fig. 85. *Illustrating the method of bleeding hydraulic brakes (Lockheed).*

It is as well always to make a point of adjusting the brake-shoes before beginning bleeding operations.

Previous remarks regarding trying out the brakes after adjustments have been carried out also apply.

Springs

When referring to car springs a semi-elliptic spring consisting of a number of leaves is the popular conception.

Modern designs, however, employ many other devices, consisting of coil springs, torsion bars and complete independent suspension units. Coil springs and torsion bars need no other attention than occasional inspection to see that their anchorages are secure. The independent suspension units vary so much in design that such maintenance as is necessary will be found explained in detail in the car instruction book. The more popular and orthodox leaf spring, however, calls for some attention.

Where gaiters are fitted, lubricators are provided for the lubrication of the leaves, and the oil-gun should be regularly applied. Some designs fit a special centre bolt with lubricator attached, so that on application of the oil-gun lubricant exudes between each leaf.

Cleaning Springs

On many springs, however, no means of lubrication is provided, but they must not be neglected in this respect and allowed to get rusty. Remove all road dirt with a wire brush and wash clean with paraffin. Jack up the car and support its weight with stands under the chassis frame. This allows the weight of the front and rear axles to "hang on the springs," and so tends to open up the leaves. Spray the spring with penetrating oil, so that the oil gets between the leaves.

The shackle pins at the front and rear ends of the springs will in most cases have lubricators fitted, and they should be attended to every 500 miles. If you do not find lubricators at the shackle pins, make sure that they are not of the rubber or silent-bloc type. These do not need lubrication and oil or grease *must not* be administered.

Shock Absorbers

In striving for riding comfort, long springs or other flexible devices have been introduced on the modern car. These being very susceptible to road inequalities, deflection is increased, and their rebound would be excessive, causing unpleasant swaying unless damped out. It is for this fundamental purpose that shock absorbers are fitted, although they may differ considerably in design.

The old friction type has been almost entirely superseded by the hydraulic type. This latter type needs regular inspection in regard to fluid level, and they must never be allowed to become empty. Inspect every 5,000 miles and top up, if required, with *the correct grade of fluid*. This is of paramount importance, as the viscosity of the fluid affects the correct functioning of the shock absorber. There are two major differences in type—the "rotor type" calls for a much thicker emulsion than that used in the "piston type." So make quite sure you are using the correct fluid as advocated for the car. You should remove all road-dirt from the filler plug found at the top of each shock absorber with a wire brush, before taking out the plug. Pour in fluid as required, but do not fill entirely to level of the plug-hole; a small air space must be left for expansion. As the shock absorbers are very often fitted in rather inaccessible positions, it may be difficult to judge the amount. In these cases fill to overflowing point and then extract a small quantity of the fluid with a syringe. When carrying out this replenishing, take the opportunity of making sure that the bolts attaching the shock absorber to the chassis are really tight. Also inspect the connecting-link rubber bushings, as these may be badly worn or entirely disintegrated, and if this is the case they must be renewed.

Looking for Leaks

If you find that the shock absorbers need far more replenishing than merely "topping up," you should look round for leaks. These usually occur round the shaft, and if an adjustable gland is fitted, as is the case with some makes, it should be tightened up with the spanner supplied in the tool kit for this purpose. If no gland nut is provided, the only solution is to fit a replacement shock absorber. This service is available at all service stations.

Should you suspect the correct functioning of your shock absorbers, even after replenishing, you can check them by disconnecting the links and working the arms up and down. If little or no resistance is felt, it may be that they have been allowed to become empty and that air has entered. In this case remove the filler plug and work the arm up and down until such time as resistance is felt, finally again "topping up" before replacing the filler plug. Should resistance still be practically nil, attempt to increase same by altering the adjuster—the adjuster is usually found directly below the filler plug—by inserting a screwdriver through the plug hole until engaging in the slot of the adjuster, then screw the adjuster right down (usually clockwise). Again, try the arm for resistance. If still inferior the shock absorber will have to be replaced. If decidedly improved, you will have to balance it with its pair on the other side. In the absence of proper apparatus the best procedure is to screw both adjusters right down and then turn back two turns. You must then judge by the way the car rides when again on the road, whether you will need to increase or reduce resistance further. Obviously if the car rides harshly, you will slacken back the adjuster to reduce resistance, or vice versa. On some types the adjuster is located in the shaft—a plug in the end of the shaft is first removed, and screwdriver inserted through the aperture. Others may be provided with two plugs and two valves—one valve controlling deflection and the other valve controlling rebound.

Never blame the shock absorbers of the car right away for the unsatisfactory riding of the car, and impetuously alter their adjustment. First of all make quite sure that your tyre pressures are correct, that your springs are functioning properly, and that all spring clips and shackle pins are in order. For it will be appreciated that the shock absorbers are originally "set" for correct operation on your particular car, before leaving the makers.

Self Testing Questions

(1) *Apart from lubrication, what regular check should be kept on the front axle?*

(2) *What do you consider the most important item in connection with the steering unit?*

(3) *Where do you make adjustments for lining wear on modern brake systems?*

(4) *Do you ever alter the brake operating linkage on modern cars?*

(5) *Where do springs of the leaf type require lubrication?*

THE ANSWERS ARE ON PAGE 444.

Answers to Self Testing Questions

LESSON 1

(1) There is only one firing stroke every four strokes, or every two engine revolutions.

(2) There are two firing strokes every two engine revolutions, or one firing stroke per revolution.

(3) It breaks the primary circuit and induces a high-voltage current in the secondary winding.
(4) It constricts the air passage near the jet, thus increasing the velocity of the air over the jet orifice.

LESSON 2

(1) Flush out petrol tank, blow through all petrol pipes, clean all filters and float-chamber bowl.
(2) A blockage in the main jet.

LESSON 3

(1) Test for spark at end of plug-lead, and if no flash, test low-tension circuit by flashing across contact breaker points when open.

LESSON 4

(1) Having allowed the engine to run and become normally warm, I should finally tighten down the cylinder-head nuts.
(2) Yes, certainly, as there is a possibility of the valves "settling down" resulting in insufficient clearance.
(3) One should follow the correct sequence as in certain designs of camshaft: correct clearance can only be obtained in this way.

LESSON 5

(1) I would immediately stop the engine and look for the fault.
(2) To check the sump level regularly and top up when necessary.
(3) Lack of water in radiator, broken fan-belt, defective hose connection, excessive low-gear driving, engine short of oil, brakes binding.

LESSON 6

(1) I should certainly not continue to drive the car, as this would be very detrimental to the friction surfaces, and might possibly ruin them. I would make sure pedal adjustment was correct, but if this did not cure the trouble, would consult the service station.
(2) To see what lubrication (if any) is necessary and regularly to carry it out.
(3) I should first of all check up the clutch-pedal setting to make sure clutch was fully disengaging. If this was in order, I should check the gearbox lubricant level.
(4) I should check the operating linkage and make adjustment on the rods with respective levers in an extreme position, *i.e.* either reverse or top.
(5) Regular checking and topping up with lubricant of the correct grade as recommended by the manufacturers.

LESSON 7

(1) The track of the front wheels should be correctly maintained, as it affects both steering stability and tyre wear.
(2) Regular lubrication with the correct lubricant.
(3) Provision is made at the brakes themselves; usually some type of adjuster is provided on the brake back-plates.
(4) The adjustment of the linkage should not as a rule be altered, certainly not for ordinary adjustment necessitated by lining wear.
(5) Apart from the shackle pins at either end of the spring, the leaves require lubricating, especially at the tips where they bear on one another.

PLUMBING

By J. Bruce Kelso

LESSON 1

Domestic Water-Supply Systems

PLUMBING is concerned with the delivery of fresh water to buildings, the removal from them of waste water by drainage, preventing the entry of water where it is not wanted, and controlling the supply of gas for heating and lighting. It takes its name from *plumbum*, the Latin word for lead, because until recent years the pipes with which the plumber is so largely occupied were almost always made of that metal. The plumber also deals with the installation and upkeep of drinking-water and hot-water systems, the flushing of sanitary apparatus, and the disposal of sewage. Roof metal-work—gutters, and so on—are also his concern, and in the country he has to look after wells, pumps, hydraulic rams and catchment rain supplies.

In this course we shall deal only with water supply, waste disposal and roof work.

The House Water Supply

In the ordinary dwelling-house, with "company's water" (see Fig. 1), the supply is delivered from a cast-iron street main through lead pipes of ½-in. or ¾-in. bore. A stop-valve on the inlet pipe from the main is usually placed on the footway just outside the house. By means of this valve the water supply to the house can be cut off by the authorities. A second valve or stop-cock is often to be found, buried about 2 ft. 6 in. deep just inside the garden, the access to it being through a narrow vertical drain-pipe. This stop-cock can be turned off only with difficulty, and it is often so hidden by silt or so stiff that it is by no means easy to turn it if a new washer is required. It is also liable to cause trouble by freezing in cold weather.

The best position for the stop-cock is within the building—say under the kitchen sink—though it is often placed under the hall floor, or in a cellar. In this case a bib-cock for draining off the water system will also be found.

From Street to Storage Tank

From the street main the communication pipe enters the house and, as the "rising main," passes directly to the roof to supply the storage cistern, a tank of galvanised sheet iron with a capacity of 150 to 200 gallons or more. The ideal arrangement is for this "rising main" to be placed close to the "flow" pipe of the hot-water system, if the building has one. Branch pipes from the rising main take drinking-water to the kitchen sink, and often elsewhere also. An overflow or warning pipe runs from the cistern to the roof under the eaves, where the outlet can be easily seen. This pipe, like all overflow pipes, must be

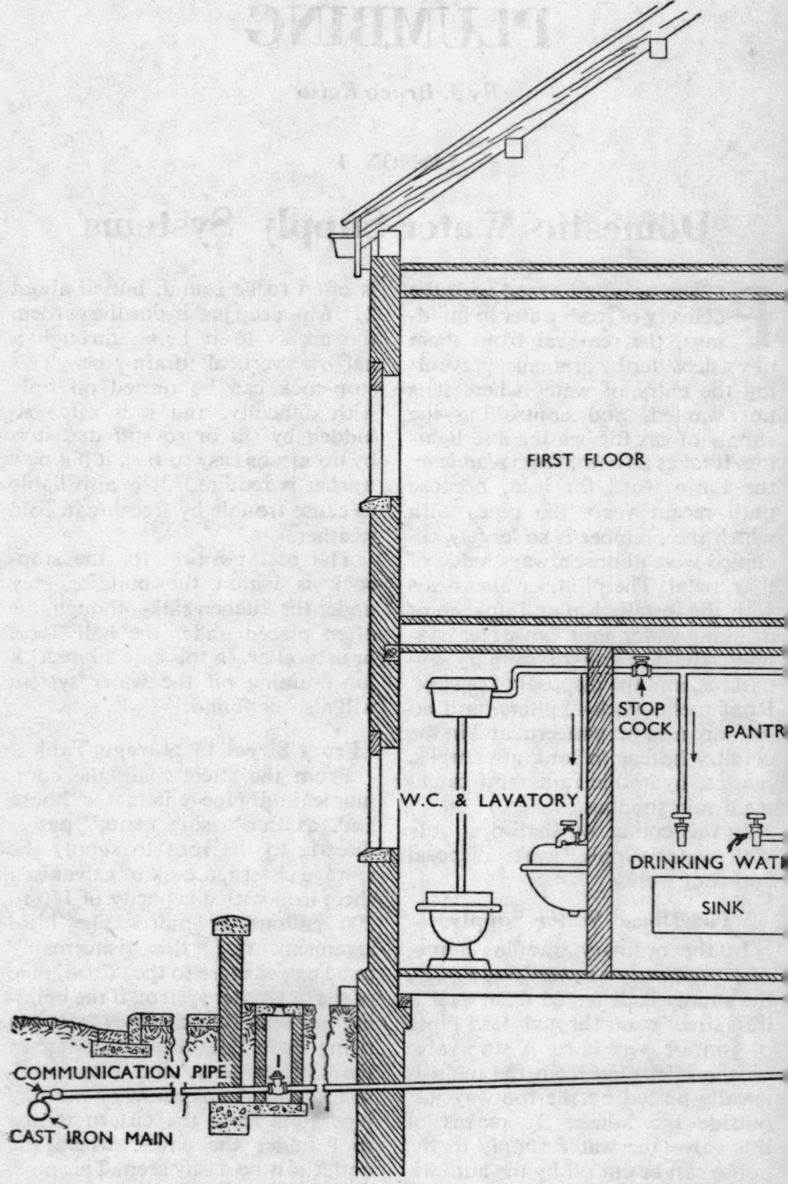

Fig. 1. *Typical arrangement of pipes in an ordinary two-storey dwelling*

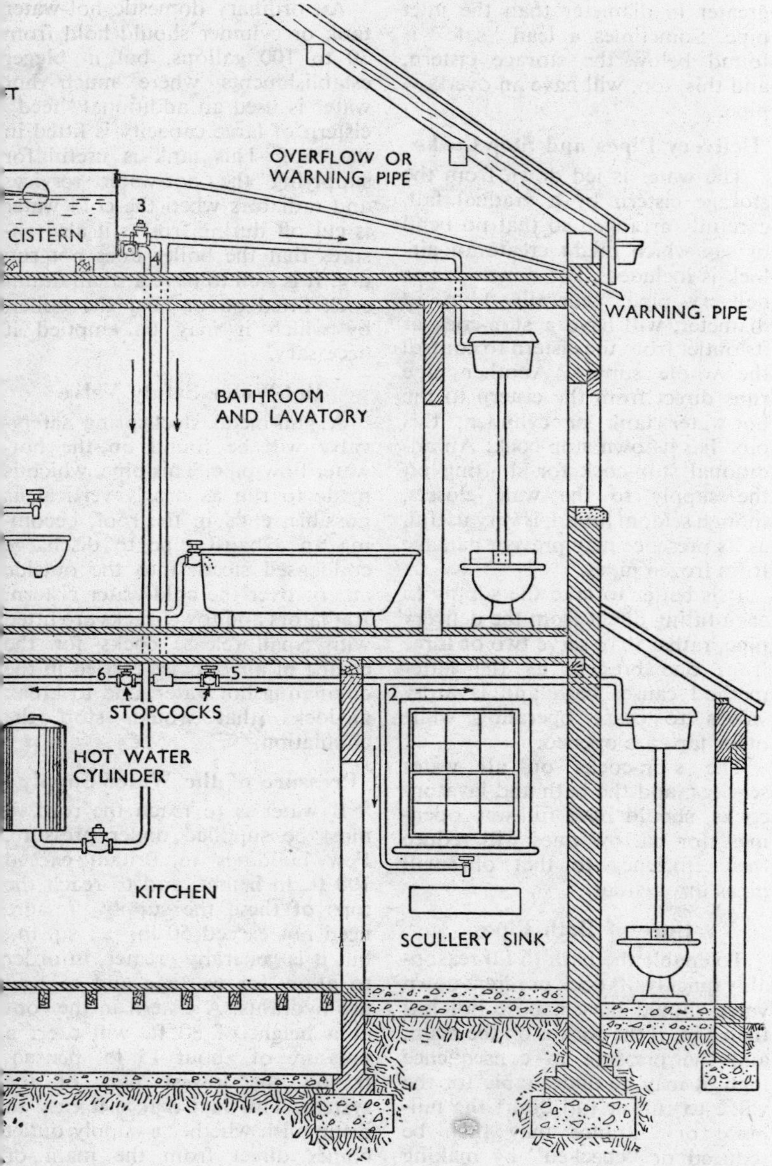

nains water supply. Stopcocks are numbered; 1 is the external cock.

greater in diameter than the inlet pipe. Sometimes a lead "safe" is found below the storage cistern, and this, too, will have an overflow pipe.

Delivery Pipes and Stop-Cocks

The water is led down from the storage cistern by a gradual fall, carefully arranged so that no bend or sag which might create an air-lock is included. The downward or delivery pipe, generally 1 in. in diameter, will have a stop-cock at its outlet from the cistern to control the whole supply. Another pipe runs direct from the cistern to the hot-water tank or cylinder; this pipe has its own stop-cock. An additional stop-cock for shutting off the supply to the water-closets, though seldom found, is very useful, as its presence may prevent damage from frozen pipes.

It is better to take the supply to each fitting direct from the delivery pipe, rather than serve two or three from one branch, as the latter method causes bath and lavatory valves to cease operating while other taps are opened.

The stop-cocks on all water services, and the bath and lavatory cocks, should have full-way openings, for narrow ones will reduce their efficiency to that of small pipes throughout.

Bore of Bath Pipe

To enable the bath to fill reasonably quickly, its cock or screw-down valve should have a bore not less than 1 in. If the cock is on the main, and the pressure in consequence high, it may be undesirable for the valve to run at full bore; the tail-piece or entrance may then be reduced or "checked" by making the hole about half the size of the outlet.

An ordinary domestic hot-water tank or cylinder should hold from 30 to 100 gallons, but in bigger establishments where much hot water is used an additional "feed" cistern of large capacity is fitted in the roof. This tank is useful for supplying the hot-water services and radiators when the cold water is cut off during frosts; it also ensures that the boiler does not run dry. It is well to have a small drain-cock fitted on or near the boiler, by which it may be emptied if necessary.

Hot-Water Safety Valve

A gun-metal steel-spring safety-valve will be found on the hot-water flow-pipe. This pipe, which is made to run as nearly vertical as possible, ends in the roof, becoming an exhaust pipe to discharge condensed steam into the outside air, or over the cold-water cistern. Radiators and towel-racks are fitted with small release cocks for the escape of air bubbles carried in the circulating hot water, and to break air-locks that would stop the circulation.

Pressure of the Water Supply

If water is to reach the roof, it must be supplied under pressure. Few buildings in Britain exceed 100 ft. in height, and to reach the tops of these the supply pressure need not exceed 50 lb. per sq. in., but it is generally greater, in order to allow for wastage and to feed fire hydrants. A cistern in the roof at a height of 30 ft. will exert a pressure of about 15 lb. per sq. ft. on the lowest part of the system. This fact makes it easy to distinguish whether a supply outlet comes direct from the main or from the cistern. Place your thumb under the tap, with the water turned on at full bore. If the supply is from the main, the thumb cannot hold back the pressure of about 60 lb., and the water will spurt out; if the supply is from a cistern, it can be easily held. If the house is very tall, however, the difference will not be so apparent.

In very high buildings, where sway and expansion are considerable, iron pipes, or brass tubing in iron-pipe sizes, is often used for cold water, the latter particularly in America.

Self Testing Questions

(1) *In ordinary houses, does the hot-water supply come from the rising-main?*

(2) *Is the communication pipe from a street main the same size as the delivery pipe from a storage cistern?*

(3) *Where should the drinking supply be connected on a water service?*

THE ANSWERS ARE ON PAGE 471.

LESSON 2

Pipe-Bending and Fixing

In almost all domestic plumbing jobs a knowledge of pipe-bending methods is called for. The points to avoid in bending a pipe are: constricting the bore, and damaging the inner or outer surface. Puckering at the bend or "throat," and bulging at the sides, can be remedied as work proceeds. Bends should be made with as easy a sweep as possible, for the sharper the bend, the more will the pipe be distorted.

There are three methods of pipe-bending: (1) inserting a steel spring; (2) filling the pipe with sand and plugging it; (3) using a wooden bobbin. The bobbin may be forced through with a driving-stick, or by following it up with other similar bobbins, which may be threaded on a cord (Fig. 2). Pipes not over $\frac{3}{4}$ in. in diameter, if they are to be bent to an angle less than 90 deg., can be shaped without these aids.

When stress is applied to a metal, it becomes crystallised, and heat is necessary to restore it to its normal state. For lead, this may be applied by the flame of a blow-lamp. The proper temperature of annealing, as this tempering process is called, can easily be found for lead pipe by splashing a few drops of water on to the pipe; when the water hisses, sufficient heating has been applied. If the water forms drops which balance on the pipe

Fig. 2. *Bending a lead pipe by bobbins. The balls, threaded on a cord, restore the diameter and remove puckers.*

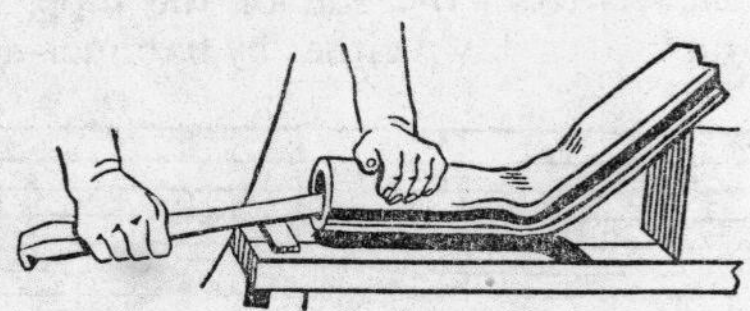

Fig. 3. *How a "dummy" is used to work out the throat of a bend. At the end of the rod is a smooth ball of solder.*

without moving, the metal has been over-heated.

Small pipes may be bent over the arched thumb or the knee, with a thick pad of carpet interposed to relieve the pressure, annealing being repeated if necessary. Lead is more pliable warm than cold. To dress back the bulged sides after bending, beat them with a mallet or with a hammer, in the latter case placing a smooth board between tool and pipe. The bend will open slightly when this is done, so, to compensate for this, the pipe should in the first place be bent a little more than is necessary.

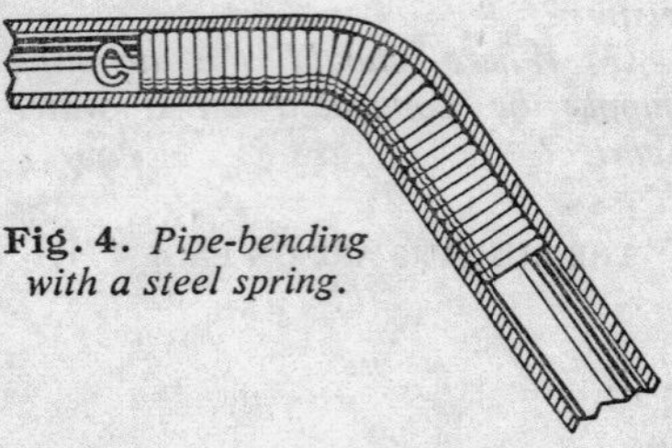

Fig. 4. *Pipe-bending with a steel spring.*

Bending Large-Bore Pipes

Large-diameter pipes should have their sides or "cheeks" beaten back to their original diameter, and the puckers then straightened out from within by driving a bobbin through. If they are seriously distorted, a small bobbin is passed through first, then one of full bore. Sometimes the puckers can be reached from the end of the pipe, and beaten down either by hammering a bar placed against them, or with a "dummy" (see Fig. 3)—a polished egg-shaped ball of solder attached to the end of a ½-in. iron rod.

Spring-Bending

In this easy method of pipe-bending a steel spring of suitable diameter (Fig. 4) is inserted in the pipe where the bend is to be made. The pipe, held between two cloth-covered pins to act as fulcrums, is then pulled back to the desired shape. Any bulging at the cheeks is dressed back as before, but with gentle blows, or the spring is pressed against the pipe interior and is troublesome to remove. To withdraw the spring, pour a little grease into the pipe and grip the end, turning it anti-clockwise. This will enlarge the spring, which will worm its way out.

Sand-bending is a quick way of making bends without tools, though as the back of the bend stretches somewhat and the puckers are not always completely removed, plumbers often prefer other methods. The pipe-end is plugged with wood, with a nail driven through to hold it. The pipe is then stood on end and filled with sand, tightly packed in by beating it with a stick. A second plug is then inserted, the portion to be bent marked off with chalk, and the lead annealed. The pipe-ends, held in the hands, are pulled together to make a preliminary bend, and any puckers formed are gently

Fig. 5. *Pipe hooks placed too far apart from each other cause pipes to sag.*

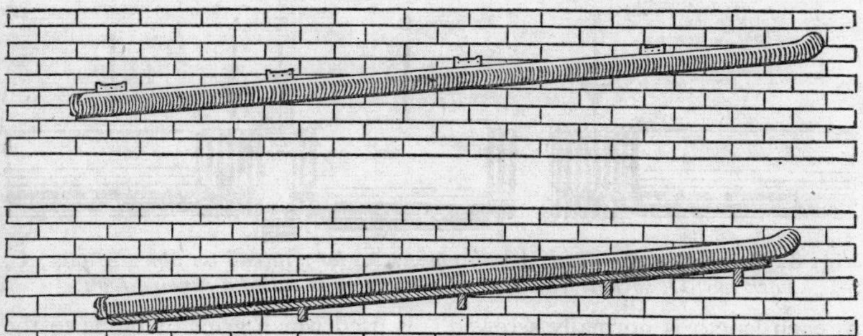

Fig. 6. *Good methods of supporting lead piping. "Tacks" as seen above, give better support.* Below, *method of supporting pipe by a wooden board.*

tapped down with a mallet. The plugs are removed and the pipe lightly tapped, and afterwards flushed with water, to clear it of sand particles which might clog ball-valves or cocks.

How to Fix Lead Piping

If lead piping is not properly secured to a support, it will sag, strain the joints and have an unsightly appearance (Fig. 5). This is especially the case in hot-water systems. To hold the pipe, thick pieces of lead, called "tacks," are soldered on about 6 ft. apart (Fig. 6), and nailed to the wall, or else screwed to wooden battens having a suitable slope or fall (Fig. 6). A pipe-hook (Fig. 7) is a wedge-shaped nail with flattened tongue-piece which surrounds half the pipe; if driven too hard into the wall it may cause the pipe to be damaged or to leak. Stamped brass clips can be used when a backboard is fixed to the wall, into which the screws may fasten.

When fixing a pipe-hook, endeavour to find a joint in the brickwork and into this force a wooden wedge. Hammer the pipe-hook into the centre of the wedge, and it will remain firm and not be loosened by vibration. A rawl-plug inserted into the brick itself will make an excellent fixing. There are numerous varieties of pipe-clips and holder-bats for all types of pipe, but the points of importance in fixing them are to see that they have a firm foundation, are secure and do not damage the pipes.

The Use of Iron Pipes

Iron water-pipes, called "barrels," are used both for cold and for hot water. Water authorities generally stipulate that underground pipes must be of iron, but in some localities chemical reaction makes it impossible to use iron in any part of the water services. One great disadvantage of iron pipes is that, unless galvanised, the interior rusts, and also becomes covered with deposits of lime or "fur." This condition may stop the supply completely, and is frequently the cause of noises being set up in the hot circulation.

To remove the obstruction, the pipes must be disconnected, but

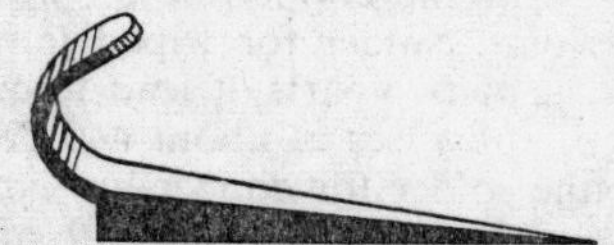

Fig. 7. *Hook for supporting pipes.*

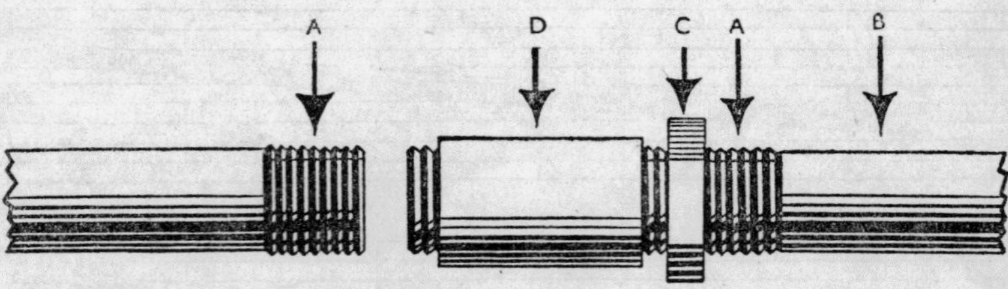

Fig. 8. *Connection for wrought-iron pipe.* AA, *long thread on pipe;* B, *pipe;* C, *back nut;* D, *socket. This type of connection is called a running-joint.*

as each length is normally screwed to the next by an elbow or socket, this would be impossible but for the fact that a special joint (Fig. 8) is used. This is called a connector or running-joint, and consists of a long thread cut on the pipe so that the socket can be screwed back to its full length. When the corresponding pipe is placed in position the socket is screwed back on to this, so that it stands half on one pipe and half on the other. The threads on iron pipes are usually made to taper slightly, so that when screwed up the pipe pinches the socket tightly, but with the long thread of the running joint this is not so. In this case a back or locking nut is used which grips or binds to the socket and prevents it working loose, some hemp and red lead paint being inserted in the threads to make the joint sound. The socket and pipes are held with pipe tongues and a spanner of "footprint" type used to tighten the joints.

Self Testing Questions

(1) *What are the main points in pipe bending?*

(2) *How are lead pipes prevented from sagging?*

(3) *What is the main disadvantage of iron pipes?*

THE ANSWERS ARE ON PAGE 471.

LESSON 3

Pipe Joining and Soldering

THE plumber uses three principal joints: soldered, compression-coupled, and lead-caulked. Here we deal only with the first of these. Soldered joints are subdivided into the plumber's wiped joint, and the copper-bit or blowpipe joint. Solder for wiped joints consists of two parts of lead to one of tin, and fuses at about 440 deg. F.; fine solder for copper-bit work has equal parts of tin and lead, and fuses at about 365 deg. F. A slightly larger proportion of tin is an advantage in either case. Remember that if heating is prolonged, the tin is liable to separate from the lead. Plumber's solder for wiped joints is worked in semi-plastic condition; fine solder is quite fluid. On clean surfaces, solders make metal-to-metal contact, and a flux is necessary to reduce capillary attraction and to retard surface tarnish. For plumber's solder the flux is tallow or oil; for fine solder, resin, zinc chloride ("killed spirits") or sal-ammoniac. Killed spirits is made by placing spirits of salts (hydrochloric acid) in a leaden jar with small pieces of zinc: it is highly poisonous. Prepared flux pastes are also on sale, but killed spirits is generally preferred for lead work.

Wiped Joint

On straight pipes this joint is elliptical in shape, in roof and cistern work a straight rib or a triangular fillet. There are three types of wiped joint: the horizontal or underhand (Fig. 9), the upright, and the branch joint (Fig. 10). The solder is wiped in a slightly plastic state. The wiped joint is much stronger than the copper-bit joint, being of greater bulk.

One of the pipes to be joined is widened out or "belled" at the end, and the corresponding pipe chamfered or bevelled to fit into the bell. To prevent the metals adhering, the ends are chalked or "smudged" with a preparation of 1 oz. of powdered chalk, 1 oz. of lamp-black, 4 oz. size, and a little water heated together till dissolved. When the "smudge" has dried, a line is scribed to mark out the joint, and from this line to the pipe-end the smudge is scraped off, together with a film of the lead, leaving a bright metal surface. The joint is smeared with tallow, firmly secured, and heated in the blow-lamp flame. A stick of plumber's solder is then applied to the pipe, any falling solder being replaced with a metal spoon. When enough solder has been applied, the joint is wiped with a wiping-cloth held in palm and fingers, till it forms an ellipse about 3½ in. long.

Wiping-cloths are made of fustian, moleskin or bed-ticking, folded about twelve times, the edges being sewn together, and the cloth thoroughly saturated with warm tallow. The usual sizes of cloth are 2½ in. × 3 in. for branch joints and 4 in. × 5 in. for underhand joints.

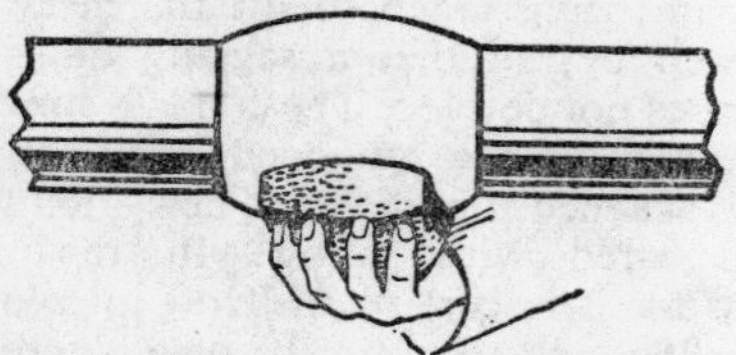

Fig. 9. *Showing method of wiping a horizontal or underhand joint.*

Branch Joints

A hole is bored in the pipe, and its edges dressed up with a steel bar, so that a collar is formed. The branch is fitted to it, care being taken that the chamfer on the branch does not reach so far into the pipe as to cause obstruction. The branch is smudged, the metal made bright and smeared with tallow and the solder deposited as with an underhand joint. Wiping is done with a small cloth, the blow-lamp keeping the temperature of the joint's edges and of its thicker part uniform.

Vertical Joints

These (Fig. 11) are made with the aid of a collar placed around the pipe about 6 in. below the joint, to catch

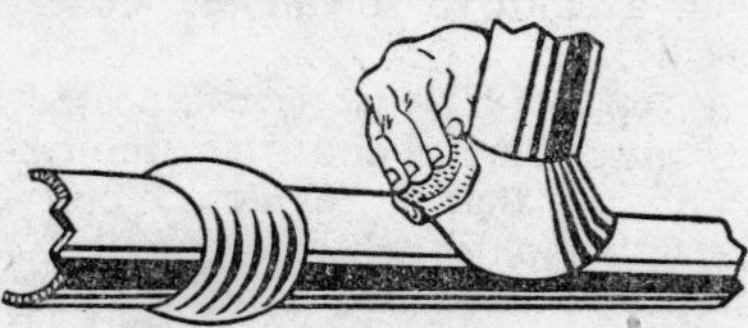

Fig. 10. *Wiping a branch joint.*

any solder that may fall, and to assist in preserving heat. The pipe is prepared as for an underhand joint, and where the collar fits, some chalk or smudge is applied to prevent the solder from adhering to the pipe. It is not easy to get the metal to adhere to the joint, but when enough has been applied the joint is wiped as already explained, care being taken to lift the metal well up, so that a sagging bulge does not develop. The collar is now removed, the smudged parts re-blackened, and the new joint smeared with tallow. In repair work it is best to melt off all old solder and to re-tin the pipe before making the joint.

In the case of a split pipe, the sides of the hole must be scraped clean and the lead dressed down so that the gap in the pipe is closed. The joint may then be wiped as already explained, or a longitudinal patch may be wiped over the split.

Fine Soldering

The heat is applied by blow-lamp, or by soldering iron or copper-bit. The latter, for good soldering, must be well "tinned"—that is, heated and covered with a thin coating of solder. The point of the bit is rasped and made bright; the bit is then put into the fire. When it attains a dull bluish colour it is removed from the heat, the bit point placed in a flux and rapidly withdrawn. A stick of solder is applied to the "face" of the bit and then rubbed with a cloth to spread the solder evenly.

A copper-bit that is overheated becomes burnt, and the tinning spoilt, so that it ceases to conduct the solder where required; a properly-heated one emits a faint fume when withdrawn from the fire. A little powdered resin sprinkled on the "face" immediately before use will keep the copper-bit brightly tinned.

The union piece is likewise tinned, and after being fitted to the pipe is held firmly in place by a stick of wood. The nut and union are called in plumbing a "cap" and "lining." To solder the joint, flux

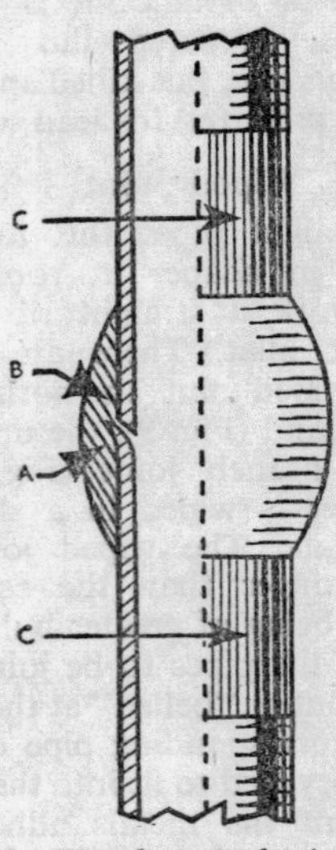

Fig. 11. *Wiped vertical joint.* A, *bell;* B, *chamfer;* C, *parts above and below joint smudged to prevent metal adhering.*

well and place the point of the soldering bit on the union itself; heat will travel down the bit and make the pipe also hot, and solder placed on the bit point will melt, flow into the joint cavity and fill it. If, however, heating is too prolonged the solder will penetrate into the interior of the pipe or union.

Self Testing Questions

(1) *What is the difference between plumber's and fine solder?*

(2) *What is the purpose of smudge?*

(3) *What is the meaning of "tinning" a soldering iron?*

THE ANSWERS ARE ON PAGE 471.

LESSON 4

Soil-Pipes and Wastes

In most modern buildings all the sanitary pipe-work is iron, except perhaps the soil-pipe outlet branches from stack to fittings. Access is provided at the elbows and junctions, which, if the set-screws are of bronze, allows of easy cleansing.

Soil-pipes are generally of 4 in. diameter, and are carried above the roof, the portion from the highest water-closet branch acting as drain-vent. If there are several water-closets on a stack, the discharge from a higher one causes a syphon action, as it falls down the pipe almost at full bore, pushing air before it and causing a partial vacuum behind. The rush of air "draws" the water in the traps of other fittings, and the water leaps over the trap-weir, emptying the trap and allowing foul gases to enter the room. To prevent this, an anti-syphon system is provided by bringing a pipe from near the crown of each trap to the roof to provide ventilation, or returning it to the soil-pipe above the highest branch. Sink wastes are dealt with in a similar manner (cf. Figs. 12 and 13).

As lead pipes are too soft to make direct contact with sanitary

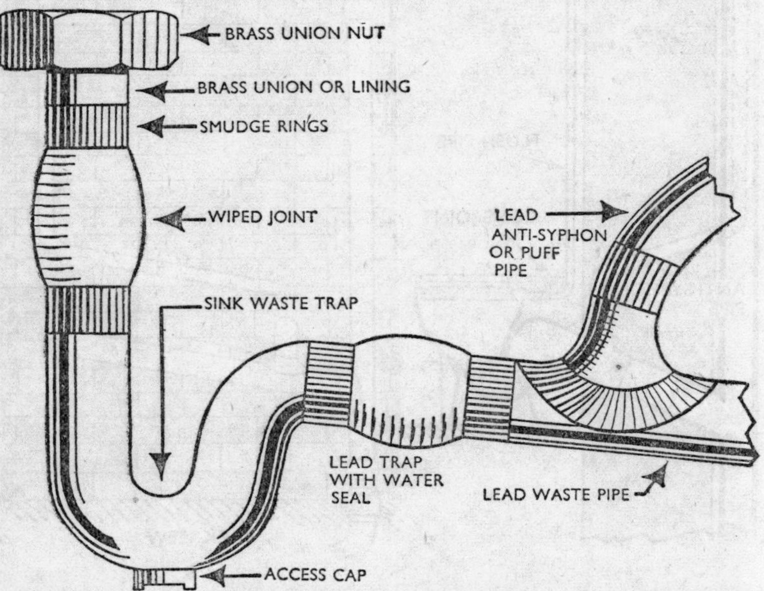

Fig. 12. *Lead sink or lavatory-basin trap with anti-syphon branch. Note how branch or puff pipe, seen on right of diagram, turns slightly in direction of flow.*

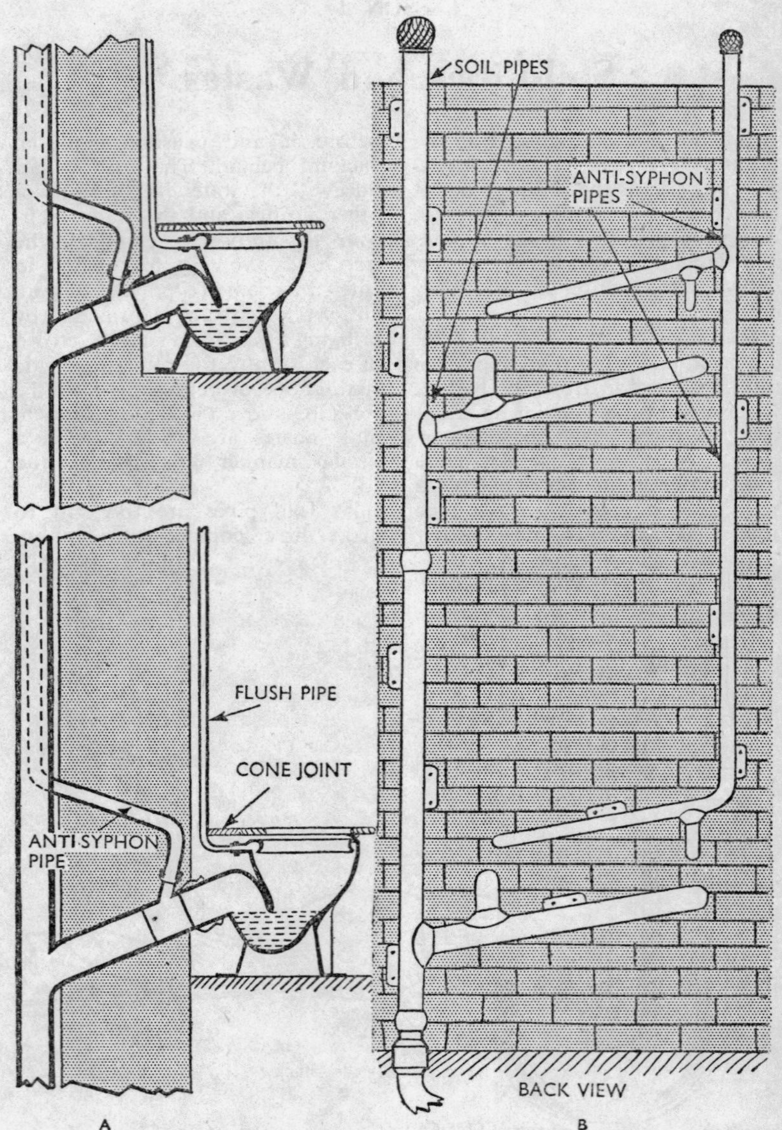

Fig. 13. *Connections of earthenware closets with a lead soil-pipe.* A, *side view or elevation;* B, *back view. Note the cone connection between down pipe and closet pan.*

fittings, and are affected by lime and cement, a brass thimble is fitted to the end of the pipe with a plumber's wiped joint, and the union with the earthenware trap made with a cement joint.

Rust Prevention

To prevent rust inside and outside sanitary pipes, they are coated with an enamel paint, known as Dr. Angus Smith's protective solution. But iron pipes where water does not pass sometimes tend to rust and clog at the bends. It is best, therefore, for all elbows to be made without acute angles, and for all ventilating pipes to have a continuous fall, so that any rust formed may fall to the bottom, where it can be removed by rodding from the manhole or access. A gurgling noise in the sink-waste or soil-pipe, or jumping up and down of the water in the closet trap when another fitment is used, means that there is rust in the ventilating shaft, and the traps are syphoning.

Cast-iron sanitary pipes are joined by pouring molten lead into the socket and caulking it well when cool. To prevent the lead getting inside the pipe, a couple of twists of hemp are placed in the faucet and rammed home.

To disconnect iron pipes, the lead must be heated by a blow-lamp and then scooped out with a flattened wire. Before replacement they should be painted inside and out to retard further rusting.

Anti-Syphonage

Anti-syphonage is a less serious problem in sink wastes; it will not occur if a 2-in. vent shaft is used and the traps are not more than 2 or 3 ft. from the shaft. By-laws, however, require anti-syphonage wherever necessary, or where a number of waste-pipes from different floors join on one stack. Anti-syphon traps, now commonly used, are dealt with in Lesson 5.

The lead down-pipe from the water-waste preventer to the closet is sometimes a weak point in domestic plumbing. The joint or connection here is usually made with a rubber cone, its large end fitting the pan, the smaller the down-pipe (see Fig. 13). The joint is often made by placing on the pipe and pan a paste made by mixing white and red lead with linseed oil, and binding with a strip of strong cloth, tied over with string or copper wire. The joint may leak through the pan not having a firm foundation, through floor movement, or because the hinged seat is pushed too hard against the down-pipe. If a small wet patch is observed on the floor of the W.C., this cone joint should be suspected. Place the hand under the pan at the joint and pull the flushing chain: if the joint is leaking, water will fall on the hand. Though this water is clean, and therefore harmless, it may cause considerable damage if the closet-pan is boxed in.

The flush-pipe may sometimes leak at the top end; if so, the joint should be re-wiped, or if the pipe is attached to the cistern by a nut, the latter should be unscrewed and a small leather washer inserted between flange and cistern.

Self Testing Questions

(1) *What is the cause of syphoning in discharge pipes?*

(2) *How can rust be prevented at bends in iron pipes?*

(3) *What is indicated by a gurgling noise in a sink waste-pipe?*

THE ANSWERS ARE ON PAGE 472.

LESSON 5

Traps and Drain-Testing

TRAPS are used in all sanitary fittings to interpose a barrier of water between the inlet and the discharge sides, so that offensive and impure gases shall not pass back into the house. In principle the trap is an S-shaped tube with an access trap for cleansing (Fig. 14); the deeper it is, if self-cleansing, the less likely is it to be unsealed. When several traps are on one stack, to prevent lower traps being blown or drawn by the breaking of the water-seal when a higher trap on the stack is discharged (see Lesson 4), they are provided with anti-syphonage devices. A pipe is taken from near the crown of each trap to the open air, so that the fluids passing can "pull" air to fill the partial vacuum created. Sometimes it is taken through the wall and not carried to the roof; it is then called a puff-pipe. But most local authorities forbid this, and require such pipes to be taken to the roof or turned into the waste-pipe or soil-pipe above the highest branch.

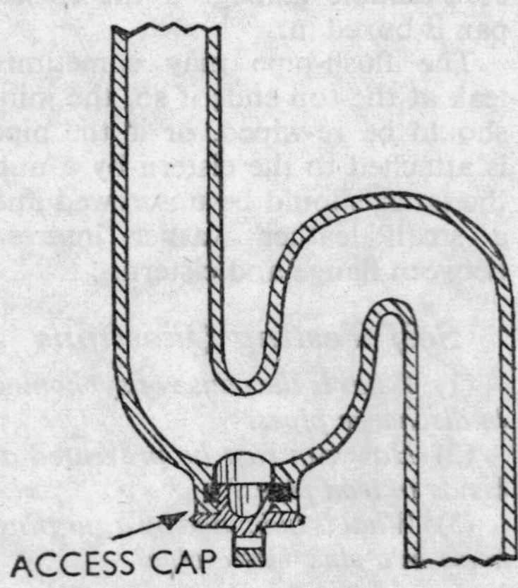

Fig. 14. *Basin trap of "S" type.*

Waste water from sinks, baths or lavatory basins is conveyed away by waste-pipes, and discharged into a gully at ground level, or under a grid, or into side-inlets; and all such waste must be trapped. Sink wastes should have a gradual fall without sags, and be free from air locks. In hot weather all traps and gullies not in regular use should be supplied occasionally with additional water, and all hair, cotton etc., removed, as these will soon lower the water in the trap by capillary attraction, and so break the water-seal.

Testing a Drainage System

At the edge of the premises near the sewer a large trap called the intercepting trap (Fig. 15) is placed to disconnect the house drain from sewer emanations. It is usually placed in an inspection chamber and a fresh-air inlet pipe prevents syphonage and allows air to circulate through the drain and up the soil-pipe, to escape above the roof.

Anti-syphon traps on waste pipes are designed to enable heavy discharges to pass through, and yet for the trap to retain its water-seal without any special air-pipe. In some there is a by-pass in which the air pressure caused by flushing takes a short circuit and forces the water along to re-enter the top portion of the trap (Fig. 16). Thence it falls to fill and re-seal the trap. In other types there is a reserve chamber where the liquids are not wholly removed by the discharge and some falls back again to re-make the seal. Yet others have an enlargement in which some of the water and air is stopped at the upper shoulder, thus causing the water to fall back again when the main discharge has passed.

There are four methods of testing a drainage system for leaks: the smoke, water, smell or chemical, and air or pneumatic tests. In the first, a smoke rocket about 8 in. long is placed, fuse end downward, in a gully or W.C. trap from which the water has been removed. The fuse is ignited, and a piece of slate placed over the top of the gully and sealed with puddled clay. After letting the smoke circulate within the drain for a few minutes, the soil-pipe top is covered. If drain- or soil-pipe is defective, smoke will be seen escaping.

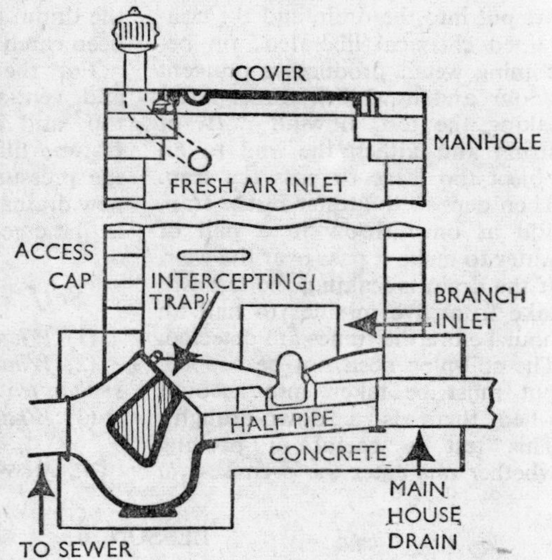

Fig. 15. *Arrangement of intercepting trap which prevents sewer emanations from reaching house.*

For the water test, fill the drain with water and place a stopper at the lowest point—which is usually the intercepting chamber at the front of the house. This test is too drastic for old drains; it tests only the part below the lowest gully, and although a leak might be indicated by a fall in the water level, it does not show where the defect is.

In the chemical test, a glass vial, or two pressed metal cups sealed with grease and bound with string,

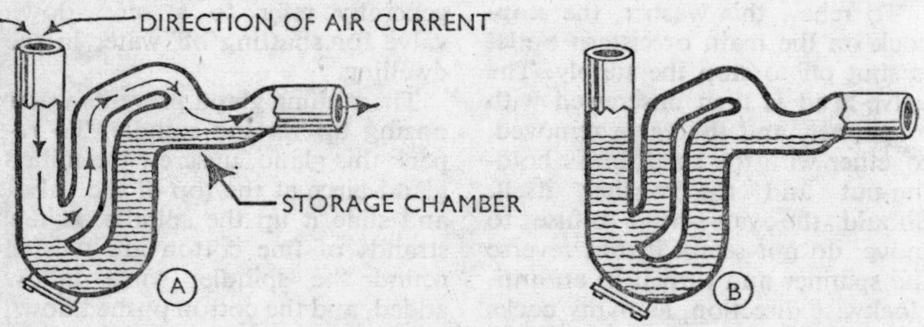

Fig. 16. *Anti-syphon trap with by-pass. The water passing causes air current in top tank which breaks vacuum and water falls back into base of trap and reseals.* A, *discharging;* B, *position of water when normal. Note access cap at bottom.*

are put into the drain and the contained chemical liberated: on becoming wet it produces a pungent odour and a whitish fume. After taking the test, unwind 2 ft. of string and attach the end to an object too large to pass the trap. Then deposit the tester in the trap, and at once throw in a pail of water to make it pass over the weir. If the drain is leaking, the test will take from five minutes to half an hour before the fumes are detected. The soil-pipe need not be capped, but must be taken into account when there is a down-draught. This test is useful in proving whether rats enter the premises *via* the drain, or if a lead soil-pipe has been eaten through by rats.

For the air test, the soil-pipe and vent-shaft are sealed at the top, and air pumped in, a glass U-tube filled with water denoting the pressure. This test is used for new drainage systems when a house is first erected.

Self Testing Questions

(1) *What is the purpose of a trap?*

(2) *What is the principle of anti-syphon traps?*

(3) *What is a puff pipe?*

THE ANSWERS ARE ON PAGE 472.

LESSON 6

Plumbing Repairs

In all domestic water systems the flow is controlled by a leather, rubber, or, for hot-water outlets, a fibre washer, screwed down to press on a ground-in seating (see Fig. 17). The washer has a centre hole to fit the turning spindle, and a small brass nut secures it in position.

Repairing Stop-Cock or Tap

To renew this washer, the stop-cock on the main or cistern outlet is shut off to stop the supply. The valve-head is then unscrewed with a spanner, and the valve removed, together with the small brass holding-nut and the washer itself. Should the valve-head refuse to move, do not strain it, but reverse the spanner and turn it in an anti-clockwise direction, as many cocks have left-handed threads to prevent the head from working itself loose accidentally when the cock is in use.

Next see that all grit and foreign matter is removed from the seating, and that the seating itself is not damaged. A new washer is then fixed on the spindle, the nut replaced, the head screwed down, and a few strands of greased cotton inserted under the small flange of the head.

In plumbing, the terms valve, cock, tap, draw-off tap are all used somewhat loosely, but they all generally refer to a screw-down valve for shutting off water in the dwelling.

The stuffing gland prevents water oozing up *via* the spindle. To repack this gland, unscrew the milled gland-piece at the top of the valve, and slide it up the spindle. A few strands of fine cotton are twisted round the spindle, some tallow added, and the cotton pushed down into the seating and the milled piece screwed down, but not too tightly. One very efficient patent

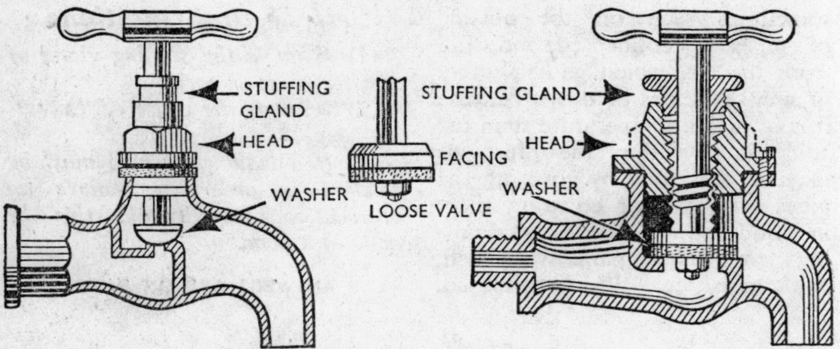

Figs. 17 and 17A. *Two types of screw-down valves showing washer on seating.*

washer acts on the ball-and-socket principle (Fig. 17A), the rounded face at the slightest pressure finding its own seating. In this the washer is very thick, and is screwed direct into the spindle, the small holding nut being discarded. The life of such a washer far exceeds that of an ordinary one.

Sink-waste and other traps may be unstopped, if the obstruction is not solidly wedged, by "plunging" with a rubber or leather disc firmly attached to a rod or handle.

Unstopping Sink-Waste Trap

The disc is placed into the trap and pushed up and down until wave motion and suction push the obstruction slowly forward. As soon as movement is felt, the plunger should be removed to let in the air pressure, and the waste will then disgorge with a rush. Long drain-canes and spiral spring waste-pipe "ferrets" can be threaded through the trap and forced around bends to remove ordinary obstructions.

When necessary, the access cap underneath the trap may be unscrewed and the cane introduced there, but care must be taken not to damage the lead trap, and the cap must be screwed in very carefully when replaced so that it does not leak.

When it is necessary to "prick" a lead waste-pipe to insert the cane, do so at a bend, and instead of sealing the hole with solder, place an access cap in the bend and solder this for use on another occasion.

Repairing a Lavatory Basin

Cracked or broken glazed earthenware, such as a lavatory basin, may be repaired as follows. Dry the edges of crack or fracture thoroughly, making sure that no part is dirty, and paint with a mixture of red lead, gold size and linseed oil, adding a little white lead putty. Then take a large linen patch, soak this in the paint, and push it tightly on to the outer surface, gently pressing it into position. The patch must be left undisturbed and no water allowed to pass for some days, when it will become quite firm. Such a patch, if painted white, will be almost invisible, and will remain intact for years.

Sweating Pipes

Though it is often believed that either lead or iron pipes may at certain seasons sweat or ooze water, this is a fallacy. The water sometimes seen on the outside of pipes is condensed moisture from the air, which gathers there in small globules or drops because it is of higher temperature than the cold water within the pipes. It may be prevented by covering the pipes with felt or encasing them in wood and sawdust, or by painting them with lead paint over which, while moist, cork dust is sprinkled.

Self Testing Questions

(1) *What is the stuffing gland of a water-valve or cock?*

(2) *What is the cause of "sweating" pipes?*

(3) *If a lead waste-pipe must be pricked in order to remove an obstruction, why should this be done at a bend?*

THE ANSWERS ARE ON PAGE 472.

LESSON 7

Flushing Cisterns and Ball Valves

THE flushing cistern, or water-waste preventer, as it is technically called, is a device used in houses for flushing water-closets and grease-traps; in the case of the latter it discharges automatically at regular intervals. Usually it is of cast iron, and about 2 gallons in capacity. Though internal designs vary, all work on the principle of syphonic action. Fig. 18 shows the various parts: float and arm (*A*), valve (*B*), bell with lever (*C*), chain (*D*) and flush-pipe (*E*).

How the Flushing Cistern Works

The ball-valve limits the height of water in the cistern, and, when the ball drops, causes it to refill by opening the valve. In the centre of the cistern is a vertical pipe rising above the water-level, and over this a bell whose top is filled with air. When the chain is pulled, the bell rises; some of the water rises with it, and, reaching the top of the vertical tube, discharges down it. When the bell falls back to its original position, the cone-shaped dome compresses the water enclosed in it; this passes up and falls down the pipe, also creating in its fall a partial vacuum. The atmospheric pressure on the water surface in the cistern is now greater than that within the pipe, so that a syphonic action occurs and continues till the tank is empty, and the air, reaching the bottom of the bell, destroys the vacuum.

The float has now fallen, opening the inlet valve, and when the tank is filled, the float-arm pushes a rubber disc on to the valve seating, and the flow of water ceases. The

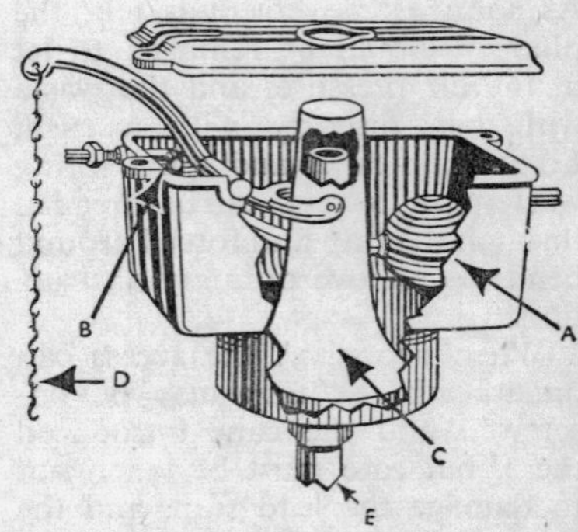

Fig. 18. *Parts of a flushing cistern.*

syphonic action cannot thereafter be repeated till the bell is again lifted and released.

Ball-valves may develop defects as a result of leaking floats, perished washers or grit and obstructions in the valve-seating. Remove the ball from the lever arm, or remove arm and ball together by taking the split pin from the valve. Shake the ball-float near the ear, and if there is water within it, the sound will disclose the fact. To remove this, prick a hole in the ball with a nail, and shake out the water; then place the float over a gas-flame, hole uppermost, and the remaining water will escape as steam.

To find a leak in the seam, place the ball under a cold tap, and then plunge it into a pail of very hot water; the expanding air will escape as bubbles, locating the defect. Clean the seam, flux it well and re-solder; re-solder the hole likewise, but do this quickly, or the solder will remain fluid and fall through the hole into the float. Before replacing the float-arm, allow the water to flow through the valve-seating to remove any grit or lime deposits.

Repairing Cistern and Ball-Valve

A "chattering" ball-valve means that the valve shuts off too suddenly, or that the washer is loose. This can be remedied by adjusting the fitting, and making the delivery hole smaller to baffle the momentum.

If the cistern overflows, or does not fill to sufficient height, the ball-valve can be bent to give more or less buoyancy; do not bend it too sharply, as, being of cast brass, it is somewhat brittle. In Fig. 19 is shown a flushing cistern with a patent valve. This consists of a float-body made in one piece of copper with a pressed-on top, and has no soldered seam where decay from electrolysis can be set up: nor can it leak from other causes. A band supporting the float allows for adjustment until the most favourable position is found. The float occupies less space than a ball, and there is less chance of damage from frictional rub against the side of the cistern. The nipple is attached to the band and not to the float, and this allows for screwing it to the arm and into position, before the float is fitted; the float will always remain upright, and cannot become detached from the arm.

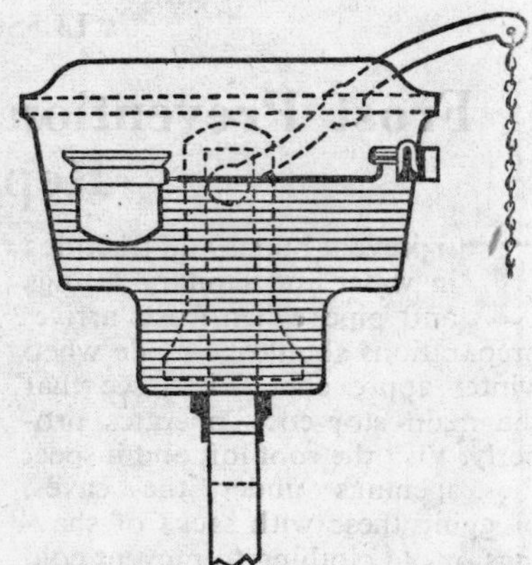

Fig. 19. *Flushing cistern or water waste preventer of an alternative type, showing "everfloat" ball—note centre tube standing above water-level.*

Self Testing Questions

(1) *What is the cause of "chattering"?*

(2) *Of what metal is a ball-float made?*

(3) *How can overflowing in a ball-valve cistern be remedied?*

THE ANSWERS ARE ON PAGE 472.

LESSON 8

Frost Prevention and Frost-Burst Repairs

To prevent bursts and fractures in water and sanitary fittings and pipes when frosts arrive, preparations should be made when winter approaches. First, see that the main stop-cock operates properly. Visit the roof loft and inspect the openings under the eaves, plugging these with sacks of shavings or old clothing to prevent cold draughts. Should the underfelt of tiled roofs be hanging, connect up the ends of the adjacent felt-sheet by pricking small holes, and join the sheets together with brass paper-fasteners.

Preparing for Winter

The storage cistern should be shielded by boxing it in with wood or asbestos boards, leaving a 2-in. cavity to be filled with granulated cork or sawdust, and a lid provided, protected but easily movable. In the roof the rising main to the ball-valve and the cistern outlet pipes should be covered with cloths; or strips of hair-felt can be wound round them in bandage form (Fig. 20), secured by string or copper wire. The ball-valve and stop-cock should likewise be protected by some suitable covering, arranged in such a way that they can be operated without delay.

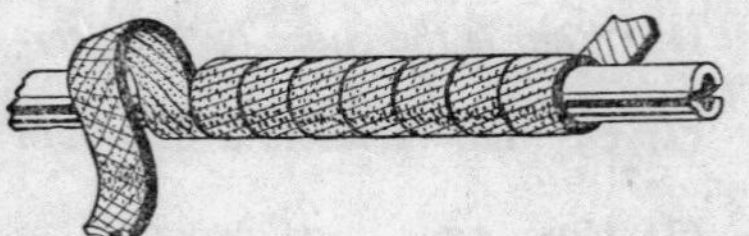

Fig. 20. *Frost protection. Method of applying hair felt to pipes as a "bandage" secured by string or wire.*

The warning or overflow pipe does not need covering, but the end in the open air should be bent downward to check any strong winds blowing through to the cistern. Felt strip is very convenient for covering external pipes, but wood boxing is more permanent: it is of little value, however, unless well packed with slag-wool, hair, or wood sawdust. The boxing should have quite a large cavity so that plenty of packing can be inserted, and the lid-piece should screw down so that rain cannot enter. Vertical hollow casing, unless well packed, will be worse than useless, for upward draughts may pass as in a flue.

External water-closet flushing cisterns can be surrounded with old cloths, and the supply pipe protected with felt; a stop-cock should be fitted to shut off the supply when necessary. The water-closet trap, also, should have its water baled out during hard frost, as this will prevent its being fractured. Should the flush-cistern be frozen, lift the lid, remove the ice, and let the water in. This may prevent the cistern from becoming frozen solid and the cast-iron tank from fracturing.

All exposed pipes and fittings should where possible be emptied and left so until the thaw. A thick sheet of ice forming on the surface of the roof storage cistern will hold the float fast so that no air can get under the ice, and the partial vacuum will stop the downflow. The ice must therefore be broken to restore normal inflow and discharge. A kettle of hot water poured into the cistern and over the ball-valve (Fig. 21) will sometimes be sufficient to thaw a local stoppage here, and hot water may be poured on any part of the surface suspected of being frozen, care being taken that the water does no damage as it falls.

Testing for Frozen Pipes

To discover what section of the service has ceased to function, turn off all draw-taps one at a time. Then turn on the main stop-cock and place one end of a stick on the rising main and the other end to the ear. If water is entering the storage cistern, a running hiss will be heard. If no noise is heard, go to the roof, uncover the storage cistern, and break any ice found there. This may free the float ball, and on pushing down the float, the water may enter. If this does not happen, the ball-valve is frozen. Boiling water may start the flow.

Next, try the cold bath and lavatory valves and W.C. flushes. If these are stopped, begin at the roof and, working from the cistern, heat the delivery pipes with a blow-lamp or hot soldering iron, or with hot water; go to the bathroom, leaving the taps open, and continue heating. As soon as the slightest trickle is observed the heating can be discontinued, for the water will form a course for itself. Next, go to the kitchen sink and continue heating the delivery pipe, going on to the outside W.C.

When the cold supply is restored, return to the roof and make sure that the cold supply to the hot-water cylinder is operating. Tapping the hot-water cylinder will generally indicate whether it is full, and the bath hot valves will prove whether that section is stopped. If necessary, continue heating. Next, test the hot-water tap over the sink; if this is stopped, the boiler may be frozen. A small ¼-in. or ⅜-in. plug is often found on the lower part of a modern independent boiler. This can be turned carefully with a spanner, and if the water starts to "weep" it is evident that it is in order. When the "return" pipe (the pipe to the boiler) is free, continue with the lamp along the flow-pipe up to the cistern and to the sink and lavatory hot supply. If water now runs normally, do not waste it, in case the cold supply is limited or cannot be immediately restored.

Thawing Out

A small fire may now be lit to warm the room and boiler. When the system shows signs of thawing out, the air which entered when the cocks were open will cause gurgling noises; this is a sign that most of the pipes are in order. Sometimes the air-locks stop the water-flow. If this does not quickly right itself, open the tap over the sink or bath, place your mouth over the tap, and suck with a steady pull, taking no notice of water which enters the mouth. A movement will soon be felt, and the water will flow in gulps as the pipes refill.

Preventing Freeze-Up

A paraffin heater or electric heater may be placed under the open trap-door into the loft so that hot air may reach the cistern and pipes. In water-closets, if the door is kept shut and ventilators temporarily sealed, a candle will suffice to keep the pipes and flush cistern from freezing. If the ball-valve is frozen, a candle should be stood with flame ½ in. from the

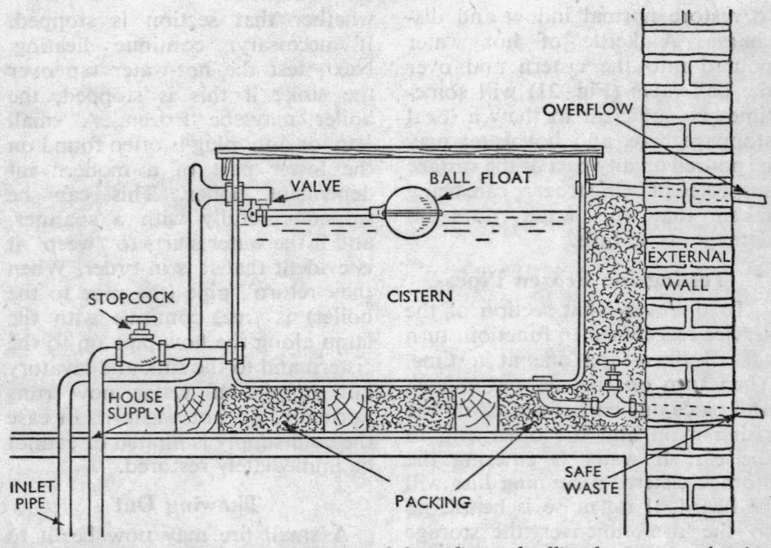

Fig. 21. *Diagram of loft storage cistern of the ordinary dwelling-house type, showing ball valve and float, inlet and outlet pipes, and discharge outlets of overflow and safe waste pipes, which pass through the wall into the open air.*

supply or by the ball-valve of the flushing cistern, and it will gradually thaw out the entire flush service.

Ventilators in a bathroom may be temporarily sealed off to prevent cold air entering, but the bath should on no account be used till the ventilator is open again. In the water-closet the sealing off of air-bricks or window-gauge may be carried out temporarily with a piece of oil-cloth cut and wedged in the openings, to be removed when the frost period has ceased.

The Running Tap Method

One of the simplest means of preventing burst pipes is to let a tap run continually at night while the frost lasts. Only a small stream is needed, provided the gully where waste discharges is covered with a board and some non-conductive material such as discarded clothing. A small weep into the sink from the hot tap will help to keep the waste pipe from freezing; but this must be constantly observed, or serious flooding might result should the waste-pipe freeze, after all. Although water companies object to this method, the waste of water it entails is far less than that from burst pipes and the emptying of systems to thaw them out. In the daytime the hot-water service can be used more freely than usual, thereby warming the sanitary fittings and sink wastes, so that night frosts are to some extent held in check.

In applying first-aid treatment to burst pipes, the main points are: turn off the stop-cock where possible; stop the water by hammering up the pipe, seal the hole by inserting a wooden plug, or bind the leak with clips and bandage. Where the leak, though it cannot be stopped, can be covered with a cloth to prevent damage to the ceiling and walls, this should be done and a bath placed beneath to catch the water. Then remove the cloth quickly, strike the pipe firmly with a heavy hammer, and completely flatten it for three or four inches.

The pipe can now be severed by cutting the middle of the flattened portion with a chisel and folding the two end pieces of pipe back upon themselves, hammering again to close the fold. Beating the pipe thus will stop the leak, but a slight weep may appear at the extremities of the fold. This can be soldered without turning off the water supply. When the burst in the pipe is a simple hole and not a split, a small piece of wood can be sharpened to a point, placed over the hole, and driven in with a hammer, care being taken not to force it through to the opposite side. This wooden wedge will remain in position for a long period, and as the wood swells it will tighten, stopping the leak completely. The wedge must not afterwards be interfered with, as it readily becomes loose under water pressure. A temporary repair may be effected by cutting out the damaged portion of pipe and replacing it with a piece of garden hose, clipping or wiring this to the pipe ends.

Treating Burst Iron Pipes

A split iron pipe may be repaired by hammering down the edges close to the hole, removing the sharpness, and covering the split with a paint of red and white lead mixed with gold size, binding it with a bandage of canvas fastened with string. As bursts in iron pipes are usually splits three or four inches long, such a repair is somewhat unsightly, but it will hold well till a new pipe or barrel can be fitted. This repair must be done when the pipe is quite dry, or a sound joint will not be made. A bandage saturated with shellac, gold size and methylated spirits may be used for iron pipes, but as the joint is somewhat brittle, it is not recommended except for a short period. A joint thus made dries very quickly.

Temporary Repairs

Small pipes under low pressure can be bound with medical adhesive tape, warmed and applied to a clean dry surface; while a rubber or cycle patch may be placed over the hole, secured by adhesive tape, which will both hold it in position and give it strength.

Fitting New Piping

To fit a new piece of piping, first force the pipe away from the wall and cut out the defective part with a hacksaw, seeing that saw-chips are not left inside the pipe. The new pieces of pipe should be about ½ in. longer than the old portion, to allow for the chamfers. The new pipe must have both ends belled out, so that the chamfers on the old pieces will fit into them. The joints are prepared as already described in Lesson 2, then soldered, and the pipe left to cool. Before pushing the pipe back into position, it is advisable to heat it for a foot or so on each side of the joints to make it more pliable. It is then pushed back into position and if necessary secured.

Iron and lead wastes on external walls may split if they become frozen solid. An iron waste can be temporarily repaired by bending a piece of sheet metal and placing it around the pipe, painting it first well with red lead, and binding it with copper wire and clips. With lead waste pipe the split is dressed back to normal size and the defect soldered over.

Clearing Waste Pipes

In freeing pipes hot water should be poured on the frozen wastes beginning from the lowest end; this will prevent a leak or defective joint starting out, as would happen if the top portion thawed first.

A waste-pipe can be cleared of ice and grease obstruction by filling the basin with hot soda water and passing a copper wire through the trap and working it backward and forward, the soda following the wire and destroying the grease. If this is not successful, the access cap under the trap must be removed, and the waste-pipe "plunged" with wire or cane from that point, care being taken to re-insert a rubber washer or twine and red lead around the thread to prevent the access cap from leaking. If frost has caused a puncture in the trap, the hole may be rounded with a penknife and sealed by placing a small cork firmly into the hole and binding with string. The cork will swell and remain in position for a long time.

Self Testing Questions

(1) *What frost-preventive covering is recommended for external pipes?*

(2) *What points must be remembered when thawing out pipes?*

(3) *How should splits in external waste-pipes be mended?*

THE ANSWERS ARE ON PAGE 472.

LESSON 9

Roof Work

METAL coverings on roofs are subject to damage from age, frost or in war-time from gun-fire; but their repair is not difficult. Eaves gutters may sag or be silted up, "falls" reversed, bolts or stop-ends dislodged, or, in box and valley gutters the metal may expand and contract, causing leaks; rough treatment or polluted air, also, perforates the metals.

The "rolls" and "capping" of zinc and copper roof-work may become loose through high winds and flashing; soakers and aprons may also develop defects. Nails left under the metals, rusting screw-heads and inequality of thickness in metal may all cause roof leaks.

In new roofing work little or no solder is used, if possible, so as to avoid galvanic action, and because solder is not so strong as the parent metal. But in repair work this objection can be disregarded.

In old, large houses the leaden gutters terminate in roof cess-pools, from which a rain-spout is taken. The wiped joint at this point often cracks, owing to the sun expanding the lead, and re-soldering the outlet with a wiping cloth will make the gutter sound again.

The separate sheets on flat roofs are connected by "rolls" or welted "drips." The roll (Figs. 22, 23), a long, straight piece of wood about $1\frac{1}{2}$ in. in diameter, is covered with a strip of metal which interlocks with the flat sheets and makes a tight but movable connection. Nailed to the under-side of the roll are strips

Fig. 22. *Lead flat with roll connections.*

of metal about 1 in. wide, and these are also folded with the roof-sheets to hold them firmly to the roof.

The "drip" is a small step-down of 2 in. to provide a fall and at the same time allow the metal sheets to join each other. The joint here is often welted, the sheet ends being folded together and dressed over to form a seam. On deep gutters the vertical sides do not reach to the top, but apron-pieces are arranged to hang over the turn-up, and step flashing metal is cut diagonally, turned over the edges and wedged into the joints of brick on chimneys and parapets. These are used in conjunction with soakers to make sound the connecting point between slates and chimney-stacks, etc.

When the roof leaks, first see that these various pieces of metal are in proper position, and if they are standing away from the walls or are otherwise out of order, dress them back tightly and secure the flashing to the brickwork joints by small wooden wedges. When the rolls are uncapped or the end-pieces loose, new ends can be soldered, fresh tie-clips placed at the rolls and the capping re-fastened.

Zinc Roofing Repairs

Eaves gutters of zinc can easily be re-soldered and patched. Both parent metal and patch must be scraped bright and tinned. The patch should be of 14-gauge metal. The job is done with fine solder and a flux of killed spirits. Tin the copper-bit well and solder in the ordinary way, but with as little delay as possible, as the solder and the zinc tend to form an alloy, making the solder on the bit pasty, and when in this condition the parent metal may easily be perforated and spoiled. For this reason the solder can be made as a rich surface deposit, and not enticed to flow into the seam.

Eaves gutters have small zinc tube-pieces placed across the top to give strength, and these frequently become unsoldered. It is best to take these, or the stop-end, completely off and re-solder them.

In all zinc repairs, all traces of flux must be thoroughly washed away, or the zinc will soon become perforated and brittle. In cleaning zinc gutters the encrusted silt must be removed very carefully, as old zinc is easily punctured, and the stop-ends are readily pushed off.

Repairing Lead Roof-Work

All loose lead and buckles should be dressed back, with the help of a little heat from the blow-lamp, and any splits or holes that are discovered soldered over. When the surfaces are level, shave both sides of the split for about ½ in., make it bright, sprinkle a little powdered

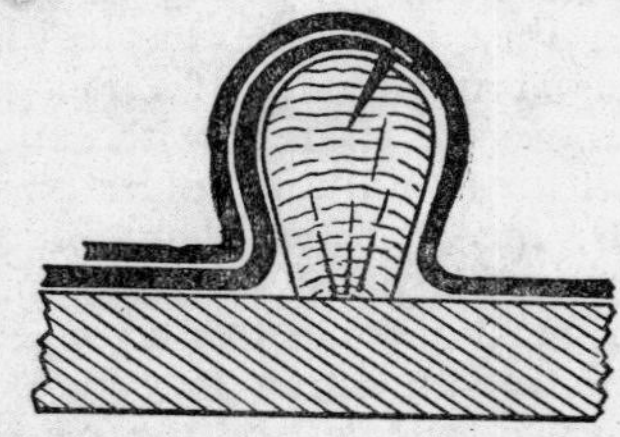

Fig. 23. *Roof roll showing how two sheets of lead are connected. Note copper tack securing lead to roll.*

resin on the cleaned part, and, with a well-tinned copper-bit and fine solder, solder it over, leaving a heavy deposit. Fine solder, however, is less satisfactory than plumber's solder, which can be wiped on with the cloth, using resin or tallow as flux. In upright splits a wiped seam is essential.

Iron gutters can be repaired by taking down, cleaning, re-painting inside and out with lead paint, and refixing, inserting new lengths where necessary. The lengths are usually 6 ft., each section having a faucet at one end into which the next length fits. The two are bolted together with a gutter-bolt and a flat nut, the joint being made sound with red lead, putty and paint.

Old Gutters are Dangerous

When disturbing old gutters, remember that they are very heavy, and, being of cast-iron, are brittle, so that they should not be dropped. The screw-heads supporting the gutter often rust through, so that it rests solely on the pegs, and careless movement may make it fall. If iron gutters are painted with lead paint inside and out, they will last for years; otherwise they soon deteriorate.

Copper Roofing

Repairs to copper roofs are seldom necessary, unless damage is done to them by falling objects. Being very light, the metal will not stand rough usage. If a fracture is discovered, clean it with sand-paper, tin it well and solder on a patch; this is better than filling the hole with solder. Never use any other metal in contact with copper, or electrolytic action may be set up, which will destroy the metal. If the welts break down it is not easy to put in a new sheet, so leaks should be soldered with the copper-bit. A large one should be used, to enable the metal to flow freely, as copper is a good conductor of heat and rapidly makes the bit cold.

Bitumen Compounds

A number of roof-repairing compounds, mainly based on tar or bitumen, exist which can be painted over roofs or gutters in the case of slight damage. But these, though they may serve for a short time, are unreliable when subject to exposure from the sun or to traffic of any kind, even though light. Coal-tar can be used in this way in dry weather, if sprinkled with fine sand after application, but this should be used only on roofs which have but a slight fall.

Copper Plumbing

The use of copper in domestic plumbing has increased considerably in recent years, owing to the durability, elasticity and greater tensile strength of copper pipes. Such pipes require few supports, as they do not sag, and the connectors can be incorporated as wall fittings.

Copper pipes can be bent, though it is best to use precast elbow tees and bends. To bend a copper pipe, first anneal to a dull red colour at the place where the bend is to be made, then fill with dry sand, resin or molten lead. A wooden bending-block with a hole which permits the pipe to pass freely should be placed in a vice, the pipe inserted into this hole, and then pulled to the radius desired. All puckers that develop in the throat must be beaten out with a ball-faced hammer before the filling medium is removed. To remove sand, extract the plug, and tap the pipe with a mallet; to remove lead, heat the pipe with a blow lamp, beginning at one end and proceeding slowly along the pipe: make sure that all dross is removed. To assist the process a little oil should be placed in the empty pipe and the latter re-heated, when the oil will absorb the oxygen of the dross and enable the lead to be freed from the pipe walls.

Joining Copper Tubes

Light copper tubes can be simply and speedily joined by capillary-soldered joints, made by a cone-collar compressed to a collar on the pipe, when the union is screwed up, forming a slight indentation which does not interfere with the bore. Capillary-soldered joints are of two types: one, in which the solder is supplied already in a grooved fitting, the other where the solder is fed normally or through a hole drilled in the fitting to assist the flow. In both types the fittings are made to fit the tube very closely.

In making these joints, first see that the pipe has no external scratches and that all burrs and filings are removed from the interior. The pipe-end and fittings are cleaned with steel wool or glass paper and slightly smeared with flux paste, and the joint assembled with a light push-on fit. The blow-lamp flame is then applied and a stick of fine solder placed on the joint; when sufficiently heated the solder will flow and fill the entire cavity between pipe and fitting, both upwards and downwards. If one joint of a tee is not ready for the pipe, a piece of wet cloth can be placed in the opening to prevent solder flow. When the joints are cooled, wipe them with clean rag and polish with steel wool.

Self Testing Questions

(1) *What is the purpose of a roll on a lead, zinc or copper roof?*

(2) *What causes metal destruction if two different metals are associated on a roof?*

(3) *Are lead, copper and zinc measured by the same gauge?*

THE ANSWERS ARE ON PAGE 472.

Answers to Self Testing Questions

LESSON 1

(1) No; the hot supply must be taken from the storage cistern or feed-cistern.

(2) No; water authorities stipulate that delivery pipes must be larger than that entering the premises.

(3) From the rising main on the house side of the stop-cock, and carried thence to the kitchen sink.

LESSON 2

(1) To keep the pipe its original size, the bore smooth, and the curves regular.

(2) By fastening them with lead-tacks or pipe-hooks, either to a wall or to wooden battens into which the tacks are screwed.

(3) Unless they are galvanised, their interiors tend to rust and to become "furred" or coated with deposits of lime.

LESSON 3

(1) Plumber's solder is two-thirds lead and one-third tin; fine solder has equal parts of lead and tin.

(2) To prevent solder from adhering to the pipe where it is not wanted, while a joint is being wiped.

(3) Brightening it by rasping, heating it, placing its point in flux and applying a thin and even coating of solder.

LESSON 4

(1) Discharge from a higher outlet pipe falling down the discharge pipe at full bore, creating a vacuum behind it, which draws the water from traps on lower fittings.

(2) By avoiding acute angles in all pipe-elbows, and providing a continuous fall in the direction of all ventilating pipes.

(3) That the traps are syphoning owing to rust or other obstruction in the ventilating shaft.

LESSON 5

(1) To prevent obnoxious gases returning to the house, by making a barrier of water between the discharge pipe and the inlet pipe to the sanitary fitting.

(2) They include a by-pass to short-circuit the air pressure and thus force water to re-enter the trap, or a reserve chamber or enlargement retaining some liquid which, after flushing, falls back into the trap.

(3) A pipe running from near the crown of a trap straight through the wall to the open air, through which air can be "pulled" with the result that it fills the vacuum caused by passing fluids.

LESSON 6

(1) A cone on both top and bottom of gland seating filled with packing which presses on the spindle and prevents the escape of water.

(2) Condensation of moisture from the atmosphere on the outside of a pipe owing to the lower temperature inside the pipe.

(3) In order that an access cap may be placed there to make it possible to repeat the operation on future occasions without re-pricking.

LESSON 7

(1) It is caused by the momentum of the water being repeatedly checked and then released, or sometimes by a loose washer. The former cause can be remedied by making the delivery hole smaller.

(2) Usually of copper; but Monel metal, composed of two-thirds nickel and one-third copper, with a trace of manganese, is better and more lasting. It may be bent and soldered in the same manner as copper.

(3) By bending the ball-float arm to alter the buoyancy as may be required.

LESSON 8

(1) Strips of felt, or wood casing packed with hair or wood sawdust.

(2) To find whether the blockage is general or local; to have a blow-lamp or other means of heating ready; and to have pails or baths at hand for catching any water that escapes from the pipe.

(3) If the pipe is of lead, by soldering; if of iron, by binding and clipping round the pipe a piece of sheet metal painted with red lead.

LESSON 9

(1) To connect the sheets, allow for expansion and contraction, and to fasten holding-clips to keep the sheets in position.

(2) A miniature electric battery is formed by the aid of the acids in the atmosphere, which causes the composition of the metals to undergo destructive changes.

(3) No; lead is measured by weight in lb. per sq. ft. or lineal yard; copper by the British Standard Wire gauge, and zinc by English Zinc gauge (usually 14 for roofs, which is approximately 21 of Standard Wire gauge).

HEATING

By J. St. Denys Reed

LESSON 1

Heat of the Body

COLD-BLOODED animals have a body temperature a little above that of the air or water in which they live, and their temperature changes with that of their surroundings. Warm-blooded animals, among which, of course, man is included, have in health a constant body-temperature—between 98° and 99° in the case of man. Since human beings live healthily in climates that have great differences of temperature, it is obvious that the body must include some means for regulating its heat—or, more precisely, for regulating loss of heat. Quite apart from differences in the temperature of the surrounding air, or the presence of warmth-producing devices like fires, or the rays of the sun, the body temperature can be raised by physical exercise, that is, by muscular activity.

Body Heat

When a person enters a room having a temperature much below 60° F. he soon begins to "feel cold," because heat flows from his body to the walls and furniture of the room, which are colder. This produces a sensation of chill to the skin. When he enters a room that is too warm he feels discomfort, and the reactions of his body mechanism in trying to adjust itself to the conditions may cause him actual pain or illness; he may feel faint.

Body-heat is produced mainly by the oxidation of carbohydrates and fats in the tissues (chiefly in the muscle); ultimately the source of heat is the food ingested, for food may be said to be burned in the body during the process which breaks down and assimilates the food materials.

Combustion of Food and of Fuel

So close is the analogy between combustion of food in the body and that of fuel outside it that the heat-producing value of a given food may be measured in calories (see Lesson 7) by precisely the same method as that of a fuel such as coal or oil intended to be burnt in a grate or a boiler. The food is placed in a calorimeter and completely burnt (or oxidised) under control—the output of heat being measured.

Given continual heat production in an appliance (whether it be a hot-water boiler or the body), the temperature must rise unless some of the heat is conveyed away or allowed to escape into the surrounding medium. Heat can escape only if the temperature of the surroundings is lower than that of the heat-producing appliance. A hot-water bottle in a bed will give off heat to the sheets and blankets, but place the bottle in a vessel of boiling water, and it will abstract heat from its surroundings till the water in it is about as hot as that in the surrounding vessel.

The amount of heat given out by

the human body is considerable: even when resting, the body has an output of about 200 British Thermal Units each hour, and in ordinary manual work this is doubled. The B.Th.U. represents the amount of heat required to raise the temperature of one pound of water by one degree Fahrenheit. Thus the output of a man while doing moderate work is enough to raise 4 gallons of water ten degrees Fahrenheit per hour.

Air entering the nose and mouth is warmed, and some body-heat is lost in this way; more is lost in evaporation of moisture and the elimination of carbon dioxide by the lungs; the balance—about four-fifths in amount—is lost at the skin surface.

Heat Loss Mechanism

Briefly there are two different types of mechanism which provide for heat loss by way of the skin:

(1) *The vaso-motor mechanism,* by means of which the blood vessels are (*a*) dilated to increase the blood-flow; or (*b*) constricted to lessen the flow; thus more or less heat is lost at the surface.

(2) *The sweat mechanism,* by which the rate of perspiration is increased or lessened, more or less heat then being lost at the skin surface by evaporation.

Heat Gain

So far we have not dealt with the question of how the body copes with the condition when the air outside it is cooler than the normal body temperature: in such a case the rate of metabolism is speeded up, so that food is oxidised away more rapidly to make up for the quicker rate of loss. It is as though a stoker were feeding more fuel to a furnace!

Note the analogy between natural and man-made mechanisms for securing heat regulation. Most of these physiological facts are so bound up with the entire question of room-warming that they should always be borne in mind in further study.

To sum up, though normally the body takes care of its own heat-regulation, we must not impose too great a task on this machinery by subjecting the body to extremes of temperature in either direction.

Methods of Heat Transmission

These may be considered in connection with the body, which for the present we can regard as a source of heat. Heat conveyed to the skin surface may be lost by conduction, convection, and radiation; there is also evaporation, as mentioned above.

Conduction. Heat is transmitted direct by contact with the air, with clothing, or with any other object touching the body. The function of clothing is to enclose around the body a layer of air, which is a good insulator.

Convection. When air becomes heated locally it expands, and so becomes lighter (for a given cubic measure) than cooler air; the cooler and heavier air displaces the warmer air, and itself becomes heated, being displaced in turn. So the process goes on, and air currents are set up which carry away heat from the skin surface. Natural air currents (*e.g.* wind and draughts) will take away the warmth similarly. This is why heating can scarcely be studied apart from ventilation.

Radiation. Any hot object will send out heat rays (only those of certain wave-length are luminous and thus visible); the rays travel in a straight line and pass through intervening air without warming this air. When the rays impinge upon an object in their path they warm that object. (Note that an object so warmed by radiation may itself dissipate heat by all or any of the three methods just enumerated.)

As to *evaporation*, we all know that a drop of alcohol (say, methylated spirit) placed on the hand will quickly evaporate and leave the surface of the hand much colder. Water does so, but less rapidly at ordinary room temperatures.

Self Testing Questions

(1) *What is the effect upon the temperature of a room when a number of persons remain it it for some time? (Vitiation of the air need not be considered here.)*

(2) *What are the three methods in which heat is transmitted naturally?*

(3) *Why is it that in winter, when the ground is snow-covered, one may feel quite warm in the sun's rays out of doors without extra clothing?*

THE ANSWERS ARE ON PAGE 499.

LESSON 2

Theory of Heating Rooms and Buildings

The warming of rooms is necessary so that the bodies of the occupants may lose heat in such a measure that comfortable and healthy conditions are maintained. Strictly speaking, this would imply also the cooling of rooms in unduly hot weather, but such adjustment is generally made by an increase in the amount of air movement through open windows, doors, or ventilating appliances. In any case, the object is the maintenance of the room temperature at such a point that the body feels comfortable—which is impossible unless it can lose its heat to the room-air at the proper rate for the time being. This object must be achieved in spite of variations in the temperature outside.

Ventilation is often taken for granted, since rooms are seldom free from draughts, and, in temperate climes at least, are not well enough constructed to need special provision for the entry of air. Windows are there, of course, and some of them are made to open, so that stuffy conditions may be relieved by the entry of fresh air and by the movement of the air already in the room by currents thus set up. Large buildings are nowadays often supplied with warmed and "conditioned" fresh air—air that is filtered and has its humidity controlled; generally, too, in order to prevent a great drop in room temperature, there is a provision for some air to be re-circulated along with the fresh supply.

Stuffiness—that feeling of discomfort so well known—appears to depend a good deal on lack of air-movement in a room, so that mere agitation of the air may remedy stuffiness. But, of course, the air must be changed every so often when there is a number of occupants, for their breathing increases the amount of carbon dioxide and lessens the oxygen content. When an ordinary room is in use by one or two people, the natural entry of fresh air is sufficient for this purpose.

The Engineer's Problem

Thus the heating engineer is faced with the problem that he must have air-change and air-movement, but unless these are properly controlled, a great deal of the warmth he provides will be wastefully expended in heating new supplies of air. The success of a heating scheme depends on finding the right balance. The question of ventilation will be discussed briefly in Lesson 7.

Practical Considerations

Assuming that a certain temperature is desired inside the rooms (60°–65° Fahrenheit is often specified), we must take a theoretical outside temperature as an average, in order to estimate the amount of heat to be supplied. The temperature of 30° F. is commonly taken. Thus we have to replace any heat lost through the walls, doors, glass, floors and ceiling of the room, plus that used up in warming the fresh air entering. The heating engineer's task is to calculate the heat losses in the rooms to be warmed, and to design a heating system that will supply the amount of heat necessary to keep the rooms at the desired temperature in spite of these losses. The aspect of the room or the building will have a considerable effect upon the losses to be made good, and a house in an exposed position will need more heat than one sheltered by other buildings.

Two *air-changes* per hour are usually allowed for, so that an amount of air equal to twice the cubic content of the room must be warmed each hour. This, of course, is an approximation, for the amount of air actually coming in will depend on the habits of the room occupants—whether they leave the window open, etc.—but it is a reasonable figure.

The amount of heat lost through any material in a given time is the same as the amount which can be transmitted through that material, and, as a result of careful experiment, basic figures have been computed for all ordinary building materials. These are quoted in terms of British Thermal Units (B.Th.U.) per square foot of surface, per hour, for every degree Fahrenheit of difference in temperature between the internal and the external surface of such material. As examples, the following figures of heat transmission coefficients for typical walls, etc., are quoted.

	B.TH.U.
Half-brick wall (4·5-in.) plastered one side	·55
One-brick wall (9-in.) plastered one side	·42
One-and-half brick wall (13·5-in.) plastered one side . .	·34
Brick cavity wall, 2-in. cavity (11-in.)	·34
Window	1·00
Floor, 1-in. board with air space under	·1
Roof boarded and tiled, with plaster ceiling beneath .	·17
Roof tiled but not boarded	1·00
Roof boarded and tiled . .	·80
Roof boarded and tiled, and under-side boarded . .	·18

In calculating the heat lost in warming the air entering a room the factor ·019 B.Th.U. is taken, but the figure ·02 is close enough for practical purposes. The cubic content of the room in question, multiplied by the number of changes required, multiplied by the factor gives the number of B.Th.U. required per hour.

It is apparent that a room with a comparatively large expanse of window area will need more heat than one with less glass. Radiators are often installed beneath windows in order to equalise the warming. From the figures given it is made clear that an 11-in. wall having an air-space of 2 in. between the outer and inner $4\frac{1}{2}$-in. walls is equal in heat-insulating value to a solid brick wall $13\frac{1}{2}$ in. thick.

The difference should be noted in the protection given by a roof tiled over boards and one merely tiled on battens. If the under-side of the rafters as well as the outer-side be boarded, the figure is almost as good as for the tiled and boarded roof with a ceiling beneath. In view of cold-weather difficulties in the roof-space, the extra protection given by boarding the under-side may be well worth the expense.

Self Testing Questions

(1) *A room measures* 14 *ft.* × 9 *ft., and the ceiling height is* 9 *ft. If two air-changes per hour are required, how many B.Th.U. must be supplied, taking the factor for heating air at* ·02 *B.Th.U.?*

(2) *The room mentioned in the previous question has a large window in one of its* 14-*ft. walls, which are* 11-*in. brick cavity walls. The window measures* 9 *ft.* × 4 *ft. Calculate the heat loss in B.Th.U. per hour per degree F. for this wall.*

(3) *Calculate the heat loss through the ceiling of the room mentioned: above the ceiling there is a tiled roof on boards.*

THE ANSWERS ARE ON PAGE 499.

LESSON 3

Different Forms of Warming Apparatus

FROM the scientific standpoint, the *open fire* is wasteful. Much of the heat of the fuel is dissipated without warming the room, and combustion is imperfect. But there are other considerations which keep it in favour. Everyone knows the feeling of comfort that is produced by the blaze from an open fire, and our enjoyment is backed up by science to this extent —that most of the warmth from such a source is "radiant" heat. Even with domestic hot-water boilers an open-fire arrangement, resulting in waste and lowered efficiency, is in popular demand.

The heat from a *stove* is given out mainly by convection currents of air which are warmed by contact with the hot body of the stove, and thence slowly circulate throughout the room. There is radiation also, of course, from the hot metal, but the convected heat predominates. The efficiency of a good stove is 70–80 per cent., whereas that of an open fire in a modern fireplace will not be much more than 25–30 per cent. Efficiency here means that out of the heat energy given forth by the burning fuel only the percentage stated serves the useful purpose of warming the room.

Radiation

There is a vitally important factor which governs the use of radiated heat: putting it mathematically, we say that radiation intensity varies inversely as the square of the distance from the heat source. Everyone knows that less warmth is felt as we move away from a fire; but the mathematical law just expressed means that if we double the distance from the fire we shall receive on any given area of surface only a quarter of the radiation; if we treble the original distance, the radiation is reduced to one-ninth.

Stoves and Warm Air Currents

Sometimes one sees a stove enclosed by a casing of an ornamental nature, with air inlets at the lower part and outlets at the top: the object of this jacket is to promote a more even circulation of air around and over the stove, so that the room-air is more thoroughly warmed by the convection currents set up.

In America much use is made of the *warm-air furnace*, in which the same principle is employed. Cool air from outside the building is led into the stove-jacket directly through a duct, is warmed in the jacket, and then conveyed by ducts to gratings in the walls of the various rooms.

Gas Fires

The *gas fire* provides what is probably the best alternative to an open coal fire, since its white-hot "radiants" give out a large proportion of radiant heat. The products of combustion are carried away by the canopy, and at the same time air from the room is entrained and passed up into the flue with which every such appliance must be provided. The cost of using it is heavier than that of an open fire, but for intermittent use the gas fire has much to recommend it; its heat becomes available at once, and the room soon becomes comfortably warm.

Electric Fires

The *electric fire* does not need air for combustion; its wire-wound heating elements are made red-hot by the resistance which they offer to the passage of electricity. The heat is somewhat local, so that though comfortable conditions may prevail in front of and near the electric fire, other parts of the room may be unpleasantly cool. No flue is needed. For intermittent and occasional use the electric fire is very convenient, and should be chosen for this service rather than for the sole heating source in room-warming. A portable electric fire, however, should for safety's sake never be used in a bathroom (a ban which applies to *any portable electric appliance*), as the presence of steam and damp is likely to cause short circuits; and there is the greater danger that a person in the bath (or one with wet hands standing beside it) may touch the metal or the flexible cord. Should the appliance be defective, a fatal shock might be received.

Electric fires are more costly to run than any of the appliances so far mentioned, though where electric current is cheap this disadvantage is reduced or may disappear.

Both gas and electric *radiant heaters* are obtainable in the form of *bowl "fires"*; these portable appliances are excellent for temporary use, and their heat can be to some degree focused. The incandescent element is set at the centre of a polished metal reflector of parabolic form. Other types of *reflector fires* are also made.

All gas-burning appliances *consume air* and *emit products of combustion* in a gaseous form. But such products, if in comparatively small quantity, will do no harm, and so an appliance with a low gas-rate can be used in a room without inconvenience.

Convector Heaters

A maximum rate of 20 cub. ft. per hour (with gas of calorific value of 500—see Lesson 7) is recommended for *flueless convectors*. The appliance warms the air, which circulates in the manner described under the heading Stoves. Its efficiency is high, but such heaters are fit only for secondary or auxiliary use, in corridors, halls, etc. A low-consumption type known as a *background heater* is used to supplement a gas fire or an open fire, serving to warm up parts of the room away from the fireplace. The appliance is made for fitting to the wall.

Similarly, *electrical convectors* are employed to warm the air of rooms, and a special type (used for factories and work-rooms) incorporates a fan to blow air through the incandescent heating bars. *Tubular heaters* consist of a heating element enclosed in a metal tube; air passing over the tube is warmed, and circulates by convection.

Panel Heating

Instead of the usual hot-water radiator (in effect a continuous series of tubes), a *panel radiator* may be used, fitted in or against a wall. Similarly, an electrically heated panel is employed, the elements being fitted in a shallow box of which the front (heating panel) is made of sheet metal. By an extension of this principle, pipe-coils may be embedded in the entire floor surface (or ceiling surface) and connected to a boiler so that hot water circulates through them. In such surface-heated systems the emission is mainly by radiation, and the method is described as "*low-temperature*" *warming*, in contradisstinction to systems in which luminous heat-sources, of much higher temperature, are used.

In the reference to panel heating, we touched on one form of central heating, and a brief description will now be given of central systems; more details will appear in the subsequent description of a typical installation for warming a house by hot water. The method of circulating warmed air from a jacket around a central furnace has already been mentioned, air being one of the three common mediums by which heat is transmitted in warming systems. The other two, of course, are hot water and steam.

Central Heating

The *hot-water warming system* must be distinguished from systems for supplying hot water for domestic or industrial use. In some systems, domestic hot water is heated by a boiler which may also serve several radiators and perhaps a towel-rail, but it is primarily a hot-water supply installation rather than a heating one; further, like most apparatus designed to serve two functions, it will not perform both equally well. Another example of a compromise is a boiler designed to heat water, cook food, and also serve as an open fire. There is no doubt that such appliances are very convenient when the duty required in all three spheres is reasonable.

In the hot-water "*boiler*," the water is delivered at about 180° F.

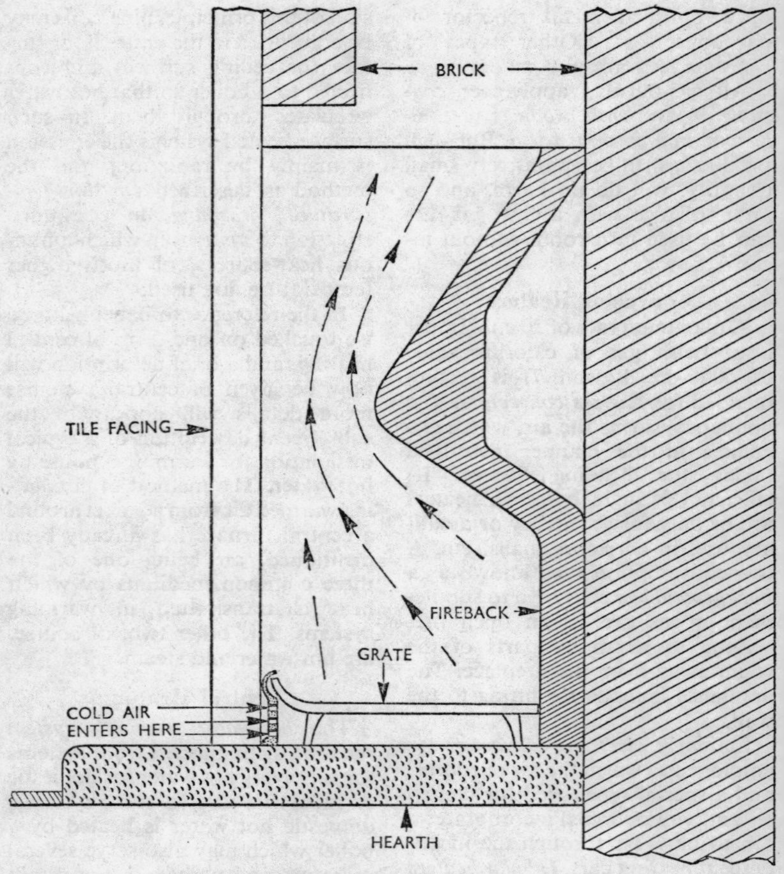

Fig. 1. *Slow-combustion fireplace with removable grate. Cold air enters through holes in damper; heated air is drawn forward where fireback projects.*

and must not boil. It is supplied by gravity from a combined *feed and expansion tank*. As water is lost by evaporation, a ball float drops and opens the cold-water inlet valve. The normal water level in the tank is low, so that ample space is left for the water pushed up out of the heating system by the expansion (one-twentieth by volume is the usual allowance) which takes place as the water becomes warm.

Water is taken from boiler to radiators by the *flow-pipe*, which is screwed into the boiler at a point near the top. At the highest point in the system a continuation of the flow-pipe is carried up above the feed-tank as an *air-vent pipe*, the end being turned down over the open top of the feed-tank. In flowing through the radiators the hot water yields up some of its heat: the drop in temperature allowed for is normally from 180° F. in the flow-pipe to 140° in the *return pipe*, to which the radiators are connected, and which goes back to the boiler, entering the latter at a point considerably lower than the level of the flow-pipe. Thus there is a continual circulation through the boiler, pipes and radiators as long as the fire is maintained.

In *heating by steam* there is a somewhat similar circuit, but the boiler is different, and has a steam space at the top instead of being completely filled with water. The steam is at a low pressure, as there is no advantage in high pressures. In evaporating water to steam, much heat is absorbed and becomes "latent" heat; 965 B.Th.U. are taken up in vaporising 1lb. of water. When steam condenses, this heat is yielded up again, although the water of condensation remains at the same temperature as the steam which produced it.

Thus steam is a convenient medium for transmitting heat; it is delivered from the boiler to radiators, where it condenses and gives up its latent heat; the water which results drains back to the boiler and is there re-converted to steam. The system is particularly suitable for large or high buildings. Radiators similar to those employed for heating by hot water are used, but must be fitted with automatic air-valves or steam-traps to allow air to escape but not steam.

Self Testing Questions

(1) *Describe briefly the characteristics of* (a) *an open fire; and* (b) *a stove.*

(2) *How does a gas fire differ from an electric fire in its effect upon the air conditions in a room?*

(3) *Convection occurs when any "fluid" is heated in an enclosed space, whether this be a room or a tank. The term fluid applies to a liquid or a gas: from what has been explained about convection, describe what happens in a hot-water storage tank when heated water enters at, or near, the bottom.*

THE ANSWERS ARE ON PAGE 499.

LESSON 4

Fires and Stoves: Choice and Installation

THE modern fireplace with its grate is constructed on the slow-combustion principle. There are many patterns and varieties, some having ingenious patented devices to procure more complete combustion of the fuel and the projection of more of the heat into the room.

Simplicity is a most important feature of any domestic appliance and sometimes efficiency has to be sacrificed in order to avoid complexity. A typical modern slow-combustion grate with fireback is shown in section in Fig. 1: the grate is removable, standing on four legs on the hearth. At the front is the damper through the holes in which air is admitted or excluded at will by a sliding member that opens or blocks the holes. (More air finds its way through the apertures at sides, top and bottom in any case, and the fretted plate is not to be compared with a proper damper such as that fitted to a boiler flue.) A complete fireplace of a similar excellent type is shown by Fig. 2.

Open Fires

When kindling the fire, open the fret, and, when the fire is well alight, close it a little. More air is needed at first than later, especially as the fireplace and flue may contain damp air, which is heavier than dry air. As the air warms, it expands and becomes lighter, volume for volume, and is displaced upward by heavier air from the room. So we get an upward movement in the chimney-flue, and a draught is created which entrains more air from the room. The draught, once started, is maintained by the fire itself. It is an old practice to ignite newspaper in a grate which has been idle for some time, in order to warm the air in the flue before starting a fire. If the chimney is foul, however, or even if there is an accumulation of soot just above the fireplace, soot may be set alight and become a nuisance.

Fig. 2. *Modern fireplace suite.*

By limiting the amount of air passing through the fuel-bed—that is, by opening the damper slide only a little—the draught may be restricted once the fire is burning brightly, and the desired slowness of combustion attained. But the heat emitted is proportionate to the amount of fuel consumed in a given period, so that we restrict the heat-emission also. The open fire is not very efficient and, as we saw in Lesson 3, only about 25–30 per cent. of the energy of the fuel is usefully expended. Early fireplaces had a vertical back, so that the heated gases were drawn straight up the chimney. Modern fireplaces, as Fig. 1 clearly shows, have a projection in the fireclay "fireback" which constrains the hot gases to flow forward on their way upward, so that more warmth is given out to the room. The student will realise that this feature, though an obvious improvement, will not make up for the disadvantage that the hot gases lose most of their warmth uselessly in the chimney.

Smoke

One important respect in which fireplaces and grates have been improved is in more perfect combustion of the fuel: this is mainly a matter of ensuring a proper air supply, for if insufficient air is provided the fuel will not be completely burned and much of its energy will be wasted in the form of smoke (unburnt particles of carbon). But in any case, when using a bituminous coal, the fire will

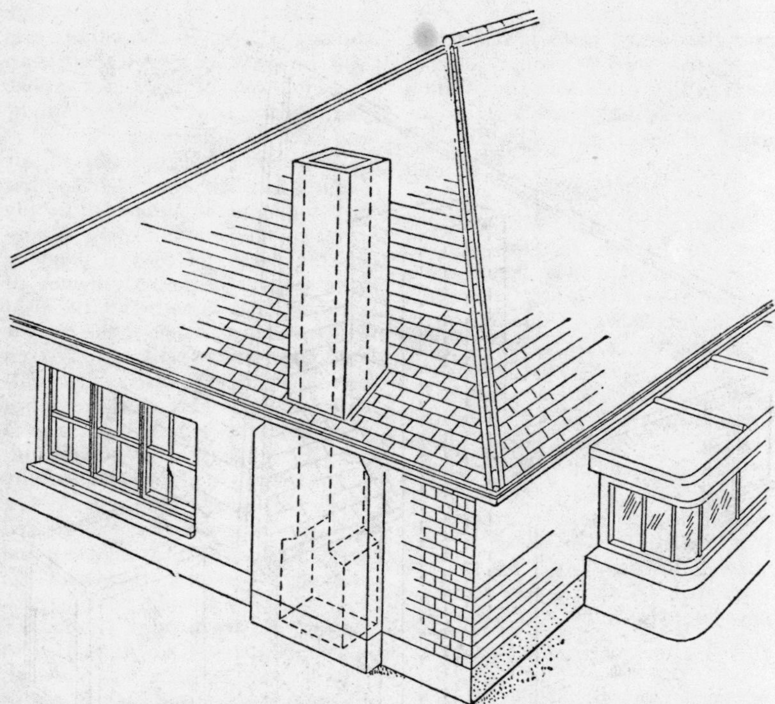

Fig. 3. *Chimney stack to bungalow. Course of flue shown in broken line.*

smoke directly we feed it more fuel, for the air, in passing through the glowing fuel-bed below, has yielded up much of its oxygen and there is not enough oxygen near the top of the fire to promote complete combustion of the new charge of fuel.

Furnace grates of large installations are often of the sort in which the fuel is fed at the bottom of the fire, thus avoiding this drawback; smoking is further prevented by a rigid control of the air supply. In the domestic fireplace it is impossilbe to ensure uniform conditions, and the fire alternates between a condition in which combustion is imperfect and one in which the entire mass of fuel is burning brightly and practically without smoke. (So-called smokeless fuels are dealt with later.)

Flues and Chimneys

These should have easy bends and be free from sharp angles. The inside should be smoothly "parged" (lined with mortar), both as a good fire-protection and to offer a smooth surface to the flue gases. The stack should come up clear of any ridge or other portion of a roof, or else air eddies may cause down-draught and smoking of the fire. The use of a cowl may ameliorate a faulty condition, but these devices would be rendered unnecessary in most cases if the building were

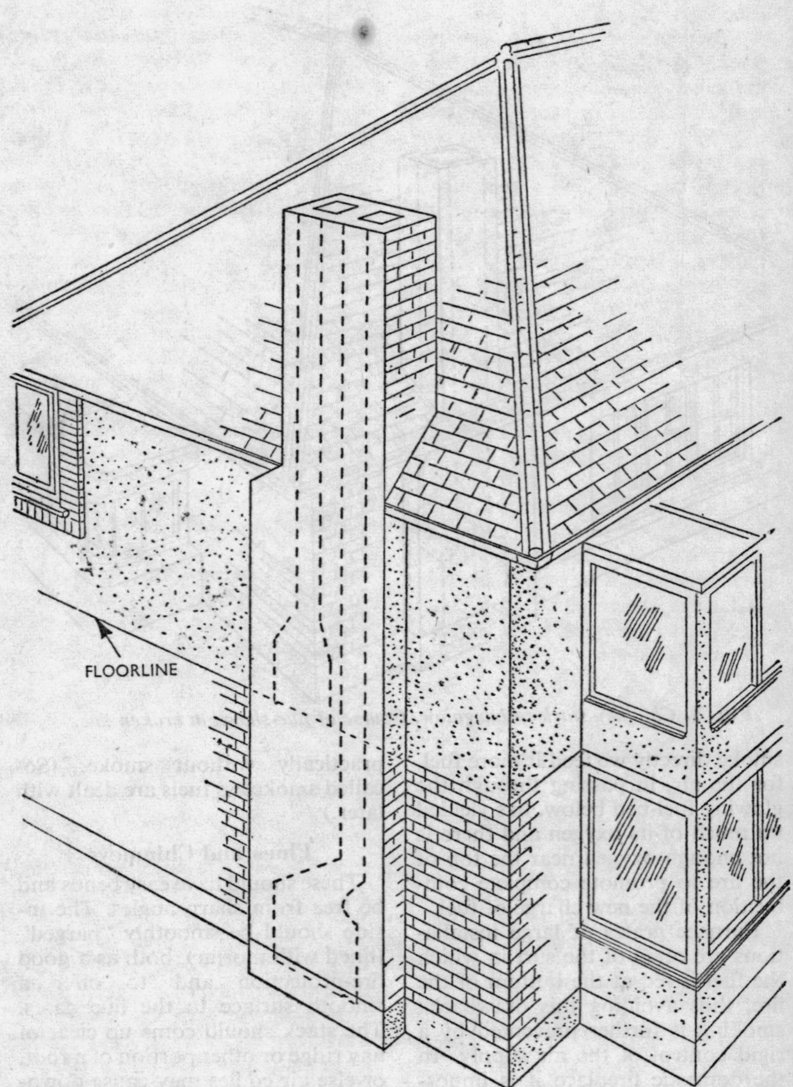

Fig. 4. *Chimney flues in two-storey villa, showing how flues are gathered over in an easy bend where necessary. The shape of the lower fireplace is shown in Fig. 5 (p. 485). For modern fires and fireplaces straight chimneys are satisfactory, as the "fireback" provides a baffle. Cowls should generally be unnecessary in a properly planned building, though they may be found useful if defects develop later.*

properly planned and constructed. (See Figs. 3 and 4.)

Where there are two or more flues in a single stack they must be gathered over as shown in Fig. 4, and some flues must thus have bends in them. But unnecessary bends should be avoided, as they restrict the free passage of the gases up the chimney. There is a prevalent idea that bends prevent down-draught: they may lessen it, but they also, in the same measure, diminish the up-draught. The true shape of a fireplace and flue-mouth is shown in Fig. 5.

The chimney should be used only for the fireplace or stove for which it was built; to connect an additional stove or boiler may result in inefficient working of the original or of the additional appliance. Chimneys should be swept regularly, and as often as necessary: the frequency will depend on the amount of use, but a much-used chimney should be seen to every three months, or else the effective diameter will be much reduced by accumulations of soot, to say nothing of the risk and nuisance of a chimney-fire. When a stack is used for a closed stove or a boiler, with connection by a stove-pipe, see that the stack is provided with a proper soot-door (see Fig. 12, Lesson 6), or else the chimney sweep will not be able to get his brushes into the flue opening. In cases where a stove or boiler is to be set in the place formerly occupied by a kitchen range, the chimney-mouth may be too big for efficient functioning of the new appliance, and may need bricking up to narrow it. Most builders employ a man who is skilled in work of this sort and understands the requirements of most sorts of appliance.

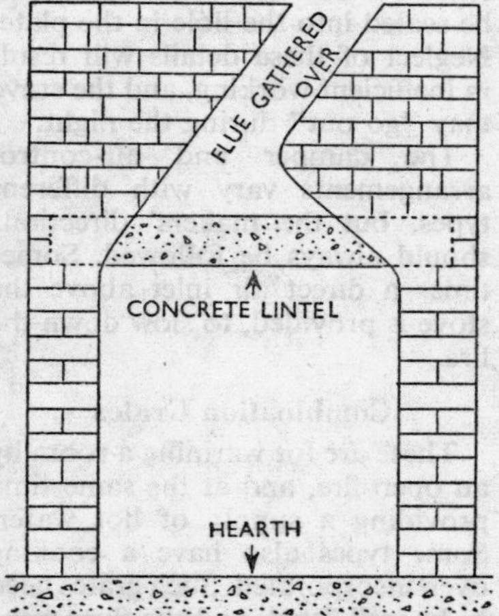

Fig. 5. *True shape of a flue and fireplace; being lower fireplace in Fig.* 4.

Stoves

The principle of stoves is explained by Fig. 6, which shows a simple type which is efficient and economical for warming schools, work-rooms, halls and other places where its plain appearance is not a disadvantage. It works on the slow-combustion principle, like the open fire described above, but here the ingress of air is much more under control and the entire combustion chamber is enclosed. When starting the fire, plenty of air is admitted, but later the supply is cut down until a slow and steady rate of burning is attained. The stove will burn for some hours on one charge of coke, and requires little attention.

A "smokeless" fuel such as coke or anthracite must be used in closed stoves, though a little ordinary coal may be used to start a coke-stove. Ornamental stoves such as those designed to burn 24 hours on one stoking (Fig. 7) are fed with anthracite, which takes up much less space for a given weight than does coke. In principle these stoves resemble the simple type shown in Fig. 6, though many have translucent mica-panelled front doors through which the cheery glow of the fire can be seen. Dampers and a shaker grate (the latter enabling the ashes to be cleared from the fuel bed without opening the doors) are provided. The fuel is fed in usually from a conical hod whose mouth fits the nozzle at the top part of the stove.

Fitting Stoves

All stoves depend on a properly controlled air supply, and the air which goes into the chimney flue must come through the stove. Thus the pipe must be sealed into the plate where it enters a fireplace, or into the brickwork of the chimney breast.

Where an ordinary grate has been converted to take—for example—an anthracite stove, the fireplace opening is usually closed by a sheet-iron plate in which an aperture has been made to take the outlet from the stove. This plate must be properly fixed so that the joints are gas-tight, and the nozzle of the stove outlet must fit properly and be sealed into the hole in the plate. Neglect of these details will result in inefficient working, and the stove may "go out" during the night.

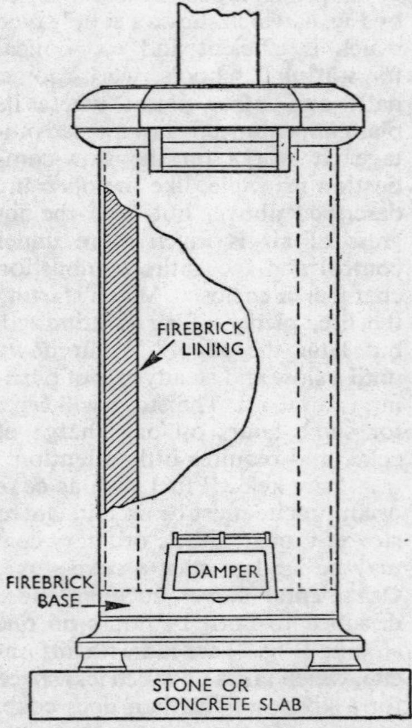

Fig. 6. *Simple slow-combustion stove.*

Fig. 7. *Anthracite stove, with a heating capacity of* 2,500 *square feet.*

The damper and air-control arrangements vary with different types, but the makers' directions should always be followed. Sometimes a direct air inlet above the stove is provided, to slow down the fire.

Combination Grates

These are for warming a room by an open fire, and at the same time providing a supply of hot water. Some types also have a cooking oven incorporated. Such grates need to be well fitted, and the flues must be kept clean and free from soot.

When the damper is set to direct

the hot gases and flames over the surface of the boiler (above and behind the fire), heat is abstracted that would otherwise go to warm the room. If both functions are to be performed equally well, more fuel must be burned than would be needed for (*a*) simply warming the room, or (*b*) heating the water. None the less, such combined grates do make use of heat that would otherwise be wasted, and serve an excellent purpose where the duty of water heating is not too heavy. Any special instructions issued by the makers should be carefully followed, both for fixing and for fuel and maintenance.

Self Testing Questions

(1) *Mention two main points in which the closed stove differs from the open fire.*

(2) *A chimney or a flue is often said to "draw" the fire and we loosely speak of the "pull" created by a chimney. How is the upward movement of air brought about?*

(3) *A tall chimney creates more "draught" through the fire than a shorter one. Why is this?*

THE ANSWERS ARE ON PAGE 499.

LESSON 5

Gas Fires and Electric Heaters

RECENT years have seen many improvements in the design of gas fires. The "radiants" have been altered in shape so that they are raised to a glowing heat by a smaller consumption of gas, and so that they project their heat in a better manner. An ordinary chimney is not necessary, and indeed may be a disadvantage, but—except for certain "flueless" types—a proper flue *must* be provided. This flue can be contrived in the thickness of the wall itself, by the building in of special flue blocks instead of bricks. A flue for a single fire can be accommodated in the thickness of a 4½-in. brick wall, and two flues back to back can be built in a 9-in. wall, so that a fire can be fitted on each side of the wall. Panel gas fires may be set into a cavity prepared in the wall, doing away with the usual mantel and hearth arrangement and saving space. The pipes are concealed, and only the operating tap is visible. Self-lighting devices are obtainable, so that turning on the gas is sufficient to ignite the fire.

When a gas fire is to be used in place of an ordinary open fire the chimney must first be swept clean. The fireplace opening should be closed with a sheet-iron plate, or filled in with brick and tiles so that only the small opening to take the outlet nozzle of the fire is left. But in old houses, where the flue is likely to become choked by fallen brick or mortar from the joints of the brickwork, it is best to leave a somewhat larger opening for access in case of need, and to fill in this with an iron plate having an aperture for the nozzle.

Heat Output of Gas Fires

The calorific value of gas (*i.e.* amount of heat produced when 1 cu. ft. is burned) varies in different districts, though the price charged (per therm) has been standardised by law. See Lesson 7 for an explanation of the basis for charging. Usually the calorific value (C.V.) is about 500 B.Th.U. The heat output of a fire will vary with the C.V. of the gas supplied, but an approximate figure can be obtained. Two types of element or "radiant" are used in gas fires: the column and the brick. The first will consume 3–4½ cu. ft. per hour; the second will take 10 cu. ft. per hour, and was designed to give the same heat output as an electric heating element rated at 1 kilowatt.

Controlling Heat Output

When warming up a room more heat is needed at the outset than is required to maintain a comfortable temperature later; a gas fire of ample capacity should be installed, having a separate control which will shut off some of the radiants at need: thus all are used at the beginning, and then some are cut out when the room has become warm. The efficiency of a modern gas fire is about 70 per cent, and as a large proportion—over 50 per cent—of the heat emitted is in the radiant form, the appliance soon produces "comfort" conditions after being lighted.

Electric Fires

Portable *electric fires* are convenient for occasional use where some other source of heat is generally used; and wherever there is a suitable plug outlet a fire can be plugged in when needed. But for regular use a built-in panel fire is preferable, since the trailing flexible—always a potential danger point—is done away with.

Electric heater panels may be provided as part of the suite of an open fire-grate, placed at the sides of the fireplace some 18 in. above floor level. Similar panels, with a larger output, can be built into the walls, giving out their heat at a convenient level. There is no reason why the heating apparatus should be at the hearth level—a position inherited from the open fire.

Types of Element

The ordinary element consists of a resistance wire secured to a shaped fireclay block and made red hot by the current flow. It is made up in bars or units having a rating of 1 kilowatt. Apart from this there are the special elements used in reflector fires; the wire is wound around a fireclay or porcelain rod or tube which itself becomes heated.

The smallest size of fire will consist of one element or bar, controlled from the room switch. Larger ones, rated at 2 or 3 kilowatts, will have one or two switches on the appliance itself; it will be noticed, in the case of portable fires, that after these have been switched off, one or more of the fire-bars will still be "alight": this is a safety precaution to ensure that the fire is switched off at the plug switch, so that the flexible is not left "live." At least one of the bars is always connected across the main terminals of the fire for this reason. "Points" are sometimes so constructed that they cannot be switched on till the fire is plugged in.

The electric fire is 100 per cent efficient, since there is no combustion and all the heat energy of the current is made available by the incandescent element. Some 60 per cent is delivered as radiant heat and the rest as convected. Unlike the gas fire provided with a flue, the electric fire does not ventilate a room: ventilation and air movement must be obtained by other means.

It can be accepted that a 2-kilowatt fire will warm 2,000 cu. ft. of room-space, but since (as explained above in dealing with gas fires) more warmth will be needed at first, a three-bar (3-kilowatt) fire would be installed in a room of this capacity, and all three units switched on at first; later one could be switched off. Many portable fires are made and used which have a loading of only 1 kilowatt; this is the safe limit for use on an ordinary lighting circuit, and larger appliances should be connected only to a proper heating circuit.

Safety Hints

Never connect a portable fire together with some other appliance (a radio set, for instance) to the same outlet by means of an "adaptor" so that the plug switch controls both; the fire while out of use may be left near a table, the wall or a chair, and someone going into the room to turn on the radio may forget about the fire and thus switch on both, with risk of fire.

Take care that the flexible is not left in the line of the fire, so that it is burnt or weakened by the heat.

Wires and Skirting Outlets

Renew all flexibles when worn or frayed, or when they appear brittle to the touch. The latter is a sign that the insulation has become perished.

Some skirting outlets are "live" always—a system not to be recommended—and have no separate controlling switch. In such cases be careful the fingers do not touch the pins of the plug in inserting or withdrawing it. Always switch off before withdrawing the plug, when a switch is provided to the outlet.

If a member of the household is unfortunate enough to receive an electric shock, the following points should be remembered in going to his assistance. Immediately switch off the electric current. Failure to do so may result in your receiving a shock when you touch the victim. If a person, however, is in contact with a live wire and you are unable to switch off the current, snatch up a rubber waterproof, rug, walking-stick, or any article that will afford you some protection in pulling the shocked person away from the source of danger. When you have managed to do this treat the patient for shock, if necessary resorting first to artificial respiration.

Self Testing Questions

(1) *The dining-room of the bungalow which forms the subject of Fig.* 8, *Lesson* 6, *is intended to be warmed by a radiator during the cold season, and therefore has no fireplace. Suppose we desired to warm it occasionally by an electric fire, what ought to be the loading of the fire? The ceiling height is* 9 *ft.; other dimensions of the room are given in Fig.* 8.

(2) *Referring to Fig.* 11, *Lesson* 6, *estimate what size of portable electric fire would be needed for occasional warming of the smaller bedroom of the bungalow?*

(3) *The dining-room of the bungalow is supposed to be provided with a fixed (panel) gas fire for use when the heating boiler is out of action. Assuming a gas fire having "brick" type radiants (stated above to have an outlet equivalent to one* 1-*kw. bar of an electric fire), how many brick units would be necessary adequately to warm the room?*

THE ANSWERS ARE ON PAGE 500.

LESSON 6

Warming a Small House by Hot Water

THE method of calculating the amount of heat required has been explained in Lesson 2. It is, of course, the amount lost through the walls, floor, ceiling, doors and windows of the room or building in question. Such calculations must be made for every individual heating installation, and there is no short cut—though, of course, an approximation can be made by reference to a similar job whose details have already been established. Then there is the heat needed to warm the incoming air according to the number of air changes to be provided for.

In the present course little can be done beyond outlining methods of calculation, for which the diagrams of part of a bungalow (Figs. 8 and 9) are included. They show different types of room, some with more window than others, and illustrate typical construction details as they affect heat-loss considerations. For simplicity a plan of the entire bungalow is included (Fig. 11) to indicate how radiators would be arranged in lounge, dining-room, bedroom and hall. The following is a brief description:

Lounge. This has a wide expanse of window, but is normally kept warm by a fair-sized coal fire. Beneath the window is a radiator for use when the open fire is not desired, or as an alternative source of heat.

Dining-Room. Another fairly large room, with a "window-type" radiator placed beneath the larger window (rear wall). No fireplace, but there is a built-in panel gas fire with a flue in the 9-in. side wall of the house. This room would be used principally for meals, when the gas fire could be lighted to give a cheerful glow and liven up things. Some little while earlier the radiator would have been turned on.

Best Bedroom. A large room with plenty of window expanse. Being a sleeping apartment—though a pleasant one that would tempt the occupants to pass many daylight hours there also—it has only a small fireplace (for occasional use on wintry nights or in time of sickness), and relies on its twin radiators under the windows for most of the time.

Hall. This, with the corridor, is adequately warmed by a radiator in the position shown on the plan.

Hot Water Supply

Domestic hot water is intended to be provided by a separate installation: a gas-fuelled multi-point instantaneous water heater. This is connected to the taps in the bathroom, kitchen and bed-room: the turning of a hot-water tap at any of these points opens the gas-valve of the heater and ensures a supply of hot water.

Although a hot-water supply can be obtained from the heating boiler, it involves complications: usually water must not be taken direct from the boiler-to-radiator circuit, but must be heated indirectly. This

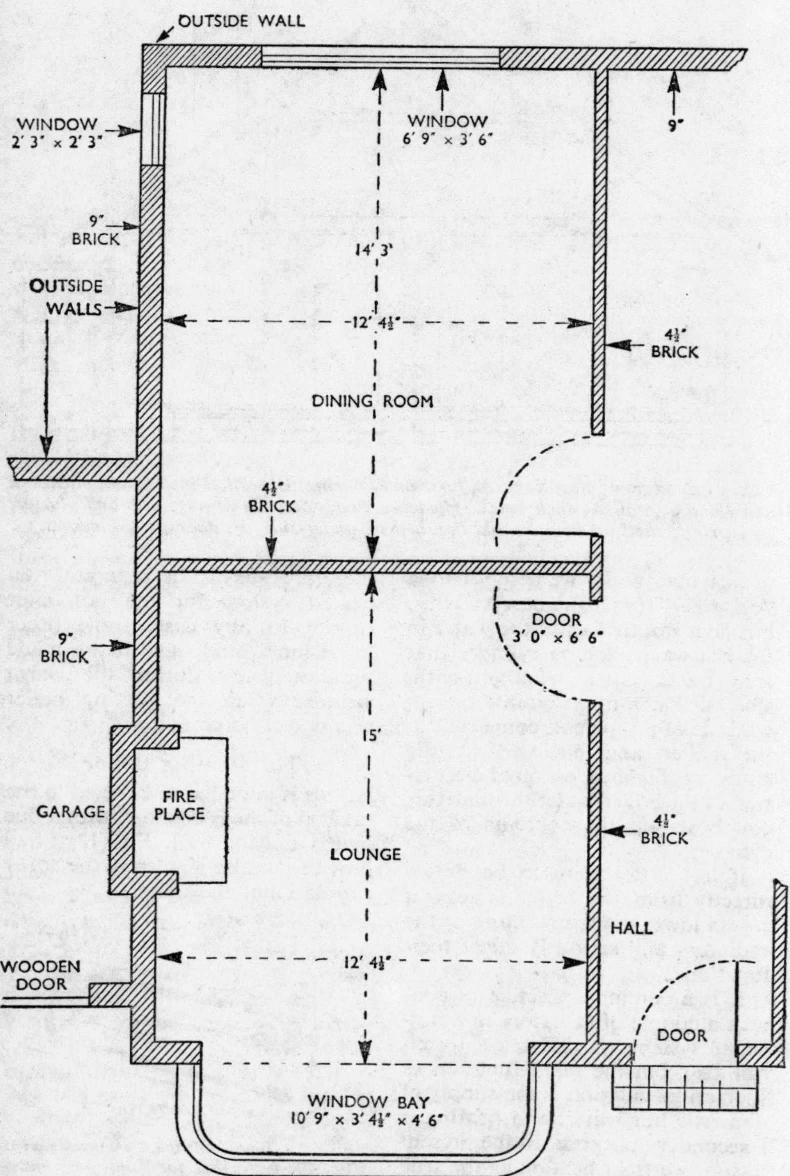

Fig. 8. *Bungalow part plan, showing typical rooms. Compare complete plan in Fig. 11.*

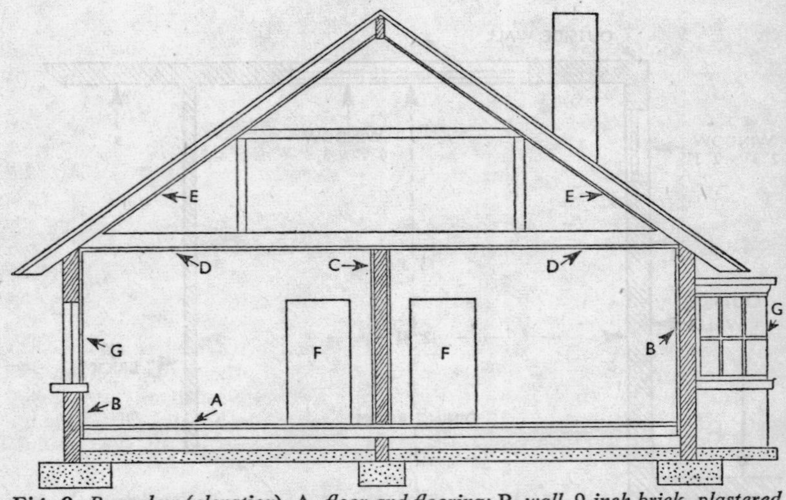

Fig. 9. *Bungalow (elevation).* A, *floor and flooring;* B, *wall, 9-inch brick, plastered one side;* C, *wall* $4\frac{1}{2}$*-inch brick, plastered two sides;* D, *ceiling, lath and plaster;* E, *roof, tiled on boards, and boarded on under-side;* F, *doors;* G, *windows.*

means that boiler-water goes to a "calorifier" (Fig. 10), where it warms, but does not mix with, the water in the hot-water storage cylinder that feeds the taps at the sink and bath. The calorifier in its simplest form consists of a pipe coil connected to the boiler and enclosed in the storage cylinder. Continual circulation of the boiler-water through this coil heats up the contents of the cylinder.

If hot water were to be drawn directly from the boiler system, it would lower the temperature of the radiators and seriously affect their functions.

It is a common practice to connect a couple of radiators to a hot-water system, or perhaps a towel-rail also, but the main function of such an installation is the supply of domestic hot water, and heating is a secondary purpose. In the present lesson, we treat heating as the true function of the installation, and therefore suggest a separate gas-heated system for the hot-water supply. In any case, some other provision would have to be made for hot water during the warm weather when the heating boiler was out of commission.

The Heating Boiler

This is intended to be fixed in the kitchen of the bungalow, with a flue in the outside wall. Fig. 12 shows how the smoke-pipe from the boiler should enter the chimney, with an

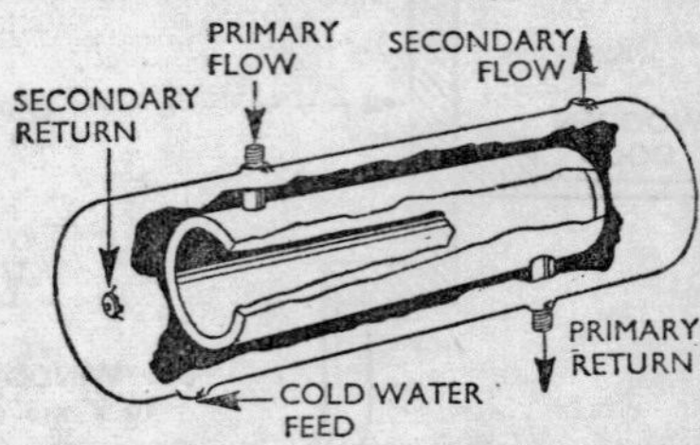

Fig. 10. *Calorifier for "indirect" heating of domestic hot water supplies.*

easy bend, flush with the inside of the flue. The soot-door is most important; also the drop below the point of entry, so that the soot may fall clear of the stove-pipe. The size of the boiler must be selected according to the duty to be performed. There are two main types: the "firepot" (Fig. 13), and the sectional boiler (Fig. 14). In the first, the water is contained in jackets around the combustion chamber and the ash-pit; the second type is built up from a number of sections, somewhat in the same manner as a radiator, and a much greater water-heating surface is in contact with the flames and the hot gases.

Pipes are run in the roof and beneath the floor to and from the various radiators, and are protected by insulating material where no heat emission is desired. The main flow-pipe runs to the roof, and so through the roof-space to the points where it drops to the radiators. In the roof the pipes are not insulated, since the heat given off there helps to warm that part of the building and lessen the heat loss from the rooms. The size of the pipes has to be calculated very carefully by the engineer, so that the requisite amount of water is passed to the radiators to give out the necessary amount of heat. When

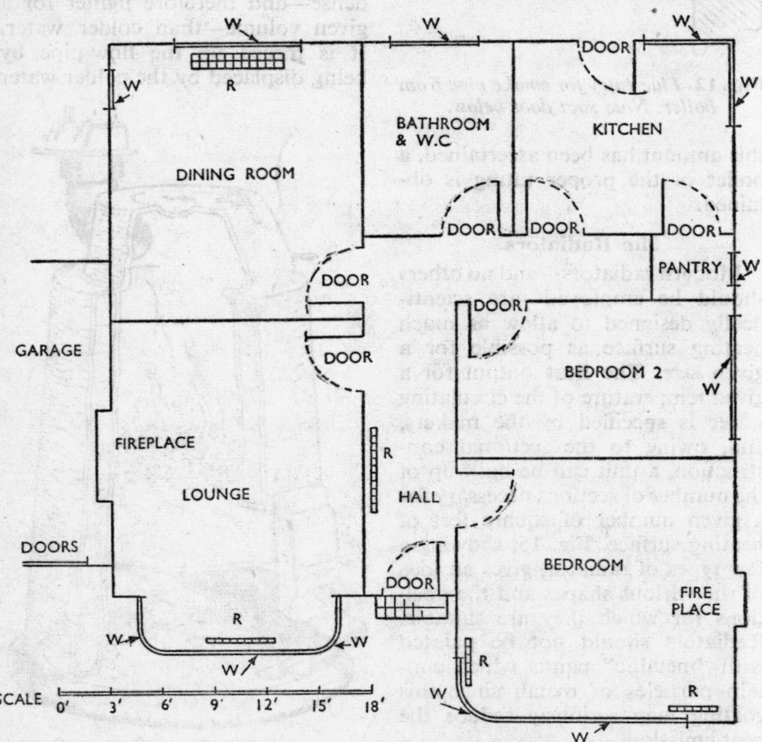

Fig. 11. *Sketch plan of bungalow, to show where radiators should be sited.*

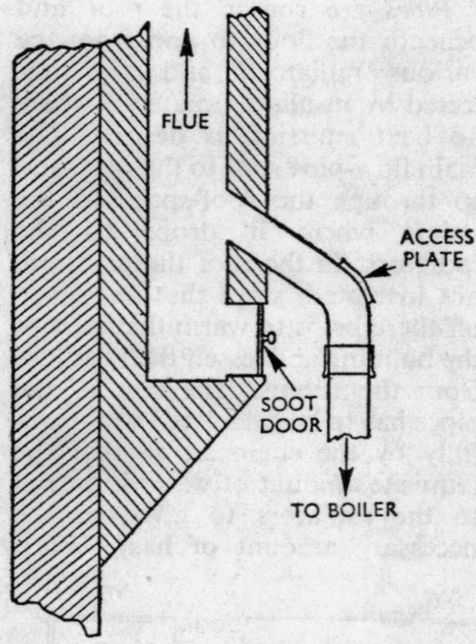

Fig. 12. *Flue entry for smoke pipe from boiler. Note soot door below.*

this amount has been ascertained, a boiler of the proper rating is obtained.

The Radiators

Modern radiators—and no others should be employed—are scientifically designed to allow as much heating surface as possible for a given size. The heat output for a given temperature of the circulating water is specified by the makers, and, owing to the sectional construction, a unit can be built up of the number of sections necessary for a given number of square feet of heating surface. Fig. 15, showing a few types of radiator, gives an idea of the various shapes and the positions for which they are suitable. Radiators should not be painted with "metallic" paints which contain particles of metal, since this coating may seriously reduce the heat emission.

It must be emphasised that the entire matter of a boiler, piping and radiators is one for the heating engineer to settle: it demands a full knowledge of theory and a wide practical experience to design a satisfactory system.

Circulation Pressure

The circulation pressure is derived from gravity and depends upon the comparatively small difference in density between a column of water at, say, 180° Fahrenheit and a similar column at 140° F. The rising column is lighter, and the descending column is heavier. As explained earlier, water after being warmed in the boiler becomes less dense—and therefore lighter for a given volume—than colder water. It is forced up the flow-pipe by being displaced by the colder water

IDEAL BOILERS & RADIATORS, LTD.

Fig. 13. *Firepot type boiler in section.*

coming into the boiler, and so a circulation is established.

If a heating system is to be kept in use during frosty weather, the radiators should be left open, so that hot water circulates through the entire system. But if the boiler is to be put out of commission—say, when the house is to be left vacant for a time—the system should be emptied of water. The cold rising main to the feed-tank must, of course, be protected in the usual manner against frost.

Central Heating Boiler Fuels

Coke or a semi-anthracite are the fuels most commonly in use for central heating, since they are "smokeless." Coke is lighter for a given volume, and takes up more space than an anthracitic coal, weight for weight. Also, unless of first-class quality and "clean," it gives more trouble by the proportion of non-combustible foreign substance present with it. Ordinary "bituminous" coal, as used for open fires, is not suitable for boilers. The coke or anthracite should be broken to a size of about 1–2¼ in.

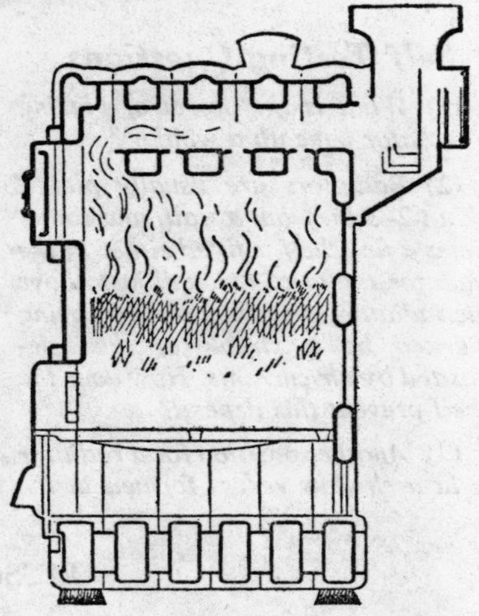

IDEAL BOILERS & RADIATORS, LTD.

Fig. 14. *Boiler of sectional type.*

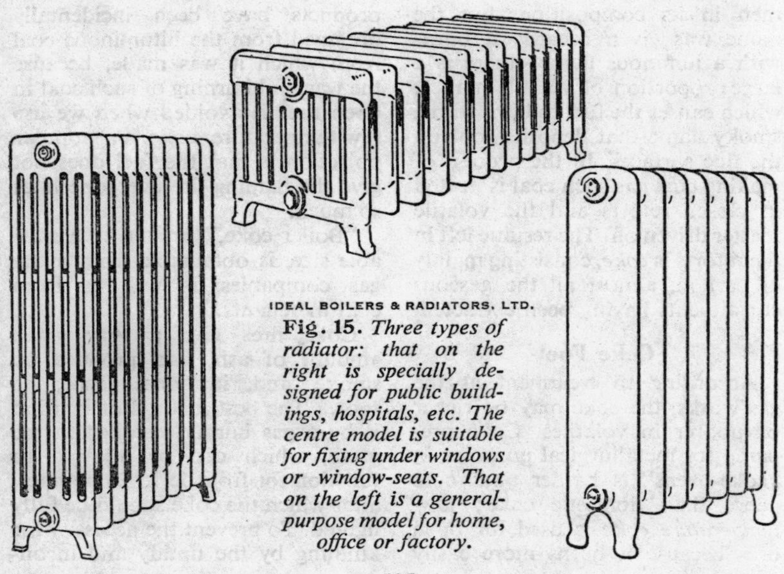

IDEAL BOILERS & RADIATORS, LTD.

Fig. 15. *Three types of radiator: that on the right is specially designed for public buildings, hospitals, etc. The centre model is suitable for fixing under windows or window-seats. That on the left is a general-purpose model for home, office or factory.*

Self Testing Questions

(1) *What is the object of placing a radiator beneath a window?*

(2) *Radiators are usually placed about 2–3 in. from a wall, and sometimes a flat shelf is fixed either to the radiator top or to the wall just above the radiator, to prevent the wall being marked by a streak of dust deposited by air currents. How does the shelf prevent this deposit?*

(3) *Another position for a radiator is in a shallow recess formed in the wall. What effect does this have on the air stream?*

(4) *Sometimes a radiator is placed in front of an air grating formed in the wall at a few inches above the floor level. The lower front part and the upper rear portion of the radiator are closed in by baffle plates. What is the effect of this arrangement?*

(5) *What is the source of the circulation pressure in a radiator system?*

(6) *What is the difference between a sectional and a firepot boiler?*

THE ANSWERS ARE ON PAGE 500.

LESSON 7

Heating and Ventilating Data

THE various fuels with which we are concerned include (*a*) "bituminous" coals, (*b*) anthracite and similar coals, and (*c*) coke. In *bituminous coal*—there is no bitumen in its composition, but the name was given because it burns with a luminous flame—there is a large proportion of volatile matter, which causes the fuel to burn with a smoky flame that deposits soot on the flue surfaces. In the process of making coal gas such coal is heated in closed retorts and the volatile matter driven off. The residue left in the retorts is *coke*, consisting mainly of carbon, almost all the gaseous constituents having been extracted.

Coke Fuel

According to treatment at the gas-works, the coke may be richer or poorer in volatiles. Coke prepared for metallurgical purposes in "coke-ovens" is harder and more dense than domestic coke; *low-temperature coke* is used for open fires because it burns more easily than ordinary coke, having more volatiles in its composition. It is generally recommended on economic grounds because it is "smokeless" and, since many valuable by-products have been incidentally obtained from the bituminous coal from which it was made, because the wasteful burning of such coal in open fires is avoided when we use low-temperature coke. A popular objection is that the fuel does not give the flaming fire everyone likes so much.

"Boiler coke," broken to a suitable size, is obtainable from many gas companies as well as from coal merchants.

Coke fires give a very small amount of ash, and produce no smoke, and, in consequence, no soot. The best method of ignition is by a gas burner installed in the grate, which can be allowed to function for from 15 to 20 minutes, after which the coke should be fully lighted. To prevent the necessity for kindling by the untidy and incon-

FUEL	CALORIFIC VALUE (B.TH.U.)	CARBON, PER CENT.	VOLATILES, PER CENT.
Bituminous Coal .	12,000–14,000	50–70	20–40
Anthracite . .	15,000	85–90	up to 8
Semi-anthracites .	14,000	75	about 14
Coke . . .	12,500	75–85	—

COMPOSITION OF SOLID FUELS

venient method of paper and wood, the similar device of the "gas poker" —a rigid rod, fitted with gas burners, attached by flexible tubing to a gas point in the floor near the fire—is now frequently installed for use with ordinary coke fires. The "poker" is thrust among the coals and the burners lighted, the poker being withdrawn as soon as complete kindling is effected.

Anthracite and Semi-Anthracite

Anthracite is the best fuel for the closed slow-combustion stoves fixed in living-rooms and sitting-rooms, and a good-quality fuel will avoid any trouble in the use of these appliances. Semi-anthracites are largely used for boiler fuel, some being sold under various fancy names. The merchant should always be informed of the intended use of the fuel, as one which would do for a warming stove might not be suitable for a boiler. Such fuels are not suited for ordinary open grates, as they require a controlled draught. Anthracite, like coke, is mainly composed of carbon, and its content of volatile matter is low. Semi-anthracites have a larger percentage but less than bituminous coals.

Heat Units

The *B.Th.U.* is the amount of heat required to raise the temperature of one pound of water through one degree Fahrenheit. The *Gram-Calorie* (metric unit) is the amount of heat that will raise the temperature of one gram of water one degree Centigrade. The *Kilo-Calorie* is the amount of heat required to raise one kilogramme of water one degree Centigrade. 1 B.Th.U. is equal to 252 gram-calories. The *Therm* is equal to 100,000 B.Th.U., and is used in the sale of town's gas. The gas undertaking has to declare the C.V. of its gas, and since gas is measured by volume in a meter, the amount of gas to one therm will vary with the C.V. Assume a declared C.V. to be 500, the number of therms for a given meter reading is found as follows:

$$\frac{\text{Number of cubic feet} \times \text{C.V. } 500}{100{,}000} = \text{Number of therms.}$$

The declared C.V. is the amount of heat given off when one cubic foot of the gas is burned completely.

In all rooms having a fireplace and a chimney ample *ventilation* will be provided for normal circumstances by the natural flow of warmed air up the chimney and the entry of cooler air through various apertures to take its place. Even when the room is not being warmed artificially, the air inside it will be warmer than that outside the building, and so there is usually a sufficient difference in air density to set up the circulation desired. Cracks and chinks in floors, at doorways and around window-frames suffice to permit ingress of fresh air; moreover, beneath the floor there are air-gratings in the wall, and unless the floor is completely covered a large amount of air enters this way.

Cross Ventilation

Windows can be opened to allow a cross ventilation, when necessary, and it is seldom in domestic houses that anything more than this is required. In hot or stuffy weather a small electric fan can be used to promote air movement, though this will not of itself induce fresh air into the room. For the latter purpose a fan with a casing opening on to the outside of the building is needed, and a simple and inexpensive type is made to fit in a circular hole in the window pane. A device of this sort expels air from the room and thus automatically allows more to come in to take its place.

Although the water in a hot-water boiler is not under pressure like that in a steam boiler, since the water must not be allowed to get hot enough to boil, it is under some pressure on account of the hydrostatic head due to the elevated feed-tank and the pipe connecting this with the boiler system. For every foot of height above the boiler water-level a pressure of 0·433 pounds per square in. is exerted by the water column. If the feed-tank water-level is 15 ft. above the boiler level, the pressure on the boiler will be $0{\cdot}433 \times 15 = 6{\cdot}49$ pounds per square in. of surface, at a temperature of 62° Fahrenheit (this temperature is commonly taken as the datum). The depth of water in the boiler is not taken into account in this simple illustration. A safety-valve, if fitted on the boiler, would have to be adjusted to open at a higher pressure than this, or water would escape from it. Often enough the valve is omitted, and reliance is placed instead on the vent-pipe (see Lesson 3) which terminates with a down-turned end over the feed and expansion tank. Undue pressure in the system would force water up the pipe, to escape from its end.

It has already been shown that water in being heated to a higher temperature takes up heat in the boiler from the fuel; from the definition of the B.Th.U. given earlier we know that when one pound of water is heated by one degree F. it thus absorbs an amount of heat equal to one B.Th.U. Upon cooling in the pipes and radiators, this same water will give up some of its heat in the same ratio, according to the temperature drop. Usually a drop of 180 (flow-pipe) to 140 degrees F. (return-pipe) is reckoned for, giving 40 B.Th.U. emission for each pound of water circulated.

Self Testing Questions

(1) *Other things being equal, what is the chief advantage of a semi-anthracite over coke as a boiler fuel (domestic installations).*

(2) *From Table on p.* 497 *choose a fuel suitable for open fires.*

(3) *A gas meter shows a consumption of* 3,900 *cu.ft. How many therms does this represent, with a gas of C.V.* 500?

(4) *What will be the pressure on a square boiler, each side measuring* 9 *in., which is situated* 37 *ft. below the level of the water-tank from which it receives the supply? Neglect the depth of the water in the boiler.*

(5) *What happens when excessive pressure occurs in a hot-water boiler which has no safety-valve?*

THE ANSWERS ARE ON PAGE 500.

Answers to Self Testing Questions

LESSON 1

(1) Owing to the heat generated by the body the room becomes warmer, and so must be cooled by the admission of outside air.

(2) Radiation, convection and conduction.

(3) Heat rays from the sun warm the body without warming the intervening air; on account of its lack of colour, the snow absorbs little heat, and so is not melted away to a great extent until the weather becomes much warmer.

LESSON 2

(1) Cubic content of room = 14 ft. × 9 ft. × 9ft. = 1,134 cu. ft.; 1,134 × 2 air changes = 2,268; 2,268 × 0·2 (B.Th.U.) = 453·6 B.Th.U.

(2) Entire wall has an area of 14 ft. × 9 ft. = 126 sq. ft.; Window has an area of 9 ft. × 4 ft. = 36 sq. ft.

Heat loss is (*a*) wall less window area, 90 sq. ft. @ 0·34; (*b*) window area, 36 sq. ft. @ 1·00.

Total heat loss is thus:
(*a*) 90 × 0·34 = 30·6 B.Th.U.
(*b*) 36 × 1·00 = 36 B.Th.U.
= 66·6 B.Th.U. per degree F.

(3) Ceiling area is 14 ft. × 9 ft. = 126 sq. ft.; 126 × factor 0·17 B.Th.U. = 21·42 B.Th.U. per degree F. difference.

LESSON 3

(1) Open fire gives mostly radiant heat, but wastes much of its warmth in the flue and chimney. Stove gives mostly convected heat, and is much more efficient as a heater.

(2) Gas fire burns some oxygen of the air, and unless properly ventilated may vitiate the atmosphere; on the other hand, it assists ventilation of the room by inducing an air current up its flue. The electric fire does not consume oxygen, but does not assist ventilation, since it has no flue.

(3) The hotter water, being lighter than cold water already in the tank, is displaced upward, and thus sets up a circulation which goes on until all the water has been warmed.

LESSON 4

(1) The draught of the stove is regulated closely by means of the damper, and the rate of combustion is thereby controlled. Little control is possible with an open fire. Further, the flue gases from the stove pass through the smoke pipe before entering the chimney, and so help to warm the room; the stove is set in the room and gives out its warmth all around.

(2) Upward air movement in a chimney is brought about by displacement of the warmed air by cooler air in the room, such cooler air being denser (and heavier for a given volume).

(3) In a tall chimney there is a longer column of warmer and lighter air than in a short chimney of the same cross-sectional area; thus there is a greater pressure difference

at the base of the chimney than would be the case with a shorter stack having the same section.

LESSON 5

(1) Cubic capacity of the dining-room is a little under 1,600 cu. ft. Therefore use a 3-kw. electric fire, having a switch by which one heating bar or unit could be cut out after the room had been warmed up from cold.

(2) The cubic capacity of the small bedroom is about 1,300 cu. ft. Therefore use a 2-kw. electric fire which could be run all-out at first and later cut down to 1-kw. by switching off one bar or unit.

(3) Fit a gas fire having three "brick" units.

LESSON 6

(1) To equalise the warming by placing the radiator at a place which is normally somewhat colder than the rest of the room.

(2) The shelf deflects the air current from the wall and diverts it outward into the room.

(3) The recessed formation promotes an outward current at the top of the radiator in a similar manner to the shelf mentioned in the previous question.

(4) The incoming air is constrained to pass over and between the hot sections of the radiator before entering the room, and is thus warmed; a ventilating effect is obtained, in conjunction with a suitable air outlet at a higher level in one of the other walls of the room.

(5) It depends on the difference in density between the two columns of water at differing temperatures: the cooler descending column is heavier than the warmer rising column, and is forced up the flow-pipe by reason of its displacement by the colder water entering the boiler.

(6) The former is built up in sections not unlike those of a radiator, so that a large water-heating surface is in contact with the flames and hot gases; in the latter the water is contained in jackets surrounding the combustion chamber and the ashpit.

LESSON 7

(1) Since anthracite is denser than coke, and takes up less room for a given weight of fuel, the boiler fire need not be fed so often as in the case of coke.

(2) A bituminous coal is suitable for the open grate; coke or anthracite require a controlled draught for satisfactory burning, though coke mixed with small coal may be used for open fires.

(3) The answer is:

$$\frac{3{,}900 \times 500}{100{,}000} = 19{\cdot}5 \text{ therms.}$$

(4) The pressure is 0·433 lb. per sq. in. of surface for every foot of height between the boiler and the tank; and the surface of the boiler is 9 × 9 = 81 sq. in.; therefore the total pressure will be 0·433 × 81 × 37 lb. = 1297·701 lb.

(5) Water is forced up the vent-pipe, and escapes from its end which is turned down over the feed and expansion tank.

BOOT AND SHOE REPAIRING

By G. L. Hanley

LESSON 1

Forms of Footwear Construction

Most handymen contemplate at some time or other the repairing of their own and the family's footwear, but although many make attempts, few succeed in making a really worthwhile job of it. Many reasons could be advanced for this, but probably the most general is the lack of any knowledge of the principles of footwear construction. The purpose of this lesson is to provide a summary of that knowledge.

Varieties and Parts

Leather footwear is made in a variety of ways, but the most common varieties are: Welted, Machine-Sewn, and Screwed and Stitched. Some component parts are common to all three; others are used in one or other type alone. The names and purposes of these components should be carefully noted, for they will be constantly referred to in the following lessons. The chief of them are: Upper, Toe-puff, Stiffener, Insole, Bottom filling, Shank, Welt, Middlesole, Outsole, Heel, Top-piece.

The *upper* is the soft flexible material covering the top part of the foot. It is generally lined with light leather or fabric. Inserted between the upper and the lining over the toe and round the back of the heel are the *toe-puff* and the *stiffener* respectively. Their purpose is to support the upper in these regions.

The shoe's foundation is the *insole*, a piece of leather or other material varying in substance according to the type of shoe. It extends throughout the inside of the shoe in direct contact with the bottom of the foot. The *welt* is a narrow strip of flexible leather extending round the front of the shoe from corner to corner of the heel. *Bottom filling* consists of felt, rubber, or a compound of granulated cork, and is used to fill the space between the insole and outsole or middlesole.

Sole Layers

The *shank*, used to stiffen the waist of the shoe, is inserted between the insole and outsole, and is made of leather, leather board, wood, or metal, or of any combination of these materials. *Middlesoles* may be half or full length; they are made of light sole leather, and are used to increase the substance of the shoe's bottom. The *outsole*, the real wearing surface of the shoe, extends from the toe to under the heel. It is generally of stout vegetable-tanned leather, but other popular materials are chrome-tanned leather, pure

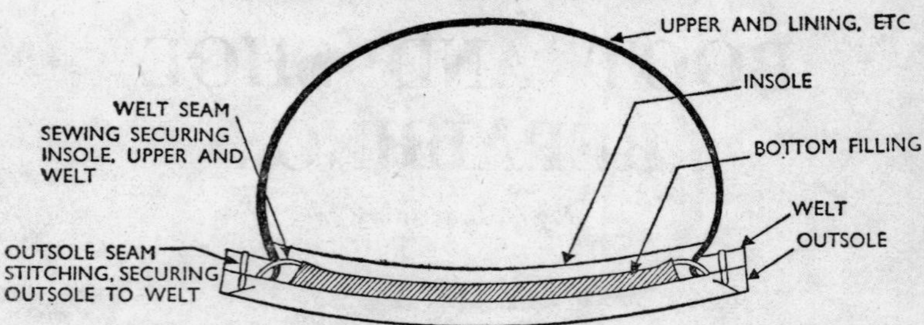

Fig. 1. *Showing details of the welted method of construction.*

plantation crepe rubber, and rubber compounds.

The *heel* may be composed of layers or "lifts" of leather or wood pulp, or may be a solid block of wood. Its purpose is to keep the foot at its correct elevation according to the "pitch" or "spring" of the shoe. It is protected on its wearing surface with the top-piece, which may be of leather or a rubber material, with perhaps a metal tip.

Welted Construction

The welted method of construction (Fig. 1) is the most popular, being unsurpassed for comfort, flexibility and its shape-retaining and wearing qualities. From the diagram it will be seen that the upper with its various constituent parts is pulled over the "feather" or edge of the insole and sewn to the welt and insole with a horizontal seam, which is largely responsible for the flexibility of welted footwear. At the "seat," as the portion of the upper and insole coming under the heel is called, a rather larger amount of upper is pulled over the insole edge and secured with tacks. This method of securing the upper in the seat is common to almost every method of construction and is always used in the three under review. The welt acts as a hinge between the insole and the outsole, and this latter is sewn to it.

The bottom filling and shank are inserted before the attachment of the outsole in the cavity made by the formation of the welt seam. While the outsole is stitched to the welt in front of the heel with a vertical lockstitch seam, it is fastened to the upper and insole at the seat with rivets, this again being common to all three methods. The same can be said of the heel's attachment, which is by nails driven from inside the shoe through insole, upper, and outsole into the heel. The top-piece is attached by a row of slugs or rivets to the surface of the heel.

Machine-Sewn Shoes

A machine-sewn shoe (Fig. 2), in which the welt is dispensed with, is simpler in construction and to repair. The upper is first folded over the edge of the insole to a width of half an inch or so, and secured along its extreme edge to the insole with very small tacks or staples. The space formed between the edges of the upper is then levelled with the bottom filling and the shank is fitted. The outsole and possibly a middlesole are then attached by the Blake sole-sewing machine. This machine sews through all the materials of insole, upper, middlesole and outsole, forming a vertical seam with a chain stitch. This uniting of the different layers

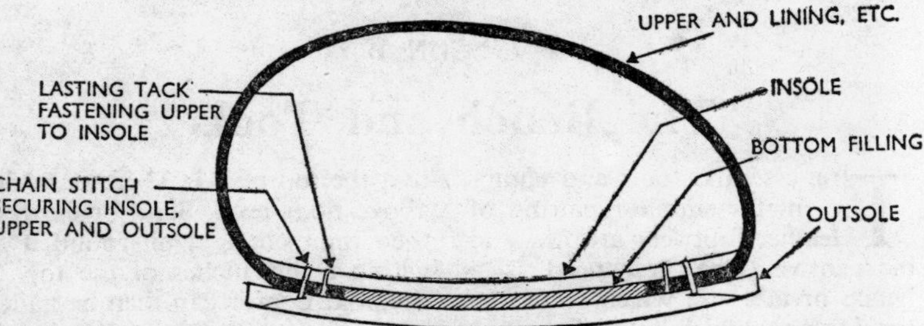

Fig. 2. *Indicating parts of a shoe constructed by the machine-sewn method.*

of materials tends to make this type of shoe somewhat stiffer in comparison with those made by the welted method. Should the heel be of wood, it is usually covered with thin upper leather or celluloid before being attached to the shoe.

Screwed-and-Stitched Shoes

The screwed and stitched method of making (Fig. 3) is essentially for very heavy footwear. The upper is "lasted" on to the insole as with machine-sewn shoes, and the bottom filling and shank are similarly positioned. One or two "through" middlesoles, that is, middlesoles extending right over the bottom of the boot from the toe to the back of the heel, are then temporarily secured with rivets, as is the outsole. All these components are then fastened together to the upper and insole with heavy brass screw wire every inch or less right round the boot and about three-quarters of an inch from the edge of the sole. The through middlesoles and outsole are also secured together with a row of lockstitch stitching round the edge from corner to corner of the heel in the same way as the outsole is attached to the welt in welted footwear.

Many other methods of construction are used by the modern shoe manufacturer, but space will permit a short reference to two only of these: the "veldtschoen" and the "turnshoe." In both cases the outsole is attached direct to the upper without the use of insole, middlesole or welt.

Veldtschoen and Turnshoes

In the first-named the upper is turned outward from the foot or last to form a "welt" and the outsole is sewn to it with a lockstitch, but in turnshoes the shoe is first assembled inside-out and the upper and outsole are secured to each other by a horizontal chain-stitch seam. The last is then slipped and the shoe is "turned" right side out, re-lasted, and the heel attached and finished. Shoes made by either of these methods are extremely flexible, and are for this reason largely employed in the making of slippers and children's footwear; but they are difficult to repair.

Self Testing Questions

(1) *What are the three most common methods of leather footwear construction?*

(2) *What are the principal components of a welted shoe?*

(3) *What components are secured by the welt seam?*

(4) *Explain why a machine-sewn shoe is stiffer than a welted one.*

THE ANSWERS ARE ON PAGE 521.

LESSON 2

The Bench and Tools

THE essential tools and equipment for simple repairing of leather footwear are few and inexpensive. The first need is a bench or table on which to fix the repair stand, which holds the last or hobbing foot. For this the average handyman's bench is suitable, especially if the repair stand can be screwed to it directly over one of the legs, which will afford solidity. If, however, it is desired to reduce noise and vibration to a minimum, and space can be spared, the provision of a special bench is a distinct advantage. This need not be elaborate or take up more than 2 ft. or so of space.

The Working Bench

A strong wooden box about 33 in. long and 20 in. or so square and a piece of heavy timber not less than 6 in.×6 in. and some 30 in. long are the main requirements, but a fairly large barrel or drum can be used instead of the box. The box or barrel is stood on end with the top open, and a few inches of earth or sand placed in the bottom and well rammed down. The piece of timber is then placed upright in the box about 3 or 4 in. from the front, so that the top of it is 33 in. or 34 in. above floor level. Sand or earth is then rammed tight all round it to within a few inches of the top of the box. Boards can then be nailed across the top to form a bench surface for the accommodation of tools, etc., and the repair stand is secured to the top of the upright timber with strong screws or carriage bolts, Fig. 4 explains the principle of the bench.

A fixed repair stand is preferable to the ordinary "triple" last arrangement, for if fitted as suggested it ensures solidity and easy working. Hobbing feet are obtainable in a variety of shapes and sizes, and the family man will require at least one for men's shoes and another for ladies', and possibly one for children's. While a hobbing foot needs to be somewhere near the shape and size of the shoe, it should be small enough to be easily inserted in the shoe.

Shoemaker's Hammer

While any form of hammer can be used, a London pattern shoemaker's hammer will be found to possess features which are advantageous. It has a large well-rounded

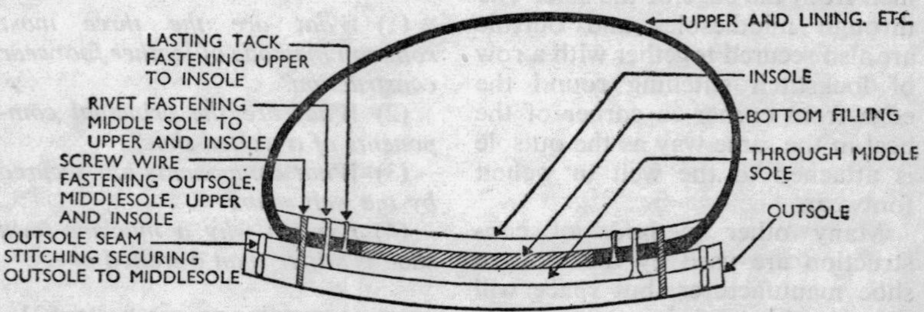

Fig. 3. *Details of the screwed-and-stitched method of shoe construction.*

face which does not damage the work and is suitable for the hammering of the leather. No. 3 is the average size. An old domestic flat-iron with the handle removed makes the best "lap-iron" on which to hammer the leather, though any piece of flat heavy metal will serve the purpose.

The Knife

Shoemakers' knives are too well known to need description, but of the many shapes available the "heel-parer" is the most serviceable, and a good-quality one more than justifies its small additional cost. A "buff-strap" or knife-sharpener is made from a piece of 2 in. × ½ in. wood 15 or 16 in. long. 3 in. or so are shaped to form the handle, and the remainder is padded on both sides with two or three thicknesses of thin leather or one thickness of close felt, such as an old felt hat. This padding should be secured with small rivets, and to one side a strip of fine emery cloth is pasted. A piece of oil-dressed leather or old razor strop is fitted to the other side. The method of sharpening the knife is to lay it flat on the emery with the edge toward the worker and the first finger pressed on it. A stroke is then made away from the body, and at the end of it the knife is turned over and a similar stroke is made toward the body. The blade must be kept flat on the emery as each stroke is made, and when the desired degree of sharpness is secured the knife is stropped on the leather surface in a similar manner.

Pliers and Nippers

A pair of pliers or nippers such as carpenters use are needed for pulling out rivets, etc., and a pair of strong cutting nippers are also useful. For the finishing operations the

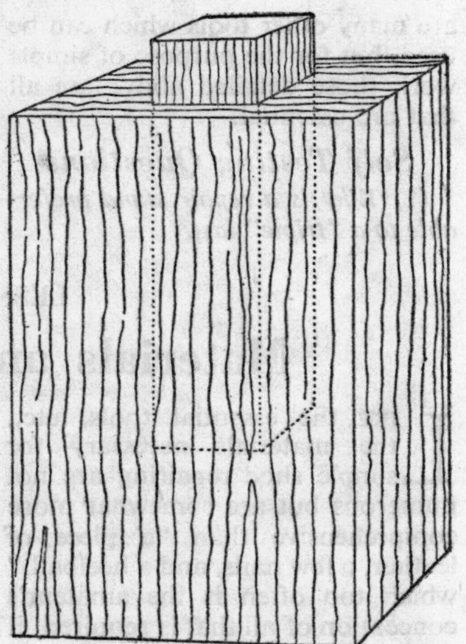

Fig. 4. *An earth or sand-filled shoemaker's bench with projection for repair stand: for construction see text.*

first essential is a shoemaker's rasp, and this should have one side smooth or file-cut and the other rough or rasp-cut. A shoe-scraper which is sharpened to possess a burred edge is generally used after the rasp, but this can be dispensed with in favour of a piece of cleanly broken glass.

Glazing Iron and Awl

A glazing iron with which the edges are burnished and heelball is distributed is the only other essential tool. A "cut-down" glazing iron enables both heel and sole edges to be burnished with the one tool. A 2¾-in. or 2⅞-in. sewing awl fixed in a suitable haft or handle should be included. This, of course, will be a curved awl.

All the tools referred to above can be obtained from the leather-seller, as can all the materials which will be referred to in the next lesson. There are many other tools which can be used, but for the purpose of simple work those detailed above are all that are essential.

Self Testing Questions

(1) *Why is a repair stand preferable to a "triple" last?*

(2) *What is a "lap-iron"?*

(3) *Which is the best shape of shoemaker's knife for general utility?*

(4) *State the purpose of the glazing iron.*

THE ANSWERS ARE ON PAGE 522.

LESSON 3

Materials and Quantities

LIKE the essential tools, etc., the materials necessary for simple shoe repairing are not numerous but are somewhat more comprehensive than "a piece of leather, a few nails, and a heelball," which too often is the amateur's conception of all that is required, if satisfactory results are to be obtained. The most important material is the leather, and as sole-leather is a complex substance which may be seriously influenced in the service it will give by the manner it is used when being attached, some thought should be given to it.

Tanning

All leather, for whatever purpose it may be used, is the preserved and dressed skin of some animal, but sole-leather is almost entirely derived from the hide of the cow or ox. It may be tanned with chrome salts or tannic acid. In the first instance the resultant leather, known as "chrome" leather, is generally of a dark green colour, and, because of the wax with which it is filled, of a very stiff board-like nature. Popular brands of chrome sole-leather are "Dri-ped" and "Western Star." Leather tanned with tannic acid is said to be "vegetable"-tanned, and, since this is most commonly used in the making and repair of footwear, its preparation deserves to receive some detailed consideration.

That portion of the hide or skin from which leather is made is a mass of gelatinous fibres which are subject to putrefaction and are surrounded by a large percentage of moisture. The work of the tanner converts these fibres into a solid string-like substance without to any serious degree altering their structure, and removes the moisture, leaving in its place mostly air spaces and a certain amount of solid material deposited by the tanning liquids. Since leather continues to possess many of the features of the hide on the living animal, it has qualities which make it particularly suitable for clothing the human foot. Briefly those features are resilience, protection against extremes of heat and cold, resistance to water and permeability to air. This last feature is the base of the hygienic superiority claimed for leather over almost every other type of footwear material.

Butt and Bends

The prime part only of the hide is converted into sole-leather. This part is known as the "butt," and is generally divided into two parts called "bends." The inferior parts are the shoulder and belly; and though not suitable for sole-leather, they are tanned by a shorter process, and are used for insoles, stiffeners, toe-puffs, middlesoles and heel lifts. A range of sole-leather is a strip cut across the width of a butt or bend. Fig. 5 illustrates the division of the hide. The cheeks and tail are sometimes tanned, but generally they are trimmed off and converted into glue or gelatine with other trimmings of the hide.

Purchasing Leather

Sole-leather can be obtained in small pieces suitable for one pair of soles or top-pieces, but it is more economical for the small user to purchase a range, which will be sufficient for three to five pairs of half-soles and top-pieces. A range suitable for men's shoes will generally be too stout for ladies' or girls', so a range for each should be kept on hand. All top-pieces should be cut from the stoutest leather available.

Choosing Sole Leather

In choosing vegetable-tanned sole-leather the following points should be noted. It should be firm, but not liable to crack on being bent. Colour is an immaterial consideration, but warble holes, brand marks or flaying cuts should be avoided. Warble holes are the result of the penetration of the hide by the maggot of the warble fly. Brand marks appear on the grain surface, and result from the branding of the animal for identification purposes. Flaying cuts are caused by the bad use of the knife in the removal of the hide, and appear on the "flesh" or under-side of the leather.

A selection of rivets must next be procured, and a range of various sorts and sizes is desirable. For the attachment of half-soles brass rivets are best, since they do not rust and

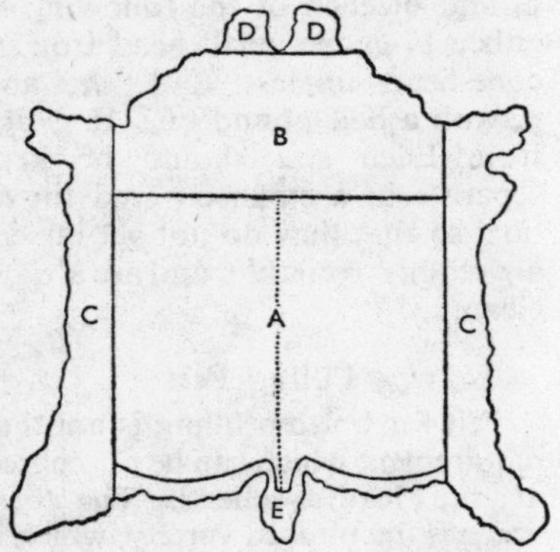

Fig. 5. *How an animal's hide is divided.* A, *butt (the dotted line shows division into two "bends");* B, *shoulder;* C, *bellies;* D, *cheeks;* E, *tail.*

therefore will not damage the shoe's foundation; but they are costly. If discretion is used in selecting the right size for the particular job in hand, some form of iron rivet will be found satisfactory. Moreover, iron rivets are more suitable for the nailing of top-pieces, because they are harder wearing. Special nails such as cutlans, slugs, and cutbils are procurable for this last purpose, but they involve considerations which space does not permit us to deal with, and the handyman will find that a discriminating use of iron rivets will amply serve his needs.

Sizes to Stock

For average work 17-gauge rivets are mostly used, but for the attachment of top-pieces to wooden heels the finer 18-gauge are not so liable to split the wood. A form of iron rivet increasingly popular with the trade is the cone-head tingle, which has a sharp point. It clinches well, is easy to drive, and gives a neat appearance. A comprehensive stock of rivets would be a half pound of each of the following in either 17-gauge small head iron or cone-head tingles $\frac{7}{16}$, $\frac{1}{2}$, $\frac{9}{16}$, and $\frac{5}{8}$, with a half pound of $\frac{5}{8}$ 18-gauge iron. Each size should be kept separate in a small covered tin or box, so that they do not get mixed, are readily available, and are always clean.

Filling Felt

Felt for bottom filling is another requirement which can be purchased at the leather-seller's. The best grade is the pitched variety, which is waterproof, easily split, and light brown in colour. It is 36 in. wide, and one may well keep a half or even a quarter yard on hand. The black tarred felt is inferior. Ladies' old felt hats make a very good alternative to pitched felt for bottom filling, but scrap leather should never be used, as it causes squeaking when the shoe is worn. Special ready-made paste for the shoeman's use can be purchased in 1-lb. tins, and a tin should be included in one's stock. Most shoe repairers make their own threads or "wax-ends," but thread-making is not at all simple, and the reader should buy a half-dozen ready made for such purposes as the repairing of welts. They should be "bristled" (not needles) at both ends. A piece of sewing-wax kept in paper with a little French chalk will be needed to replenish the threads as they are used.

Other Materials

Finishing materials are the only other essentials. The first of these is a sheet or two of No. 1½ or No. 2 sandpaper. Sole and heel edges have to be coloured, and for black work the old-fashioned black burnishing ink is preferable for the hand worker. It can be purchased in very small bottles, but the pint size is the most economical. Brown burnishing ink can also be obtained, but a suitable colouring matter such as jeweller's rouge or Bismarck brown can easily be mixed in water for the staining of brown edges. Indeed, brown edges can be burnished to a very good tone by simply moistening them with a little spittle or clean water, as will be fully explained later.

Sticks of heelball are better to use than the small round balls, and the best quality is necessary for good finishing. Good heelball should be bright, hard and brittle, and to buy any that is of a soft greasy nature is a waste of money. Heelball is obtainable in a variety of brown shades as well as black, and a dark brown or chocolate shade is most general for brown work, although the colour of the heelball does not greatly affect the colour of the finished surface. One stick each of black and brown is sufficient.

Adhesives

If any soling material other than leather, such as Uskide or crepe rubber, is to be used, the worker will need an adhesive other than paste to secure the material to the foundation of the shoe before it is riveted or sewn. The reason for this is the degree to which these materials will spread during wear, thus throwing an undue strain on the medium of attachment, *i.e.* the rivets or sewing, and by first securing the sole with an adhesive this possibility is greatly reduced. The best adhesive for applying to the shoe's foundation is latex, and to the soling material an ordinary rubber solution. A half-pint tin of each will be sufficient for many pairs. Latex is also a very satisfactory adhesive to use for sticking light leather soles to light footwear when riveting or sewing can be dispensed with. Other materials such as rubber tips, rubber heels, etc., are best purchased separately as they are required.

One's stock of materials should be stored tidily in a small cupboard or box, so that they are kept clean and can always be easily found when required. The same can be said of the tools which have already been referred to in the preceding lesson.

Self Testing Questions

(1) *What is a "bend?"*

(2) *What sizes of rivets are mainly required?*

(3) *What are the features of good heelball?*

(4) *Why are soling materials other than leather secured with an adhesive?*

THE ANSWERS ARE ON PAGE 522.

LESSON 4

Benching

FOOTWEAR that is in use naturally requires repairing at some time or other, but the amateur shoe repairer will quickly appreciate the truth of the adage "A stitch in time saves nine," and if wise he will proceed with the work before the worn condition of the shoes involves a number of complicated details. From what has been learnt in Lesson 1 it will be seen that the only components that are really wear-resistant are the outsole and the top-piece, and immediately either of these needs replacement is the time for the repairing to be done. To continue wearing a shoe after these components cease to perform their function not only complicates the repair operation, but it is most uneconomical, for the other components which then become exposed to wear are quickly ruined. Moreover, a badly-worn shoe rapidly loses its shape because of the strain which is thrown upon its many components, and this is almost impossible to rectify. A heel worn down through two or more lifts causes irreparable distortion of the stiffener, and the continued exposure of a welt-seam or insole to the elements will soon result in a number of difficulties.

Assuming that a pair of boots or shoes are not extravagantly worn, their repair is easy, and the purpose of this lesson and the next is to describe the simple half-soling and heeling of them. This will be done in a composite manner, taking note of the different features presented as they arise by the three main methods of construction previously described.

Making the Pattern

Whatever the method of construction, the first thing to be done is to take a paper pattern of the half-sole and/or top-piece. This is done by placing one of the shoes on the hobbing foot and, after placing a piece of strong paper, in the case of a half-sole, with a straight edge across the waist of the sole to the extent the half-sole is to reach, filing downward lightly all round the sole with the smooth side of the rasp. The line of the half-sole across the waist should be more or less parallel to that of the "joints"

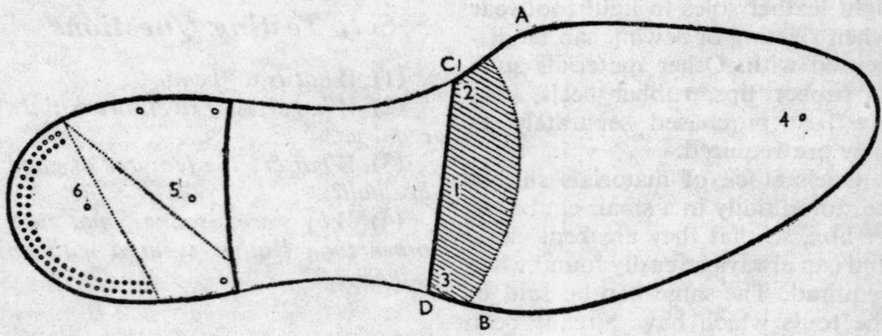

Fig. 6. *Half-sole and top-piece (left foot). References are explained in text.*

(marked *A* and *B* in Fig. 6) and from 1 to 1½ in. below. When new top-pieces are to be fitted a full pattern of one of them is taken in like manner.

Cutting the Leather

From these patterns the necessary leather is cut for both shoes, allowing ¼-in. fullness all round. Take care to reverse the patterns, so that one "left" and one "right" of each is obtained. These soles and heels are then wetted and mellowed. Although this "conditioning" of the leather is a simple operation, it is an important one, for it not only makes for easy working, but has a material effect upon the service the leather will afford in wear. It is done by first immersing the leather in clean water for a half-hour or so, and then, after standing it on end for a while to drain, wrapping it in damp cloth or paper for at least twelve hours. By this means the leather will assume a cheesy condition because, while in the water, its air content will be replaced by the water which will gradually permeate the tight bundles of fibres during the time it is wrapped.

Meanwhile the shoes can be "stripped," or in other words prepared for the reception of the new leather. First mark the line of the half-sole *C-D* (Fig. 6) across the waist of the shoe, and remove the main portion of the worn outsole by cutting the stitches securing it. With the shoe on the repair stand and the toe toward the worker's body, insert the point of the knife between the outsole and the next component at a point equivalent to *A* (Fig. 6) in the case of the left foot and cut the stitches right round to *B*. After lifting the sole thus partially severed at the toe, cut it across as indicated by the dotted line (Fig. 6). The area of leather remaining from the old sole between the line *C-D* and the cut edge is then skived to form the splice of the old sole by thinning it down with the knife so that the full substance is left at the waist line and the extreme edge is reduced to nothing. If a concavity is given to the skived surface as indicated in Fig. 7 (*A* to *B*) it will aid the neater fitting of the new sole.

Moving the Filling

Should the bottom filling be worn or in a bunched lumpy condition it should be completely removed forward from the edge of the splice, and a piece of pitched or other felt cut to shape and secured in position with a little paste or rubber solution. This completes the

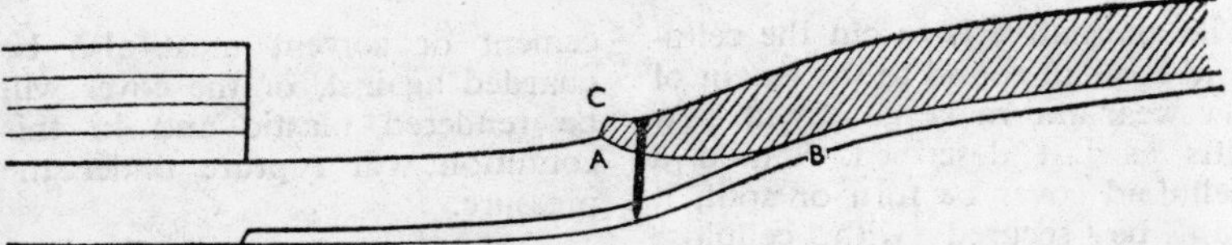

Fig. 7. *Half-sole splice. Note the concavity of the skived surface* AB.

stripping of the sole, but if the shoe is a welted one it is as well to wet the welts slightly and rub them out square to the upper with the bevelled end of the wooden handle of the knife. When lifting the sole of a screwed and stitched boot after cutting the outsole stitches, care must be taken not to pull out the brass wire screws. As each one is reached it should be cut off flush with the surface of the middlesole with the cutting nippers.

The Heel Lifts

After removing the worn top-pieces, the preparation of the heels is confined to making good any damage to the top lifts. If the heel is a small one it is best to replace any worn lifts with new ones of a like substance, but with larger heels it is more economical to piece the worn lifts. This piecing, however, should not be at all small, or solidity will be lost, and, as the extent of the worn part decides, the lift should be cut vertically across as denoted by one or other of the dotted lines in the heel portion of Fig. 6. In removing the worn lift or portion of lift, take care not to disturb the heavy "heel pins" or nails holding the heel on. These nails are then cut flush with the surface of the under lift and the new lift or piece is secured in position with $\frac{5}{8}$-in. iron rivets a full $\frac{3}{8}$-in. from the outer edge of the heel and fairly wide apart. As the lifts do not form a wearing surface, the leather used can be of inferior quality, such as the extreme edges of the bend, or small pieces of belly or shoulder leather purchased for the purpose. These small pieces of leather are called "rising" by the leather-seller. Harsh brittle leather should never be used for heel lifting, as it is liable to be split by the top-piece nailing.

Wooden Heels

With covered wood heels the ravages of wear beyond the substance of the top-piece can be most damaging to the cover. If the wood is at all worn the cover should be carefully turned back all round to a little below the extent of the wear, and the wood then knifed, sawn, or rasped level. The cover is then returned and secured with a little paste or rubber solution; the latter will generally be found simpler and cleaner to use. All reduction of the height of the heels occasioned by this levelling of the wood is corrected by fitting one or more leather lifts secured with $\frac{5}{8}$-in. 18-gauge iron rivets, unless the reduction has been very small, when the use of extra stout top-pieces will make good the deficiency. It should be noted that the maintenance of the original heel height is very important, and the practice of lowering or increasing the height of a heel is to be deprecated, for it throws the whole shoe out of pitch and results in undue strain being thrown on its many components.

With celluloid-covered heels it is impossible to turn the cover back.

The alternative is to cut the celluloid level all round to the extent of the wear and make good with new lifts as just described. Should a celluloid cover be torn or split, it can be secured with cellulose cement or a celluloid solvent such as amyl acetate. To do this, carefully remove all dust and dirt from under the fracture, and then give the thinnest smear of the cement or solvent to the under-side of the celluloid. While still wet it is pressed into contact with the wood with the thumb or palm of the hand. The pressure is maintained for a minute or so to secure adhesion, but rubbing must be avoided. Extravagant application of the cement or solvent must also be guarded against, or the cover will be rendered plastic and in this condition will rupture under the pressure.

Self Testing Questions

(1) *When should a repair be undertaken?*

(2) *Describe the method and result of mellowing leather.*

(3) *At what distance should a half-sole extend down the waist of the shoe?*

(4) *Why use* 18-*gauge rivets for fixing the top-piece on a wood heel?*

THE ANSWERS ARE ON PAGE 522.

LESSON 5

Re-soling

After preparing the shoes for the reception of the new soles and top-pieces, attention is next given to the leather itself. While the wearing propensities of the leather will be mainly dependent upon its quality, a careful hammering of it in its mellowed condition will considerably enhance the wear it will give; but unless the leather is properly mellowed as previously described, any hammering will have a disastrous effect, as it will cause the breaking up of its fibrous structure, with the result that it will more or less powder away in wear.

Before hammering the soles they should be skived across the waist, or straight edge, to facilitate the fitting of them to the skived splice of the old sole. This is done by placing the sole flesh, or under-side, uppermost on a "skiving board" (a piece of board 18-in. × 6-in.) with the straight edge to the right. The worker will find it most convenient to hold the board at an angle by resting one end against his chest and the other against the base of the repair stand. Holding the sole firm on the board with the left hand, the leather is skived with the knife, as shown by the shaded portion of Fig. 6, from approximately the curved line to the straight edge *C-D*. The depth of the skive should be such as to leave the straight edge not less than $\frac{1}{16}$ in. thick, with a gradual increase to the full substance of the leather at the other extreme of the skive. If the edge is skived too thin it will be too weak to hold the rivets securing it to the shoe.

Hammering

The hammering of the leather is done by placing the lap-iron on the right thigh just behind the knee, the worker being seated on a low stool or chair, with the right foot solidly placed on the floor and the left heel slightly raised, so that this knee will provide support to the end of the lap-iron. The leather, held flesh side uppermost on the lap-iron with the left hand, is then solidly hammered all over, beginning at the centre and gradually working outward to the edges. In this way thorough hammering condenses the leather and gives it a concavity from the under or flesh side which facilitates the fitting of it to the shoe. Once the leather has been hammered, every effort should be made to avoid bending it, as this would nullify the advantages hammering gives.

Attaching the Piece

The actual attachment of the leather to the shoes is then proceeded with. One shoe is placed on the hobbing foot with the toe away from the worker, and the appropriate half-sole is placed in position on it so that the straight waist edge comes a full ⅛ in. below, or toward the heel, of the skived portion of the splice on the old sole and the outer edges of the sole evenly overlapping the shoe all round. A rivet of a suitable length is then inserted centrally along the waist and about ¼ in. from the edge (1, Fig. 6), followed by others (2, 3, and 4) as indicated. If the rivets used are long enough just to clinch on the surface of the insole when driven right home, these four will be sufficient for the initial attachment of the sole. Before inserting the fourth rivet the shoe should be pulled well back on the hobbing foot and kept as straight as possible, with the sole carefully pressed down to it at the toe with the thumb of the left hand while the fingers hold the shoe back on the foot. To facilitate the driving of the rivets, the insole should be pressed into close contact with the surface of the hobbing foot at the point at which the rivet is to be inserted. Therefore it will be seen that a re-positioning of the shoe is necessary for the driving of every rivet.

Rounding

The top-piece is then fixed with two ⅝-in. rivets (5 and 6, Fig. 6), remembering to use the finer 18-gauge for wood heels. With the other sole and top-piece attached in like manner, both shoes are "rounded." Rounding consists of shaping with the knife the new leather to the more or less exact shape determined by the welt or middle-sole or, in the case of single-sole machine-sewn, by the insole edge, and for top-pieces by the top lift or top of the heel. The shoe is removed from the hobbing foot for rounding; it is generally easier to do it seated on a low stool or chair. With the shoe held firmly sole downward, the fingers of the left hand should hold the upper away from that part of the sole being cut, and with the welt or middle-sole as a guide the new leather is shaped a fraction full (⅛ in.) all round. With single-sole machine-sewn work the operation is a little more difficult; a little practice will soon enable the worker to use the edge of the insole as his guide to the shape of the sole, but in this case the fullness should be rather more (¼ in. or so). The top-piece is rounded fairly close, and in all instances the cut edge of the leather must be kept as square as possible.

The final benching operation is the riveting of the soles and top-pieces. Although this is comparatively simple, the manner in which

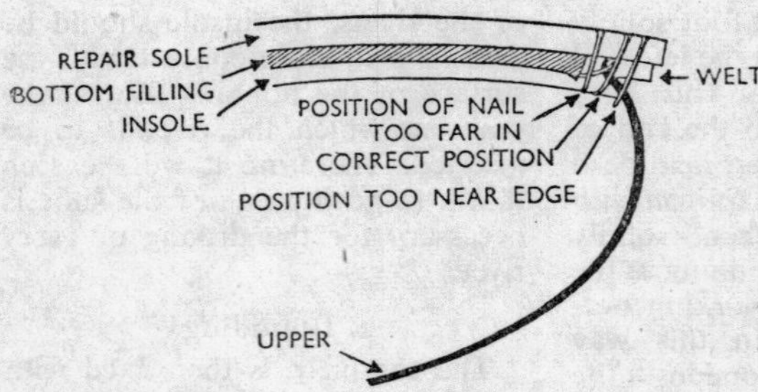

Fig. 8. *Correct and incorrect riveting of welted footwear.*

it is done has a serious effect upon both the appearance of the work and the service it will afford. In the attachment of the sole the row of rivets virtually constitutes a vertical seam uniting the half-sole to the shoe, and to be fully effective it must be uniform throughout. The careful choice of the length of rivets used and their even spacing are the main essentials in securing this uniformity. If the rivets are too long, serious damage is done to the shoe's foundation, and irregularity in spacing and alignment causes insecurity and discomfort.

Marking for Rivets

A line should first be marked right round the sole about ¼ in. to ⅜ in. from the edge and across the straight waist edge in line with the three rivets already inserted. The position of each rivet should then be pricked along these lines with the point of a sharp awl, which will not only assure equal spacing but will also make the insertion of the rivets easier, as the mark will have punctured the hard grain of the leather. For average work the rivets should be spaced about four to the inch around the sole, with those across the waist a little closer, although for stout work the spacing can be slightly increased. In determining the length of rivet to use, the golden rule is that it should be just long enough when hammered right home for the point to clinch on the surface of the insole, and it will generally be found that a slightly shorter rivet is needed across the waist than around the sole.

Begin riveting by inserting a rivet which is rather on the long side in every fourth hole all round the sole, and then fill up with a slightly shorter length of rivet. When riveting soles on machine-sewn or screwed-and-stitched footwear the rivets are inserted quite vertically, but on a welted shoe they need to be driven slightly at an angle. The reason for this precaution is the necessity for each rivet to secure all the components. If the rivet is driven vertically rather close to the edge of the sole it will probably be visible outside the shoe between the upper and welt and fail to clinch on the insole. On the other hand, if vertically inserted farther in from the edge it will miss the welt entirely and penetrate the welt-seam, which, as the shoe bends during walking, will be broken. By driving the rivets at an angle it is possible to secure all the various components without damage to the welt-seam, and so that they are not visible. These points are illustrated in Fig. 8.

Clinching the Rivets

When the riveting of the sole is completed, give it a firm but light hammering all over to level it out and to clinch all the rivets completely, taking care that the portion of the shoe to be struck is really making solid contact with the hobbing foot for each blow.

The riveting, or "nailing," as it is called, of the top-piece is rather different, for while a certain number of the rivets are necessary to secure the top-piece to the heel, the majority of them are utilised to reinforce the leather at the point of greatest wear. For this reason they are placed relatively close together and nearer to the edge of the top-piece. A line is first made right round the top-piece a bare $\frac{1}{8}$ in. from the edge. For a leather heel of a medium or heavy shoe it is usual to place two close rows of rivets on the "tread" at the back as indicated in Fig. 6, but for lighter shoes or on wood heels a single row, the outer one, is sufficient. After pricking the position of the rivets, insert, for a leather heel, five $\frac{5}{8}$-in. fixing rivets one at each of the following points: at each corner of the heel, centrally at the back, and midway along each side. The one or two rows are then completed with $\frac{7}{16}$ or $\frac{1}{2}$-in. rivets. For wood heels only three $\frac{5}{8}$-in. 18-gauge rivets are necessary for fixing, one at each corner and one centrally at the back, while the row is completed with $\frac{7}{16}$-in. The top-piece is finally hammered all over to level it.

Self Testing Questions

(1) *Why is hammering of the new leather done?*

(2) *What results from hammering dry leather?*

(3) *What does the row of rivets securing the sole constitute?*

(4) *Why are top-pieces nailed?*

THE ANSWERS ARE ON PAGE 522.

LESSON 6

Finishing

The purpose of finishing is not only to improve the appearance of the completed job by colouring and polishing the edges of the new leather, but, as will be demonstrated later, the operation has a utility value inasmuch as it also imparts hardness and water-resistance to the soles so that they do not spread or lose their shape in wear.

After trimming off all surplus leather around the edges with the knife and at the same time cutting the bulge of leather across the waist as indicated by *C* (Fig. 7) off level, the edges of the soles and top-pieces are well rasped with the coarse side of the rasp. The rasp is held between the thumb and first finger of the right hand, with the thumb resting on the smooth side about an inch or less from the end. The first section of the finger is turned under the rasp, so that while acting with the thumb in holding the tool the side of the finger can be brought in contact with the surface of the sole or top-piece as a guide or control. The rasping is done with short forward strokes, and the edge should be slightly moistened with water or spittle beforehand. In this way the rasp compresses and hardens the edge and closely unites the various layers of leather, besides removing all evidence of knife marks.

The edge is again slightly moistened and then scraped really smooth with the scraper. This tool is held between the thumb and first two fingers of the right hand with the third finger tip acting as guide against the sole or top-piece surface. The amount of scraping should be sufficient only to remove all the rasp marks, and afterwards the edges are lightly sandpapered with a piece of folded sandpaper. Any burr of leather along the corner of the edge with the surface of the sole or top-piece is removed with the scraper, or if on the welt side of the edge is cut off with the knife.

Colouring

The work is then ready for "colour," when black or brown burnishing ink is applied with a soft brush after being well shaken. When put in colour the shoes should be stood aside to dry, or rather almost dry, for a certain degree of dampness should remain in the coloured edge for the following operation of "burnishing." When the coloured leather has become mellow-dry it is brushed with a soft shoe-brush to remove any excess of ink or extraneous matter. The glazing iron is warmed on a gas-jet or spirit lamp until it is a little more than comfortably hot to the palm.

The "cut-down" portion of the iron is used to burnish the sole edge by fitting the shoulder against the surface of the sole with the face of the "cut-down" flat on the coloured edge while the handle of the iron is grasped tightly in the right hand, the thumb being uppermost. The iron is then moved backward and forward short distances in an oscillating manner, with as much pressure as possible exerted on the face of the iron all the time; but care must be taken not to mark the edge with the corner edge of the iron. This operation imparts a hard burnish or glaze to the edge all round the shoe.

As with all shoe repairing operations which are carried out seated, the worker will find advantage in being seated on a low stool, for it enables full control to be exercised over the work while it is rested on the knees. The heel edge is burnished in a similar manner to the forepart, except that the larger and more rounded face of the iron is used, but the "cut-down" is best to use for the single leather top-piece edge of wood heels.

When the burnishing is completed a little heelball is applied to the edges by lightly melting the heelball in the gas or spirit flame and dabbing small smudges all round. The glazing-iron, warmed sufficiently to melt the heelball, is then used to distribute it evenly all over the edges in the same way as the burnishing is done. The final operation of finishing is "rubbing-off" with a piece of serge or similar fluff-free cloth. The cloth is folded tightly over the thumb, and a vigorous rubbing will smooth the heelball, but this is not quite sufficient, for actually almost all the heelball should be removed from the edge in "rubbing-off." Therefore the deposit of heelball given to the edge in the first place should be kept at a minimum. The purpose of using heelball is to improve the water-resistance of the burnished edge by imparting to it a very thin transparent veneer of wax, the main ingredient of heelball.

Self Testing Questions

(1) *What is the main effect of rasping?*

(2) *How is burnishing achieved?*

(3) *Why is heelball used?*

(4) *Give the reason for using a fluff-free cloth for rubbing-off.*

THE ANSWERS ARE ON PAGE 522.

LESSON 7

Hand-Sewn Work

It is difficult to realise why it should be so, but the phrase "Hand-Sewn" seems to be more closely associated with good quality footwear than with any other commodity, and the ability to "hand-sew" implies a high order of proficiency in the shoe-repairer. Accordingly we shall consider this type of work—especially that part of it which has a bearing upon what the reader has already learnt. In particular, this will be the repairing of welts and the attachment of half-soles by sewing instead of riveting.

It often happens that the stitches of the welt seam break during wear. The correction of this condition is essential before a satisfactory repair can be completed. The method of doing it is to remove first the bottom filling so that access can be obtained to the welt stitches coming along the insole. Then remove any broken stitches from the welt. Parts of the broken stitches will generally be found firmly embedded in the seam where they hold the upper and the lining in close contact with the insole, and it is inadvisable to attempt to remove them.

Holding the Thread

With the shoe on the repair stand the actual sewing can next be done. Hand-sewing is always done toward the worker, which means that the inside of the seam should be toward the right hand and the welt toward the left. The shoemaker uses a fairly stout thread called "a pair of wax ends," because it has a bristle attached to each end. Hold one end of the thread with the thumb and finger of the left hand and grasp the awl with the right hand. To make the first hole the point of the awl is inserted a little back from the commencement of the broken stitches from the inside and bottom of the seam, and to facilitate its penetration of the materials, it is gently wriggled as pressure is applied to the end of the handle with the palm of the hand.

Sewing Hints

The awl should penetrate the work so that its point breaks the surface in line with the original sewing, and, to ensure solid sewing, the hole made should be as small as possible—which means that the smallest fraction of the awl's point should actually penetrate right through the materials. As the awl is withdrawn, the point of the bristle held in the left hand is made to follow it, and, without losing grip of the awl, the worker should steadily pull through the bristle for three or four inches with the finger and thumb of the right hand. Any semblance of snatching at the bristle must be avoided, or it will part company with the thread. Maintaining hold of the bristle, hook the middle of the little finger round the thread close to the seam and pull through another twelve inches or so of the thread.

This method of drawing the bulk of the thread through with the aid of the little finger is repeated until the thread is centrally halved in the work. The first stitch is then completed by again inserting the awl as before but a quarter inch or so from the previous hole. This quarter inch, of course, will be the length of the actual stitch, but the length of stitch will vary with the substance of the work. In theory the stitch should be of the same length as the original, but with machine-made footwear it is generally sufficient to re-sew in every other hole of the original sewing. Before inserting the awl the bristle of each end is taken up by the finger and thumb of each hand, and, as the awl is withdrawn, the left bristle is made to follow it as previously described. Before pulling it right through, however, the right one is inserted from the other side and the two are drawn through together in reverse directions for a few inches. Each thread is then grasped by the little fingers and pulled through as before until the complete stitch is made.

Tightening the Thread

The final tightening of it is secured by twisting the now left thread right round that hand, and the right thread round the end of the awl handle, and by steadily straining on each. To protect the left hand when twisting the thread round it the shoemaker uses a "hand leather," but the amateur worker will find that an old leather glove with the fingers cut off, mitten fashion, will serve the purpose as well.

Sewing Wax

The thread should be rubbed down with a piece of sewing wax when every four or five stitches have been completed. Sewing wax acts both as a lubricant to the thread and as a water-resisting preservative, and, by setting hard, helps to secure the stitch when it is pulled tight. When the sewing is completed, the two ends are tied in a knot on the insole side of the seam and cut off. The work is then completed by replacing the bottom filling and the repair is proceeded with as previously described.

Half-Soles

For sewing a half-sole on a welted shoe follow the advice given in Lessons 4 and 5 up to and including rounding. Then cut a "channel" right round the sole to accommodate the stitches. Starting at the outside corner of the half-sole in the case of the right shoe or the inside corner of the left shoe an incision is cut with the point of the knife at an angle of 45° to a depth of half the leather's substance and about $\frac{1}{8}$ in. from the edge. This incision is then forced open (as illustrated at *B* in Fig. 9) with a screw-driver or similar tool. The sewing is done with the shoe held on the right knee by a "stirrup" (a piece of rope or strap) passing over the knee and round the foot with the shoe on its side so that the surface of the sole faces the left hand. The awl is made to pierce the welt just behind the original outsole stitching, but not so far back as to interfere with the welt stitches and to emerge in the bed of the channel. The manipulation of the thread to form the stitches, which for average work should not be longer than four to the inch, is identical with that described for welt sewing. When the sewing is completed the stitches both along the welt and in the channel are rubbed smooth with the

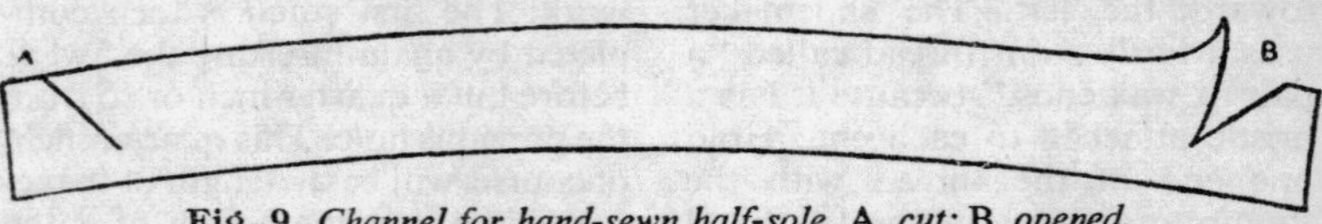

Fig. 9. *Channel for hand-sewn half-sole.* A, *cut;* B, *opened.*

bevelled end of the knife handle and the channel is closed by first rubbing a smear of paste, rubber solution, or latex in it, and by pushing the turned-up lip down with the peen of the hammer followed by a light hammering. The straight waist edge of a sewn sole is riveted across in the same way as for a riveted half-sole.

Self Testing Questions

(1) *Is hand-sewing done toward or away from the worker?*

(2) *For what purpose is sewing wax used?*

(3) *What is a "stirrup"?*

(4) *What is a channel?*

THE ANSWERS ARE ON PAGE 522.

LESSON 8

Sole Attachment with an Adhesive

A POPULAR and simple method of attaching repair soles to very light-welted or machine-sewn shoes is to stick them on with an adhesive, and the best form of adhesive for the amateur's use is latex (Lesson 3). Start by preparing both the shoe and the new half-sole as previously described up to the point of the actual attachment of the sole, which should then be allowed to dry thoroughly. The two surfaces are roughened or scratched to provide an anchorage for the latex. This roughening can be done with a coarse hacksaw, wire brush, or a piece of wire "carding." The whole surface of the new sole is treated in this way, but it is necessary only to do certain parts of the shoe.

Welted Shoes

In the case of a welted shoe, the important parts to roughen thoroughly are the skived splice of the old sole and the surface of the welt seam, or all the materials coming between and held by the stitches. The welt itself should be lightly roughened, but its loose texture does not make it suitable for really secure adhesion: hence the importance of particular attention being paid to the welt seam.

Care must be taken not to break or weaken the welt stitches. The skived splice of the old sole and that portion of the upper overlapping and secured to the insole are the parts of a machine-sewn shoe to be roughened. Before attempting this all the tacks fastening the upper to the insole should be hammered so as to secure them thoroughly; and then the upper, from the point where it folds over the edge of the insole to its edge where it makes contact with the bottom filling, should be lightly but thoroughly roughened.

Applying Latex

Remove all dust with a clean stiff bristled shoe brush. Latex can then be applied with a brush all over both sole and shoe bottom. A small wad of clean rag is still better as it can be thrown away afterwards. The adhesive should be worked into the surfaces fairly liberally, and the work then stood aside to dry. A little gentle heat will accelerate this drying. Never expose the latexed surfaces to direct rays of sunlight, however, as this will ruin the thin deposit of pure rubber which the coating of latex gives. When the latex is thoroughly dry, it will assume a shiny brown appearance; then the sole can be pressed in position, and lightly hammered. After rounding up the sole proceed with the finishing.

As a precaution a few rivets may be inserted. They should not be many, however; three across the straight waist edge as indicated by Nos. 1, 2, and 3 in Fig, 6, with another centrally at the toe about a quarter of an inch from the edge, and yet another about an inch on each side of it and the same distance away from the edge.

Care for Footwear

In conclusion, here is some useful advice on the care and maintenance of footwear: wet boots or shoes should never be dried by such artificial means as placing them on a hot surface or near a fire, for wet leather is very easily burnt without the burn becoming visible to the wearer. Filling the shoe with dry clean newspaper will facilitate normal drying.

Deposits of mud should be washed off, and, after the shoes have been thoroughly wiped, a plentiful supply of vaseline should be rubbed into the uppers. If the shoes are then left for a day or two in a dry but not artificially heated spot, the grease will revive the natural oils of the leather. If the shoes must be polished before they are perfectly dry, the addition of some paraffin to the shoe polish will be found very helpful.

Shoe Cleaning Hints

In cleaning shoes remember that the securing of a high polish is not the only desirable effect, for leather, both by its contact with the elements and by the effect of heat and perspiration from the foot, loses certain of its properties, and this can be corrected only by using a good dressing which contains certain waxes. An occasional light washing with tepid water and soap is beneficial, for by this means all dirt and accumulated polish can be removed, thus leaving the leather ready to receive when dry the full benefit of the cream or polish used. Shoe cleansers should be applied only in small quantities, or the surplus left on the surface will merely collect dust and dirt.

Crocodile or reptile-skin shoes should be cleaned with a white shoe-cream. An occasional application of cream or milk to patent-leather shoes will be found to keep them soft, pliable and free from cracks. Suede shoes may be stuffed with paper and cleaned by applying with a rag some spirits of turpentine, well rubbed in, or with one of the special cleaning preparations sold for the purpose. Rubbing with emery paper will remove shine from the toes.

Use of Dubbin

Heavy footwear on which the securing of a polish is not essential can be profitably treated with some form of grease such as dubbin or neat's-foot oil, and even polished footwear can be improved if a little dubbin is rubbed over it occasionally after polishing, without the polish being seriously affected.

It is sometimes desired to blacken a pair of old brown shoes which have become stained or discoloured. This may be done by rubbing them well with the cut surface of half a raw potato, and then polishing them in the ordinary way with black polish to which a generous quantity of black or blue-black ink has been added. Salt or sea-water stains on brown shoes will yield to the application of a little warm milk in which some washing soda has been dissolved.

For squeaky shoes the best treatment is a linseed-oil bath. The shoes should be arranged so that the bottoms of the soles are just covered with the oil, and left standing for about two days.

The use of good fitting trees is advantageous in preserving the shape of shoes, but they should never be inserted while the footwear is excessively wet.

Rubber Heels

The fitting of extraneous rubber soles and heels has a serious influence upon the service footwear will give, and while they can be used with advantage if discretion is exercised in their choice and fitting, abuse of their use is very often evinced. Probably the most common way in which they are employed is the fixing of a rubber heel on top of the original top-piece, with the result that the shoe is thrown out of pitch. This distortion not only affects the wearer's gait, but it throws a tremendous strain upon the various parts of the shoe, and results in broken seams in upper, welt and outsole, cracked uppers occasioned by the unnatural creasing of them, and even broken shanks. The obvious precaution is to reduce the height of the heel proportionally before fixing the rubber. It is generally permissible to fit a shaped rubber direct to the lifts, but in the case of revolving heels the top lift of the reduced heel should be replaced with a wear-resisting leather top-piece before the rubber is screwed in position.

Rubber Soles

There may be said to be two types of rubber soles, other than those that are used definitely as a substitute for the leather outsole, *i.e.* the nailed or screwed-on soles and those that are attached with an adhesive. For average footwear the latter are to be preferred, for they are lighter and do not impose the same amount of strain upon the shoe. Neither type can be regarded as an alternative to half-soling, and the outsole should always be in a good condition before they are fitted.

Should the outsole be badly worn it is impossible to secure proper adhesion of a "stuck-on" rubber, and the thinness of it will be an objection to nailing one on. Directions for fitting are generally supplied with the reputable makes, but it will be found as well if the nailed-on types are first secured in position with rubber solution, for not only will this provide a more permanent attachment, but it will also prevent the ravages of dust and dirt, which will otherwise get between the rubber sole and the outsole.

Self Testing Questions

(1) *What type of footwear is the adhesive method of sole attachment suitable for?*

(2) *How are the surfaces roughened and why?*

(3) *Why should wet footwear not be subjected to artificial heat?*

(4) *What are the best dressings for heavy footwear?*

THE ANSWERS ARE ON PAGE 522.

Answers to Self Testing Questions

LESSON 1

(1) Welted, machine-sewn, and screwed and stitched.

(2) Upper, insole, welt, bottom filling, shank, outsole, heel and top-piece.

(3) Insole, upper and welt.

(4) Because the vertical seam made by the Blake sole-sewing machine tends to make the various layers of material into one solid thick-

ness, whereas the welt seam, being horizontal, possesses greater flexibility, and the welt, being soft, acts as a hinge between this flexible seam and the stiffer outsole.

LESSON 2

(1) Because being fixed it provides for solidity and easier work.
(2) A piece of flat metal such as the bottom of a domestic flat-iron on which the leather is hammered.
(3) "Heel Parer."
(4) To burnish or polish edges and distribute heelball.

LESSON 3

(1) Half a "butt," which is the prime part of the hide suitable for leather.
(2) $\frac{7}{16}$, $\frac{1}{2}$, $\frac{9}{16}$ and $\frac{5}{8}$ in. 17-gauge small head iron rivets, or the same sizes in cone-head tingles, and $\frac{5}{8}$ in. 18-gauge iron rivets.
(3) Good heelball should be bright, hard and brittle.
(4) To reduce their tendency to spread, and thus strain the medium of attachment excessively.

LESSON 4

(1) Immediately the worn part of the shoe or boot ceases to fulfil its purpose.
(2) Mellowing, which consists in immersing the leather in water for about half an hour, allowing it to drain, and then wrapping it for at least twelve hours in damp cloth or paper, renders the leather cheesy and easy to work.
(3) 1 in. to $1\frac{1}{2}$ in. below and parallel to the joints.
(4) Because their thinness will reduce the risk of splitting the wood.

LESSON 5

(1) To condense it, and thereby increase its wear-resistance, and to impart a concavity to it which facilitates its fitting.
(2) The breaking up of its fibres.
(3) A vertical seam.
(4) To increase their wear-resistance.

LESSON 6

(1) The hardening of the edges of the soles and top-pieces.
(2) By the oscillating action of the warm iron under pressure.
(3) To improve the water resistance of the burnished edge by giving it a veneer of wax, which is the main constituent of the heelball.
(4) To impart a clean, brilliant surface to the edge and to remove surplus heelball.

LESSON 7

(1) Toward.
(2) To lubricate and preserve the thread and to set the stitch.
(3) A piece of rope or strap passed over the knee and held by the foot to hold the shoe during sewing.
(4) An incision made round the sole to accommodate and protect the stitches.

LESSON 8

(1) Very light welted or machine-sewn.
(2) With a hacksaw (coarse), wire brush, or piece of wire "carding". The roughening is done to provide an anchorage for the adhesive.
(3) Because leather is very susceptible to the effects of heat, especially when wet.
(4) Dubbin or neat's-foot oil.

WATCH AND CLOCK REPAIRING

By Donald de Carle, F.B.H.I.

LESSON 1

Repairing English Pendulum Clocks

In this course you will learn much about clocks. You will learn the features of the various types of clock in common use, and discover how to make the necessary adjustments—usually simple in themselves—that will cause a clock or watch which has stopped to function normally again. You will be shown how to take clock-work to pieces and how to put it together—how to clean and oil and adjust the working parts of a clock.

Clockmaker's Tools

What are the necessary tools for dismantling and cleaning clocks? Procure first a bench, which should be fitted with a vice. Now provide yourself with a pair of flat, square-nosed pliers. When they are new, the inside of the jaws of these pliers is usually rough, and as this is undesirable for clock work, file or stone this roughness away until the jaws are reasonably smooth. You will also need cutting pliers, two screw-drivers, one with approximately $\frac{1}{4}$-in. blade and the other with $\frac{1}{8}$-in. A hammer shaped as in Fig. 1, a pair of tweezers, a watchmaker's eyeglass of 3-in. range, a pin-vice and a fairly fine file of about 6 in. in length, are also necessary. Other tools we shall discuss as we proceed, but for the present those mentioned are sufficient. Most of them, even the eyeglass, can be purchased for a small amount at any good iron-monger's. There are trade "tool shops" in most of the big towns of England and Scotland, and they can easily be found by reference to the local directory.

Grandfather Clocks

The clock with which we shall begin is the familiar Grandfather clock. The vast majority of Grandfather clocks, and, indeed, most large clocks, stop (*i.e.* "go wrong") because of the oil becoming dried up. It will be shown first how to give one a partial clean, but the information given, together with that in Lesson 2, will enable you to take the movement to pieces and clean such a clock thoroughly should the partial clean not prove sufficient. The Grandfather clock is good to experiment with, first, because of its size, and secondly, because the general principle of the average Grandfather striking clock is the same as that of most clocks.

Before you can dismantle and clean the clock, you must remove the works or mechanism—technically known as the "movement"—from its case. To do this it is necessary

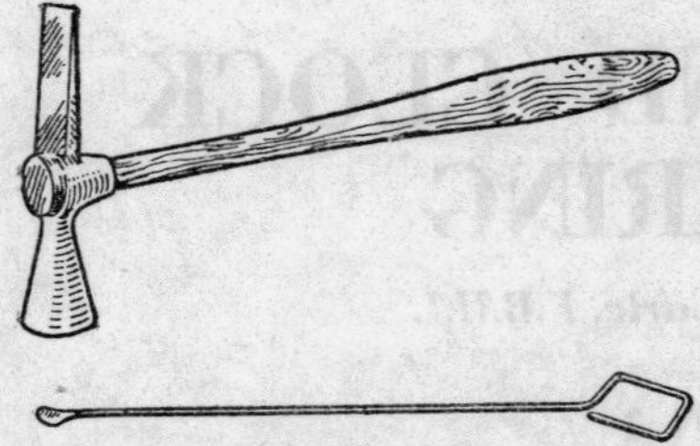

Fig. 1. (Above) *clockmaker's hammer;* (below) *oiler, which can be home-made.*

to draw forward the hood, *i.e.* the upper part of the case. The hood is sometimes bolted from the inside, so open the door of the case and put your hand up to feel if there is any form of bolt or turn-button within. Draw the hood off carefully, and the movement will now be exposed, as in Fig. 2. Next you will find that the weights will unhook from the pulleys, so remove and mark them to ensure that they are replaced on the correct side. The weight on the striking side of the clock is usually the heavier of the two, and, if you are facing the clock, it is to your left.

Next remove the pendulum. To do this, hold the pendulum-rod with the left hand, and with the right guide the suspension-spring block out of the pallet bridge and carefully lower the pendulum with the left hand. (Unfamiliar terms

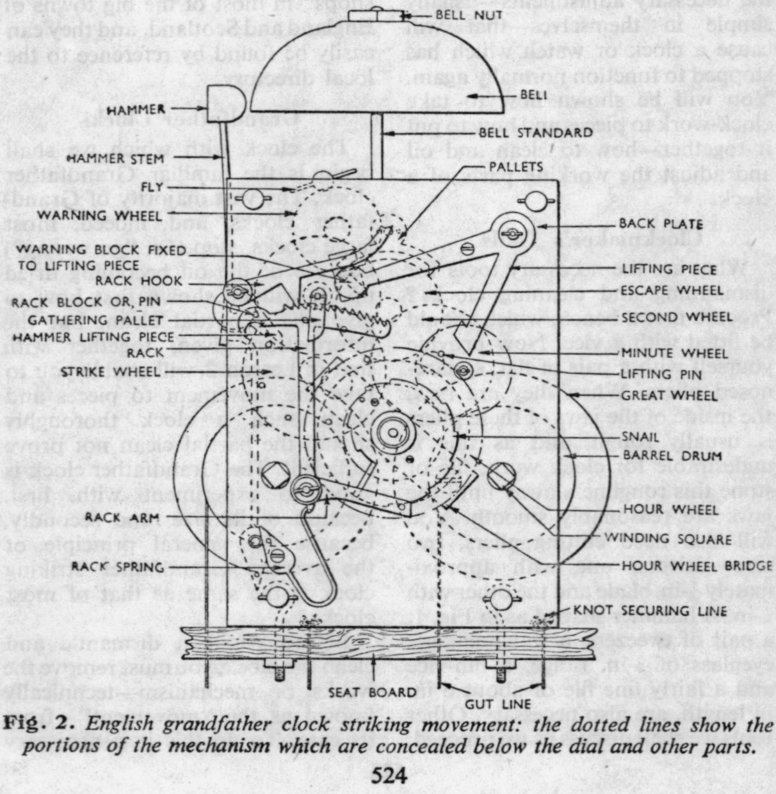

Fig. 2. *English grandfather clock striking movement: the dotted lines show the portions of the mechanism which are concealed below the dial and other parts.*

will be explained later.) Take great care to guide the suspension-spring block through the crutch fork, and then remove the pendulum from the case. The safest way is to lay the pendulum flat on the floor, because the pendulum bob is proportionately heavier than the pendulum rod and the suspension spring is delicate. If you stand it upright, the rod may be bent or the spring damaged.

Meaning of Terms

Now to explain the terms that have just been used: the suspension spring is the spring fixed on the top of the pendulum, and it is by this spring that the pendulum is suspended. The suspension-spring block is the small piece of brass riveted to this spring, and the pallet bridge is the bar or bridge from which the pendulum hangs and is also one of the bearings for the pallets. The pallets are shaped as is shown in Fig. 2, and are fixed about the centre of an arbor or spindle. At one end of the pallet arbor is a piece of wire or thin rod, which terminates in a flat piece of metal with a rectangular slot in it. This wire or rod is the crutch, and the flat piece at the end is the crutch fork, so called because one end of the slot is sometimes left open so as to form a fork. The pendulum bob is the weight at the end of the pendulum, regulating its swing.

Removing the Movement

Having removed the weights and the pendulum, you can now remove the movement. This is usually screwed to a board known as the seat-board, which is, in turn, sometimes screwed down on to the main part of the clock case. Remove the seat-board with movement attached. Push the gut-line through the board; then undo the knot which holds the line in position. Do this to both sides, and the pulleys will be released. Now unscrew the screws holding the movement to the seat-board. This frees the movement. Before you proceed further, take care to have a box handy in which to put the parts as the clock is taken to pieces.

Remove the hands and the dial; withdraw the small pin which holds the hand-work in position. The minute hand will be inclined to spring forward, so take care not to lose the small brass collet or washer. The hour hand is next removed by taking out the small screw which holds it in position. The second hand (if there is one) is best removed with the fingers. It is held in position friction-tight, and, if it is held firmly between the thumb and forefinger, and twisted slowly backward and simultaneously pulled outward, it will come away with ease. The dial is held on by four pins which can be seen from the back. You will take them out in removing the dial, but it is methodical to replace them in their holes until wanted for the re-assembly of parts of the clock.

Cleaning and Oiling

The clock can now be partly cleaned, and oiled.

First, remove the bell and unscrew the two screws holding the pallet-cock in position. If we take out this piece, we shall be able to remove the pallets. The wheel into which the pallets engage is the escape wheel, and this, together with the pallets, is known as the escapement.

Have ready a small vessel of benzine or petrol and a piece of clean linen rag. With these, clean the pallets, making sure to remove all congealed oil, especially from the parts which directly engage the escape wheel. Now stretch the piece of rag over the forefinger and dip it into the liquid. With this clean as thoroughly as possible the teeth of the escape wheel; well clean with peg-wood both the pallet holes as explained in Lesson 2. Then replace the pallets.

An efficient oiler can easily be made from a piece of brass wire of about the thickness of a large hairpin and 6 in. in length. Hammer the end flat and file it to shape as shown in Fig. 1. Bend the other end as shown in the drawing.

Clock oil is the best to use, but machine oil answers well. Pour a little oil into a small pot of about an inch diameter, to a depth of about an eighth of an inch. If we place the oiler in the pot of oil so that it touches the bottom, the right amount of oil is carried. This is important, because applying too much oil is almost as bad as using too little.

Parts to be Oiled

Now apply one oiler full of oil to each pallet, and then employ a little force with the hand to the barrel, moving the crutch backward and forward so that the teeth of the escape wheel move forward and receive some of the oil. After one revolution you may find it necessary to use more oil. Apply an oiler full of oil to all the pivot holes and also put a little on each of the pins on the strike-wheel, which is the wheel that operates the hammer. Other parts of the striking mechanism should also be oiled where friction is caused. You can now replace the dial and hands: the minute hand fits on to a square, so make sure that it is fitted on to the correct square and that the hour hand points to the hour when the clock strikes. The brass collet, which fits over the minute hand, will have to be pressed inward so as to allow the pin holding the hand in position to be replaced. We now fix the movement on the seat-board, thread the pulleys on the lines, pull the lines through the seat-board and re-tie the knot. Place the movement in the case and hang the weights.

Pulleys and Weights

In doing so, make sure that the pulleys are the right way up; and see that the line runs in the groove of the pulley and does not slip between the pulley and the wire loop, otherwise the clock will not run for the full time. When the weights were taken off, the clock may have been half wound; in this case the lines must be unwound before the weights are hung. For this purpose, hold the line which comes directly from the barrel, and at the same time pull it gently, with the tweezers or small screw-driver, hold the click that works on the barrel ratchet wheel out of position, and pull the line out to its full length. Replace the weights and wind the clock slowly, observing at the same time that the lines run correctly in the grooves on their respective barrel drums.

Now with a piece of rag and some petrol clean that part of the pendulum to which the suspension spring is attached, and which works in the crutch fork. Replace the pendulum, apply a little oil to the crutch fork where the pendulum works, and set it swinging.

It is essential that the beat of the clock should be even. If you are certain that the clock itself is upright but find that the tick is irregular, the crutch must be bent a little. A very simple method is to

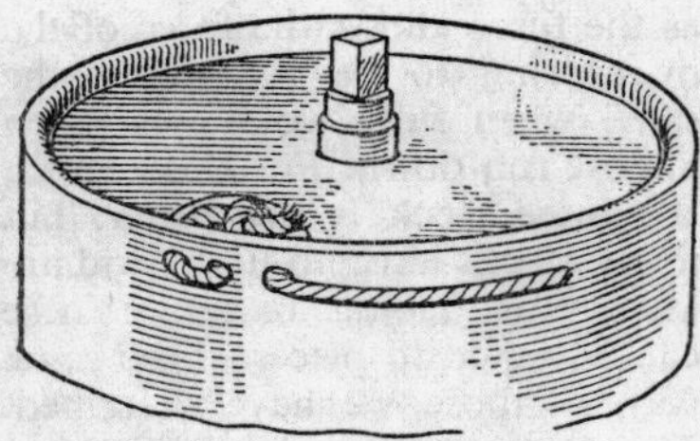

Fig. 3. *Method of attaching line to barrel.*

stop the pendulum and let it hang still. Then move it very gently until you hear a tick, note the extent of the arc through which you have moved the pendulum, and let it rest again. Now move it in the other direction till you hear a tick, and again note the distance. Should you find that it was necessary to move the pendulum more to the right than to the left, the crutch must be bent to the left; if otherwise, to the right. To bend it to the left, for instance, hold the forefinger of the left hand on the side of the crutch, somewhere near the top, and push the lower part of it over with the right forefinger. Replace the hood, and the job is complete.

Fitting a New Line

Occasionally clocks of this type stop because the line has broken. New line, which is usually made from gut, can be purchased from the tool shop. A "hank" of gut is sufficient for two lines, and as we retain the old line we can measure off the amount required.

To fit the new line it may be necessary to take the clock to pieces, but sometimes the line can be manipulated without doing this. Thread the line through the hole in the part of the barrel where the grooves are (Fig. 3), then manipulate the end through the hole at the side, tie a knot, cut the gut to about $\frac{1}{4}$ in. of the knot, then just burn the end with a match—this causes the gut to spread, and it will be impossible to pull the knot out. When fitting the line make sure not to catch it on any sharp edges, because, although of great strength, it is easily damaged.

Dial or Kitchen Clocks

A popular type of clock is the English fusee dial, sometimes called the kitchen or office dial.

To repair such a clock, proceed in the following manner. The pendulum must be removed before the clock is taken down. To do this open the small door underneath the clock and also that at the side. Hold the pendulum with the left hand and exercise the same precautions as explained for dealing with the Grandfather clock. Now take down the clock and place it face up on the table. Open the front door, or bezil as it is called, and remove the hands; these are fitted in a manner similar to those of the Grandfather clock. You will find four wooden pegs immediately behind the dial; remove these and you will be able to lift out the front of the clock, together with the movement. Place this face downward on the table, remove the four pins which hold the movement in position and lift the movement upward, leaving the dial fixed to that part of the case. Now place a piece of wire about 6 in. in length in the arms of the escape wheel, and work the crutch backward and forward until the wire stops any further movement of the escape wheel.

The pallet cock and then the pallets can now be taken out. Remove the wire carefully and the clock will begin to run down.

While this is in progress, oil all the pivot holes, and when it has run down, clean the escape wheel and pallets as already described.

Re-assemble as directed for the Grandfather clock. Hang the clock on the wall and replace the pendulum in the same way as it was removed, judging the beat and adjusting the pendulum as was done with the Grandfather clock.

If the line of the fusee clock breaks, it is necessary to take the clock to pieces to fit a new one. A special quality line is used for these clocks, and is usually sold in about the correct lengths. To make sure, however, knot the line into the fusee first, burning the end as for the Grandfather clock line; then wind the line on to the fusee and estimate the length required from the fusee to the barrel, cut off the surplus and knot the line to the barrel. Some fusee clocks are fitted with a chain instead of the gut line. If the chain breaks it must be re-riveted.

Re-Winding the Fusee

When the clock is re-assembled the procedure in connection with the fusee is as follows: having placed the train in and pinned up the plates, leave the line to one side. Now wind the line on to the barrel, set the barrel up—that is, wind the mainspring by the barrel arbor square—about three-quarters of a turn, and tighten up the click; then wind the fusee slowly, making sure the line rides in the grooves correctly. Should you find the line inclined to run off the grooves of the fusee, push it into position; then continue to wind to the top and see that the line lifts the stop piece correctly and so ultimately stops the winding. We may then let the clock run down a little to make sure all is free; arrest the escape wheel, put the pallets in position and continue the assembly and oiling, etc.

In the spring-driven clock, the cone-shaped piece which is known as the fusee allows the force of the mainspring to be practically the same when fully wound as when almost run down. For this reason, the fusee clock is the better, but many clocks have no fusee, and are known as "going barrel." These can be taken to pieces in the same way as those we have described. The movement may not be fitted to the case in the same manner, but there are so many methods adopted today that it would be futile to attempt a description of all. The procedure, however, will be obvious.

The minute hand is usually held in position by a collet and pin, but there may be no spring to be pressed down when replacing this pin.

The hour hand of such a clock is usually held in position by friction, and can be removed with the finger and thumb. In some clocks the minute hand may be held by a screw collet, while in others it may be held on friction tight without a collet. Examine each clock thoroughly before taking it to pieces and always bear in mind that clocks and watches are delicate instruments, and that to use undue force must have disastrous results.

Self Testing Questions

(1) *How would you remove the hands of a Grandfather clock?*

(2) *What is a "going-barrel" clock?*

(3) *Are the pallets essential to clock mechanism?*

(4) *What is the crutch of a clock?*

(5) *When is a clock in beat?*

(6) *Is the line an essential part of a clock?*

(7) *Should you apply oil to the pendulum of a clock?*

(8) *What is the escapement?*

THE ANSWERS ARE ON PAGE 546.

LESSON 2

French Clocks

As the French clockmakers have specialised in delicate work, French clocks are smaller and very much finer—though not better made—than English. For this reason, the simple repair that may suffice for a large and more robust English clock, may not be satisfactory for a clock of French make.

In this lesson, therefore, we shall explain how to take a French clock to pieces and how to re-assemble it; for there are hundreds of thousands of French clocks in the British Isles. They are familiar to us in their marble or decorative gilt cases.

Nearly all French makers use the same method of fixing this particular type of movement in its case.

Taking to Pieces

Lift the clock carefully, tilting it slightly forward in order to steady the pendulum and to prevent injury to the suspension spring. Open the back door of the clock and remove the pendulum. If the bell proves to be an obstruction, unscrew and remove it. The pendulum hangs from the suspension spring (in some of the earlier movements silk is used as the suspension), and the top part is fitted with a hook. This hook rests on a pin which runs through the brass block attached to the suspension spring. Immediately inside the door you will see two screws which are screwed into long brass straps fixed on to the front part of the clock. Unscrew these, at the same time holding the front of the clock, and you will find that the back door with its fitting will come away. The movement can now be drawn out from the front.

Remove the hands and draw out the pins which hold the movement to the dial. Place the key of the clock on the winding square and turn as if winding; this will enable the click to be lifted out of position; now unwind the clock, or, to be more correct, the mainspring. It is advisable to unwind only half a turn at a time and to let the click return into position and to re-grip the key. Unwind both mainsprings in this manner. The pallets must not be removed until these things have been done. The pivots are so fine that, were the clock allowed to run down as was the case when we were repairing English clocks, they might break off. Now we can remove the pallets and the parts on the front plate. (The front plate is that which faces the dial, and has attached to it the strike mechanism and the wheels which operate the hands; the back plate is at the back of the movement, *i.e.* the plate which faces you when the case is opened at the back.) Fig. 4 will show where these parts are placed. Remove the winding ratchets and the small wheel with the long pipe, to which the minute hand is attached. This is held on by a spring grip, and can be pulled off if given a slight turn backward.

Procure a small lidless box of about 4 in. square, and on it, with its back plate uppermost, lay the clock.

We can now unpin and remove the back plate. As was the case with the English clock, all the wheels,

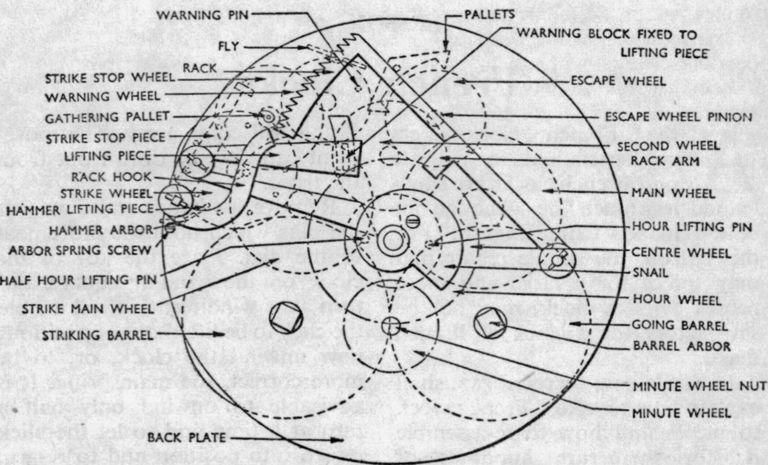

Fig. 4. *French clock movement, showing details of striking mechanism and other parts which are normally concealed by the back plate in dotted lines.*

etc., will be left standing up on the front plate. Take out the wheels and scratch a small "s" on the strike barrel. You will find that the wheel next but one to the fly of the strike part will not come away; leave this until the last; then, turning the plate over in the hand, with a light hammer tap the extended pivot to release the small steel piece (the gathering pallet).

It is a good plan when taking the wheels out to place them on the table in their correct position. That is to say the fly should be at the top, then the wheel with one pin, and the extended pivot, down to the barrel. Treat the going train in the same manner. (The word train means a set of wheels.)

We shall now clean the clock with petrol or benzine. Pour a little of the liquid into a bowl. Dip in a brush—a watchmaker's brush does well for this, and is similar to the domestic plate brush—and clean all the wheels, etc. Be sure to remove all congealed oil. The barrels can be opened by prising up the cover with a small screw-driver, at the point where a segment has been cut away. To remove the arbors (the steel pieces with the winding square) turn them slightly backward, and unhook them from the mainspring. Clean them and the barrels, but do not allow the spirit to get inside to the mainspring.

Now dry all the pieces with a clean linen rag and brush them with a clean dry brush. With a piece of rag clean out the holes of the barrel —both the cover and the barrel. (Clockmakers use long strips of chamois leather for this purpose.)

Replacing Barrel Cover

Replace the barrel arbors and see that the mainspring hooks on. Apply four or five oilerfuls of oil to the top edges of the mainspring and put back the covers. The side of the barrel has a small dot which is the position of the cut-out segment. The covers should snap on, but if they are stiff, proceed as is shown in Fig. 5, using a piece of wood as the block. The large holes of the plates are cleaned in a similar manner to the barrel holes, while the smaller holes are cleaned with "peg-wood" (a special wood which can be purchased at the tool shop). An orange stick such as is used in nail-cleaning will answer well for this purpose, but a thin stick of ordinary soft wood will do. Sharpen the wood to a long point and twist well in each hole until the wood leaves the hole quite clean. Sharpen or scrape the point before its re-insertion. Cut the piece of wood chisel shape and work it up and down the cogs or pinions of the wheels until they are quite bright. The holes of the pieces from the front plate which are fitted on to posts must also be cleaned. If the holes are large enough, use the strip of rag, otherwise the wood.

Re-Assembly

When all is perfectly clean and dry, we are ready to re-assemble the works. Replace the front plate on the box and place all the wheels in position, not forgetting the two steel pieces of the striking side. An oilerful of oil should be applied to the two pivots of each barrel—that is, to the pivots which work in the barrel itself—before the barrels are placed in position.

If you examine closely with an eye-glass, you will see that the pinion next to the wheel with the strike-pins has a small piece of one of its leaves cut away. (The teeth of a pinion are called leaves.) On the wheel engaging the pinion—the wheel with the strike-pins—you will find a dot between two teeth. This notched pinion leaf must work between the two teeth marked. Now replace the top plate and pin it up with two pins. Take great care to get all the pivots into their holes in the plate. Use a little pressure on the plate and get the larger wheels into position first. To accomplish this you will have to use tweezers.

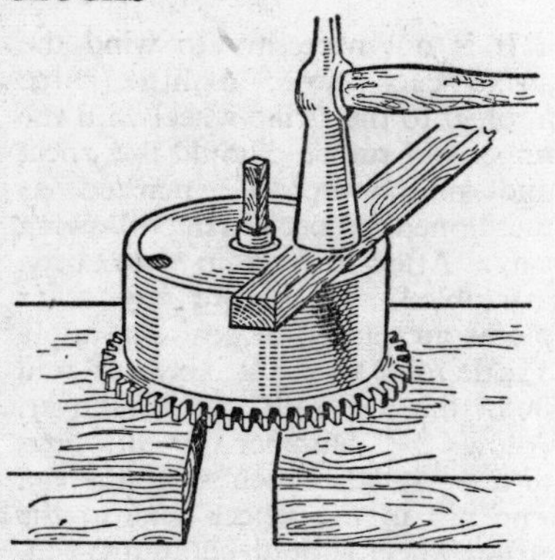

Fig. 5. *How a tight barrel cover is replaced by using a wooden block.*

We can now oil all the pivots of the front plate and re-assemble the ratchet and click-work. Wind the clock two or three clicks on both sides to see that all is free and that the trains run well. Replace the striking pieces, oiling the posts slightly first, and apply a little oil to the long arbor before placing on the long pipe with the wheel. Wind the strike train a few clicks, making the clock strike: when it has finished and the train is locked, place the gathering pallet in position, with the sharp edge, or acting part, upright, or farthermost from the rack with which it engages. When the strike is at rest, the pin on the wheel next to the fly must be immediately under the fly. This allows half a turn run before it is arrested by the small lever projecting into the movement from the front plate. If the pin is not in the position required, let the mainspring down, remove one pin and lift the plate one side, only just high enough to allow you to disengage the pinion referred to, and turn it round where required. You may have to make one or two attempts before it is correct.

It is not necessary to wind the strike each time; a little force applied to the strike wheel with the finger will suffice. Should the wheel and pinion not be marked as mentioned, proceed in the following way. After the train has been assembled, and before any other pieces are placed in position, apply a little force to the strike wheel and hold the fly with the forefinger. Allow the hammer to lift and directly it has fallen stop the fly. The pin in the wheel next to the strike wheel should be about $\frac{1}{8}$ in. away from the steel block which arrests it when the strike is finished. If this is not the case, unpin the plate (see above) and correct the position. When you are satisfied that the striking is accurate, place the other two plate-pins in position and tap with a light hammer to make secure. English clocks are not so marked, and, as the gathering pallet-tail arrests the striking by butting on to a pin or block on the rack, this gathering pallet-tail must be about $\frac{1}{8}$ in. away from the pin or block when the hammer falls. The position of the pin on the wheel next the fly must be under the fly as just stated.

Oiling French Clocks

Now we replace the pallets as with the English clock, and also the dial. You should use less oil when oiling a French clock. It is advisable to make another oiler and to use thinner wire. Place the minute hand on temporarily and let the clock strike the hour. Remove the minute hand and put on the hour hand, pointing to the hour, as indicated by the number of blows struck. The general oiling and putting into correct beat, etc., are as were explained for the English clock.

The construction of carriage or portable clocks is the same as that of the French clock just dealt with, but a platform escapement is used instead of a pendulum. This is virtually part of a watch, and its cleaning will be described in Lesson 6.

Turn the clock upside down, and you will find a small screw in the centre of the plate. Remove this and the plate will come away. At each corner screws with long heads will be seen. Remove these. Now lift up the base of the case, and with it will come the movement. Care must be taken with the case part, as the glasses and door are liable to fall inward. First let down the mainsprings, remove the four screws securing the escapement and lift it away. The wheel which gears into the escapement has its teeth on the side, and is known as the contrate wheel. It is important to see that this wheel has the minimum end shake (freedom between the plates). When assembling, adjust any excess of freedom by means of the small screw provided at one end.

Replacing the Escapement

Assuming the clock to have been cleaned and assembled, we are ready to place the escapement in position. The holes in the plate or platform are left a little large to allow for adjustment. You will understand what follows better after reading Lesson 6. The balance and balance-cock are placed in position last. Screw the platform in position, but do not screw tightly. With an eye-glass examine the gearing, or intersection of the wheel with the escape pinion, and see that the depth is correct. Tighten the screws and examine again. If a small adjustment is necessary as a result of the screws drawing, a light tap with the hammer on the edge of the platform should suffice. The balance and balance-cock can now be replaced.

Some French clocks are fitted with what is known as a hanging escapement. In this the escapement hangs vertically. In such clocks the wheel which gears with the escape wheel is similar to the rest of the train.

Self Testing Questions

(1) *What would you use to clean a clock with?*

(2) *What is the gathering pallet?*

(3) *How would you put the striking mechanism right?*

(4) *Would it be correct to oil the wheels of a clock?*

(5) *How would you set the hands of a French clock to coincide with the striking?*

(6) *What is the essential adjustment in connection with the escapement of a carriage clock?*

THE ANSWERS ARE ON PAGE 547.

LESSON 3

Foreign Clocks

HERE we shall deal with American and German clocks as distinct from French. Generally speaking, they are of cheaper manufacture, and in recent years many clocks of similar construction have been made in England. In fact, unless such a clock is named or marked, it is difficult to say whether it is English or German (Fig. 6). American clocks, however, usually have some characteristic marking. The instruction given here will, therefore, have wide application. Some of the better foreign clocks are fitted with barrels for the mainsprings. If so, the instructions given in Lesson 2 will usually apply. The clock which we propose to clean and oil now has striking mechanism and no barrels. Hence the mainsprings can be seen in the movement. Begin by examining the clock to see how the movement can best be removed from the case. In some foreign clocks the dial is fixed to the case so that the hands must be removed whilst the clock is still cased up. The movement will, therefore, come away from the back. Others are straightforward.

Having taken the pendulum off, the movement out of the case and the hands and dial off, proceed in the following way. Place a piece of wire in the escape wheel and continue as explained in Lesson 1.

To clean, procure a large bowl and, if possible, sufficient petrol to half-submerge the movement when it is laid flat in the bowl. Remove the wire and allow the clock to run down in the petrol. When it has half run down, turn it over so that the other side receives the same treatment. With a brush—a clean varnish brush of about ½ in. width will do—brush thoroughly all the parts accessible whilst the movement is still in the petrol; brush the pivot-holes well to remove any old oil, and give the teeth of the escape wheel a good cleaning also. When the movement is clean take it out of the bowl and shake off as much of the petrol as possible.

Wind the clock and allow it to run down. Next, wipe the plates with a piece of clean linen rag. Then wind the clock again and let it run down once more. Put the movement on one side for about half an hour to let it dry. The mainsprings being exposed, all the spirit will have evaporated before you re-oil.

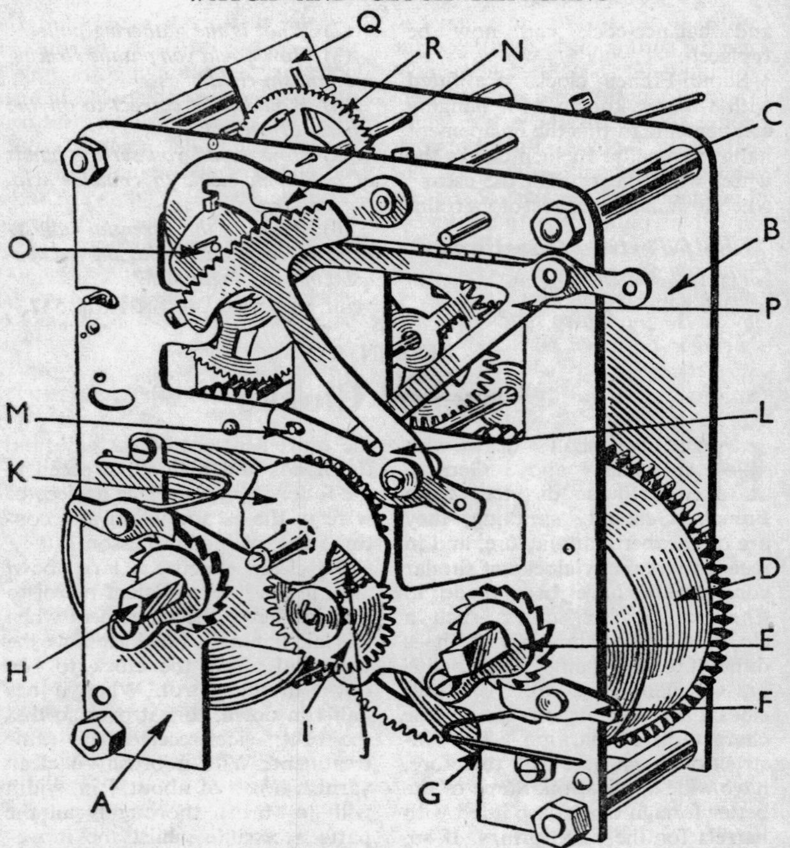

Fig. 6. *English striking movement of foreign design.* A, *front plate;* B, *back plate;* C, *plate pillar;* D, *barrel;* E, *ratchet;* F, *click;* G, *click spring;* H, *winding square;* I, *minute wheel;* J, *hour wheel;* K, *snail;* L, *rack;* M, *rack arm;* N, *strike locking piece;* O, *gathering pallet;* P, *lifting piece;* Q, *fly;* R, *pin wheel.*

In the meantime clean the pallets, the pallet cock and pendulum, and any other parts which have been removed. As the pallet holes are fine, they can be cleaned with wood as described in Lesson 2.

Oil all the pivot holes and wind up the mainspring about five or six clicks to ensure that the oil works into the holes. Now assemble and oil the escapement as in Lesson 2. Wind up the mainsprings fully and oil the top edge of each spring as was done when oiling the French clock.

It now remains to replace the dial and hands, exercising the same precautions as explained in Lesson 2, when placing the hands in position.

We will now consider the foreign-made alarm clock. In dealing with this the removal of the movement from the case is simple. After doing this, remove the hands and dial. In order to do so, you may have to use the cutting pliers to take off the minute hand; hold the pliers under the centre of the hand as if you were going to cut off the arbor which carries it. Apply a little pressure, and the hand will come away. The hour hand and the alarm hand can usually be pulled off with the fingers. With the hands and dial removed, hold the movement in the left hand and, using the flat-nose pliers, remove the pin which holds the hair-spring in position. Turn the balance (*i.e.* the wheel to which the hair-spring is attached) until the end of the hair-spring—or more correctly the balance-spring—is free from the piece to which it was pinned and also from the index or regulator. You may have to use the tweezers; just touch the spring, which will then free itself and jump out.

Removing the Pallets

When the spring is quite free, unscrew the screw with the square head opposite to the regulator, using the flat-nose pliers. This will release the balance, which must be lifted out carefully and put on one side. Place a piece of wire in an arm of the escape wheel and work the pallets with the tweezers until the wheel is bound. The plate of an alarm clock is usually held together by nuts; unscrew all four nuts about half a turn, and the nut nearest the pallets two or three turns, or sufficiently to allow that end of the plate to be lifted high enough for the pallets to be removed. The plates are pierced to economise in metal, and the pallet hole is left on a thin strip of brass. This is convenient, because in removing the pallets all we have to do is to guide to one side the pivot which has been removed. Then it will be free, and the pallets can easily be removed.

Care should be taken that the plate is not lifted more than is necessary in removing the pivot, otherwise the escape-wheel pivot may be released, with disastrous results. The pallet pivot is usually left short by the manufacturers to facilitate its easy removal. Screw the nuts up tightly again. Wind the alarm mainspring as well as the works or going mainspring, and place the movement in the petrol bath, where the clock is allowed to run down. Remove the wire from the escape wheel, and proceed as for cleaning the striking clock.

Cleaning the Pallets

When the movement is clean and dry, clean the pallet holes with wood: also the countersinks of the screws into which the balance pivots work.

Place the pallets and the balance to which the spring is attached into the petrol. Brush the pallets well, especially the two small pins and the fork end. These pieces are delicate, and great care should be exercised. Brush the balance pivots and the pin which operates in the pallet fork very carefully indeed, making sure not to touch the balance-spring. Dry the pallets with a soft brush, and wipe the balance pivots with a piece of clean linen rag.

We are now ready to re-assemble. The movement, having run down, must not be wound until the balance is in position. Loosen the four nuts as before and place the pallets in position. Replace the balance between the two countersunk screws and screw up that which is opposite to the regulator. Tighten this screw until the balance has a little shake but is at the same time free. Turn the balance round so that the pin works into the fork of the pallets, and then manipulate the balance-spring so that it passes between the index or regulator pins. The end of the balance-spring must then be guided into the hole of the piece to which the spring is fixed. The balance-spring will, no doubt, show where it was secured before. Replace the pin to secure the spring, but first lightly, and see that the pin in the balance works so that it brings the fork of the pallets exactly opposite to it. The clock should then be in beat.

Arranging the Spring

If this is not so, unpin the spring and either push it farther into the hole or pull it farther out so that the balance pin brings the pallet fork to a central position as explained. Now press in the balance-spring pin tightly. Wind the clock, and it should start working immediately. Oil all pivots as before, applying a little oil to each of the pallet pins and to the balance pivots, making sure not to touch the balance-spring with the oil. Apply the merest trace of oil to the balance pin which works in the pallet fork. Also apply a fair amount of oil to the edges of both the time-keeping and the alarm mainsprings, winding them fully first. Replace the dial, and then turn the alarm hand set piece slowly until the alarm is set going. Now place the alarm hand at 12 o'clock and the hour hand at the same hour; press on the minute hand lightly, pointing it about three minutes to the hour. Set the alarm hand to one o'clock, turn the other hands round slowly, and the alarm should release at about three minutes to the hour. If it is not correct, lift the minute hand off and replace it correctly.

When you are satisfied that it is correct, hold the movement so that the end on to which the set hands piece is fitted rests upon something solid, such as a stake or the anvil of the vice. Then, with the movement facing upward, give the centre of the minute hand a tap with the hammer to secure it. The movement is now ready for replacement.

Self Testing Questions

(1) *How would you dry a movement which has been cleaned with petrol?*

(2) *Is there any general rule as to fitting the movement to the case?*

(3) *When is an alarm clock in beat?*

(4) *How do you set the alarm right?*

(5) *What is the balance?*

(6) *Should the balance-spring be oiled?*

THE ANSWERS ARE ON PAGE 547.

LESSON 4

Electric Clocks

As the synchronous motor, or mains plug-in, is the most popular, we shall discuss this first.

The mechanism of such clocks is very simple indeed. They have no mainspring or escapement, but just a train of wheels terminating in a rotor. Synchronous clocks are made to work from the rotor—or escapement end of the mechanism—backward to the centre wheel. Apart from their requiring oil, there is little that needs attention in these clocks, provided that the electrical part is in order. If one of

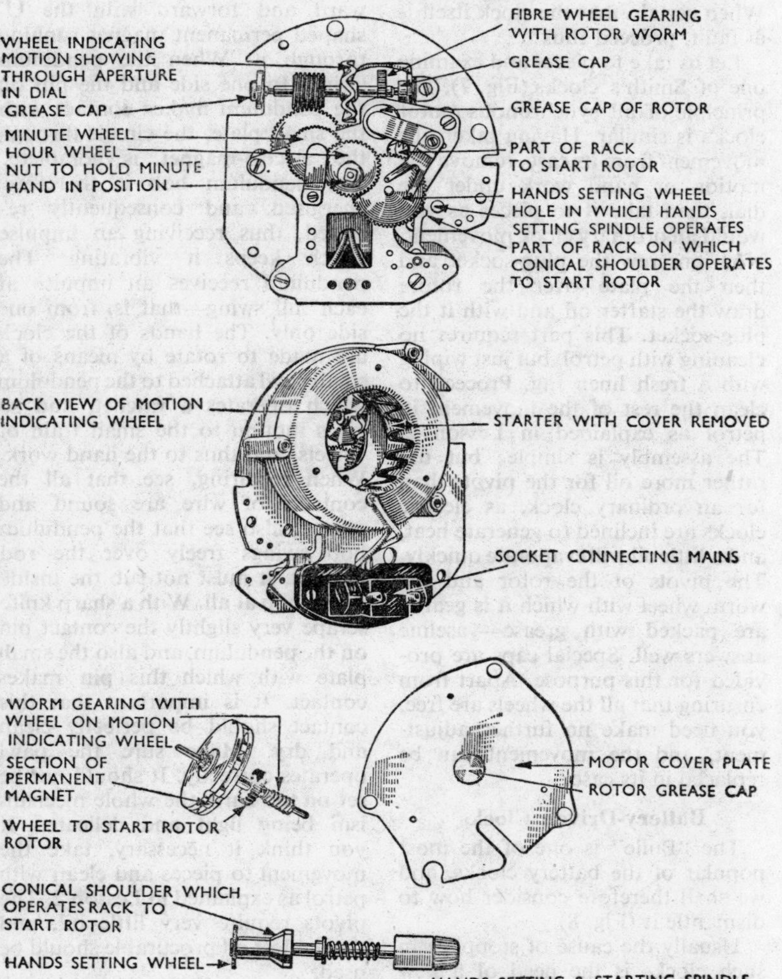

Fig. 7. *Parts of Smith electric clock, a typical synchronous motor clock.* Above, *movement with dial removed;* below, *back of movement with motor cover removed.*

these clocks stops, do not start to take it to pieces until you have made sure that the power has not been cut off. Some of these clocks are self-starters; others will stop if the power is cut off, even for a short period. The self-starters have the disadvantage of showing the incorrect time should the power be temporarily cut off. Make sure the connections of the plugs to the mains and those to the clock are in order.

When certain that the clock itself is at fault, proceed thus:

Let us take to pieces and examine one of Smith's clocks (Fig. 7). The principle of all synchronous motor clocks is similar. Having taken the movement from its case, remove the motion or hand work under the dial, then take it to pieces as you would an ordinary clock movement. Now unscrew the plug-socket and then the plate over the rotor; draw the starter off and with it the plug-socket. This part requires no cleaning with petrol, but just wiping with a fresh linen rag. Proceed to clean the rest of the movement in petrol as explained in Lesson 2. The assembly is simple; but use rather more oil for the pivots than for an ordinary clock, as electric clocks are inclined to generate heat, and a little oil will evaporate quickly. The pivots of the rotor and the worm wheel with which it is geared are packed with grease—vaseline answers well. Special caps are provided for this purpose. Apart from ensuring that all the wheels are free, you need make no further adjustment, and the movement can be replaced in its case.

Battery-Driven Clocks

The "Bulle" is one of the most popular of the battery clocks, and we shall therefore consider how to dismantle it (Fig. 8).

Usually the cause of stoppage in such clocks is the need of a new battery, so satisfy yourself that there is sufficient power in the battery to drive the pendulum. If there is any doubt on this score, it is advisable to fit a new battery before doing anything else. If you understand how the clock functions, you will find its repair simple.

The pendulum bob, which consists of a solenoid, swings backward and forward with the U-shaped permanent magnet running through it. When the pendulum swings to one side and the pin on the pendulum makes contact with the small plate, the circuit through the electro-magnet is complete. The pendulum bob is therefore energised, and consequently repelled, thus receiving an impulse which keeps it vibrating. The pendulum receives an impulse at each full swing—that is, from one side only. The hands of the clock are made to rotate by means of a small pawl attached to the pendulum which operates a ratchet, and so gives motion to the small train of wheels, and thus to the hand work. When repairing, see that all the contacts of wire are sound and secure; also see that the pendulum bob swings freely over the rod magnet. It must not rub the inside of the bob at all. With a sharp knife scrape very slightly the contact pin on the pendulum, and also the small plate with which this pin makes contact. It is important that this contact should be perfectly clean and dry. Make sure the pawl operates correctly. It should not be set on too hard, the whole mechanism being light and delicate. If you think it necessary, take the movement to pieces and clean with petrol as explained in Lesson 2. The pivots require very little oil, and the lightest oil procurable should be used.

If after being set in motion the clock still fails to function properly, it may be necessary to renew the solenoid pendulum bob, as there may be a fracture in the winding. This fault, however, is most unlikely. The clock is in beat when the pendulum bob is in the centre of the U-shaped rod when at rest. As, however, the pendulum receives impulse from one side only, the accurate levelling is not vital, always providing the bob is free of the rod as mentioned before. Regulating the clock is effected as with an ordinary pendulum clock.

Self Testing Questions

(1) *What is the first thing you would look for when a mains clock stops?*

(2) *If a mains clock loses or gains, how would you regulate it?*

(3) *How would you regulate a Bulle clock?*

(4) *Do electric clocks need oil?*

(5) *Are electric clocks accurate time-keepers?*

THE ANSWERS ARE ON PAGE 547.

LESSON 5

Portable or Travelling Clocks

THE clocks which we propose to discuss in this Lesson are the type usually fitted into fancy chromium or leather cases, with a supporting strut at the back. Such clocks are really large watches, and greater care must be exercised in their repair than when dealing with the clocks described in previous Lessons. The causes of the stopping of such clocks or of their not keeping good time are many, so we must give a general survey.

It is correct to say that most clocks fail to function owing to the presence in their works of dust or dirt. Thick or congealed oil is a common cause, but we must realise that even a speck of dust may be sufficient to stop a clock of the type we are now considering. Absolute cleanliness is therefore vital when repairing these time-pieces. We have mentioned dust and thickened oil. Broken mainsprings are another cause of failure. In this Lesson, therefore, let us assume that the clock we are repairing needs a new mainspring. At the same time we shall freshen the oil in the more vital parts as we would if we were merely cleaning and overhauling a watch. In the next Lesson we shall take a watch to pieces, and much of the information given there will apply here too.

First, we shall need three watch-

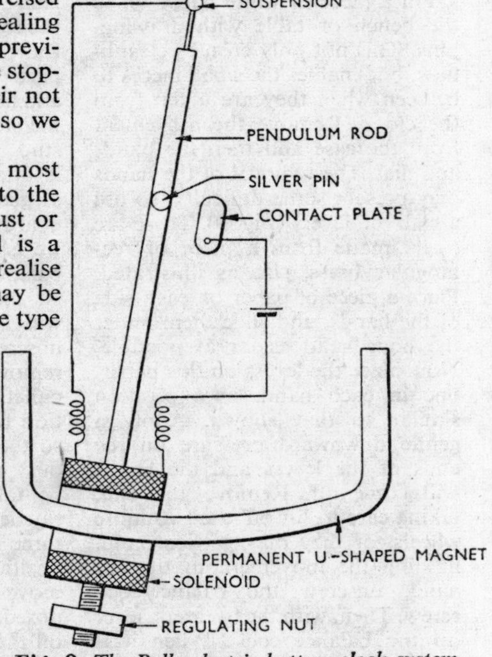

Fig. 8. *The Bulle electric battery clock system.*

Fig. 9. *Showing method of using the hand lifting levers.*

maker's screw-drivers, an oiler of about the dimensions of an ordinary sewing-needle, and a watchmaker's brush. It would be advisable also to have some peg-wood, one or two pieces of pith, and a piece of chalk with which to clean the brush, and benzine.

All the above-mentioned articles can be secured at a very small cost.

Pin a piece of white paper on to the bench or table with drawing-pins. This not only ensures cleanliness, but enables the small pieces to be seen when they are taken from the clock. Remove the movement from the case and then the hands and dial. The removal of the hands may present some difficulty, so use a pair of levers (Fig. 9). These are easily made from a piece of rectangular brass, size as illustrated. Place a piece of paper on each side of the hands, and slide them under the hour hand as far as possible. Now place the levers on this paper, one in each hand, in a position similar to that shown. Apply a gentle downward pressure on the ends of the levers and the hands will come off. Remove the dial, taking care to lift off the two loose wheels, or they may get lost, and, holding the movement in the left hand, unscrew the balance-cock screw. Then, with the tweezers, lever up the balance cock. When it is loosened, hold it with the tweezers and lift it up very carefully; the balance will also come with it. It is quite safe to hold it so, and the balance will hang downward by the balance-spring. Lower it carefully on to the bench or table; then, when the balance touches the bench, turn over the balance-cock and lay it upside down. Now lift the balance up and, turning it over, lay it on the cock in its original position. Place the forefinger of the left hand on the foot of the balance-cock, on the part where the steady pins are, and hold the cock down firmly. With the small screw-driver, unscrew the stud to which the balance-spring is attached. If the index pins have a guard over them—usually the guard forms one pin—turn this and we shall be able to remove the balance with its spring complete. As the mainspring is broken, there will be no power on. So we can unscrew the pallet cock, lever it up, remove it, and then take out the pallets. Most clocks of this description have a separate bar or bridge, so the barrel can be removed without the whole clock having to be taken to pieces. Unscrew the ratchet winding wheel, and then the three screws which hold the bar in position. Lever this bar up and remove it; the barrel will now be exposed. Remove the barrel and prise off the cover as explained in Lesson 2. Fig. 11 in Lesson 6 will explain any technical names not at the moment clear.

If the mainspring is broken in the centre, the barrel arbor will be removed easily, and with it a broken piece of spring. Hold the barrel in the left hand, and with the tweezers in the right hand grip the broken end of the mainspring. Pull it gently, and the spring will come away. When you feel it uncoiling, release the spring from the tweezers and hold the entire barrel in the left hand, well into the palm, and close the fingers over it. Manipulate so that the spring uncoils completely. By following these directions you will be sure not to lose the barrel.

Fitting a New Spring

If it is broken in the centre, a new spring will have to be fitted. Should the end which is attached to the barrel be broken, however, you can use the same spring again. The instructions for re-hooking the spring apply also when a new one is fitted. There are several methods of attaching the mainspring. A good one is to rivet a short piece of mainspring on to the spring. In the case of a new spring it will, no doubt, be necessary to shorten it, so we could use a piece of that. To mend it, however, a short piece must be broken off the spring; this will leave it a little shorter, which does not, as a rule, matter. Having broken off a piece of about ⅜ in. long, proceed in the following way.

Heat the end of the spring to soften it, making sure that the heat does not run too far up the spring. Then drill a small hole in the end. Treat the small piece of spring in a similar manner. Clean the ends of the mainspring and of the short piece with an emery stick; pin the short piece on to the mainspring, cut the pin short and rivet (Fig. 10).

Fig. 10. *Showing method of riveting piece to main spring to form a hook.*

Clockmakers use a special tool with which to wind the spring back into the barrel, but this can be done quite satisfactorily with the fingers. Hold the barrel in the left hand and coil the spring back, starting at the end to which the short piece has been fixed. Re-assemble and oil the barrel as explained in Lesson 2. Replace it in the clock and screw the bar into position.

The pith now comes into use. Hold the balance in the left hand, and with the pith dig the balance pivots into it. This may seem drastic, but it is quite safe. Unscrew the plate into which is set a jewel end-stone, from the bottom plate—the equivalent of the front plate of the larger clock—and, with a pointed piece of peg-wood, clean the balance hole and the pallet holes and also the jewelled end-piece. This should also be done to the balance cock.

It will be better to dip the pallets in benzine and brush carefully with the soft watch-brush. Wind up the clock about a dozen clicks. Hold the movement upright in the left hand, and, while the train is still running, give the edge of the movement a few light knocks with the back of the watch-brush. Any pieces of loose dust, etc., will thus be released.

Oiling

Now replace the pallets and pallet-cock, wind the mainspring a few clicks and apply a very small amount of watch oil to the pallet-cock pivot. Apply a little oil to the acting faces of the pallets, and work the pallet backward and forward a few times so that the oil is carried to all the teeth of the escape wheel. Apply a little oil to the balance hole, and, when the balance is replaced, the pivot will push the oil into the parts where it is required. Attach the balance and the spring to the cock in a similar manner to that employed when it was removed. Lift the balance a little away from the cock and apply oil to the hole. Particular care must be taken to ensure that no oil touches the balance-spring. Replace the balance in the watch and see that the pin on the balance—the ruby or impulse pin—works between the fork of the pallets. No oil is applied to this pin. The clock should now start off. Apply oil to all the pivots, reassemble the dial and hands, and fit back into the case.

To clean the watch-brush draw it across the chalk three or four times; then rub the bristles well with clean tissue paper; finally give the brush one or two sharp taps on something solid to ensure it is free of dust.

Pith, as the name suggests, is a soft pithy substance taken from the stem of a plant, and is sold by the tool shops in bundles.

Self Testing Questions

(1) *Why would you liken the movement of a travelling clock to that of a watch?*

(2) *How are the hands of such clocks held in position?*

(3) *What is the ruby pin?*

(4) *How do you oil the balance pivots?*

(5) *What is likely to make this type of clock stop?*

(6) *With what part must particular care be taken when oiling and what part must not be oiled at all?*

THE ANSWERS ARE ON PAGE 548.

LESSON 6

Watches

THE repair of watches is probably more fascinating than the repair of clocks. Watches, although mysterious contrivances, are quite simple, but they require the utmost patience and a delicate touch. In no circumstances should force be used.

As with clocks, most repairs to watches mean simply the removal of dust and dirt from the works, and freshening the oil. Unlike clocks, however, watches will not run for such long periods without attention. Let us take to pieces a watch, and make some small adjustment and clean it. First, pin a piece of white paper on the bench as in Lesson 5. Then remove the movement from the case. To do this the winding piece must first be taken out and then the case-screws (Fig. 11).

Remove the hands and dial as in the previous Lesson. With an eye-glass, examine the balance-spring carefully. Frequently a watch is made unserviceable because its balance-spring has got caught up, or because two coils of the balance-spring instead of one get jerked between the index-pins. On the other hand, oil may have got on to the spring and made the coils stick together—which can cause the watch to gain time mysteriously. Should you find that there is anything amiss, make a mental note of it. Remove the balance-cock with the balance, and dismantle the watch as explained in Lesson 5.

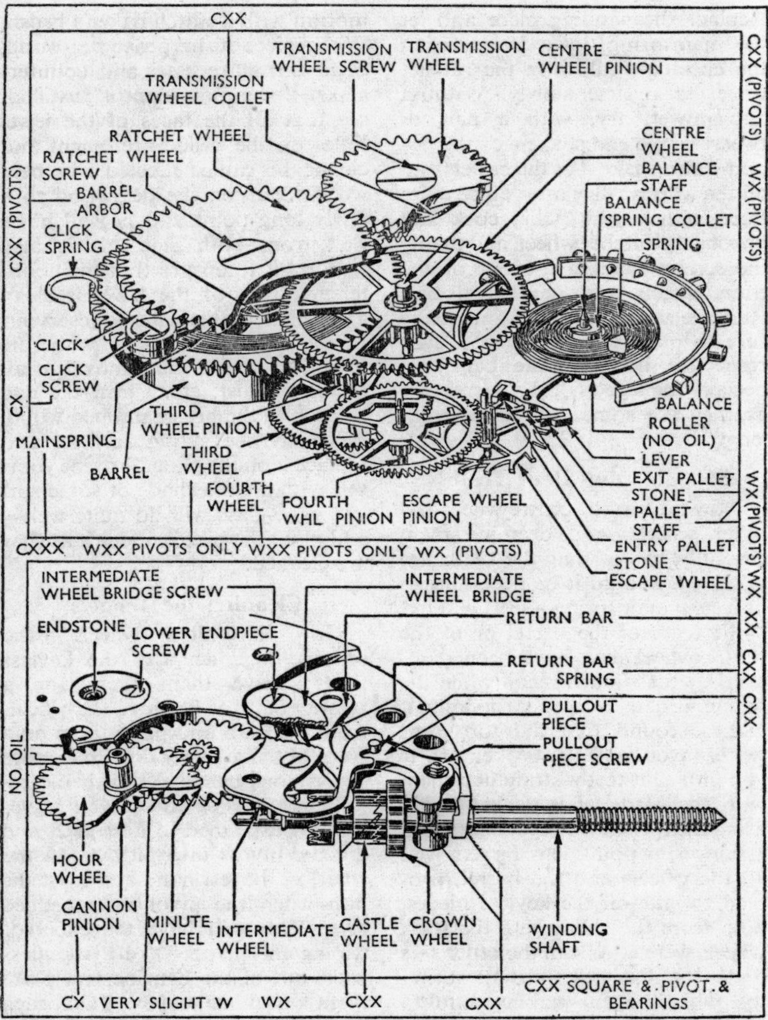

BY COURTESY OF OMEGA WATCH CO. (ENGLAND) LTD.

Fig. 11. Above: *watch mechanism, with bridge work, etc., cut away to show the working parts.* Below: *the same watch under the dial, with some of the bridge-work cut away. Oiling parts, and the oil to be used, are thus marked:* C, *clock oil;* W, *watch oil.* XXX, *oil generously;* XX, *oil moderately;* X, *oil lightly.*

After the dial has been removed, the hour and minute wheels can be lifted off. With a pair of flat-nosed pliers, which have the jaws lined with brass, remove the canon pinion; this will come off quite easily with a gentle backward twist if you pull up at the same time.

Replace the winding piece and let the mainspring down by releasing the click and allowing the ratchet wheel to reverse slowly. Without any power, try, with a pair of tweezers, the end shake—or the up-and-down shake—of the pallets and all the wheels; they must all be quite free. Remove the pallet cock and pallets, the ratchet wheel, and finally the screws holding the bar of the train wheels and the barrel bar. Remove these two bars and make sure to place the screws into their respective holes in the bars; especially the screws of the barrel bar, as they are sometimes of different lengths.

Straightening Bent Teeth

Now lift out the centre wheel and other wheels, and examine them carefully to see that the teeth are not bent. Should it be necessary to fit a new mainspring—see Lesson 5—the teeth of the barrel or of the centre wheel may have been damaged by the sudden recoil when the spring broke. Very occasionally it will be found that the top third wheel pivot has been broken off. If you find bent teeth, straighten them with the blade of a pocket knife, using the root of the preceding tooth as a levering point. Having removed all the wheels and the barrel, proceed to take off the keyless pieces, both from the side where the train wheels were and from the other side under the dial. Lay them all out on the white paper, making sure to place the screws with their respective parts. Remove the lower end piece and place the lower plate, or bottom plate as it is called—the plate on which the wheels stood—in the benzine bath. Remove the plate and dry it with a piece of clean linen rag. Hold it in a piece of tissue paper, and brush it in a circular motion with a watchmaker's brush. With a piece of sharpened peg-wood, clean out all recesses and countersinks. If the movement is jewelled, see that all the faces of the jewel holes on the inside are bright and clean; this can be effected with peg-wood. Sharpen the peg-wood to a fairly long point and peg all holes well from both sides. It is also important to ensure that the countersunk part of the jewel is clean and bright, as this is the oil reservoir. Finally, dab the plate with the brush, to ensure the removal of all pieces of dust, etc. Clean the end piece with the brush and peg-wood, especially the acting surface, and replace it on the plate. Provide yourself with a glass shade of some sort—a wine-glass will do quite well—and place the pieces under it as they are cleaned.

Cleaning the Wheels

Now, place all the wheels in the benzine together with the keyless parts; leave them there for a minute or two. Remove the wheels from the bath and place them on a piece of tissue paper first, to remove superfluous benzine, and then carefully brush. Peg the pinion leaves well, as explained in Lesson 2, and dig the pivots into pith. Hold the wheel in the left hand and twist the pith when the pivot is embedded in it. This will have the effect of wiping the pivot. Take the keyless parts out of the benzine and place them on tissue paper. Take each piece in turn from the paper and, holding it down on the white paper with the tweezers, brush it well; then turn it over and brush the other side. Such pieces are usually too small to be held in the fingers with tissue paper, and to hold them without paper invites the steel parts to rust.

Remove the keyless wheel from the barrel-bar and place both the bar and the wheel in the bath with the train-wheel bar. Clean these pieces as previously instructed. Take the barrel to pieces and clean it as described in the last Lesson. The pallets are cleaned in a similar manner to the keyless pieces. Make sure that the jewelled pallet stones are bright, especially the acting surfaces. The fork is cleaned with a piece of peg-wood cut chisel-shape; rub the inside of the fork up and down very carefully. Clean the pallet cock well. We are now ready for the balance cock and balance, so remove the balance with its spring from the cock (see Lesson 5). Remove next the two small screws from the under-side of the balance cock in order to release the index and with it the end piece. Place all these pieces in benzine. Remove the cock and clean it as you did the plates. Re-assemble the index after cleaning the end piece and pass the chisel-shaped piece of peg-wood, newly cut, between the index pins to ensure their freedom from oil.

Cleaning the Balance

Now place the balance on the tissue paper to help to absorb the superfluous benzine; hold the balance with the tweezers, balance-spring uppermost, and, with the watch-brush, give the spring a few light dabs. Great care must be exercised when doing this. All traces of oil will now be removed. Now proceed, as explained in Lesson 5, to finish cleaning the balance. The watch is then ready to be assembled.

Assembling the Watch

Hold the bottom plate with tissue paper in the left hand; having oiled the barrel during assembly, place in position, first oiling both pivots which work in the plates; then the pull-out piece screw. Apply a little clock oil to both the pivots of the centre wheel before placing it in position—it is most advisable when oiling watches to use the recognised watch and clock oil as supplied by the tool shop. Now screw the barrel bar in position, and then place the third and escape wheels in position and screw the bar on, taking care to guide the pivots into their respective holes, using very little pressure on the bar in so doing. Assemble the keyless work, oiling at the same time with clock oil all parts where friction takes place. Now wind the watch up a few clicks and see that the train runs freely. We are ready to assemble the escapement (see Lesson 5).

Oiling

Oil very slightly with clock oil the arbor on to which the canon pinion fits. Sometimes this will snap on with a little pressure with the tweezers; but should there be any difficulty, hold the canon pinion in the brass-nosed pliers and twist it on—this time with a forward twist and slight pressure downward. Apply watch oil to all the pivots which have not already been oiled, then complete the assembly of the motion work, dial and hands. With an eye-glass examine the balance-spring. It *must* be free, running from the stud to which it is fixed, between the index-pins, and so to the fixing on the balance itself; it must not rub on the under-side of the balance cock or on the balance itself. The spring can very easily be bent to make free, if freedom is wanted, but the greatest care must be used. Far better to make several attempts with ultimate success than one bold dash and damage the spring beyond repair. Even experienced watchmakers sometimes fail when it comes to adjusting the balance-spring.

Finally, a few hints on the care of watches will not be out of place:

I. Wind your watch in the morning. This especially applies to wrist watches; the reason being that the watch is better able to withstand vibrations and jerks, etc., during the day when the mainspring is at its strongest.

II. When your watch stops, do not continually shake it and knock it. If you are able, proceed as instructed. If not, take it to a watchmaker.

III. Do not pour oil indiscriminately into the mechanism of your watch. This course will have taught you why.

IV. Should you drop your watch into water and be unable to take it to pieces at once, open the case and shake out all the water you can first; then pour a little spirit into it to dry off the remaining water; then pour in oil. After such treatment an advanced amateur may be able to make a repair, but the spirit, such as methylated, whisky, or any other volatile spirit, may have upset the setting of the pallet stones and ruby pin which are held in position with shellac.

Self Testing Questions

(1) *When a mainspring breaks is that the only damage likely?*

(2) *What makes a watch gain considerably?*

(3) *When is the best time to wind a watch?*

(4) *How do you oil the centre wheel of a watch?*

THE ANSWERS ARE ON PAGE 548.

Answers to Self Testing Questions

LESSON 1

(1) Remove the small pin in front of the centre of the minute hand, taking care that the collet does not spring away; remove the small screw which holds the hour hand in position. Twist the seconds hand backward, gently and slowly, pulling off at the same time.

(2) "Going barrel" is distinct from the fusee, as the power of the mainspring is transmitted direct to the mechanism and not through the line and fusee.

(3) Yes, the pallets are most essential. Without them, the clock would run down as soon as it was wound up.

(4) The crutch is the wire or rod which is attached to the pallet arbor and is the means of transmitting the force to the pendulum to keep it in motion.

(5) The clock is in beat when the beat or ticks are even.

(6) Yes, the line, or its equivalent the chain, is essential if the clock is weight-driven or is fitted with a fusee, but is not used in going barrel clocks.

(7) Oil should be applied to that portion of the pendulum which works in the crutch fork.

(8) The escapement consists of the escape wheel and pallets together with the crutch, and is that part of the clock which allows the force of the falling weight, or coiled mainspring, to escape.

ANSWERS TO SELF TESTING QUESTIONS

LESSON 2

(1) Benzine or petrol is used to clean clocks, and the pivot holes are finally cleaned with pointed wood. The large holes are cleaned with strips of rag.

(2) The gathering pallet is the piece which gathers up the rack, and the rack controls the number of blows struck.

(3) If the striking is marked, the notched pinion-leaf gears between the marked teeth. If not marked, the pin on the wheel next the strike wheel must be about an eighth of an inch away from the piece which arrests it, when the hammer drops: in other words, this wheel must have about an eighth of an inch run after the strike has finished. Also when the strike is completed, the pin in the wheel next the fly must be immediately under the fly.

(4) The only wheels oiled in clocks are the escape wheels, and, in the case of alarm clocks, the alarm wheels, which are actually escape wheels. The *pivots* receive oil, and also the pins on the wheels of the striking part.

(5) Before fixing the hands in position, place the minute hand on temporarily, turn until the clock strikes the hour, when the minute hand should be pointing to the hour. Count the number of blows struck and place the hour hand pointing to that hour. If the hour hand has been replaced it can be turned to the right position, but it is better to proceed as suggested.

(6) An essential adjustment of the carriage clock is the correct depth of the escape-wheel pinion with the wheel into which it gears.

LESSON 3

(1) The movement is dried, after a petrol bath, by first shaking it. Then wind up the mainsprings and allow them to run down once or twice. Wipe the plate with a piece of clean linen rag. On no account must the movement be dried before a fire or an exposed naked light whilst using petrol.

(2) No, there is no general rule for fixing foreign movements into their cases: a careful examination must be made in each case.

(3) An alarm clock is in beat when the pin in the balance brings the pallet fork exactly opposite to it. The clock will then have an even tick.

(4) Wind the alarm mainspring, and turn the alarm-set handpiece carefully until the alarm rings. Place all three hands in position pointing to the same hour, taking for example 12 o'clock. It is usual for the minute hand to be set 3 minutes before hour.

(5) The balance is the wheel to which the balance-spring is attached and virtually takes the place of the pendulum.

(6) On no account should the balance-spring have any oil on it. Were this to happen, a slight jar might cause two coils of the spring to stick together, and the clock would gain rapidly.

LESSON 4

(1) When a mains clock stops first re-start it. Some of these

clocks are not fitted with self-starting mechanism, with the result that if the electric power is cut off the clock stops and remains stopped.

(2) It is not possible to regulate a synchronous motor mains clock. The regulating takes place at the power-station. Should, therefore, your mains clock lose or gain it means the electric power from your power-station is not "time controlled" and the power supplied is not suitable to drive such clocks.

(3) The Bulle clock is regulated in a similar manner to any other pendulum clock. The bob is screwed up to make the clock gain and unscrewed to lower to make it lose.

(4) Yes, electric clocks need oil, and they need rather more oil than an ordinary clock. Battery clocks need little oil, using a light oil.

(5) Synchronous motor clocks, when driven by time-controlled A.C. power, are most accurate time-keepers. Battery-driven clocks can be good time-keepers, but they suffer from the weaknesses of ordinary clocks.

LESSON 5

(1) These travelling clocks are similar to watches because in reality they are large watches and have all the component parts of a watch, plus an extra train wheel when the clock goes for eight days.

(2) The hands of these clocks are pressed on in position; they are held in position friction tight, no pins being used.

(3) The ruby or impulse pin, as it is sometimes called, is the pin which operates in the pallet fork. (The pallets, with the fork, are known as the lever.)

(4) Oil is placed in the hole before the balance is put in position. The balance pivots work the oil through to the parts where required.

(5) The most likely cause of these small clocks stopping is the presence of small particles of dirt, dust, or grit, and in some instances the oil becoming thick and sticky. As a certain percentage stop because of broken mainsprings, it is worth mentioning here that the springs of such clocks are more liable to break than those of the larger clocks.

(6) Care must be taken not to over-oil the top pallet pivot; too much oil would run through to the under-side and cause the pallets to cling to the pallet cock. The ruby or impulse pin must not be oiled.

LESSON 6

(1) When the mainspring breaks some of the teeth of the barrel or centre may be bent over. Sometimes the top third pivot is broken.

(2) Lack of freedom of the balance-spring will make the watch gain; also oil on the spring has the same effect, or more than one coil between the index pins.

(3) To get the best results watches should be wound in the morning or before they are taken into use.

(4) The centre wheel pivots are oiled *before* this wheel is placed in position during assembly.

HINTS AND WRINKLES FOR THE HANDYMAN

By T. Leicester O'Malley

I

Inside the House

In this section will be found a few notes on some small miscellaneous domestic jobs that frequently call for attention. They are arranged in alphabetical order.

Ball-Float Valves to W.C. Cisterns

If water overflows through the "warning pipe" the water-level may be too high, and the rod of the ball valve may need bending downward to shut the water off sooner: do not attempt to do this without first removing ball and rod. Then bend the rod down a little at a time.

If, when this cure has been tried, the water still comes up too high, the valve may need a new washer. Carefully pick out the old one and get a similar one from the ironmonger. Ease in the new washer and try the cistern. Sometimes the water creeps up very slowly, and it may be an hour or two later that the water will be seen to overflow. Take off the ball-float and shake it to make sure water has not leaked in. If this should prove to be the trouble, find the hole of entry (it can be located by immersing the ball in water and watching for air bubbles), and enlarge the hole slightly so that the water can be shaken out.

Sometimes the worker may have to make another small hole elsewhere, in order to permit air to enter, before the water can be got out. Drop a spot of solder on each hole, and the job should be satisfactory.

Newer types of float are sealed with a rubber washer at the stem-socket and with a rubber gasket between the flanges where the two hemispheres abut. These cannot be mended in the way described. In all cases where the ball float is unsatisfactory and cannot be mended, fit one of the new flat-topped floats complete.

Bathroom Fittings

Do not use ordinary spanners or pliers or wrenches on plated bathroom fittings. Cover the jaws of the tool with an old wash-leather or a thick duster so that there is no metal-to-metal contact. Special "strap-wrenches" are used by plumbers and fitters, with a leather strap that is put round the fitting and tightened, but the makeshift device mentioned is satisfactory if carefully applied.

Bolts: to Remove

Apply paraffin as for screws; use a spanner with care. If too much leverage is used (very easy with a long spanner), the bolt-head may be wrenched off. Give the paraffin plenty of time to work. If the further end of the bolt is accessible, clean up the thread with a sharp piece of steel so that it will come through the nut more easily. When the bolt turns with the nut (for instance, in the case of a coach-bolt used to fasten together parts of a sectional building) and the bolt-head cannot be chocked or gripped, file a square on the protruding end of the bolt, and grip the bolt with one spanner while another is used on the nut.

Failing all other measures, when the object is simply to separate two parts held together with a bolt, sever the bolt with a hacksaw blade.

Burst Pipes: First Aid

A small burst may sometimes be stopped by hammering in a tapered hardwood plug while the pressure is turned off. Even a meat skewer has been known to answer for such a repair. Tap down the metal around the plug before turning on the water again. Emergency "repairs" such as closing the pipe by hammering flat make the subsequent mending of the burst pipe more expensive. The first thing, of course, is to shut off the water. If the supply pipe from an overhead cistern has no stop valve, the water can be shut off by means of a length of broomstick tapered at the end so as to fit into (and block) the opening in the bottom of the cistern where the pipe leaves. Such a plug ought to be prepared and fitted beforehand, and then kept in readiness close to the tank.

Cements

Glass can be united by a cement made of Canada balsam dissolved in benzol. This preparation can be bought ready made from a dealer in microscope accessories; it takes some time to set hard.

A cement for leather (also useful for stopping holes) is made by dissolving small pieces of gutta-percha in carbon bisulphide. The latter is very inflammable and has an unpleasant sulphurous odour, but it is a solvent of rubber and similar substances and is valuable on that account.

Iron pipe joints can be sealed with rust cement, made by mixing iron filings or turnings with powdered salammoniac. About 1 part by weight of salammoniac with 80 parts of iron is a good mixture; some people add two parts by weight of flowers of sulphur. The pipes are positioned and caulked with yarn, and then the rust cement, moistened with water, is filled in on top of the yarn. The mixture oxidises and expands, eventually holding the joint firmly.

A cement for securing felt lagging to hot-water pipes or a tank is made of whiting, 8 parts by weight; red lead, 1 part; and white lead, 3 parts. These ingredients are mixed with enough boiled linseed oil to give a syrupy consistency.

Cistern: How to Mend a Hole in It

A small hole in a cistern of the open type may be mended by means of a stout bolt (threaded close up to the head), two large-diameter washers, and a couple of nuts. Open out the hole to take the bolt, and insert the latter, having one washer on the outside, against the head. Put on the other washer inside the tank, and then one nut. Now put on a hemp grummet at each side, under each washer, and tighten the nut. Finally lock the first nut by putting on the second one and twisting it down with the spanner.

Door Bells

Spring-operated bells sometimes stick because the plunger stem binds against the side of the hole in the door-frame. Take off the spring mechanism and move it slightly until it is free from obstruction.

The ordinary electric trembler bell should be firmly screwed to the wall in a vertical position gong downward, so that the armature (to which is attached the bell-clapper) hangs freely and can swing in pendulum-fashion from its spring suspension. Where two or more bells are mounted it may be worth while to plug the wall and attach a short batten or backboard by screws. The bells are then screwed down to the wood, making a better job than if fixed directly to the wall. It is often mechanical rather than electrical defects that cause faults in bell circuits. The hammer shank may need bending slightly in or out, and this should be done with pliers while the shank is held with the fingers. If the hammer is too close to the gong, the note will not be clear. Before adjusting the contact-screw, loosen the grip-screw that holds it at its present setting; twist it in or out very slightly, testing the bell each time by operating the push.

Often the contact point has become worn away to a slant, and a half- or a quarter-turn of the screw may be sufficient to secure a vigorous action. Fasten at the best setting by screwing in the locking-screw.

Door Knobs

Often a knob becomes loose because the grub screw fails to grip the squared spindle. If there is a recess in the spindle, drill a hole clean through and use a longer screw that will penetrate some distance into the spindle. If the thread in the knob has worn away, enlarge the hole slightly and then tap for a larger screw. Another method is to leave a clearing hole in the knob and to tap the hole in the spindle.

Glazed Tiling

Loose or broken tiles to a hearth or wall can be re-set with Portland cement and sand (hearth) or with Keen's cement (wall). The backing must usually be chipped away a little to allow room for the new cement backing. Wet the tiles thoroughly, as this material is very absorbent and the cement will not stick otherwise. Only a thin buttering of cement is needed, and it must not be too wet. Press the tiles gently into place; after a short time the surface can be gently rubbed with a wad of newspaper to clean off superfluous cement.

Glazing New Wood Sashes

Putty will not adhere to bare, unpainted wood, since the linseed oil is sucked in and the putty is thus left dry. Paint all new woodwork before attempting to glaze it. The glass should be cut somewhat smaller than the opening in the sash, and an allowance of about $\frac{1}{16}$ in. is sufficient (all round). Sashes may not be dead true and square; test for this before cutting the glass.

Kitchen Chairs, Mending

Spindles and rails of these chairs become loose. Deal with the trouble as soon as it is noticed, or else the chair will quickly get so rickety that mending it will be a much bigger job. Take out the loose member by prising the legs, etc., apart just enough for the purpose. Get off the old glue with a scraper or sand-paper; apply hot glue to the joint and clamp up strongly till the glue has set and hardened.

In positions where a cramp cannot be used, make a tourniquet with cord and a stick and twist up until the members are securely held in the proper position. If the rail or spindle has broken away at the end, make a new one out of stout dowel rod (say, ¾-in. section) and insert, tapering the end to fit the hole, which must, of course, be cleared out.

In jobs of this sort, be careful not to spring the legs in too much so as to put negative tension on them; the aim should be to keep them at the former distance, and this can be done only by accurate length in the new member, with proper tapering of the ends. A chair back can sometimes be mended with a steel repair plate screwed on at the rear, after the break has been glued.

Kitchen Table, How to Mend

The table top can be planed down level, and any warping remedied by inserting a few fine screws. But it may pay to take off the boards and relay them with close joints. Examine the under-side of the top to see how it is fixed. Good tables are fastened with clamps or buttons that allow a certain amount of movement and thus avoid warping. In an old article of furniture it may be worth while putting on an entire new top, made from t.-&-g. board, ¾ in. or 1 in. nominal thickness. The drawer usually needs attention; the kicker rails may want renewing, and the runners also. A drawer that goes right in is a first-class source of annoyance in the kitchen, and this behaviour can easily be cured by renewing or replacing the stops at the back. A good examination of the article before beginning the task will save time and labour. If the table top has to come off, this will enable the inside work to be done much more readily.

The drawer-knob may be loose; if it is a wooden one with a stem going into a hole in the drawer front, the hole will probably be too big now. Coat the stem with glue and quickly wind around it a turn or two of narrow tape; put on more glue and insert the stem into the hole. Tap in tight and leave to set. Where knobs are broken and difficult to replace, plug the holes and fix on metal drawer-pulls instead.

If the leg-joints are loose they should be re-glued and cramped up, a pair at a time. An old knife can be used to clean out the old glue from the joints of rail and leg; the same implement can serve to work hot glue into the joint, the table being turned into such a position that the glue will run down where it is wanted. A broken leg may be replaced by a new one bought at a cabinet works or timber yard; all the other leg-joints will need to be glued up afresh, as they are sure to be disturbed in getting out the broken leg. Cut the latter off close to the rails, and then with a tenon saw and chisel clear out the stump. Mark the new leg for the mortises, cut these, and then glue in the leg. Let the table rest on its top, upside down, until the joints have set. A table can be stiffened up considerably by inserting a brace between the long rails, mid-way in their length. Cut this from a piece of stuff of the same section as the rails themselves, long enough to fit tightly between them, its lower edge just coming flush with that of the rails. Drive two nails in at each side, through rail and endwise into the brace; punch in the nail a little and fill the hole with stopping (plastic wood, for example).

Leaded Lights

When inserting repair panes to leaded lights, bed the glass on a mixture of putty and red lead. Open up the cames with a wooden tool, wedge-shaped and pointed. At the corners it is difficult to raise the cames, and usually they are lifted a little and the glass pane is cut at the corners just enough to clear the came. Press down the cut cames with a flat piece of wood.

Any soldering needed should be done with a hatchet-shaped bit; it should be nicely hot and should rest only momentarily on the lead-work.

Mirrors

When these are to be framed the edges of the glass should be painted black, or else a reflection from the edge will show in the mirror. When inserting a mirror panel in an article such as a wardrobe door the glass is held at the back by thin wooden slips bradded to the rebate between the side of the glass and the woodwork. The slips are cut from stuff like glue-blocking, triangular in section and about ½ in. × ½ in. across the flats. Plate-glass mirrors can be mounted flat upon a wooden backboard by the use of clips and corners, screwed to the backing. The latter must be flat and free from warps or twists. Should there be any inequality, let the glass take its own level and do not force it down flat and close by screwing on the clips too tightly.

A mirror from a door-front can be taken out and made into a useful pier-glass by mounting upon a backboard and then fixing to the bedroom wall in a convenient position. The edges of the backboard (which can be deal or whitewood) should be planed and papered smooth, and then be stained and polished to match the existing furniture. Screw on three brass lugs to the back of the backboard—two at the top and one at the bottom—and, while the mirror (ready mounted) is held in the proper position on the wall by an assistant, or supported on some such thing as a stool or a box, mark the holes in the wall through the lug-holes. Take down the mirror and drill out holes in the wall for rawl-plugs, when the fixture can be finally fastened to the wall. If the glass is bevelled, the usual clips will need to be bent in slightly, but avoid anything like pressure on the glass from the clips, or the edge will break.

Before taking out a mirror, have the bench or table clear, and covered with a thick cloth or several layers of soft paper. This will safeguard the silvered back from damage.

Nails: to Withdraw

Bent or clenched nails should be straightened first. Then use a stout pair of pincers, gripping close to the wood. Gouge out a recess in order to make room for the pincers or claw-tool if necessary. Sometimes it may be better to cut off the nail-head and then to punch the nail out through the reverse side of the wood. A piece of sheet metal between pincers and the timber will protect the surface of the wood. A hacksaw blade can be used to sever the shank of the nail between two pieces of wood so that the nail can be drawn or punched out in two parts.

Nails in floorboard can usually be punched out downward to release the board; after the board has been lifted, the protruding end of the nail can be gripped with pincers. Do not use an ordinary nail punch for such jobs, as a parallel pin-punch of suitable diameter will do the work better and will not split the board.

Screws: to Remove

Screws in outside work or other positions exposed to damp are often difficult to withdraw. When in a wood-to-metal joint, apply paraffin sparingly and leave for an hour or so; then select a driver that fits well, and carefully try to shift the screw. If the slot is damaged, clean it out or deepen it with a file or a hacksaw. Sometimes a screw can be started by trying to turn it *in* a little first. Do not apply too great pressure at first, or the screw-head may be driven off.

Should the screw refuse to budge, try to tap it round with a narrow cold chisel applied to the edge of the slot; after it has been made to move, the task can be completed with a driver. After the screw has been got out a little, take a strong pair of pincers and turn the screw thus. Failing other methods, when a screw has become rusted in, drive a cold chisel under the head so as to lift the latter, and then use pincers or a tack-lifter.

When the head has rusted away, try to file a square or two flats on the end of the shank so that a small spanner or a hand-vice can be brought to bear on the end. In the case of a tight screw whose head is sunk in flush with woodwork, chisel out a recess around the head with a small gouge so that pincers can grip the shank beneath the head. If the head has been broken off, file or saw a new slot in the shank and use a screw-driver in this. A "round-the-corner" screw-driver is just the tool for this job: it is a metal bar with two ends turned down at right angles, somewhat like a timber dog in shape, and the blades are formed on the ends.

Sink and Basin Traps

When a sink or a basin is blocked, try using a force-cup to urge the blockage downward; alternatively, try and bring it up by a sucking motion of the rubber cup. There must be a fair amount of water in the basin for success.

Stand a pail beneath the trap and unscrew the little access plug with a pair of large pliers. Look after the washer or gasket between plate and seating. Drain out the water, and fish for any obstructing matter with a hooked and bent wire. Usually one or all of these methods will do the trick. Replace the plug carefully and screw up tight. Sometimes a length of spring curtain "rod" can be passed along the pipe from the open trap and taken out through the outlet to clear an obstruction in that part of the waste-pipe. Otherwise immovable blockages will sometimes give way if the top of the pipe is filled with broken soda crystals, wetted with hot water, and left over-night.

Taps: New Washers

When the screw of the jumper-stem has become corroded the jumper can be replaced with a type which has the fibre "washer" permanently fixed to the stem. Take out the old jumper and insert the new one. If the nut on a jumper is fast and will not easily turn, cut away the remains of the washer, hold the plain end of the stem in a vice, and unscrew the nut with a small spanner that fits it nicely. If the nut has become deformed so that a spanner will not grip it, use a pair of gas-pliers carefully to start it turning. Always use a hard (fibre) washer on the hot-water taps. Before replacing the tap body, always unscrew the tap handle as far as it will go first. If the supply cannot be turned off—this is often the case when the supply comes from a tank and not from the main—open other taps on the same supply to decrease the flow and the pressure; have a house-cloth or a swab handy to clap over the top of the tap when the top is unscrewed and removed. This will stop the water spurting upward and will lessen the mess. Have all tools handy, with the new washer, before unscrewing the tap, so that no time is lost.

Taps to Lavatory Basin

Avoid undue pressure in unscrewing the tap body, or the basin may be cracked; hold the tap nozzle with one hand while using the spanner on the other part. Sometimes the tap on a basin becomes loose in the hole and must be tightened. Do this carefully, and insert a piece of tow (or string unravelled) between tap-flange and top of basin. The nut underneath the basin is difficult of access, but a "basin-wrench" can be bought quite cheaply, and this has a thin head that will enable the nut to be gripped and turned. Sometimes, when a new washer is to be put on, the tap is too tight to be unscrewed without risk to the basin; in such a case (having first shut off the water supply) unscrew and remove the

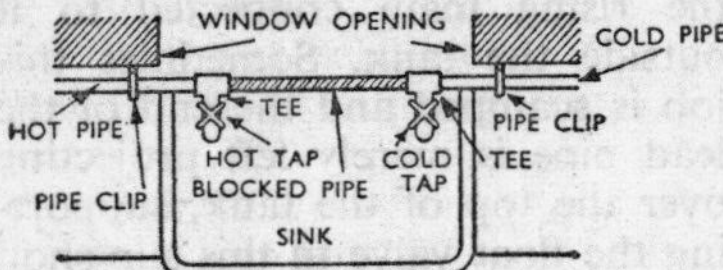

Fig. 2. *Taps over a sink below a low window-sill should be fixed in this way.*

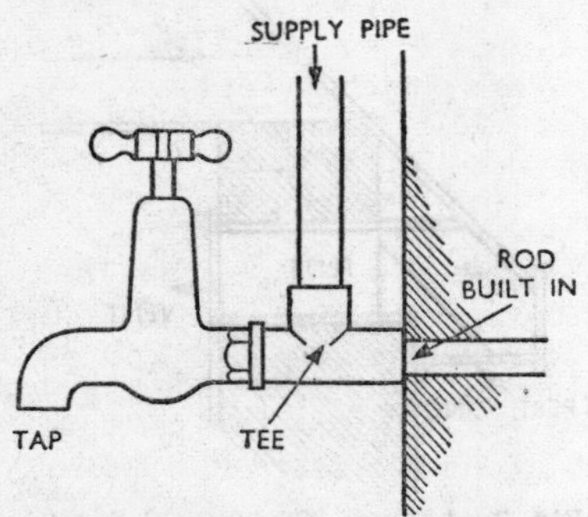

Fig. 1. *Screwing a sink tap to an iron tee in this way prevents distortion.*

tap from the rising pipe, and then it can be loosened at the bench. Use great care in undoing and replacing the union connecting tap tail to the supply pipe.

Sink Taps

The cold water tap over a kitchen sink when fixed to a lead pipe nearly always gets distorted after a period of use. If the tap is screwed to an iron tee so that it occupies one end of the cross-piece, which at the other end has a short length of iron rod screwed in and pinned into the wall, then the lead pipe jointed to a brass union screwed to the tail of the tee (either vertically or horizontally) makes a firm fixing (Fig. 1).

In cases where the sill of a window behind the sink is too low to permit proper fixing for hot and cold taps, it is a complete solution to screw both taps to iron tees, with a length of *blocked* tube between, crossing the window as a horizontal rail. Secure fixing by pipe clips can be arranged at either side of the window opening (Fig. 2).

Simple Ventilators

Rooms not provided with smoke flues are required to be furnished

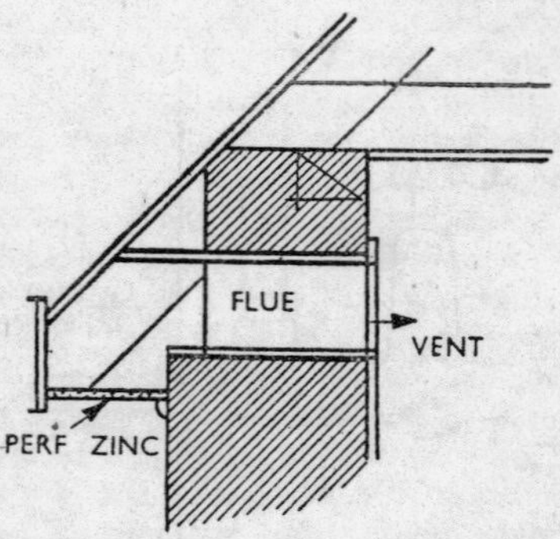

Fig. 3. *A square of perforated zinc thus fixed forms a good ventilator.*

with independent means of ventilation. There are many objections to the customary air brick for this purpose—birds' nests, draughts, and emission of light-rays being not the least. Where a close eaves with facia and soffit is formed, inconspicuous and efficient ventilators can be formed by the insertion of a square of perforated zinc in the soffit between a pair of rafters, and continuation from thence of a boarded flue through the wall to the room adjacent. A hit and miss or flap at the inner end allows control if desired (Fig. 3).

Water Closets

The joint between pan and soil pipe is important. The pan is screwed down to the floor, and in a newly built house there will be a certain amount of shrinkage of the woodwork, causing movement of the pan. If a rigid joint (as generally provided) connects the pan to the outlet pipe one of two things may happen: the joint material will crack and allow the pan contents to leak; or in bad cases the pan itself may crack somewhere at the bend. Moreover, concussion from a nearby explosion may fracture the pan. The remedy is to connect the pan to the soil pipe by a short length of lead pipe, which will permit movement.

The joint of the flushing pipe to the pan also needs consideration. Here it is recommended that a rubber cone connector be used over the usual red-lead cementing. The cone fits over the end of the flushing pipe and when the jointing compound has been applied in the usual way the larger end of the cone is pulled over the inlet to the pan and fastened down.

Water Tanks, Cleaning

Nowadays, the drinking-water supply is taken direct from the rising main, while the cold supply for baths and basins is generally obtained from a tank at the top of the house, whence also comes the cold feed to the hot-water cistern. The open tank should be drained every year and cleaned out. Scrub the sides and bottom with a brush if necessary, and flush out with clean water before putting into service again. The opportunity could be taken to examine the lagging of the rising main and to renew it if needed. The tank should be fitted with a wooden cover to exclude dirt and animals. Examine the washer of the ball float valve on the rising main; if it looks to be much worn it will be worth while to replace with a new washer and thus save an awkward job at a less convenient time.

The float-valve fitting should be fixed through the tank wall, and the rising main connected to it outside the tank. Sometimes this job is scamped and the end of the lead pipe is merely left projecting over the top of the tank, supporting the float valve in this slip-shod manner. It is impossible to adjust the ball lever in such a case, and the lead pipe gradually bends down and upsets the water level, besides restricting the bore. The connection to the overflow pipe needs inspection, for it may be loose in the tank wall and permit water to leak through and run down the outside of the tank instead of conducting it outside the house. The back-nut in such a case should be screwed up tightly.

Access to the tank will be made easy (and damage to ceilings avoided) if a track of rough boards is laid from the trapdoor entrance over to the tank itself. Nail the boards to the ceiling joists so that they do not shift when in use. An electric light in the loft is a great convenience; besides making it easy to inspect the tank arrangements and do any necessary work, the light can be left burning in frosty weather and may prevent a freeze-up. It is dangerous to take a lamp on a flexible lead into the loft when engaged in work on the tank or pipes. The latter provide such a good "earth" that an unsuspected defect in the flexible or the lamp-holder may result in a shock to persons coming in contact with the cable, and at the same time touching the pipe or tank.

II

Out of Doors

Brick Steps

A COMMON failing of brick outdoor steps is the dislodgment of the angle brick. This can be prevented if the exposed corner, instead of being laid with brick on edge as usual, is formed by a brick on end, with the lower portion buried to greater or less degree in the substance of the next lower step or paving (Fig. 4).

Concrete Paths or Paving

To avoid unsightly cracks in paving, the area should be divided into sections divided by open joints so that no section has a greater measurement than about 6 ft. × 5 ft. The appearance of any considerable expanse of paving is greatly improved if this necessity is made the occasion for a visible division such as a line of paving bricks, tiles, knapped flints, or other permanent strips which will cut the area into panels.

Clothes-Line Posts

Permanent (not dismountable) posts should be protected at the top by a capping of zinc or lead projecting an inch or so on all sides; cut the top of the post to a taper wedge-shape and nail on the capping. If pulleys are used out of doors, see that the entire pulley is galvanised and thus made rust-proof. Ordinary indoor pulleys generally have a japanned framework, with the wheel left plain; these quickly rust and soil the clothes line.

Damp Walls

See that the air bricks are unobstructed by earth or leaves or rubbish outside. See also that earth has not been heaped up against the wall *above* the cement rendering that acts as a vertical damp course. Look out for leaky down-pipes: water may stream on to a wall from a crack in the rain-water pipe,

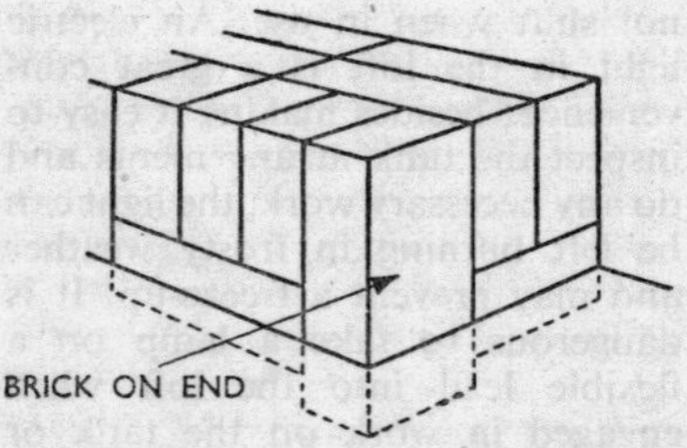

Fig. 4. *The angle brick of a step will not be dislodged if placed thus.*

or from an obstructed gutter or rain-water head. A warning pipe from a W.C. cistern or from a tank in the roof, if allowed frequently to overflow, may seriously affect a wall and cause dampness that will take weeks to dry out.

Dormer Checks

A dormer window situated in a sloping roof is usually made needlessly clumsy by the fancied need for studwork as a basis for covering the sides or checks. If the window-frame is erected and stayed by ceiling-joists running back to the roof structure, the sides can be adequately formed by stout boarding *parallel to the roof slope*, nailed at one end to the end ceiling-joist and at the other to the back of the window-frame. To this the external covering of lead or tiles can be fixed; internally, either counter-lathing and plaster or wall-board completes the check (Fig. 5).

Fences

When a fence (particularly a close-boarded one) begins to sway it should be stayed at the weak places to prevent further damage.

Cut off a few pieces of quartering of suitable length, with a bevel at the top end to fit close against the boarding when the lower end has been sunk some 9 in. in the ground. Put a stay at each post,

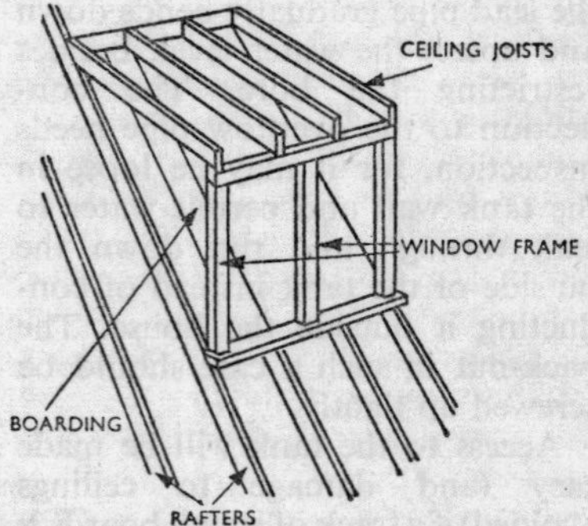

Fig. 5. *This is the best arrangement for the sides of a dormer window when it is situated in a sloping roof.*

driving a nail through the stay sideways so that it enters into the post. Push the fence upright and then, while the fence is held in this position, bed the foot of the stay firmly and cover it with earth. Lastly, drive in a short stake of 2 in. × 2 in. near the foot and nail the stay to this.

Such a repair, though of a temporary nature, will hold the fence for some time. Later the fence-posts, if still sound, can be cleared of earth and well rammed with hard core, or packed with concrete at the butts. If unsound, a new half-post can be inserted alongside, coming well up the old post and bolted through to the latter.

The main thing with fences is to repair them as soon as weakness becomes evident. The thrust of a stay against earth can be taken by a piece of stout board about 9 in. wide, interposed between the grounded end of the stay and the side of the hole in the soil. The rear face of this hole should be dug at a suitable angle.

Garden Chairs: Repairing

Deck chairs generally break at the rails, and these parts can be replaced with others cut from $\frac{3}{4}$-in. dowel rod. With a rasp form a neat shoulder at each end, leaving a stub just big enough in diameter to fit the holes in the sides. Should it be difficult to draw the short nails that hold the broken stems, cut off the latter close to the shoulder and use a gouge or $\frac{1}{2}$-in. chisel to clear out the holes. Since glue would be useless in these outdoor articles, we must rely on a tightly fitting joint to hold the rail safely. Tap in a nail at each end to replace those extracted. Broken arms or sides can be replaced, perhaps from members taken from a derelict chair too far gone to repair.

Incidentally it should be noted that the wood from these chairs is excellent for odd workshop appliances such as cramp-arms, etc., and should not be wasted. Tool-handles can be made from it, and many other useful articles.

Rivets sometimes pull through the metal clinch or washer, and, if not bent or crippled, can generally be closed down again. Failing this, substitute a $\frac{3}{16}$-in. coach-bolt of suitable length; put on a washer at each side, and file down the square beneath the bolt-head to the same cylindrical diameter as the shank. After the nut has been turned on to the proper tightness, saw off the projecting threaded end, leaving just enough to rivet down over the nut. Do not omit the riveting operation, or the nut will work loose, and may let down the user with dangerous results.

Gully Traps

The bend of the gully trap found at the foot of a rain-water downpipe should contain water to seal off gases in the drain and prevent them reaching the air around the gully. But in dry weather this water seal may be lost by evaporation and there will be nothing to stop smells from the drain. Pour a pail of water (a little disinfectant may be included) down the gully so as to ensure that the seal is established. Fish up the grating with a bent iron rod and, holding it in this manner, wash and brush the grating in a pail of water to which some soda has been added. Then replace the grating.

Gratings to gullies beneath sink and bath waste outlets are usually thickly coated and clogged with soapy matter, which may smell badly, and in any case will impede the flow of water. Sometimes the straight part of the trap gets an accumulation of grit which in time will block the entry to the bend and result in a blocked and overflowing gully unless the trap is scooped out at intervals.

It is of little use sprinkling the trap with one of the "carbolic" powders to remedy smells: these powders may not be soluble. Use instead some carbolic fluid, but remember that it is dangerous and corrosive, and should be kept in a proper Poison bottle in a safe place. Mix up a small quantity of the diluted disinfectant when needed and swill out the gully. But the better plan is by proper and frequent treatment of the drains to prevent bad odours, not merely to mask the bad smell by one of disinfectant.

Gutters

In autumn, after the leaves have fallen, all house gutters should be cleared of leaves and dirt carried down by the rain. A potting trowel is a useful tool for this job, as it is shaped to a similar curvature and fits in the gutter. A cranked trowel can be fitted with a long handle so that from a ladder a greater distance can be reached by the worker. Push the trowel along the gutter and scoop out any soil, etc., therein.

At the same time, the rain-water heads should be looked to, in case they have become blocked at the tops. Make sure that the guttering does not sag anywhere, thus forming a catchment and preventing the free flow of water.

Gutters should slope in a slight fall from the end toward the rain-water head where the down-pipe is situated. Inspect the brackets and screw up tightly any that are loose.

After a fall of snow, when the thaw is well established, use the trowel to clear the guttering and rain-water heads: this will hasten the dissolution of the snow and save much dampness from reaching the walls. Failing this precaution, the snow will pile up at the eaves and water will run over on to the house walls.

Jumper for Wooden Posts

Light wooden posts can be inserted in preformed holes made by means of a jumper. Suppose a pergola is to be erected having a number of posts all of 3 in. × 3 in. section: procure a 4-ft. length of sound oak of similar section to act as a jumper. Carefully saw off four facets at the end to form a fairly sharp point, but leave a shoulder $\frac{1}{8}$-in. deep where the taper joins the parallel portion. Now armour the taper part with sheet iron, cut to shape and nailed on at the top and at one side (overlap here). The iron should come flush against the shoulder. At about 9 in. from the top end of the jumper bore a hole through to take an 18-in. piece of broom-stick to serve as a handle. Pass the stick right through so that it projects equally at each side.

In use, the jumper is held steady by an assistant while the worker drives it with a wooden mallet to the desired depth; the jumper is then joggled slightly, or given a tap or two to loosen it, and pulled out ready for the post to be inserted.

The head of the jumper can be shouldered, if desired, to take a wrought-iron band, which will lengthen its life considerably.

Manholes

Open up these occasionally and flush out the chamber with a hose and plenty of clean water. Sometimes, when the runaway from a drain is sluggish, the cause may be found in an accumulation of matter at the end of the pipe entering the inspection chamber: a vigorous hosing plus gentle use of a rod at the outlet will often cure this and avoid more drastic remedies higher up in the drain. If the manhole lid is tight in the cover, clean out any dirt around the edges and prise gently to loosen it.

Rain-Water Butt or Tank

It is a convenience to have a draw-off tap on a rain-water tank, but this should be one of the old-fashioned "plug" type. The screw-down type of tap, which requires a fair head of water to lift the jumper, is not suitable. A hole can be cut in a galvanised iron tank very readily by use of a "tank-drill" which has a centre pilot drill and an adjustable radial cutter.

Do not omit to fit an overflow near the top of the tank, if it is fed by a rain-water down-pipe, as this will avoid the mess and dampness of frequently over-running water. The overflow can be taken by an old piece of gas barrel, or by a short length of shuting, to the nearest gully. Fit a cover to the top of the tank, but leave holes so as to ensure the free entry of air.

Roof Repairs

Soft slippers should be worn when working on lead or zinc flats, or on gutters covered with these metals. The nails in ordinary heavy boots will be likely to damage the roof covering. When making repairs to tiles or slates, the utmost care must be taken or adjoining parts of the roof will be damaged. A proper duckboard should be employed, having hooks to fit over the ridge and support it.

An alternative is a double board, hinged at the middle, which hangs over the ridge on both sides of the roof.

Do not put any weight on the eaves gutter, which is held only by screws and is not strong enough to cope with any undue stress. It is very dangerous to mount the roof-slope on a ladder resting on the guttering at one end and merely lying on the roof.

Thatched Roof, How to Fireproof

The following solution can be sprayed on to an existing roof, and new straw for a repair may be soaked in it before use. A liberal application is needed in order to render the straw resistant to fire.

In 50 gallons of water dissolve the following quantities of chemical: Ammonium sulphate, 28 lb.; ammonium carbonate, 14 lb.; boracic acid, 7 lb.; borax, 7 lb.; alum, 14 lb.

Vent Pipes to Drains

The pipe at the top should be fitted with a balloon grating to prevent birds building a nest in the open end. This pipe, in conjunction with a fresh-air inlet elsewhere in the drain line, is intended to promote a free flow of air through the pipes; if inlet or outlet becomes blocked the drains may smell. Frequently the fresh-air inlet gets covered up with plants or shrubs; its flap valve, which should allow entrance but not exit of air, is often found to be broken. Sometimes the vertical pipe to which the F.A.I. is fitted is only a few inches above ground. Attention to points such as this will save expense and annoyance.

When the balloon grating becomes rusted, it may not fit tightly enough to stop the entry of birds, and should be renewed.

Water Stop Valve Outside House

The outside valve is generally at the bottom of a piece of drain pipe set up vertically below ground and covered at surface level with a hinged access plate. The valve may be the usual tee-handled one as fitted inside the house, and must be turned by a long-handled iron key with a crutch that fits on to the tap. As often as not, when in time of emergency it is necessary to turn off the water outside the house, the shaft will be found to be blocked by leaves and soil for some distance up from the bottom; at the best, the tap will be hard to turn, because of infrequent use.

The remedy is to inspect the valve from time to time and to clear out the shaft. Give the tap a few turns to ensure that it works with reasonable freedom. Hang up the key in a conspicuous place in an outhouse or outside W.C., and let responsible persons know where it is. In many cases no such key is provided by the builder, and the occupants of the house are ignorant of the need for such an implement.

There should also be fitted a stop valve inside the house, where the rising main enters; but in frosty weather it may be well to empty the underground pipe from outside valve to house valve. Moreover, if there is a garage, the supply for car-washing will probably come off the pipe before it enters the house, and only the outside stop valve in such a case will affect the garage pipe. The garage service, on account of its colder surroundings, is specially prone to freezing.

III

Workshop Hints

Site for Workshop

A DRY and well-lighted shed makes a good workshop, provided some simple precautions are taken. The ground must be firm and well drained. There is nothing to beat a concrete floor for a building of this kind, and the only drawback—that it is somewhat cold to stand upon—can be overcome by laying a floor of 1-in. board just in front of the benches. If an entirely new shed is to be built, set out the floor area with pegs and lines and clear out the ground to a level. The concrete floor (6 in. thick) should extend some 6 in. beyond the shed walls on each side, and the projecting portion be worked off smoothly to a slight fall outward in order to throw off rain. When the floor is set hard, the wood sills for the shed sides may be laid; they are secured to the floor by rag-bolts cemented into holes cut in the concrete and projecting through the sills, to which the latter are fastened by a nut and washer at each point.

The use of a concrete floor enables benches and machines to be firmly fixed to the floor—the bench legs by means of angle plates screwed to the wood and bolted to the floor; and the machines by the use of rag-bolts. If it is more convenient, a machine can first be bolted to wooden bearers (3 in. × 2 in.), and the bearers in turn fastened down by bolts. Benches are usually placed close to a wall on one long side, with the idea of saving space and of permitting a firm fixing. This practice is not so good as a more central location, which would allow the worker to get at all four sides.

Where really heavy work is to be done the supporting framework of the shed should be stout, the main uprights of not less than 3 in. × 2 in. section, and the horizontals of the same at the window level. Diagonal braces should be built in from the sill line to the first horizontal timber, so as to stiffen up the lowest bay of the framework. Door and window openings must be properly framed. A lean-to shed is satisfactory, and somewhat simpler to construct than one with a span roof; a fixed roof-light can be included without much difficulty, but a window which opens in the roof demands more care as it may leak at times.

A proper lean-to building could be constructed if there were a convenient house-wall to form its back support, and in such case a brick structure might be desirable, with roof covering to match that of the house itself. The roof covering of an independent shed would usually be corrugated asbestos-cement sheets or corrugated steel. The latter is very hot in summer. Another alternative is tiles of asbestos-cement. It must not be forgotten that most local authorities require plans to be submitted for approval in the case of permanent structures, whether attached to a house or standing free, and the rating of the house might be affected.

A portable shed could be bought or constructed, and provided it stood on a concrete floor such as that described above (securely bolted down), would be almost as good as a permanent building. But many of the sheds offered for sale in sections are made up of ridiculously small scantlings and are virtually useless for our present purpose. In building a sectional workshop more timber and labour are required than in a permanent shed, but beyond this there is nothing against such a choice. The sections, however, must be of stout construction, properly stiffened and braced, and put up securely.

Workshop Doors and Windows

A framed door should be used, and one with a glass panel will give valuable extra light. A ledged door is not suitable for a proper workshop in which good tools and materials are to be kept. In fitting the hinges it may be worth while to use lift-off butts, as then the door can be lifted off at need in order to leave a wider opening when taking large work into the shed. For the windows we recommend a two-light casement (to open) in one position, with a fixed pair having a ventilating fanlight above in another wall. Proper frames and sills should be provided, to stop water entering in bad weather. Two ventilating gratings ought to be built in high up in the walls.

Workshop Lighting and Heating

A small cylindrical slow-combustion stove of the "Tortoise" or similar brand is about the cheapest source of heat when the workshop is to be used for hours on end; it is started with coal and thereafter burns coke. Protect nearby woodwork with sheet iron, and take the smoke-pipe out through the roof; the latter should have a properly constructed outlet, weathered to prevent the ingress of rain. For short periods of use a 1-kw. electric fire will do to warm the shed. This can be run off the lighting circuit.

A couple of electric drop lights with funnel-shaped opal shades should be arranged in suitable positions over benches or machines. The cable from the house supply ought to be run in permanent fashion and nothing of a temporary or makeshift nature attempted. See that the workshop circuits are properly fused and protected. If power supply is wanted for a lathe or other machines, a line of ample capacity must be arranged for.

Use of Garage

A built-on brick garage, if its sole use can be secured, is perhaps the ideal workshop. The sole drawback is the big entrance doors, which allow draughts to enter and are troublesome in other ways. But if there is another and a smaller doorway, as is often the case, the big doors can be made draught-proof and opened only on occasion. If the garage has to be used also for a car, it will not, of course, be of much value to the worker.

There is sometimes a difficulty with the walls, which are usually cement rendered and which cannot be penetrated by nails. In order to provide hanging space for tools, two or three runs of 2 in. × 1 in. batten might be screwed to the wall on one side, holes being made for rawl-plugs. Then any large and light tools such as saws could be hung from nails or hooks in the battens without damaging the wall surface. A garage floor will have a fall toward the entrance, and must be levelled where benches or machines are to stand.

Tool Accommodation

The woodworker's tools should be kept in a different box from those of the metal-worker. For either kind, two small boxes are better than one large and unwieldy tool chest, especially when goods have to be removed.

It is advisable to make a shallow box specially for the wood saws, which are always a problem to protect. A whole kit of joiner's saws can be accommodated in this way, and no weight need rest upon the blades.

Racks for chisels, gouges, etc., can be made by the worker and screwed to the wall above the bench; a rack fixed to the bench itself is a nuisance, as the tools chatter and get shaken off during planing operations. Keep a recognised place for each sort of tool, so that it can be got at readily.

Do not make a dump of odd lengths of timber beneath the bench, but sort out useful pieces from waste and keep the former in a box; firewood can be turned over to the housewife. Tools may be lost for days under an untidy bench.

The tool chest will be smaller than the carpenter's box, but will have to stand a heavier load; this is another argument for the use of several boxes. Have compartments for short files in a tray that can be lifted out; long files will have to go at the bottom of the box in their own compartment. Heavy tools should go at the bottom or in a special box of their own.

There are many small tools, such as reamers, broaches, fine files, punches and so on, that are best accommodated in tin boxes. The common "flat-fifty" cigarette tins are excellent for this and for housing twist drills. Squirt a little oil over them in the box to prevent rusting. Keep spare hacksaw blades well greased and in a place where they will not be damaged by other implements.

Storing Drills

Stands are sold for twist drills, having a hole for each size; experience shows that the drills get taken out and not replaced, or get knocked or shaken out of the stand. It is probably better to keep them in boxes, where they can be placed in order of size almost as easily as in a stand. Smaller boxes will do for small taps and dies.

A rack for hammers is a convenience. It is made by boring out holes of suitable size for the handles in a ledge of $\frac{3}{4}$ in. stuff about 5 in. wide and 18 in. long, which is fastened to the wall of the shed. The hammers are put in at the top and are kept from falling by the heads.

The horizontal timbers of the shed (it is presumed to be unlined) will afford support for shelves, and others can be fixed to brackets screwed to the verticals. A ledge of $\frac{5}{8}$ in. × 1 in. slip tacked at the front will prevent the fall of articles by vibration during workshop operations.

Drilling Machines

These take up a good deal of room on the ordinary work-bench, and if there is space in the workshop for a bench especially for such tools, it will be a wise provision. The bench need not be very wide from back to front, and could also accommodate a grinder. A good light is needed, of course. A polishing head might be mounted at one end of the same bench, with a foot-wheel beneath; it is very useful for many odd jobs of polishing, and if furnished with a drill chuck (generally the case) at one end of the spindle it can be made to rotate small arbors, etc., while they are filed or trued up. There is usually a mounting for a small grindstone on the polishing head, or a small-diameter saw; the latter is of limited use, but a fine-grained grinding wheel will come in very handy for finishing small tools. Small drills can be run in the chuck, and work, after being centre-punched, can be held up to the drill—though this is not the most accurate method of drilling. The belt from the flywheel below to the pulley on the head is led up through the bench top. Another way of driving the head is by a fractional h.p. electric motor screwed to the under-side of the bench top, with a switch on top; the diameter of the motor pulley must be so proportioned that the head spindle runs at a reasonably slow speed.

Small Lathe

For the worker to whom a bigger lathe does not appeal one of the little "plain" lathes (say with 2⅛ in. centres or thereabouts) would be a useful workshop adjunct, viewed purely from its value in the hundred-and-one jobs where a small part has to be run between centres for some operation and no other method will answer. Such a lathe costs little, and will soon earn its keep in the time it saves. The machine can be driven by a foot-wheel in the same manner as a polishing head. Among other odd jobs for which a small lathe is adapted are the winding of small springs and the winding of electrical coils—extremely awkward to perform by other means.

Sensitive Bench Drill

This is another light pulley-driven machine that could be fixed on the extra bench mentioned in another paragraph. In the usual type the belt comes up and changes direction at two idlers at the rear of the vertical spindle, then passing around a horizontal pulley on the drill spindle. In conjunction with a heavier drill press, this machine would take care of almost all the jobs arising, being adapted particularly for accurate light drilling.

Driving Light Bench Machines

Two machines—for example, a polishing head and a sensitive drill—could be driven alternatively by the same foot-wheel by use of a simple countershaft arrangement at the rear of the bench. Since a quick change-over would not be essential, the change from one machine to the other could be done by merely slipping the belt off the pulley for the machine not required, leaving the other machine engaged. Of course, if a motor drive were installed, a proper countershaft with a belt striker could be fitted. A self-contained electric drive unit is obtainable which includes a pedal-operated clutch and brake. This unit is mounted beneath the bench, the pedal control unit being fastened in a convenient position to the floor. Thus the operator's hands are free.

Bench Anvil

These are made from about 1½ lb. to 10 lb. in weight. A 4-lb. anvil could be bolted to the general metal-working bench, but unless he also has a much larger one (smith's anvil, 12 lb. upward) mounted on a block the worker would do well to install a 10 lb. bench anvil (nearly 1 ft. long, including the horn), fixing this on a low and strongly built platform of its own. A bench should not be used for hammering jobs. The platform for the 10-lb. anvil might with advantage be made up with splayed legs, so as to give a broader base and greater stability.

Brazing Equipment

For work of some size and fair quantity a gas blow-pipe is desirable, so that a service pipe will have to be taken into the workshop. A bellows or a blower is needed: a foot bellows (double-blast type) is more convenient for one-man jobs, as when its knack is acquired it can be controlled and kept in blast very easily, leaving the hands free. In order to protect the bench-top, a piece of stout-gauge sheet iron should be cut about 24 in. wide and long enough the other way to reach from back to front of the bench and project some 2 in. The projecting part is bent down at right angles so that when in use it butts against the front edge of the bench. The work to be brazed should be supported on bricks, or placed in a brazing tray on top of the sheet iron. Another idea is to make up a stout table, topped with rough boarding and covered with sheet iron, the latter being turned down all round and nailed. The table could then be stood in the centre of the workshop, well away from the wooden walls, etc. Another advantage is that in hot weather the table could be taken outside and the job done in the open.

Brazing Lamps

The smallest size lamp (paraffin fuel) with which jobs of any importance can be brazed is one of 2½–3 pints capacity. The proper brazing lamp is not merely a big blow-lamp such as a painter or plumber might use; it has a larger reservoir, and the burner is mounted horizontally. A safety valve is provided in some of the larger lamps, and there may be an arrangement by which the burner unit can be detached and connected to the reservoir by a flexible metal tube, giving a greater range of use.

The reason why petrol-burning lamps are not here recommended is that the use and storage of such fuel may involve risks in the hands of novices. Many first-class lamps are marketed which burn petrol, and they are in common use. But paraffin is a safer fuel to store, is usually available in the house, and depends for its "pressure" on air-pressure furnished by the pump incorporated in all paraffin-burning blow-lamps or brazing lamps.

Some workers mix a little petrol with the paraffin when filling the lamp, claiming that it gives a hotter flame and more lively action. If this is done, the petrol should be added to the paraffin in a metal filler-can outside the building, and certainly not poured separately into a lamp which is still hot.

INDEX

INDEX

INDEX

INDEX

INDEX

INDEX

INDEX

INDEX

T647/4RS. Made and Printed in Great Britain by Richard Clay and Company, Ltd., Bungay, Suffolk.
Reprinted 1947